The Holt Science Program

SCIENCE 1 *Observation and Experiment,* by Davis, Burnett, and Gross

SCIENCE 2 *Experiment and Discovery,* by Davis, Burnett, and Gross

SCIENCE 3 *Discovery and Progress,* by Davis, Burnett, and Gross

MODERN BIOLOGY by Moon, Mann, and Otto

MODERN CHEMISTRY by Dull, Metcalfe, and Williams

MODERN PHYSICS by Dull, Metcalfe, and Brooks

LIVING THINGS by Fitzpatrick and Bain

MODERN PHYSICAL SCIENCE by Brooks and Tracy

MODERN HEALTH by Otto, Julian, and Tether

● HUMAN PHYSIOLOGY by Morrison, Cornett, and Tether

HUMAN
PHYSIOLOGY

THOMAS F. MORRISON
FREDERICK D. CORNETT
J. EDWARD TETHER, M.D.

HENRY HOLT AND COMPANY . . . . NEW YORK

The Authors of **HUMAN PHYSIOLOGY**

THOMAS F. MORRISON is a member of the Science Department and a teacher of physiology at Milton Academy, Milton, Massachusetts.

FREDERICK D. CORNETT is Head of the Science Department and a teacher of physiology at Santa Monica High School, Santa Monica, California.

J. EDWARD TETHER, M.D., is Assistant Professor of Neurology, Indiana University Medical Center and School of Medicine, Indianapolis, Indiana.

59P9

Preface

The role of physiology in the general plan of education is to familiarize students with the functions of their own bodies and to prepare those who are interested for further specialized work in the field. In this text, the authors have had the former as their chief objective because they believe the more advanced and technical journals will give specially interested students the additional knowledge required for professional courses.

HUMAN PHYSIOLOGY is an introductory text written for secondary school students who wish more detailed explanations of some of the functions of the human body beyond those already covered in the standard biology or health courses. In this volume the authors have attempted to develop the basic knowledge of physiology as represented by the latest advances in the various areas of the subject, but have deliberately avoided the inclusion of findings of a highly theoretical nature or those supported by incomplete data not yet proved. Although a background knowledge of biology and chemistry may be helpful, students using this text can assimilate the material without either course because complete explanations are given for each physiological principle and all terms and concepts are defined and explained clearly. Thus, the book may be used as either a second course in the biological sciences or an introductory course in physiology without previous experience in this field. It may also be used with equal effectiveness as a text in those junior colleges which offer a course in physiology or in schools of nursing where elementary physiology is an integral part of the curriculum.

Throughout HUMAN PHYSIOLOGY illustrations appear wherever they are required to help explain the topics under discussion. Some have been borrowed from other sources, but the majority are new illustrations drawn especially for this book. The authors appreciate the excellent work of the artists: Stephen Rogers Peck, Mrs. Pauline Burr-Thomas, and Tom Morgan, whose drawings add greatly to the teachability of the text. Certain of the illustrations represent original drawings by Mr. Morrison, the senior author. The inclusion of the "Trans-Vision" inserts of the human body, the eye, and the ear should help the student in his understanding of the structure and functions of the more important organs.

At the end of each chapter are various aids to direct the learning process. Teachers will probably wish to use all of these, modifying them as desired to meet individual or group differences. The PHYSIOLOGY WORKBOOK, a combination workbook-laboratory manual, and the TESTS IN PHYSIOLOGY which accompany the textbook will provide a complete program for all the students.

In common with all introductory science courses, there is a vocabulary load that must be mastered in order to understand physiological concepts clearly and concisely. To aid in this mastery, all physiological words and terms are printed in **boldface italics** the first time they are used. The more important words have been collected at the end of each chapter in the material titled *Speaking of Physiology*. The authors suggest strongly that the student check carefully his knowledge of the meanings of each word appearing in these lists, since they are basic to the course.

In *Test Your Knowledge* are included questions which will stimulate the student to think about the material presented in each chapter. *See for Yourself* contains suggested projects and activities related to the chapter, but not necessarily specifically discussed in the text. These will especially challenge those students who hope to enter professional fields, but will also be of interest even to those who may never take a future course in physiology.

At the end of the text is an *Appendix* containing various conversion factors which can be used to translate some of the data given in the text into more familiar terms. There is also a complete *Glossary* containing definitions of the important physiology terms occurring in the text. The authors have also included a *Bibliography* listing reference books and articles that may be helpful to both teachers and students. This contains a large number of references so that each school may, if desired, select from it those titles that are most appropriate for the school library.

The authors hereby extend their sincere gratitude and appreciation to Miss Ruth E. Weimer, Washington High School, Massillon, Ohio and to Mr. Charles E. Herbst, Beverly Hills High School, Beverly Hills, California for invaluable assistance. These two classroom teachers of physiology have read the entire manuscript and have offered many helpful comments and suggestions. The authors also wish to thank Dr. Alexander T. Ross, Professor and Chairman of the Department of Neurology, Indiana University Medical Center, for his excellent and constructive comments on the chapters dealing with the nervous system, each of which he carefully analyzed in manuscript.

The work of Laurence Lustig, who designed the cover and general format of the book, is also gratefully acknowledged. Thanks are due, too, to The University Prints, which kindly granted permission to use the photograph of the discus thrower appearing as an integral part of the design throughout the book.

Table of Contents

UNIT 1: The Body as a Whole

Chapter

1. The Meaning of Physiology   2
2. The Physical Basis of Life   8
3. The Cell—Its Structure, Functions, and Reproduction   20
4. The Grouping of Specialized Cells   28

UNIT 2: The Bones and Muscles

5. The Skeleton   40
6. The Physiology of Skeletal Muscle   62
7. The Action of Some Skeletal Muscles   73

UNIT 3: The Nervous System

8. The Structure and General Functions of the Nervous System   82
9. The Structure and Functions of the Central Nervous System   95
10. The Structure of the Eye and the Physics of Vision   115
11. The Physiology of Vision   126
12. The Structure and Physiology of the Ear   139

UNIT 4: The Digestive System

13. Foods: Their Composition and Use   152
14. Enzymes and Vitamins   166
15. Digestion in the Mouth   181
16. Digestion in the Stomach   190

17. Digestion in the Small Intestine: The Liver and Pancreas   **199**
18. The Large Intestine   **211**

UNIT 5: The Respiratory System

19. The Respiratory Structures and the Mechanics of Breathing   **216**
20. The Physical and Chemical Processes in Breathing   **225**
21. Artificial Respiration and Phonation   **234**

UNIT 6: The Circulatory System

22. The General Functions of the Circulatory System   **246**
23. The Solid Parts of the Blood   **252**
24. Plasma, Hemorrhage, and Transfusions   **262**
25. The Structure and Action of the Heart   **273**
26. The General Plan of Circulation, the Spleen, and Lymph   **288**

UNIT 7: The Skin, Metabolism, and Excretion

27. The Skin   **304**
28. The Regulation of Body Temperature   **312**
29. Metabolism   **320**
30. The Kidneys and Their Function   **331**

UNIT 8: The Endocrine System

31. The Endocrine Glands: The Pituitary and the Thyroid   **340**
32. The Parathyroids, the Adrenals, the Pancreas, the Pineal Body, and the Thymus   **352**

UNIT 9: Genetics

33. The Inheritance of Characteristics   **362**

APPENDIX   **381**

BIBLIOGRAPHY   **382**

GLOSSARY   **385**

INDEX   **395**

The Body as a Whole

CHAPTER 1

The Meaning of Physiology

CHAPTER 2

The Physical Basis of Life

CHAPTER 3

The Cell—Its Structure, Functions, and Reproduction

CHAPTER 4

The Grouping of Specialized Cells

The Meaning of Physiology

Physiology, a biological science. In the broadest sense of the term, the biological sciences may be said to include all phases of knowledge dealing with living things. These sciences may be purely descriptive in nature or they may consist of a highly detailed examination of the relationships between living things and their environment. They may also involve experimentation. The ever-changing pattern of life constantly presents a challenge to the student of these sciences. Very few laws can be established to explain how living things will behave under all conditions, but progress is being made toward a better understanding of the processes involved in what we call life.

There are still many unanswered questions. Many of these are of fundamental importance, but their solution must wait until further advances are made in the fields of chemistry and physics. These fields promise the greatest hope to the biological scientist in his search for answers to his problems.

Physiology is that branch of the biological sciences that deals with the activities of living things. It is a dynamic subject because it is concerned with all of the physical and chemical processes that occur within the body of a living animal or plant. All of these processes imply transformations of energy from a quiet or potential form as it is found within the living material of the body to an active or kinetic state that results in the manifestations of life.

As shown in Fig. 1-1, the relation of physiology to some of the other biological sciences is threefold. On the one hand, there is a group of sciences dealing primarily with the *structure* of the body. These are generally spoken of as the **anatomical sciences** and include a study of the **anatomy** of the individual, the structures that can be seen with the unaided eye. Historically, this is probably the oldest of all of the biological sciences. It is primarily descriptive in nature, although modern anatomical studies include some discussion of the func-

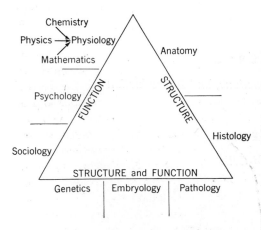

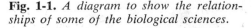

Fig. 1-1. *A diagram to show the relationships of some of the biological sciences.*

tion of an organ to make a knowledge of its role more complete and satisfying. With the development of the microscope, study of the finer details of structure became possible, and a separate branch of anatomy appeared, **histology.**

A second side of our triangle is composed of the branches of the biological sciences that are primarily *functional* in nature. Here, in addition to physiology, we have noted **psychology.** This deals with the thought processes of the individual, which very frequently have a profound effect on the physiological well-being of the person. Certain types of behavior are receiving an increasing amount of attention, and for want of a better designation, are spoken of as the *psychosomatic* conditions. The word has been coined from the two Greek stems of *psyche,* meaning soul or mind, and *soma,* referring to the body. Such conditions as gastric ulcers, colitis, and certain types of skin disorders may be examples of the body's response to stresses and strains placed on the nervous system. Man's relation to his fellow beings constitutes the material for the field of **sociology.** This may be considered a functional aspect of the biological sciences because it frequently involves problems affecting the health and physical welfare of members of a community.

A third group of the biological sciences consists of subjects that combine *descriptive and functional* elements. One of these, **pathology,** is the basis for the study of medicine. It includes the study of abnormal functioning of the body and also deals with changes in bodily structure which may affect normal procedures. Two other branches of biology combine a study of function and structure. These are the fields of **embryology** and **genetics.** Embryology deals with the early development of the individual, and recent experiments in this field, conduct-

ed on animals, shed light on the processes occurring in the early stages of human development. Genetics is a study of the manner in which various characteristics are transmitted from one generation to the next. The pattern of inheritance exhibited by any person is established at the very beginning of his existence. Not only are physical features determined at this time, but certain physiological traits are also fixed, due to the activities of transmissible materials.

The history of physiology. Physiology in its present form is a relative newcomer on the stage of the biological sciences. Some of the earliest work in the field was done by the Greek physician Galen (131–210?). His many experiments might have laid a foundation for further studies, had it not been for his interpretation of his results. Galen lived at a period when animals were considered to be governed by laws quite different from those governing inanimate objects. It was thought that all living things were controlled by a mystical influence called the "vital force." Although some of Galen's experiments led him to the threshold of discovery of important physiological facts, the concept of a special type of behavior among living things prevented him from grasping the true significance of his observations. For many years after Galen, the science of physiology continued to be shrouded in mysticism, and then for a brief period there was a trend toward a more logical approach to the subject. A German whose real name was Theophrastus Hohenheim (1490?–1541), but who wrote under the name of Paracelsus, attempted to study the action of the body in much the same way we do today. He was not successful, however, because the field of chemistry was too undeveloped to furnish him with the necessary information or techniques. His great contribution to the study of the biological sciences was that he developed methods which actually form the basis for many of the modern procedures.

One of the great names in the development of scientific thought in general and physiology in particular is that of the Englishman William Harvey (1578–1657). In 1628 he published a small book, written in the language used by all scientists at that time, Latin. Although this book was only 72 pages long, it had the extraordinary title of *Exercito anatomica de motu cordis et sanguinis in animalibus.* This may be freely translated as *An Anatomical Dissertation on the Movement of the Heart and Blood in Animals.* The importance of this work was that it demonstrated clearly that

Fig. 1-2. *William Harvey, one of the early pioneers in the study of physiology. (Bettman Archive)*

the flow of blood around the body is really a circulatory movement in which the arteries, veins, and capillaries form the conducting channels. Due to the fact that microscopes had not reached a satisfactory stage in development at his time, Harvey had to imagine the presence of the smallest blood vessels, the capillaries. In 1632, however, their presence was demonstrated by the Italian anatomist, Marcello Malpighi. Harvey's methods were so painstakingly and carefully developed and his thinking so clear that this small report is considered to be one of the finest examples of the scientific method. Prior to the appearance of Harvey's book, the course the blood followed in passing around the body was unknown. Paracelsus, for example, believed that there were small openings in the wall which separates the two sides of the heart through which the blood passed. Others believed that the arteries were tubes which carried air around the body, because after death the blood frequently leaves the major arteries to collect in the veins and tissues.

From Harvey's time onward, great strides were made in the biological sciences. As the microscope was perfected, more details of structure could be observed and linked with the activities of various parts of the body. The development of the fields of chemistry and physics and the application of mathematics to many of the problems of physiology have given a clearer insight into the functions of the tissues and organs of the human body.

The general structure of the body. Before embarking on a study of the details of the body's structure and functions, it is wise to review certain general terms that will be used from time to time throughout this text.

Man, like all of the vertebrates (back-boned animals), has a type of body symmetry that is known as **bilateral.** This is determined by passing a plane lengthwise through the body from the middle of the skull in such a manner that it will bisect the vertical column and the breast bone. When such a division has been made, it is found that each half of the body is essentially like the other if it is viewed in a mirror. An example of this is found in the shape of the two hands. Their general form is such that the right hand is like the left, if you view the reflection of the left one in a mirror. Internally, of course, the plane does not divide the body into two exactly equal halves because the various organ systems have developed different growth patterns.

When the human race began to walk upright, the relative position of the body surfaces changed. In a four-footed animal, the upper surface along which the back bone lies is called the **dorsal** side, while that along the belly of the animal is the **ventral** side. In man, the dorsal side has therefore become the **posterior** (back) area, and the former ventral side, the **anterior** (front) portion of the body. Since these terms are sometimes used

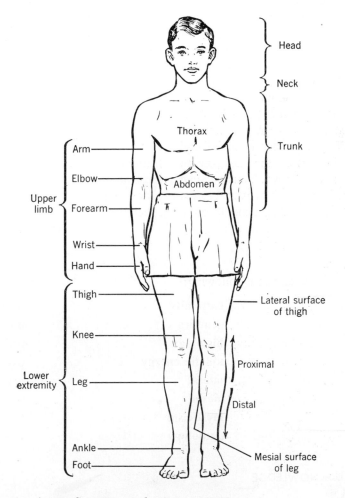

Fig. 1-3. *Anterior (ventral) view of the human body to show its general regions and the orientation of its parts.*

interchangeably, their original use should be kept in mind.

The main axis of the body consists of the three principal regions of the **head, neck,** and **trunk;** attached to it are the **limbs,** or **extremities,** which make up the **appendages.** In Fig. 1-3 are indicated the two principal parts of the trunk. The upper part is the **thorax,** a region that is usually spoken of as the chest. Its lower limit is marked by the course of the lowest (9th) rib that can be easily felt. Below the thoracic region lies the **abdomen.** Within its cavity lie the various organ systems shown in the Trans-Vision insert (following page 312). The abdomen can be roughly divided into four quarters, or **quadrants,** two of which lie on either side of the middle line.

Several terms are applied to an appendage to describe the position of its parts in relation to each other and to the main axis of the body. The **proximal** end of a limb is the region that lies toward the main part of the body. Thus one can say that the upper arm is proximal to the forearm, or the shoulder proximal to the arm. Likewise, the region that lies toward the free end is spoken of as being **distal** to other parts that are nearer the point of attachment. In this case, the hand is said to be distal to the forearm.

Two other terms are used in connection with a limb. The surface that is toward the side of the body is known as the **lateral** surface to distinguish it from the **mesial** surface that lies toward the middle line of the body. If the **palmar** surface of the hand is held upward as in the motion of asking for something, the hand is said to be in a **supine** position. The same term is used to describe the position of the body when lying on its back. If, however, the hand is extended with the palm facing downward, it is in the **prone** position, as is the body when lying on the anterior surface.

All these terms will be found very useful in the study of physiology. One of the most important aspects of science training is exactness in describing the location of a structure or the nature of a process. To do this correctly requires a specialized vocabulary.

SPEAKING OF Physiology

Briefly identify each of the following:

abdomen	**extremity**	**posterior**
anatomy	**genetics**	**potential energy**
anterior	**histology**	**proximal**
appendage	**kinetic energy**	**psychology**
distal	**lateral**	**psychosomatic**
dorsal	**mesial**	**sociology**
dynamic	**mysticism**	**thorax**
embryology	**pathology**	**ventral**

Test YOUR KNOWLEDGE

1.   How would you define the word *biology?* List as many as you can of the courses offered in high school or college that are classified as biological sciences.

2.   Why is the study of human physiology becoming increasingly dependent upon research in the fields of chemistry, physics, and mathematics?
3.   What is the educational significance of the triangle as represented in Fig. 1-1?
4.   Why did the study of human physiology have such a "stormy passage" historically?
5.   Who were some of the great scientists who contributed to our present-day knowledge of physiology? What was the great achievement of each?
6.   What is bilateral symmetry? Is this characteristic only of man? Why?
7.   Why do the names of the positions of the body surfaces change with reference to an animal that stands on two legs as compared to one that stands on four legs? Describe what changes occur.
8.   What is the difference between a *supine* position and a *prone* position?
9.   Why is vocabulary building essential for any scientific study?

See FOR YOURSELF

1. The method used by scientists in the solution of problems follows a definite plan. This same plan can be used by all students in the solution of their problems. We call this plan the *scientific method*. In order that you may become more familiar with this idea, write a report on the procedure used in the scientific method. You might use a hypothetical problem to show the significance of each step.

2. Write a paragraph on your reason for taking a course in physiology. What educational and/or vocational benefits do you expect from the knowledge gained by such a course? Do you feel that a course in physiology should be required of all students? At the end of the course, reread your answer to this question to see if your ideas have changed.

3. Prepare a written or oral report on the contributions of one of the following men to the science of physiology: Galen, Paracelsus, Harvey, Malpighi.

4. Make a chart showing how the use of the terms *dorsal, ventral, anterior,* and *posterior* differs with reference to the anatomy of men and four-footed animals.

CHAPTER 2

The Physical Basis of Life

The composition of matter. Matter may be defined as anything that has weight and occupies space. It can be recognized in one of three forms—as a **gas,** a **liquid,** or a **solid.** Matter is composed of individual, infinitely small particles— the *atoms.* Each of these is of such minute size that if we had sufficiently delicate balances, we would find that an atom of the familiar oxygen would weigh 0.000,000,000,000,000,000,000,026,5 gram (1 gram = 0.035 ounce). Chemists usually write this number as 2.65×10^{-23}. Since oxygen is taken as the standard of atomic weight, an atom of hydrogen would weigh $\frac{1}{16}$ of that amount and an atom of carbon $\frac{3}{4}$ as much. On the other hand, an atom of sulfur would weigh twice as much as an atom of oxygen.

Structure of the atom. Atoms, though very tiny, are quite complex in structure. In the center of the atom is the part known as the **nucleus,** usually composed of two different particles: positively charged **protons,** and **neutrons,** which have no electrical charge. Negatively charged particles, called **electrons,** move about the nucleus in fairly definite regions called shells or energy levels. Early in the present century, the movement of the electrons was thought to resemble that of the planets as they revolve around the sun. Today there is evidence that the movement is not so definite. Nuclear scientists now picture the electrons as resembling a swarm of bees moving about a hive (the nucleus).

The total number of electrons must equal the total number of protons in the nucleus if the atom is to remain electrically neutral. The paths followed by the electrons as they spin around the protons are the shells of the atom. If an atom, such as hydrogen, has a single electron, there is only one shell present. Oxygen, with eight electrons, has two shells (Fig. 2-1); uranium has its 92 electrons arranged in seven major shells. The newly discovered elements beyond uranium have still higher numbers of electrons in their shells.

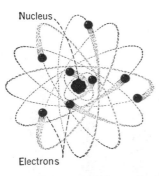

Nucleus

Electrons

Fig. 2-1. *Diagram of the oxygen atom. The nucleus contains eight protons and eight neutrons. There are eight electrons in two shells.*

Isotopes. The same type of atom may exist in several different forms, called *isotopes.* In these the number of protons and electrons is always equal, but the number of neutrons varies. An example of this is seen in the atomic structure of hydrogen. The common hydrogen atom has one proton in its nucleus and one electron in its single shell. One rare isotope of hydrogen, called heavy hydrogen or deuterium, has a neutron and a proton in the nucleus. Another, tritium, has two neutrons and one proton.

In some heavy atoms, the nuclei are unstable. These atoms break down spon-taneously to produce atomic particles of varying sizes. They also release pene-trating radiations at the same time. Such atoms are said to be naturally radioac-tive. It is possible to make some atoms artificially radioactive by bombarding them with atomic particles from nuclear reactors, and by the use of other complex machines, such as the cyclotron. The Oak Ridge and Brookhaven Laborato-ries have produced radioactive iodine (I^{131}), for use in the treatment of dis-eases of the thyroid gland, and calcium (Ca^{45}) for the study of bone and muscle activity. A naturally occurring isotope

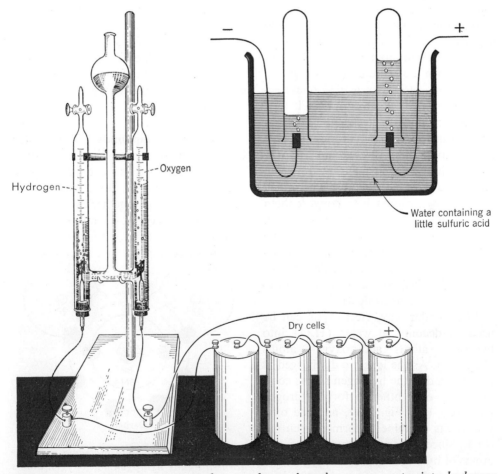

Fig. 2-2. *Two types of apparatus that can be used to decompose water into hydrogen and oxygen.*

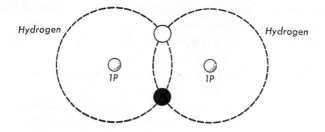

Fig. 2-3. *Two atoms of hydrogen sharing electrons to form a molecule of hydrogen.*

of carbon (C^{14}) is now being widely used to determine the age of very old materials.

Ions and molecules. When an atom gains or loses electrons, it becomes negatively or positively charged and is known as an **ion.** For example, table salt (sodium chloride) is composed of one atom of sodium combined chemically with one atom of chlorine. In this combination the sodium atom has lost one electron to form the sodium ion (Na^+), and the chlorine atom has gained one electron to form the chloride ion (Cl^-). If a direct current of electricity is passed through *melted* sodium chloride, the salt is decomposed into sodium and chlorine. The sodium ions are attracted to the negative electrode (cathode) where they gain one electron each to convert them into sodium atoms. In the opposite way, chloride ions are converted to chlorine atoms as they lose electrons at the positive electrode (anode). The decomposition of chemical compounds by electricity is known as **electrolysis.**

In a similar way, electrolysis can be used to decompose water (H_2O) into hydrogen atoms and oxygen atoms (Fig. 2-2). As the ions are discharged at the electrodes, the hydrogen atoms combine with each other to form hydrogen gas (H_2) (see Fig. 2-3), and the oxygen atoms combine to form oxygen gas (O_2). Since water is composed of two atoms of hydrogen to one of oxygen, two volumes of hydrogen gas are evolved for every volume of oxygen.

A **molecule** is formed when two or more atoms unite by sharing or exchanging electrons. Molecules are thus electrically neutral. If all the atoms composing a substance are of the same kind, the substance is called an **element.** Thus, in the electrolysis of water, all of the gas appearing at one electrode is composed of the element hydrogen, while that appearing at the other is the element oxygen. There are 92 different elements that occur naturally on the earth. Since the early days of World War II, ten new synthetic elements have been produced by nuclear scientists.

Chemical compounds. The water from which the hydrogen and the oxygen were obtained is an example of a **chemical compound.** In a compound, the atoms are held together by their electrical charges (Fig. 2-4) and cannot be

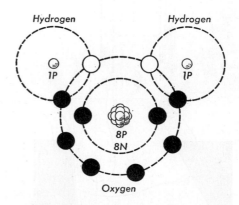

Fig. 2-4. *Diagram of a molecule of water formed by the hydrogen and oxygen atoms sharing electrons. This is an example of a chemical compound.*

separated by means that do not involve an expenditure of energy. The hydrogen and oxygen in water will not separate on standing; electrical energy is required in this case to separate the bonds that hold these elements together.

A second characteristic of a compound is that the number and relationship of the atoms that compose it must always be the same. In water, there are always twice as many hydrogen atoms as oxygen atoms, so that the **chemical formula** for water is H_2O. Under certain conditions, hydrogen and oxygen can be made to unite in such a manner that the number of oxygen atoms equals the number of hydrogen atoms. This will produce a very unstable liquid, hydrogen peroxide (H_2O_2), which has properties quite different from those of water. Therefore, a change in the relative number of atoms in a compound will produce a new substance.

The relative position of the atoms within the molecule will affect the properties of a substance. This is well shown by two simple sugars that play important parts in our body's chemistry. *Glucose,* a very common sugar manufactured by green plants, is composed of 6 atoms of carbon, 12 of hydrogen, and 6 of oxygen ($C_6H_{12}O_6$). Within its molecule, the atoms are arranged as in Fig. 2-5, right. If these same atoms are arranged in a slightly different manner, another sugar is formed that has properties quite different from glucose. This is *fructose,* the formula for which may also be written as $C_6H_{12}O_6$. Since these two sugars are so nearly alike, ordinary chemical tests will not distinguish between them. However, if each is exposed to a beam of polarized light, the glucose will twist the light to the right and the fructose to the left. (Glucose is sometimes called *dextrose,* from the Latin *dexter,* meaning "right,"

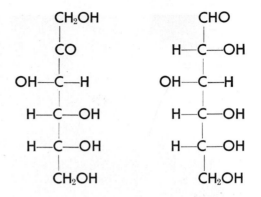

Fig. 2-5. *The structural formulas for fructose (left) and glucose (right). Note that although these compounds have the same general formula ($C_6H_{12}O_6$), the arrangement of the atoms in the molecules is different.*

and fructose is known as *levulose,* from the Latin *laevus,* meaning "left.")

A fourth characteristic of a compound is that its properties are quite different from those of the substances that produce it. Water is a liquid composed of two elements that appear as gases in nature. Similarly, common table salt has properties quite different from those of the sodium and chlorine which compose it. Sodium is a soft, gray, highly active metal that will react violently with water. Chlorine, on the other hand, is a yellow gas used during World War I as a poison gas. However, if these two elements are chemically combined by sharing electrons, the resulting compound is table salt, a white crystalline substance which is easily soluble in water and is essential for all animal life.

Colloidal suspensions. Living matter is vastly complex in its composition and structure. Its basic nature is that of a mixture of extremely minute particles of solid matter suspended in a liquid. This is known as a **colloidal suspension** (Greek, *kollos,* glue). These particles may range in size from 0.000001 millimeter to 0.0002 millimeter. These size

Fig. 2-6. *The Tyndall effect. Note how the beam of light in the jar on the left, which contains only water, shows very little scattering. Compare this with the jar on the right, which contains a suspension of gelatin.* (*Bennett*)

limits are rather arbitrary in defining a colloidal suspension because larger particles tend to settle out from the liquid in which they were suspended, whereas colloidal suspensions never settle out. The colloidal particles are sometimes single huge molecules, as in the case of some of the proteins, while at other times they represent groups of molecules that stick to each other in clumps.

If a colloidal suspension is viewed under the ordinary microscope or is seen in direct light, it appears to be transparent. But if a beam of light is passed through it at right angles to the viewing angle, it will appear turbid because the particles scatter the light. This is called the **Tyndall effect** (Fig. 2-6). The size of the particles in a colloidal suspension also prevents them from passing easily through a parchment or an animal membrane. Thus it is possible to separate a colloidal suspension from a

true solution (solution of crystalloids) by a process known as **dialysis** (Fig. 2-7).

The relation between the suspension and the liquid in which the particles are suspended can change from time to time. A well-known example of this property is seen when gelatin is mixed with water. Gelatin, a simple type of protein, will form what appears to be a clear solution when it is heated with water. In this condition, the colloidal particles of the gelatin are in a greatly folded or contracted condition and are quite widely scattered among the water molecules. In this state it is called a **sol**. As the gelatin cools, the particles straighten out or expand to form a firm network that traps the water within its meshes and forms a **gel** (Fig. 2-8).

The physiologic significance of colloidal particles lies in the fact that, being extremely small, they expose a tremen-

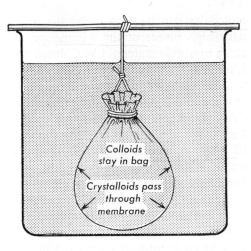

Fig. 2-7. *Diagram illustrating dialysis. The colloidal particles are too large to pass through the walls of the membranous bag.*

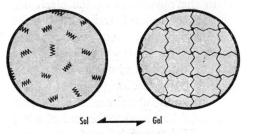

Sol ← → Gel

Fig. 2-8. *The colloidal state. Left, the colloidal particles are shrunken and folded among the molecules of water that are represented by the small dots. Right, the particles have straightened out and now form a network that traps the water. As the arrow indicates, the sol state can be changed into the gel state, or the process can be reversed. (From Marsland,* Principles of Modern Biology, *Holt, 1957)*

dous amount of surface over which chemical reactions can occur. It has been estimated that if a one-centimeter cube of a substance were divided into particles of colloidal size, its total original surface area would be increased from 6 square centimeters to over 6 million square centimeters. Since living material is colloidal in nature, this means that within each cell there is a vast amount of surface area over which chemical reactions can occur.

Emulsions. An *emulsion* is a type of colloidal suspension in which a liquid is suspended in a liquid. In milk, for example, cream will separate out and rise to the top if the milk is allowed to stand. If the milk is homogenized, the fat is broken down into colloidal particles that remain suspended in the rest of the liquid. In this latter state, milk is an emulsion. We are all familiar with what happens when we try to mix oil and water. The oil becomes divided into fine droplets if we shake it vigorously with the water, but soon the two will again separate into distinct layers. If soap is present, the oil remains suspended in the

water and gives it a milky appearance. The soap surrounds the fat droplets and prevents them from recombining, thus forming an emulsion. The soap acts as an *emulsifying agent* (Fig. 2-9). In our discussion of the digestive system (Chapter 17) we will see how bile acts as an emulsifying agent in the digestion of fats.

Motion of molecules. Matter, as we have seen, is composed of atoms and combinations of atoms (molecules). Atoms are in a constant state of motion,

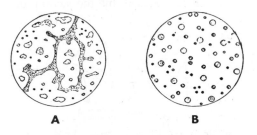

A   B

Fig. 2-9. *The action of an emulsifying agent. In A, when an emulsion, made by shaking oil and water together, is allowed to stand, the oil particles tend to run together. In B, the emulsifying agent surrounds the particles and a stable emulsion is formed. (After Marsland,* Principles of Modern Biology, *Holt, 1957)*

due to the movement of the electrons. This atomic motion is transmitted to the molecules so that there is a constant minute motion in all substances. It may be rather difficult to imagine this occurring in a bar of lead or a piece of gold— both very solid substances. But if a piece of pure gold is fused to the end of a bar of pure lead, atoms of gold will slowly migrate into the lead and atoms of lead into the gold. This movement can only be explained on the basis of the motion of molecules. In a *solid* the spaces between the molecules are infinitely small, and the distances permitted the molecules for their movements is correspondingly minute. In a *liquid,* the spaces between the molecules are much greater. The result is that they can move with more freedom. This also explains why a liquid takes the form of its container —the molecules can shift on each other and adjust themselves to the shape of the glass or bottle in which they are placed. The spaces between the molecules of a *gas* are, relatively speaking, very great and the molecules have great freedom of movement. Since these spaces are large, it is difficult to restrain a gas; the molecules always move away from each other.

Movement caused by the action of

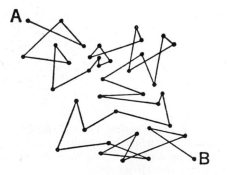

Fig. 2-10. *The paths taken by a particle moving by Brownian movement from Point A to Point B. (From Bawden,* Matter and Energy, *Holt, 1957)*

molecules can be seen under the ordinary high power of the microscope. If some insoluble material like Chinese ink is finely divided and put in a drop of water, the particles of ink will be seen to move with a jiggling motion. These relatively huge particles are much larger than colloidal particles, but they can still be affected by the small and invisible water molecules which are constantly bombarding them. The water molecules strike them first from one angle and then from another. Each time the particle is struck, it is knocked in one direction only to be immediately knocked in another direction by another water molecule. The final result of this motion is the scattering of the ink particles through the water. Such visible evidence of the activities of colloidal particles is called **Brownian movement** in honor of the English scientist, Robert Brown, who first described it in 1828 (Fig. 2-10).

Diffusion and osmosis. One of the most important processes occurring in living cells is based on the fact that molecules have the power of independent movement. As we have mentioned, the molecules of gold pass into the lead bar, and those of the lead into the gold. In each case there is a movement of the molecules from an area where they are highly concentrated (that is, in great numbers) to a region of lower concentration. This process is known as **diffusion.** Exactly the same process occurs in living bodies; materials have a tendency to pass from a region where they are in relatively high concentration to a region of lower concentration, and this usually occurs through a cell membrane. Thus, when materials are present in higher concentration outside the cells, these materials often have the ability to enter the cells by diffusion.

A special type of diffusion occurs through the membranes of cells under certain conditions. There is good evidence that the cell membrane is sieve-like, with openings of a fairly uniform diameter. These will permit certain molecules to pass through the membrane quite freely, but prevent other, larger molecules from doing so. A membrane of this type, showing a selective action, is called a **semipermeable membrane.**

If a certain kind of semipermeable membrane is placed between a sugar-water solution and pure water, we find that more molecules of water enter the solution than leave it. The simple apparatus shown in Fig. 2-11 will demonstrate this process. A solution of sugar is placed in the bell of the thistle tube, and the opening is covered by a semipermeable membrane. The tube is then inverted in a beaker of water. Within a few hours the sugar solution in the thistle tube increases in volume and rises above its original level. The reason for this is that there are fewer water molecules in the sugar solution than there are in the beaker which contains only pure water. Since the semipermeable membrane allows the small water molecules but not the larger sugar molecules to pass through, the water moves by diffusion from a region of high concentration (the beaker) to a region of lower concentration (the tube), thereby increasing the quantity of fluid within the tube. Theoretically, this process will continue as long as there is a difference in the concentration of water molecules on the two sides of the membrane.

Diffusion through a semipermeable membrane is called **osmosis,** and the pressure that is developed is known as *osmotic pressure.* Osmosis is the basic principle involved in the process of dialysis mentioned earlier.

The osmotic pressure under various conditions must be carefully considered in any work with living cells. Any treat-

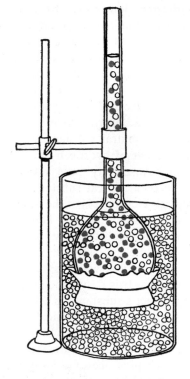

Fig. 2-11. *A demonstration of the process of osmosis. The colored dots represent the sugar molecules and the small circles the water molecules.*

ment affecting the composition of the blood and other body fluids must be delicately adjusted. Unless the composition of these fluids exactly balances the composition of the materials within the cells they bathe, excess fluids may enter the cells, or fluids may be drawn from the cells, with harmful results. For example, a saline (salt) solution is often injected into a person's blood stream following a serious loss of blood as a result of an injury or after a serious operation. If this saline solution contains too little salt, the resulting osmotic flow carries an excess of water into the blood cells, causing widespread destruction of these cells. Likewise, if too much salt is used in the solution, water is removed from the cells and they are destroyed.

Hydrogen ion concentration (pH).
We are all familiar with the fact that some substances are acid and have a sour flavor, while others are either alkaline or neutral. The difference between an acid and an alkali (base) is the presence of an excess of hydrogen ions (H^+) in an acid, and of hydroxide ions (OH^-) in a base. Neutral substances have an equal number of hydrogen and hydroxide ions. Absolutely pure water is an example of a neutral substance. In the biological sciences it is of the utmost importance to know exactly how acid or how alkaline a substance is; living material is extremely sensitive to any change in its environment with respect to these two features. It is easy enough to determine whether a substance is acid or basic by testing it with a chemical that will change color accordingly. Litmus is an example of such an indicator; it will turn blue in the presence of a base and red in an acid. Litmus does not indicate, however, the degree of acidity or alkalinity. Other indicators can be used for this purpose.

To meet the needs of chemists who work with substances that react only slightly to the indicators, methods have been devised to measure with great accuracy the number of hydrogen ions present in a solution. Some of these methods depend on how easily a solution will carry a definite amount of electric current, while others use delicate indicators that change color in the presence of small amounts of hydrogen ions. An exactly neutral substance like absolutely pure water will neither carry an electric charge nor bring about a color change in an indicator because of the balance between the hydrogen and hydroxide ions. This neutral point has been given a value of 7 on a scale that has been developed to measure the acidity of a solution. On this scale, acid substances have values from 0 to 7 and alkaline substances have values from 7 to 14. Thus a solution of hydrochloric acid may have a value of 1.1 as compared with a value of 13 for a solution of sodium hydroxide. A statement of the theory on which this scale is based can be found in an advanced text in chemistry or physiology.

In the body, each cell and its products have become adapted to a very definite hydrogen ion concentration, which is usually called the **pH** of the material. If their normal acidity or alkalinity is upset, their various chemical reactions are affected. For example, in the mouth the saliva will digest starch if the pH is between 5.6 and 7.6. If it is lower, the acid will attack the teeth, and if it is higher, no digestion will take place. The action of the saliva will eventually be stopped in the stomach where the gastric juice has a rather low pH value (about 2). When the gastric juice passes into the small intestine, its action is stopped by the higher pH of that region, which may reach a value of between 7 and 8. Figure 2-12 shows the relative pH of some of the body fluids.

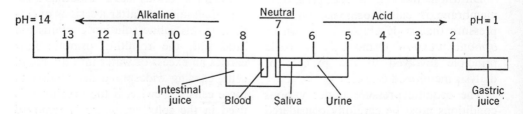

Fig. 2-12. *The hydrogen ion (pH) scale.*

Oxygen	65.00%
Carbon	18.30%
Hydrogen	10.00%
Nitrogen	2.65%
Calcium	1.40%
Phosphorus	0.80%
Potassium	0.30%
Sodium	0.30%
Chlorine	0.30%
Sulfur	0.20%
Magnesium	0.04%
Iron	0.004%
Iodine	0.00004%
Silicon, Zinc, Fluorine, Cobalt, Copper, Manganese, Bromine, Aluminum, and others	Minute traces

Protoplasm. The fundamental material of which all living organisms are composed is **protoplasm.** This highly complex material is in a constant state of change, never being the same for two consecutive moments of time. It is continually being broken down by the chemical reactions occurring within it and is just as continually being re-formed. This cycle of destruction and rebuilding gives protoplasm the living quality.

There are approximately twenty different chemical elements present in the living material of the body. Identification of these elements is rather easy, but the part each plays in the living process is sometimes difficult to determine. The reason lies in the fact that the property of life depends on a very delicate balance between chemical compounds and reactions. These conditions are so easily upset that as soon as an attempt is made to analyze protoplasm, the material is so altered that it loses the living quality. When that occurs, we are no longer working with living material in which vital chemical reactions are taking place.

Many analyses have been made of protoplasm to determine its chemical contents and to measure the percentage by weight of each of its elements. These percentages will vary among different individuals, depending on what elements each is able to obtain from his environment, but they will approximate those in the table at the left.

One must remember that these elements are not found in their free states in the protoplasm of cells. That is, one does not find pure carbon or hydrogen or potassium in the body. Instead, the elements are combined into compounds. The following table gives the approximate distribution of these:

Water	80%
Proteins	15%
Fats, oils, and other fatty substances	3%
Inorganic salts	1%
Other compounds including carbohydrates	1%

Protoplasm has a slightly grayish-green appearance when viewed under a microscope. Within the material can be seen small masses of a granular nature, which may be either cell structures or products of the cell's activities. The background material is colloidal in nature.

The characteristics of protoplasm. Those features which one usually associates with the condition of being alive are actually manifestations of the activities of protoplasm. This substance is the basis for all traits which distinguish a living from a nonliving object. These attributes of living organisms may be grouped under four main headings:

1. Protoplasmic organization. The protoplasm of the body of any animal is always contained in unit packets, the *cells.* An adult human body of average size is estimated to contain about 26,500,000,000,000 cells. A protozoan, such as the ameba, has only one. In any case, the cell contains a quantity of protoplasm which carries on those various processes, the sum total of which results in the state of living. Thus we find that the body is composed of cells and the products of cells.

Not only is protoplasm responsible for the functions of the various cells, but it is also the material from which the parts that may be considered nonliving have been formed. In certain cells in the bodies of all animals, the protoplasm is replaced by nonliving material which either gives strength to the region or serves as a protective layer for underlying parts. In man, parts of the bones, teeth, and skin are examples of regions where living matter has been replaced by nonliving materials. It must be remembered, however, that in all cases these are modified cells that have once been living and filled with protoplasm; they are the products of highly specialized action within the living cell.

2. Metabolism refers to all chemical and physical processes that occur in the body: how the cells use different types of food; how they produce energy from these substances; and how they manufacture the many types of materials for which they are responsible. The efficiency of the body can be measured in terms of the metabolic reactions within the cells; hence "basal metabolism" refers to how ably we use the materials we take in to meet our various energy requirements.

3. Irritability. A third characteristic of protoplasm is its power to respond to environmental changes. A single-celled animal like the ameba is quite sensitive to differences in its surroundings, al-

though it lacks a definite nervous system or specialized organs to register these changes. This is an example of how protoplasm, without benefit of any highly differentiated parts, can respond to variations which may affect it either adversely or beneficially. An increase in size makes it necessary to develop highly specialized organs which can receive stimuli from outside the body. Other parts must be able to transmit these messages to relatively distant regions, which set up a chain of events that constitute the reaction to the original stimulus. Thus, in the more advanced forms, certain cells of the body have developed to a high degree the function of irritability, and we find a nervous system appearing as an essential part of the animal's organization. Man's real claim to superiority lies in the fact that he has the most highly specialized nervous system found among animals. This permits him to respond to stimuli in a variety of ways and also gives him power to originate within his body other stimuli which appear as the thought patterns known as human intelligence.

4. Reproduction. The continuation of the race of any living organism is dependent on its ability to produce others of a like nature. One-celled animals simply divide the material of the cell into two halves, each of which then develops into a new individual. The increasing complexity of the higher animals has made it necessary to develop specialized cells for this purpose. These cells insure that the characteristics of the race shall be transmitted in an essentially unaltered form from one generation to the next. Thus, the inheritance pattern of the individual is closely associated with the process of reproduction, and the increasing complexity of the organisms requires the sharing of this responsibility by two sexes.

SPEAKING OF Physiology

Briefly identify each of the following:

acid	**element**	**molecule**
atom	**ion**	**osmosis**
base	**irritability**	**pH**
chemical compound	**isotope**	**protoplasm**
colloidal suspension	**matter**	**reproduction**
diffusion	**metabolism**	**semipermeable**

Test YOUR KNOWLEDGE

1. What conditions must exist if an atom is to remain electrically neutral?
2. Water can exist in three states: as a gas (steam), as a liquid, and as a solid (ice). What changes in molecular activity occur in each of these states?
3. How does an ion differ from an electrically neutral atom?
4. State briefly, in your own words, three characteristics of a chemical compound.
5. How does a colloidal suspension differ from a sugar solution?
6. How are isotopes used by man today?
7. Give three examples of diffusion, other than those listed in your text.
8. Why is the process of osmosis so vital to all living organisms?
9. Why is protoplasm defined as the "unit of function and activity" of a living organism?
10. List four characteristics of nonliving substances. Compare and discuss the differences, if any, between your suggestions and the four principal characteristics of living material given in your text.

See FOR YOURSELF

1. If a microscope is available, obtain a small bottle of pond water, making sure that you collect some of the green scum at the edge of the pool. Place a drop of this water on a clean microscope slide and cover it with a cover slip. Observe through low power to see if any living forms are present. How many different kinds of living animals can you find? Note those activities which are characteristic of living cells. Draw examples of the forms you see. If the water evaporates under the cover slip, note what happens to the living cells. Why? (Before starting this experiment, be sure that you have received instruction on how to operate a microscope.)

2. Prepare a report, either for oral presentation or as part of your class notebook, on the cell theory and how it has affected science.

3. Make a series of structural models of atoms. You may use modeling clay, small round corks, rubber balls, ping-pong balls or any other round object. Use different colors for electrons, protons, and neutrons. Hydrogen is made up of one electron and only one proton; carbon is made up of six electrons circling a nucleus made up of six protons and six neutrons. Oxygen contains eight electrons moving around a nucleus of eight protons and eight neutrons. You might even construct these models as mobiles to be hung from the ceiling of your classroom or your own room at home.

CHAPTER 3

The Cell—Its Structure, Functions, and Reproduction

The study of the minute structure of living matter was dependent on the invention of the compound microscope. It was not until this instrument had been developed to a point where it could be used for the examination of these parts that man was able to see the fine structures that made up the human body. This invention came during the seventeenth century. In 1665, Robert Hooke, an English scientist, cut very thin sections of cork and examined them under this new instrument. He saw that the sections were composed of numerous walled structures that he called "cells." Hooke's use of this term for what he saw differed from our use of the same term. What he actually saw were the dead cell walls of the cork and not the "stuff of life" which they had at one time contained.

During the next fifty years, many basic discoveries were made by such men as Marcello Malpighi, Jan Swammerdam, and Anton van Leeuwenhoek, who opened up the field of microscopic anatomy. Today, with the help of micro-dissection techniques, the electron microscope, and improved methods of chemical analysis, new facts are being discovered about the details of cell structure. Although much has been learned about these structural units during the 300 years that have elapsed since Hooke's time, there remain many unanswered questions.

The cells of the human body differ greatly in shape and size. Some are minute disk-shaped objects, like the red blood corpuscles, which are so small that between 5 and 5½ millions of the cells are contained in $\frac{1}{25}$ of a drop of blood. Others, the nerve cells, have a very irregular outline with exceedingly thin projections, several feet in length. Still other types of cells are spindle-shaped with cross-markings that distinguish them as muscle cells attached to the bones of the skeleton. As we shall see in the next chapter, the shape and size of the cells are usually associated with the particular function they perform.

A cell is a unit of structure, function, and heredity in a living body. Not only do cells serve as "building blocks" for the body, but they also determine its various activities. This is because the functions of the body as a whole are the result of the combined activities of the individual cells. Furthermore, each cell contains the materials that control the inheritance of the individual, although these actually determine heritable characteristics only in the reproductive cells. To accomplish all these activities, the internal structure of a cell must be highly complex although superficially it may appear to be quite simple in structure. No cell of the human body, regardless of its apparent simplicity or complexity, is self-sufficient. A cell cannot supply its own needs without help from other cells. All of the body's millions of cells are highly specialized for specific functions; hence, they are not capable of meeting all of the problems that arise. The diagram given in Fig. 3-1 may be considered a composite of a large number of cells. Few cells contain all of the structures shown here, but all are present in one or another type of cell.

Plasma membrane. The outer covering of an animal cell is a very thin layer of material called the **plasma membrane** (or **cell membrane**), composed largely of proteins. It is one of the most important cell structures. One of its functions is to contain and protect the inner parts of the cell. This membrane, which is semipermeable, also regulates the passage of materials into and out of the cells. The regulatory action is very selective, permitting the entrance of a substance at one moment and then preventing the same substance from leaving when the cell requirements change. This action results in the maintenance of a balance among the different groups of materials within the cell. Just how this selective action is accomplished is not clearly understood at present.

A second feature of the plasma membrane that makes it unique is the method of its formation. Although generally considered a living part of the cell, under certain conditions it behaves as though it were a product of chemical reactions that take place when the contents of the cell come in contact with the surrounding fluid. For example, if, during a microdissection experiment, a plasma

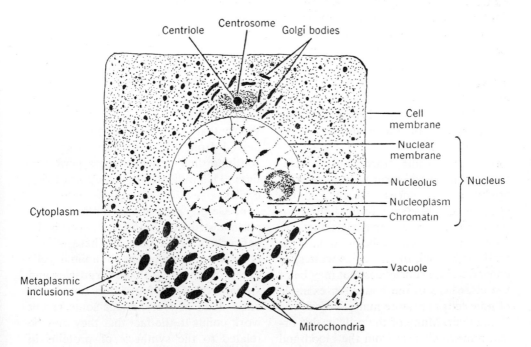

Centriole   Centrosome   Golgi bodies

Cell membrane

Nuclear membrane

Nucleolus — Nucleus

Nucleoplasm

Chromatin

Cytoplasm

Vacuole

Metaplasmic inclusions

Mitrochondria

Fig. 3-1. *Diagram of a typical animal cell.*

membrane is torn and the contents allowed to escape, a new membrane will form if calcium ions are present in the surrounding fluid. If no such ions are present, the contents of the cell will continue to flow through the break. However, in the case of a small puncture of the membrane, the gap is healed spontaneously.

Cytoplasm. All of the ground substance (protoplasm) of the cell lying between the cell membrane and the nucleus is called cytoplasm. This jellylike substance has all the characteristics of living material. Embedded in it are some nonliving substances which are the products of the activities of the protoplasm. As the result of this combination of living and lifeless materials, a highly complex type of organization may exist in the cytoplasm. This may contain some, or all, of the following structures:

a. Centrosome. Lying quite close to the nucleus is the centrosome, a collection of very fine granules within which lies a larger solid granule, the **centriole.** As we will find when we study the process of cell division, the centriole plays an active part in the division of the cell. That it is probably not essential to this process is shown by the fact that a centriole is absent from or has not yet been seen in cells of the majority of the higher plants.

b. Metaplasmic inclusions. Metaplasm is a general term used to refer to nonliving substances present in the cytoplasm. These are formed by cytoplasm and represent materials that are temporarily stored to be used later as food for the cell, discarded as wastes, or converted into substances that may be of use elsewhere in the body. An example of how cells may store materials is found in the liver. Many of the cells in this organ remove glucose from the blood and then convert it into a starchlike com-

pound, glycogen. This glycogen is stored in the form of granules in the cells until such time as the body requires a source of quick energy; then it is reconverted into glucose.

c. Vacuoles. Just as solids may be stored in the cytoplasm, liquids may also be present as minute droplets of fluid within **vacuoles.** Each of these is surrounded by a very thin membrane, the **vacuolar membrane,** which separates it from the rest of the cytoplasm. Some of these liquids are stored material, such as fat. Others are manufactured substances which the cell may liberate through the cell membrane for use elsewhere. Still others are waste materials.

d. Mitochondria. Within the cytoplasm of nearly all animal cells are found mitochondria, the importance of which is just being realized. These small bodies may take the form of rods, spheres, or oval structures, and they are most common in those regions of the cell where the rate of chemical activity is the highest. Mitochondria are composed of proteins, fatlike compounds (phospholipids), and other chemical compounds, all of which are connected with the release of energy from the various food materials present in the cell. Recent work on the structure of the cell has shown that if the mitochondria are removed from the cytoplasm, they will continue their activities for a period of time. This indicates that they are living bodies.

e. Golgi network. Another cytoplasmic structure found in the cell is the network of Golgi bodies. These minute objects are present in all animal cells except mature red blood corpuscles and sperm cells. Their function is not clearly understood at present, but some recent work points to the fact that they may be related to the synthesis of proteins in the cells. By means of special staining techniques, they can be distinguished from the mitochondria. (The members of the Golgi network stain red when neutral red is used, and the mitochondria stain green with Janus green.) The Golgi bodies are frequently found in the vicinity of the nucleus or the centrosome.

Nucleus. The nucleus of a cell functions in two important ways: (1) it controls and regulates the metabolic activities of the cell as a whole, and (2) it plays a leading role in the process of cell division. The protoplasm within the nucleus is called **nucleoplasm.** A *nuclear membrane* separates it from the cytoplasm. This thin layer of material behaves in a manner similar to that of the plasma membrane. The important parts of the nucleus are as follows:

a. Chromatin. The word "chromatin" is taken from the Greek word *chroma,* which means "color," because chromatin has the ability to absorb a variety of basic dyes. From a chemical standpoint chromatin is composed of a type of protien known as a **nucleoprotein.** These substances are combinations of a protein and a nucleic acid. The nucleic acid typical of all living cells is *desoxyribonucleic acid* (DNA). We shall have more to say about DNA when we discuss the subject of heredity (Chapter 33).

When a cell is not actively dividing (reproducing), the chromatin granules are usually in the form of long threads so thin and interwoven that they give a netlike appearance to the contents of the nucleus. However, when a cell is in the process of dividing, this network becomes aggregated, forming thick, rodlike bodies, the *chromosomes.*

b. Nucleolus. One or two nucleoli may be present in the nucleus of some cells while other cells seem to lack them. In fact, this structure may be present during some of the stages of the life of a cell and absent at other times, or it may divide into two or more pieces. During the process of cell division, the nucleolus disappears entirely, only to reappear after the new cells have been formed. The exact function of this body is not clearly understood, but there seems to be increasing evidence that it is associated with the formation of nucleoproteins.

Growth of cells. The growth of a living body is dependent on two factors which occur in sequence: (1) the increase in the volume of the individual cells and (2) the increase in their numbers.

Individual cells grow in volume as a result of a process known as **assimilation.** During this process the cell takes in food and, under the influence of chemical materials produced by specialized parts of the cytoplasm, is able to form new living material. This increase in size occurs within the confines of the cell membrane and thus differs from the so-called "growth" of nonliving objects, such as icicles and stalactites, which increase by the addition of new material to the outside.

A result of this type of cell growth is that the volume increases more rapidly than the surface area. Thus, if a newly formed cubical cell measures 10/25000 of an inch on each edge, its growth may double its dimensions to 20/25000 of an inch on each edge. This would mean that its volume would be increased eightfold, while the surface area had increased only four times. Since cells depend on the amount of food and oxygen they can absorb through their cell membranes, this difference between volume and surface makes continued growth impossible. If the cell grows larger, it will die because it cannot absorb enough of the necessary materials to supply its ever-increasing volume, nor can it get rid of all the wastes it produces. Cells, therefore, are limited in size by this surface area-volume relationship. When an individual cell reaches the maximum volume its surface area can support, it divides in half to restore the balance between area and volume.

The rate of normal division of individual cells is obviously a direct result of their rate of growth. In the human body, cells divide at varying rates of speed, depending on their functions. The result is that some parts of the body may grow very rapidly for a period of time and then slow down, while other parts grow slowly or not at all, once they have been formed. Good examples of how different kinds of cells grow at varying rates of speed are the cells of the middle and inner ear, and those in the outer layers of the skin. The tiny bones of the ear and the hearing apparatus have reached their maximum size some time before birth and do not grow after that time. The outer layers of the skin, however, are in a constant state of active growth because they are being constantly shed and replaced by new cells formed by the underlying skin layers.

Tissues are formed by cell divisions (Chapter 4), and when a sufficient number of cells have been formed to meet the requirements of the individual, they stop dividing. In the majority of tissues, even replacement of lost or injured cells is not possible once the "check" has come into play. Occasionally, this check disappears for some currently unknown reason, and some of the cells in a tissue may begin to divide rapidly and in an abnormal manner. When this occurs, these abnormal cells invade regions occupied by normal cells and upset their metabolic activities. The result is a tumor or a cancer. When a more complete understanding of the processes occurring in normal cells has been reached,

the problems concerned with their abnormalities may possibly be solved. Basically, the control of cancer involves the riddle of cell growth and division and an understanding of why cells behave as they do.

Cell division. The process of cell division results in the growth of the body as a whole, for it is by this means that the total number of cells is increased. As a general rule, those cells that grow slowly divide with a corresponding slowness, so that it may take days for them to go through the same process that more rapidly growing cells accomplish within twenty minutes.

The most common process by which cells divide is called **mitosis** (Greek, *mitos,* thread). During this process, the cell passes through a series of quite complicated stages which result in the formation of two new cells. Each of these daughter cells contains an amount of chromatin that equals that found in the other, not only in quantity but also in quality. This even division of the chromatic material of the nucleus is of extreme importance in the case of those cells responsible for the transmission of characteristics from one generation to the next. Without a process that would guarantee the exactly equal distribution of chromatin among these cells, there could be no assurance that the characteristics of the race would remain constant from one generation to the next.

The process of mitosis is a continuous one and is usually of fairly short duration. For the convenience of study, the various stages through which the nucleus passes in its division have been grouped into five principal phases. It should be remembered, however, that although each phase has its own peculiarities, these are really parts of a continuous process. It is possible, therefore, to arrange them under the following headings: *interphase, prophase, metaphase, anaphase,* and *telophase.*

Interphase. This is, strictly speaking, not a stage in the process of mitosis but represents that growth period in the cell's life when it is not actively dividing.

Prophase (Fig. 3-2). One of the first indications that a cell is about to divide is given by the centriole. During the interphase, this body lies within the centrosome; but as the time of division approaches, it splits in half and the two parts move slowly away from each other toward opposite poles of the nucleus. As the centrioles separate, lines of granules (the **spindle**) appear between them; around each centriole similar fibers (**asters**) radiate into the cytoplasm. The exact function of these granules is in doubt, but that they are very definite structures can be demonstrated by microdissection. If a fine hooked needle is thrust into the cell, the spindle can be stretched and drawn out of position, indicating its fiberlike consistency.

Within the nucleus, changes occur in the chromatin. The netlike appearance of the chromatin is lost, and for the first time its true threadlike character is seen. The chromatin now appears as long double threads which are loosely coiled. These double threads then become shorter, thicker, and more distinct as separate bodies, the **chromosomes.**

For many years the chromosomes were thought to be single structures, but recent advances in the techniques of staining cell parts show that they are not. In fact, what appears to be a single rodlike body turns out to be a double thread surrounded by a sheath of material that is held to it by a very thin layer of protein. It is this surrounding substance that is stained by ordinary dyes and gives the impression that the chromosome is single. If special stains are used, the inner structures can be seen.

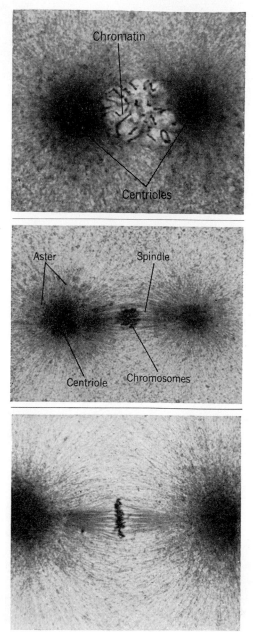

Fig. 3-2. (*Top*) *Early prophase. The chromatin appears as pieces of cut thread. The centrioles have moved to opposite poles of the cell.* (*Middle*) *Late prophase. The chromosomes and spindle appear in this stage.* (*Bottom*) *Metaphase. The chromosomes are arranged along the equator of the cell.* (*General Biological Supply House*)

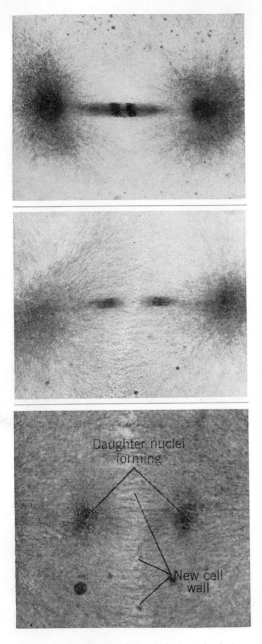

Daughter nuclei
forming

New cell
wall

Fig. 3-3. (*Top*) *Early anaphase. The halves of the chromosomes separate and move toward opposite poles of the cell. (Middle) Late anaphase. The chromosomes move farther apart and the spindle begins to break down. (Bottom) Telophase. A new cell wall appears and two distinct daughter nuclei are formed. (General Biological Supply House)*

These consist of the two chromosomes attached to each other at a single point by a very small piece of chromatic substance, the **centromere**. This double nature of the chromosome explains how some of the later processes occurring in mitosis can take place. Both the nuclear membrane and the nucleolus disappear during the latter stages of this phase.

Metaphase (Fig. 3-2). The metaphase is characterized by the separation of the halves of the chromosomes. Up to this time the halves have been attached to each other by the centromere, but in this phase they break apart and the halves separate. Prior to their actual separation, under the influence of the spindle fibers, the chromosomes have become neatly arranged along the center (*equator*) of the cell.

Anaphase. Following the separation of the halves of the chromosomes, each half turns away from the other and moves toward an opposite pole of the cell (Fig. 3-3). Just how this movement is accomplished is not clear, but the spindle fibers probably play a role in the process. As the halves separate, an indentation appears in the cell membrane at a point approximately in the middle of the cell. This indentation begins to divide the cytoplasm of the cell in half.

Telophase (Fig. 3-3). The final stage of mitosis is the one in which there is complete division of the parent cell into two daughter cells. This is accomplished when the new cell membranes have met and fused, resulting in the formation of two new and separate cells. The chromatin material of each daughter cell then rapidly goes through a threadlike stage and eventually assumes the network appearance typical of the interphase. The nuclear membrane forms around the chromatin of each new cell, and nucleoli may reappear.

SPEAKING OF Physiology

Briefly identify each of the following:

anaphase	cytoplasm	nucleolus
assimilation	Golgi network	nucleoprotein
cell	interphase	nucleus
centriole	metaphase	plasma membrane
centrosome	metaplasm	prophase
chromatin	mitochondria	telophase
chromosome	mitosis	vacuole

Test YOUR KNOWLEDGE

1. Describe the functions of the plasma membrane.
2. If a cell membrane is severely damaged, what must be present in the surrounding fluid for it to repair itself?
3. Why are cells considered the unit of structure, function, and heredity of a living organism?
4. List and describe five structures present in cytoplasm.
5. Why is the nucleus considered the "controlling center" of a cell?
6. Explain the relationship of surface area and volume to the growth of a cell.
7. The rate of growth determines the rate of cell division. Why is this not constant for all cells?
8. Summarize the activities which generally occur in each of the five phases of mitosis.
9. What are the physical and chemical properties of cytoplasm?

See FOR YOURSELF

1. Get a prepared slide showing the mitotic cell divisions. With the aid of a microscope find examples of cells which show each phase of mitosis as described in your text. Make a series of drawings of these stages and compare these with the photomicrographs in your text. Describe the significant changes that occur in each phase.

2. Prepare a report for oral presentation or as part of your notebook on the discovery and development of the microscope, or a summary of the contributions of Robert Hooke, Marcello Malpighi, Jan Swammerdam, and Anton van Leeuwenhoek.

CHAPTER 4

The Grouping of Specialized Cells

The very simplest animals have bodies composed of a single cell or, at best, a loose grouping of more or less similar cells. These few cells suffice for primitive forms of life. However, in those animals which are more complex in structure, the need for specialized parts to meet the demands of the larger body size becomes increasingly apparent. In human societies no single individual can be simultaneously a successful plumber, lawyer, artist, farmer, and merchant. Likewise, a group of similar cells cannot possibly carry on all of the functions of a complex body. The work of society is conducted by groups of specialists, and the same is true of the work of the human body. **Division of labor** in the body is accomplished by the specialization of the various tissues and organs that comprise it.

The cells which are the basic units of structure become adapted and changed for specific purposes and are grouped together to work with greater efficiency. Each of these groups of similar cells is called a **tissue.** When various tissues are combined to carry on a particular function or activity, the structure is called an **organ.** Organs which act together in the performance of some major vital role constitute an **organ system.**

This chapter will deal with the structure of tissues and their functions. The tissues of the body may be classified in a variety of ways depending on whether they are studied from the standpoint of their structure or function or both. For the sake of convenience, the following division will be used: *covering tissue* (epithelium); *moving tissue* (muscle); *nervous tissue* (nerve); *circulating tissue* (blood cells); *reproductive tissue* (sperm and egg cells); and *connective tissue* (including bone and cartilage).

TISSUES

Epithelium. This is the general name given to all those tissues which cover the body surfaces, both externally and internally. The cells are arranged in one or more layers and serve as a protection against invasion by bacteria or as a buffer against mechanical injury. Some types of epithelium also produce materials useful to the body in localized areas, such as the serous fluid which lubricates adjoining surfaces. These tissues may be classified on the basis of the general appearance of the cells that comprise them.

1. Squamous epithelium. Cells of this type of epithelium are flat and slight-

Fig. 4-1. *Squamous epithelium.*

ly irregular in outline (Fig. 4-1). All tissues composed of such cells are extremely thin, the average depth being approximately 0.0001 inch. Since they are so thin, they serve admirably as the lining of blood vessels and the heart. They are also present in the covering of the lungs (pleurae) and heart (pericardium). In the case of the coverings of the heart and lungs, the cells secrete fluid which reduces friction between the actively moving organ and its covering. This is the serous fluid which, in the case of the covering of the heart, is called the **pericardial fluid,** and when found between the layers of the pleurae, is known as the **pleural fluid.** The layer of cells forming the thin inner walls of all blood vessels is a specialized type of squamous epithelium called **endothelium.**

2. Columnar epithelium. The cells of this type of epithelium are much taller than they are broad and are packed close together to form a protective covering

for the inner surface of an organ (Fig. 4-2). The lining of the stomach is composed of cells of this type. In some regions of the body these cells are modified so that they are able to produce materials (secretions) which aid in a particular body function. This is true of those found in the walls of the stomach, where many of the cells manufacture the various components of the gastric juice. In some tissues, cells of the columnar type have been modified to produce **mucus,** a lubricating material. These are the so-called **goblet cells** (Fig. 4-3). An example of the formation of excess mucus is found in the condition arising when a person has a head cold. At that time the amount of mucus formed by the nasal membranes is substantially increased.

3. Ciliated epithelium. Fig. 4-3 also shows a group of ciliated epithelial cells. These cells are modified columnar epithelium that has the function of moving small particles of debris or individual cells along a surface or through a tube. The free end of each cell is equipped with numerous small hairlike projections, the **cilia.** When viewed under a microscope, the beating of the cilia reminds one of the passage of a slight breeze over a field of standing grain. By the continuous movement of the cilia, particles of dust and dirt can be moved

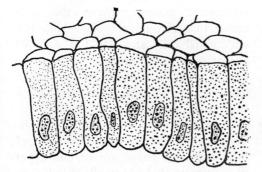

Fig. 4-2. *Columnar epithelium. Note the height of the cells that make up this type of tissue.*

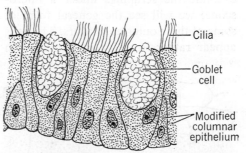

Cilia

Goblet cell

Modified columnar epithelium

Fig. 4-3. *Ciliated epithelium with two goblet cells.*

up the trachea (windpipe) from the lungs, or eggs and sperm can be swept through the oviducts or seminal tubules.

4. Cuboidal epithelium. The simple cuboidal epithelium cells are somewhat heavier and stouter than the squamous type. The cells are not real cubes, as will be noted from Fig. 4-4, but the name has been applied to them because of their approximation to this form when seen in a section cut through the middle of the cell. Cuboidal epithelium is not a common type of tissue; the tissue covering the ovary is perhaps the best example of this type.

5. Stratified epithelium (Fig. 4-5). This is a highly complex type of epithelial tissue. Its primary function is the protection of some body surface that may be subject to mechanical injury. This tissue is composed of several layers of cells for added strength. The lowest layer is composed of cells that are tall and cylindrical in shape. Above these are irregularly shaped cells which are gradually transformed into flat cells that cover the surface. In the skin, for example, the outermost cells may eventually become nonliving because their protoplasm is replaced by a harder and more resistant material (**keratin**) that protects the more delicate lower layers. If we gently scrape the inside of the cheek with the blunt end of a toothpick and then examine the scrapings under a microscope, we will see the general form of some of these outermost layers. The cells appear rather irregular in outline with

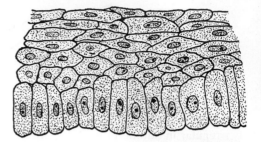

Fig. 4-5. *Stratified epithelium. A tissue of this type lines the cheeks.*

gently folded surfaces. They lack the keratin that is present in the corresponding layers in the skin because they are not subjected to the same degree of mechanical abrasion.

6. Endothelium. A type of squamous epithelium, highly specialized as to structure and function, is the tissue known as endothelium. The cells comprising it are flat and quite irregular in outline, resembling in shape the epithelial cells of the lining of the cheeks. An outstanding characteristic of these cells is that they are held together by a cementlike substance that changes in permeability as the occasion demands. The walls of the smallest blood vessels, the capillaries, are composed of endothelial cells. The diffusion of substances through the capillary walls to the surrounding tissues is thus regulated, since some part of the substances passes between the cells rather than through the cell walls. The endothelial cells also line the walls of the arteries and veins, as well as the cavities between bones at the joints. This tissue will be discussed more fully in Unit 6.

Muscle tissue. The movements of the body organs are due to the activities of muscle tissue. There are certain types of movement that are so slight that they are only visible with the aid of a microscope, as for example, the motion of cilia. In the ordinary sense, however, the

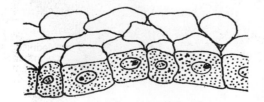

Fig. 4-4. *Cuboidal epithelium.*

movement of any part of the body, whether it is rapid or slow, depends on the type of cells that comprise the muscle tissue. Muscle tissue can be classified on the basis of the types of cells that compose it.

1. Striated, skeletal, or voluntary muscle. If a piece of lean meat is carefully torn apart with needles so that its fibers are separated, it will be seen under the microscope that the cells making up the tissue are crossed by very delicate lines. This marking is typical of muscles that are attached to the skeleton of an animal, each individual line being known as a **striation.** In human muscles, these cells may vary from 1 millimeter to over 40 millimeters in length and from 10 to 40 microns in width (1 micron = 0.001 millimeter). Since the muscle cells are relatively large and very active, they require several centers (nuclei) to regulate their activities. It is not unusual, therefore, to find that each cell may contain twenty or more nuclei which lie in the protoplasm outside of the main body of the cell but surrounded by a very thin membrane, the **sarcolemma.** Internally,

the muscle cell is made up of many small fibers which lie parallel to each other and run lengthwise in the cell. These in turn are composed of still finer fibers, called *filaments*. When a muscle contracts (shortens), each of the filaments shortens due to chemical changes occurring in the proteins they contain. More will be said about these changes in Chapter 6. The majority of the striated muscles require conscious effort to make them contract. They are therefore often called **voluntary muscles.**

2. Smooth muscle. Whereas a striated muscle cell may be more than an inch in length, the length of the smooth muscle cells is measured in thousandths of an inch. Their general appearance also is quite different because they lack the cross-markings which are characteristic of striated muscles (Fig. 4-6). Another difference is that each smooth muscle cell has a single nucleus which lies in the approximate center of the cell. Smooth muscle cells are found in the walls of the organs of the digestive system. Their slow movements pass food along the canal during the process of

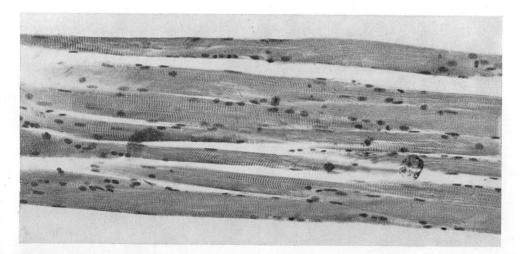

Fig. 4-6. *Striated muscle tissue (photomicrograph). Note the numerous nuclei. (General Biological Supply House)*

digestion. They are also present in the walls of arteries and veins. Here their contraction and relaxation controls the flow of blood to various parts of the body. Their action is not controlled by the will; hence they are called **involuntary muscles.**

3. Cardiac muscle. This type of muscle tissue beats in a rhythmic manner. The word "cardiac" always refers to the heart and it is only here that cardiac muscle tissue is found. The cells of the heart (Fig. 4-7) are unlike those of either smooth or skeletal muscles in that they are greatly branched and join each other in such a way as to form a protoplasmic network. The muscle cells show some striation, but it is not as distinct as that found on skeletal muscles. Also, disks are present which cross the muscle cells at more or less regular intervals. The nuclei are found in the middle of the cells. Functionally, the most important characteristic of this type of tissue is its ability to contract without being stimu-lated by a nerve-borne impulse. No other type of muscle tissue will do this normally. It is therefore possible to remove the heart from a freshly killed animal and have it continue to beat when completely separated from the body.

Nervous tissue. The cells that comprise this type of tissue are adapted for the function of relating the individual to his surroundings. Some of the cells receive stimuli. These are the **receptors.** Others transmit the nervous impulse from one part of the body to another, while still other types bring about a response to the stimulus. In the well-coordinated individual, all of these work harmoniously.

The basic unit of structure in the nervous system is the nerve cell, or **neuron.** This type of cell shows many variations in form and size depending on the part of the body in which it is located and what its particular function is. In the brain, for example, the cells may be relatively short but extremely branched,

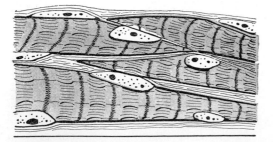

Striated muscle

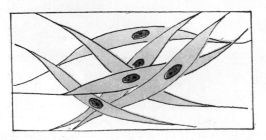

Smooth muscle

Fig. 4-7. *Note the differences in appearance of the three types of muscle tissue.*

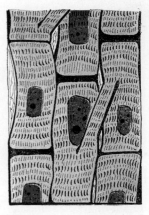

Cardiac muscle

while in other parts of the body some of the extensions of the nerve cell may be several feet long. One of the characteristics of nerve cells is their branching nature. It is by means of these branches that the various parts of the body are connected and their activities coordinated. The details of the structure of the neuron are found in Chapter 8.

Circulating tissue. All of the cells of the body must be supplied with food and oxygen and have waste products removed from them. To accomplish this end, there is a transportation system that is essentially liquid, carrying cells that are not grouped together like other tissues, but each of which helps to meet a requirement of the body. The functions of these cells will be discussed much more fully in Chapter 23.

The blood is composed of two distinct parts: a fluid portion, or **plasma,** and the solid elements, the **corpuscles.** The particular characteristics of each of these will be dealt with in later chapters. For the time being, let us note that the solid parts of the blood can be divided into three main types of cells. These are the *red corpuscles* (*erythrocytes*), the *white corpuscles* (*leukocytes*), and the *platelets* (*thrombocytes*) (Fig. 4-8). We should also note that the fluid which is present in the cells, and which bathes the cells and tissues, is formed from the plasma.

Reproductive tissue. One of the primary characteristics of living things is their ability to reproduce themselves and thereby continue the race. To accomplish this, specialized cells have been developed which not only assure the continuity of life but also determine those characteristics that are typical of the race and the individual. These cells are the **gametes.** This term is a general one and is used to refer to any reproductive cell.

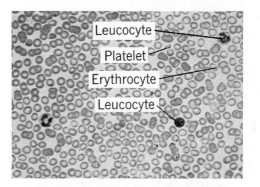

Fig. 4-8. *Human blood cells. This photomicrograph of a thin smear of blood shows several types of cells. When in a body, the cells float in the plasma. (Carolina Biological Supply Co.)*

1. Ova. The ova (sing., *ovum*) are formed in specialized organs of the female, the **ovaries.** Following a complicated series of cell divisions, these cells move from the interior of the ovary toward the outside as they mature. When completely developed and freed from the ovary, the human ova measure about 0.09 millimeter in diameter and contain a large and distinct nucleus. The cytoplasm is plentiful and within it is a small amount of nonliving *yolk* material. This yolk, together with other materials that are present in the cytoplasm, serves as a source of food material for the early embryo until further provision is made for its development (Fig. 4-9). There is much more of this stored food material in the ova of lower animals than there is in the human ovum.

2. Spermatozoa. The spermatozoa, or **sperm** (Fig. 4-10), are formed by the male reproductive organs, the **testes.** Compared with most of the other cells of the body, the sperm are very minute. The total average length of a sperm cell is about 0.05 millimeter—the *head,* which contains the nuclear material, being only 0.003 millimeter in length. Behind the head region is a part usually

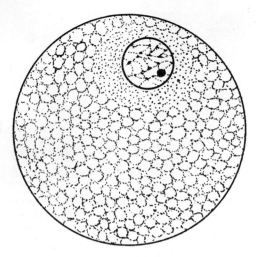

Fig. 4-9. *A diagram of the ovum, or egg cell.*

There are certain cells in the body whose primary function is the connecting of one tissue, or group of tissues, to another; these are the **connective tissues.** The majority of these are composed of long, loosely joined cells. If, for example, one separates the skin and subdermal tissues from the surface of a muscle, he will find that there is a sheet of quite tough thin cells that hold these two layers together. Under the microscope, this layer of connective tissue will show numerous nuclei, but the cell walls may be quite indistinct or they may appear as disorganized threads without any apparent cellular structure.

1. Adipose tissue (Fig. 4-11). Fat tissue is quite widely distributed through

referred to as the *middle piece,* which contains the mitochondria and the centrosome. In back of the middle piece is the *tail,* which serves as a locomotor organ. Aside from the tail, there is very little cytoplasmic material in a sperm cell. The functions of the sperm are to add its chromatin material to the ovum at the time of fertilization and to initiate the development of the ovum into a new individual.

The importance of the chromatin of the gametes in the formation of chromosomes, and the functions of the chromosomes in determining hereditary characteristics will be discussed much more fully in Chapter 33.

Connective tissue. Many of the tissues which are classified under other headings help to connect parts of the body to each other. Each of these, however, has another function to perform which is more important than that of joining one part of the body to another. Thus it might be said that muscles help to hold the bones together, but this is a very minor role for them; their principal function is to move the bones and other organs of the body.

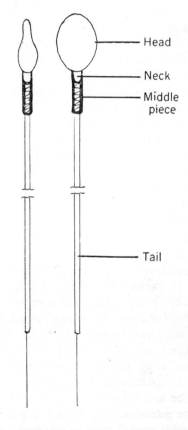

Fig. 4-10. *Spermatozoa. Left, side view; right, top view.*

the body. The cells that make up this type of tissue are relatively large and contain a single vacuole in which a droplet of fat has been deposited. Fat accounts for a sizable percentage of the total body weight; in males it is approximately 18 percent of the total weight and in females about 28 percent. Fat plays three important roles in the body. It serves as a reserve supply of energy-producing materials. It also serves as padding to absorb the jolts and jars to which the body is being constantly subjected. Fat tissue is deposited in quantities around the eyes, in the palms of the hands, in the soles of the feet, and between the joints. The third function of fat is that it serves as an insulator. Deposits of fat beneath the skin help to maintain the normal body temperature by preventing the loss of heat generated within the body tissues.

2. Cartilage and bone. The framework of the body consists of two types of supporting tissues: cartilage and bone. Although other types of tissues play some role in the general support of the body, these two are the principal ones, since they make up the skeleton. Most of the bones of the skeleton first appear as cartilage structures, although in some instances special membranes form the bases into which bone cells migrate. This process of bone formation (**ossification**) by the replacement of cartilage or the invasion of membranes proceeds slowly throughout life. In a very young child the skeleton is characterized by the presence of a relatively large number of living cartilage cells and their products. In an elderly person the majority of the cartilage has been replaced by nonliving calcium and phosphorus salts that have been laid down by the bone-forming cells. Thus, a young person has quite flexible bones, but those of an older individual are brittle because they contain

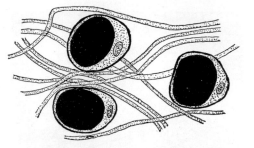

Fig. 4-11. *Adipose tissue: three fat cells shown among strands of connective tissue.*

much more of these inorganic salts.

Bone tissue is composed of two general types of cells, one that forms the bony material, the **osteoblasts,** and one that is connected with its constant reabsorption, the **osteoclasts.** By the action of these two opposing types, the skeleton undergoes a continual series of changes that result in the building up of new bone and the sculpturing and reabsorption of old material. The bone-forming cells originate in the membrane that surrounds the cartilage. As the osteoblasts grow into the cartilage, they form a very compact type of bone into which the osteoclasts will migrate. These latter cells hollow out pathways for the nerves and blood vessels. The canals thus formed constitute the **Haversian system** that is so typical of the microscopic structure of mature bone. The osteoblasts then arrange themselves in concentric circles around Haversian canals and surround themselves with bony material. Just how this process is carried on by the cells is not yet fully understood. After the osteoblasts have become surrounded by bone, they are known as **osteocytes.** The spaces in the bone that remain after the bone has dried appear black under the microscope. The layers of bone thus formed make up the lamellae of the bone, which can be seen in the photomicrograph, Fig. 5-5.

Cartilage, commonly called gristle,

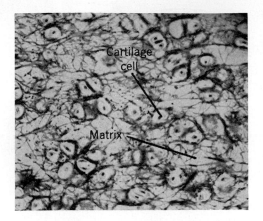

Fig. 4-12. *Elastic cartilage: photomicrograph showing the relation of the cartilage cells to the matrix. (General Biological Supply House)*

is a very flexible but quite firm material. As we have said, in the early stages of development it forms the mold for the future bones. In the adult, cartilage is present in those parts where flexibility is a desired condition. Thus we find the ribs attached to the sternum (breast bone) by cartilage in order to permit their movement during breathing. It is also present in the tip of the nose and the external ear. The majority of cartilage is composed of a nonliving material, the **matrix**, through which are scattered groups of **cartilage cells.** These cells may be in groups of two, four, etc., each group surrounded by a capsule of semitransparent material. Microscopically, it is possible to distinguish several different types of cartilage. Two of the more common forms are the **hyaline cartilage,** with a uniformly clear matrix, and the **elastic cartilage** (Fig. 4-12), in which there are strands of denser substances between the cells.

ORGANS AND ORGAN SYSTEMS

Organs. An **organ** can be defined as a group of tissues which function to-gether in the performance of some vital activity. These tissues are not necessarily all alike in structure or function, but by the coordination of their individual activities they form a distinct part of the body.

The hand may be taken as an example of an organ. Here we have a collection of different tissues, all of which work together to give us a very useful part of the body. The outside of the hand is covered by a highly complex type of stratified epithelium which in certain areas has become folded into ridges (the fingerprints). These ridges supply a slightly roughened surface to aid in grasping. Embedded in the skin are highly sensitive nerve receptors. Also in the skin and throughout the entire hand are blood vessels that carry the blood to supply the tissues with needed food and oxygen. In the walls of the blood vessels are smooth muscle fibers, while the fingers are moved by the action of striated muscles, many of which are located in the forearm, although there are some in the hand to perform its more delicate motions. Bone and cartilage serve as the supporting elements of the hand, and there is adipose tissue in the palm and elsewhere to absorb shocks. All of these various types of tissues are held together by bands of connective tissue. Here then, we have an example of a part of the body that serves a definite purpose although composed of diverse tissues.

An **organ system** is a grouping of several organs which function together in carrying out some major bodily activity. The division of labor in the body is accomplished not only by tissues and organs, but on a more elaborate scale by the organ systems. In the table (page 37) the various organ systems are listed. These systems are further subdivided to show the organs and tissues that comprise them.

ORGAN SYSTEMS	PRINCIPAL TYPES OF TISSUES						
	Epithelium	Muscle	Nerve	Blood	Reproductive	Bone and/or cartilage	General connective
Digestive							
Mouth	X	X	X	X		X	X
Esophagus	X	X	X	X			X
Stomach	X	X	X	X			X
Intestines	X	X	X	X			X
Circulatory							
Heart	X	X	X	X			X
Arteries	X	X	X	X			X
Veins	X	X	X	X			X
Capillaries	X		X	X			X
Lymphatics	X		X	X			X
Skeletal							
Skeleton			X	X		X	
Respiratory							
Nasopharyngeal area	X	X	X	X		X	X
Trachea	X	X	X	X		X	X
Lungs	X	X	X	X			X
Pleurae	X		X	X			X
Diaphragm	X	X	X	X			X
Intercostal muscles	X	X	X	X		X	X
Excretory							
Kidneys	X	X	X	X			X
Ureters	X	X	X	X			X
Kidney tubules	X			X			X
Urinary bladder	X	X	X	X			X
Urethra	X	X	X	X			X
Reproductive							
Ovaries and testes	X		X	X	X		X
Associated organs	X	X	X	X			X
Nervous							
Brain and spinal cord	X		X	X			X
Sense organs	X	X	X	X		X	X
Muscular							
Muscles	X	X	X	X			X
Integumentary							
Skin	X	X	X	X			X
Endocrine							
Endocrine glands	X		X	X			X

SPEAKING OF Physiology

Describe or define the following words:

adipose	gamete	osteoblast
cardiac	goblet cell	ova
cartilage	lymph	plasma
cilia	matrix	receptors
corpuscle	neuron	spermatozoa
endothelium	organ	striation
epithelium	organ system	tissue

Test YOUR KNOWLEDGE

1. Why is the specialization of cells, tissues, and organs necessary in the more complex animals?
2. Why can you classify epithelial tissue as the first line of defense against the invasion of bacteria and other harmful agents?
3. Compare the similarities and differences of structure and function in each of the following: squamous epithelium; columnar epithelium; and cuboidal epithelium.
4. In what way does the stratified squamous epithelium of the skin differ from that of other areas composed of the same type of tissue? Why?
5. How can you distinguish between voluntary muscle, involuntary muscle, and cardiac muscle by their appearance? By their function?
6. Why is nerve tissue considered the coordinating mechanism of the human body?
7. Why is blood described as a circulating tissue?
8. Classify the following as a tissue or an organ: (*a*) skin, (*b*) lining of the stomach, (*c*) finger nails, (*d*) teeth, (*e*) heart. What is the basis for your decision in each case?
9. List the ten organ systems of the human body. In what part of the systems are the principal types of tissues found?

See FOR YOURSELF

1. Construct a series of clay models of the various types of epithelial cells, i.e., squamous, cuboidal, and columnar. Try to gain your knowledge of proportion, shape, and appearance from microscopic observation, drawings, and photomicrographs.

2. If a microscope is available, prepare a slide of your own body cells in the following way: with the flat end of a toothpick, gently scrape the mucous lining of the inner cheek wall. Rub the material collected on a clean microscope slide. Place a drop of dilute aqueous solution of iodine on the material and cover with a cover slip. Observe under low power until you find some individual cells. Change to high power and draw a few of these cells. Label as many of the parts as you can.

The Bones and Muscles

CHAPTER 5

The Skeleton

CHAPTER 6

The Physiology of Skeletal Muscle

CHAPTER 7

The Action of Some Skeletal Muscles

The Skeleton

The bony connective tissue that makes up the general framework of the body constitutes the body's **skeleton** (Figs. 5-9 and 5-10, pages 48–49. There are about 206 named bones. The bones that make up the skeleton vary greatly in size and shape: some are extremely small, such as those of the middle ear, while others are large and heavy, as the thigh bones. Their shapes range from long and cylindrical to thin and curved, such as those of the skull. Regardless of their size and shape, all of the bones are joined together by tough, fibrous bands of tissue, the **ligaments.** This is true even in the case of the bones of the skull, although here the softer ligamentous tissue may be replaced by bone as the individual parts fuse.

The functions of the skeleton are (*a*) to afford a supporting framework for the soft parts of the body, (*b*) to protect delicate inner structures, (*c*) to serve as a place for attachment of muscles, (*d*) to supply the body with certain types of blood cells, and (*e*) to provide a storehouse of minerals that the body can draw on in times of necessity.

Not all bones can perform all of the functions listed above: some are more highly adapted for specific activities than others. The function of protection is illustrated by the bones of the skull that enclose the brain and by those of the thorax (the ribs, breast bone, and part of the vertebral column) that enclose the heart, lungs, and other internal organs. Attached to the outer surfaces of bones are muscles that supply the force that enables us to use our bones as a series of levers in such motions as walking, lifting, and sitting (see Chapter 7). The long bones of the body, such as those of the upper arms, the ribs, and the breast bone, supply many of the solid parts of the blood. That the skeleton as a whole can supply minerals to other parts of the body in times of need is especially evident during pregnancy. At this time the mother furnishes the developing child with the calcium and phosphorus salts it needs for the formation of its skeleton.

The hardness of bone is due to its high percentage of mineral content. Inorganic and organic salts of calcium, phosphorus, and magnesium are the chief constituents of bone, but important, though small, amounts of potassium, fluorine, sodium, and iron are also present. All of these materials are absorbed from the food the individual eats, or from other tissues where they may have been stored.

Structure of bone. There are two types of bone tissue: **spongy** and **compact.** Spongy bone, which is found in the interior of a bone, is more porous and contains more blood vessels than does the compact bone of the surfaces. In a long bone, such as that of the upper arm (Fig. 5-1), the shaft (**diaphysis**) is composed almost entirely of compact tissue, while the ends (**epiphyses**) contain mostly spongy bone. The compact bone of the diaphysis encloses the long cylindrical **medullary canal** which contains the **marrow.** The marrow consists of blood vessels, fat cells, and those cells from which blood corpuscles are derived (see Chapter 23). Lining the medullary canal is a membrane called the **endosteum.** Covering the bone is the **periosteum,** a thick double-layered membrane containing blood vessels, nerves, and the bone-forming cells. The growth and development of bone is initiated from this membrane.

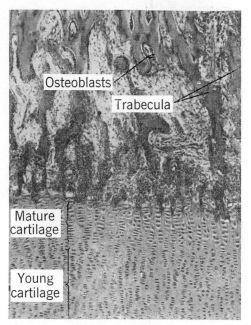

Fig. **5-2.** *Developing bone. The hyaline cartilage is being rapidly transformed into bone. Masses of solid bone, the trabeculae, may be seen toward the top of this photomicrograph. (General Biological Supply House)*

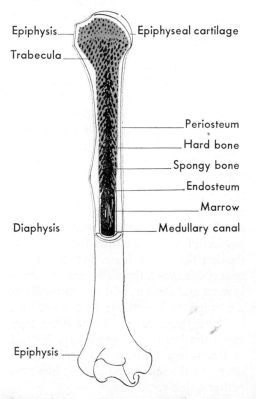

Fig. **5-1.** *A section through the humerus to show the internal structure of bone.*

Bone formation. The general form that the adult skeleton will take is determined long before birth. In the early embryo the potential skeletal framework is laid down in two forms: flexible hyaline cartilage and fibrous membranes. As long as seven months before birth, bone cells begin to replace these with bone tissue. This process of ossification continues throughout life, but the major activity occurs in the first twenty-five years. Thereafter, bone tissue is capable of local growth, as in the healing of a fracture. Most of the bones of the body are formed from cartilage. The cartilage of the embryo is not strong enough to bear the weight of the human body, though it serves as an excellent model for the laying down of the strong bony tissue that characterizes the mature skeleton.

Cartilage consists of cartilage cells in a large amount of gelatinous matrix (Fig. 5-2). As the young cells mature, they produce a chemical substance that brings about the calcification of the matrix. The cells are surrounded by this hardened material and are cut off from their source of nutrition. They eventually die and most of the calcified matrix dissolves. Simultaneously, bone cells (osteoblasts) move rapidly from the periosteum into the area and begin to manufacture their own ground substance, the bone matrix, in long columns (*trabeculae*). It is interesting to note that though bone matrix also becomes calcified, the bone cells do not die, as do the cartilage cells. This is because the osteoblasts have long processes that come in contact with the branches of other bone cells and with the capillaries. During the formation of the bone matrix these provide channels for the passage of nourishment to the cells. After the matrix is laid down and calcification begins, the processes are drawn back into the cell, leaving **canaliculi** (small canals). These are filled with fluids, thus continuing the flow of life-sustaining fluid between the osteoblasts and the capillaries. By this unique mechanism bone cells are able to give to bone the quality of living tissue, in spite of the fact that about 70 percent of bone is composed of a mixture of mineral salts with extremely hard texture.

The process of ossification begins in the center of the diaphysis and proceeds rapidly toward the epiphyses. After this primary **center of ossification** has its work well under way, a similar ossification center arises in each epiphysis and begins its slower replacement of cartilage. In the X-ray photograph (Fig. 5-3) of an infant's hand, the epiphyses appear to be separated from the bone. Actually there is a band of cartilage connecting them to the shaft. In the adult hand (Fig. 5-4), this division between the epiphysis and the diaphysis is indicated by a narrow line, the **epiphyseal cartilage.** The continued growth of this portion of cartilage allows for growth in the length of the bone. At about the twenty-fifth year, these two centers finally meet and form a solid structure. Since the epiphyseal cartilage is a weak link in bone structure, a violent blow may cause the bone to separate here instead of fracturing. This often occurs in children, but the separation usually heals together quickly.

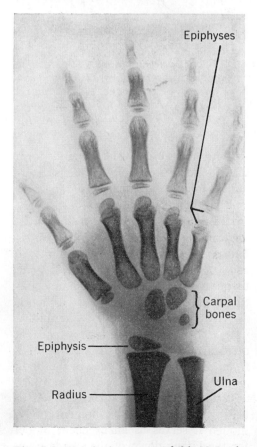

Fig. 5-3. *Hand of a young child. Note the absence of solid bone formation in the wrist and the separation of the epiphyses.*

While replacement of cartilage continues in the interior centers of ossification, osteoblasts between the periosteal membranes are laying down layer after layer of thin bone, forming a collar around the shaft. This type of ossification differs from that of replacing cartilage. The bone matrix is laid down by osteoblasts between the membranes and is calcified directly. A similar process occurs in the formation of the skull bones, for which membrane rather than cartilage serves as the model for the future bone.

Because all bone tissue, when first formed, is of the spongy type, these external layers of the long bones and the first bony formations of the skull are only temporary. They must be replaced by compact bone by the processes of destruction and rebuilding. Destruction is probably the work of the osteoclasts, large cells with many nuclei that are thought to dissolve bone tissue. In the interior of the long bones these cells carve out a large cylindrical space, the medullary canal, which fills with marrow. In the flat bones of membranous origin, such as those of the skull, the spaces hollowed out by the osteoclasts contain blood vessels and nerves. At this stage, newly formed bone is very porous, with many spaces between the long columns of bone (trabeculae). It must now be converted to more compact bone by building the layers into a more closely woven network with fewer and smaller spaces.

To do this, concentric layers (**lamellae**) of bone are laid down on the inside surface of the channels between the trabeculae. As these layers are added, the channel is gradually narrowed to form the Haversian canals, which contain blood vessels and lymphatics. The osteoblasts (bone-forming cells) come to lie in cavities (lacunae) between the lamellae and are then called osteocytes (bone-maintaining cells).

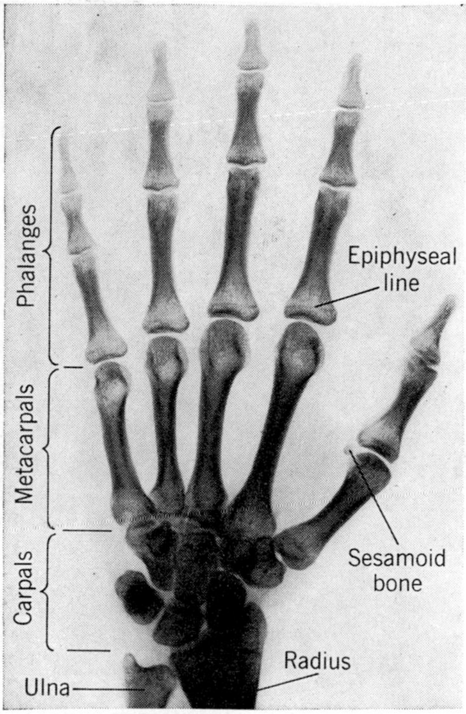

Fig. 5-4. *Adult hand. Compare the development of bone tissue in this photograph with that shown in Fig. 5-3.*

The unit of structure of compact bone, then, is the Haversian system (Fig. 5-5) with its lamellae in concentric layers around the Haversian canal, the osteocytes lying in the lacunae between the layers of bone, and the tiny canaliculi that channel the tissue fluid between the cells and the blood vessels in the canal. Because of this intricate, interconnecting system of canals there is an extensive blood supply throughout the bone.

Joints. The junction of two or more bones is a **joint.** Such an **articulation** (joining) may be freely movable, as the shoulder joint; slightly movable, as the joint formed by the rib in its articulation with the spine; or immovable, as the bones of the skull. The degree of flexibility is determined by how closely the bones are joined together by ligaments

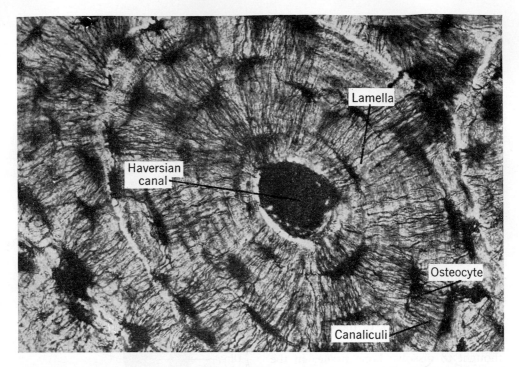

Fig. 5-5. *Bone tissue (photomicrograph). Note the arrangement of the bone cells around the Haversian canal. (Carolina Biological Supply Co.)*

and the amount of freedom permitted them by nearby structures.

There are several **types of movable joints,** described according to the type of articulation and the range of movement (Fig. 5-6). The **ball and socket joint** provides the freest movement. One bone with a rounded head moves in a cuplike cavity of the other, as the thigh bone in its articulation with the hip bone. **Hinge joints,** such as the elbow, allow powerful movement in one plane only. **Pivot joints** provide a rotary movement in which a bone rotates on a ring or a ring of bone rotates around a central axis, as is seen in the turning of the skull on the spine. The vertebrae of the spine are good examples of **gliding joints** in which the articulating parts of one vertebra slide on those of another. An **angular joint** is formed by the articulation of an oval-shaped surface with a con-

cave cavity, as in the wrist. It permits movement in two directions. A **saddle joint** is similar to the angular joint in its range of movement, but the bones that form the joint each present a concave-convex articulating surface. The thumb joint is an example.

There are several terms which describe the movement of joints, and these terms will also be used in Chapter 7 which deals with the muscles and their action. **Flexion** is bending or decreasing the angle between the parts, as when the leg bends back toward the thigh. **Extension** is the opposite action, stretching out, as when the leg is straightened. **Rotation** is turning on an axis, much as the earth turns on its axis, except that in the body complete rotation is impossible because blood vessels, nerves, and other tissue would be torn. **Abduction** is drawing away from the middle line of the

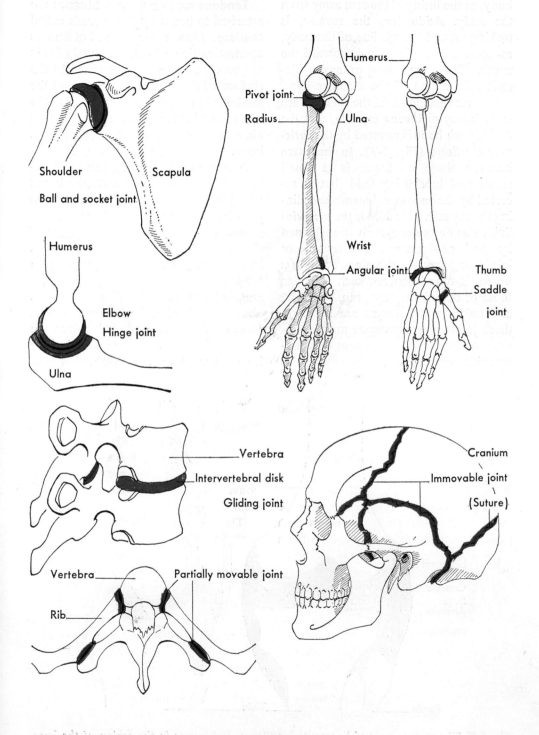

Fig. 5-6. *Types of joints.*

body, as the lifting of the arm away from the body. **Adduction,** the reverse, is turning toward the midline of the body, as when the arm is brought toward the trunk. These last two examples describe the action of the shoulder joint.

The movable joints of the skeleton are enclosed by a **fibrous capsule,** and the end of each bone is covered by the **articular cartilage** (Fig. 5-7). In the space between these cartilages is a small amount of lubricating fluid that is secreted by the endothelial membranes lining the capsule. This fluid is the **synovial** fluid. The fibrous capsule is strengthened by bands of ligaments. Another type of lubricating and cushioning device, a **bursa,** is found between such bones as those of the elbow, knee, hip, shoulder, and ankle joints. Bursae are found in those joints where pressure may be exerted or where the attachment of a tendon rides over a bone.

Tendons and ligaments. Muscles are attached to bones by tough cords called **tendons.** These are composed of fibrous connective tissue to which muscle fibers are fused, and they are attached to the surface of the periosteum. Through the tendon, the muscle exerts traction on the bone to which it is attached, and is thus able to control the movement of the bone.

A **ligament** is a strong band of connective tissue which connects the bones of a joint. Its function is to support the joint by holding the bones in place.

Bones as levers. The movements of the muscles and joints provide action in which the bones act as levers. From the standpoint of elementary physics, a **simple lever** is a rod that can be moved about a fixed point, the **fulcrum,** to exert force for the movement of an object. We may consider the bones as levers and the joints as the fulcra. Muscle action sup-

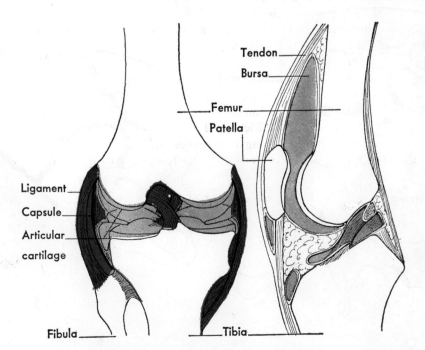

Fig. 5-7. *The arrangement of ligaments, cartilages, and bursae in the region of the knee. (Left, back view; right, side view.)*

plies the force. Simple levers are classi-fied in one of three groups depending on the relation of the effort (E) and the load (R for resistance) to the fulcrum (F). In Fig. 5-8 these three classes are illustrated by the motion of the foot. In this case, the same bones are involved in all three instances, but as the effort is applied in different directions the type of lever changes. These simple levers are more useful in moving small loads rap-idly than they are in moving a heavy load because their mechanical advan-tage is low. When the body is required to move heavy loads, it uses another type of lever that is seldom found among man-made machines because of its com-plex structure. This is the **end-loaded compound lever.** This consists of two or more long levers (bones) connected by joints in such a manner that the load comes at the end of the levers when they are almost straightened. Examples of this type of lever are found in the up-ward thrust of the leg when it is almost straight or the out-thrust arm of a boxer at the end of a jab. In these levers the mechanical advantage is great and ac-counts for the fact that considerable weight can be moved or force exerted. A common example of the mechanical advantage obtained by this type of lever is the "scissor jack" used in lifting an automobile when a tire is to be changed.

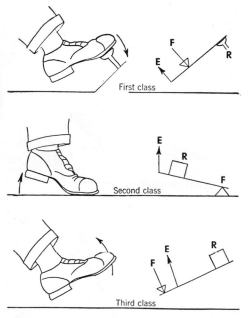

Fig. 5-8. *The three classes of simple levers illustrated by different motions of the same part of the body. (From Miller and Haub,* General Zoology, *Holt, 1956)*

THE STRUCTURE OF THE SKELETON

The skeleton as a whole can be di-vided into two main divisions: the **axial** portion and the **appendicular** portion. As the name implies, the former makes up the main axis of the body, while the appendicular portion makes up the ap-pendages and those structures which at-tach them to the axial part. In the axial part we find the skull, the vertebral col-umn, the breast bone, and the ribs. The appendicular portion consists of the shoulder girdles and arms and the pelvic (hip) girdles and legs.

The axial skeleton. The **skull** is com-posed of two distinct regions: the cra-nium, which houses the brain, and the facial bones, those irregularly shaped bones which support and guard the mouth, nose, eyes, and ears. The bones of the cranium are generally membra-nous in origin, while those of the face are largely cartilaginous in origin. Some of the facial cavities are composed of both bone and cartilage. For example, in the nasal cavity the **nasal bones** form the upper part of the bridge of the nose, while the lower part is cartilage.

The **cranium** consists of relatively thin, slightly curved bones. In infancy, the edges of these are held snugly to-gether by an irregular line of connective tissue called a **suture.** This tissue is later

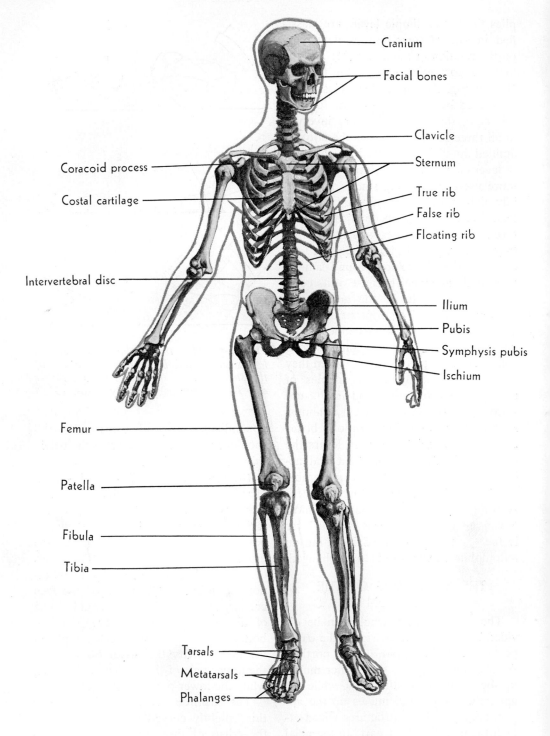

Fig. 5-9. *Front view of the human skeleton.*

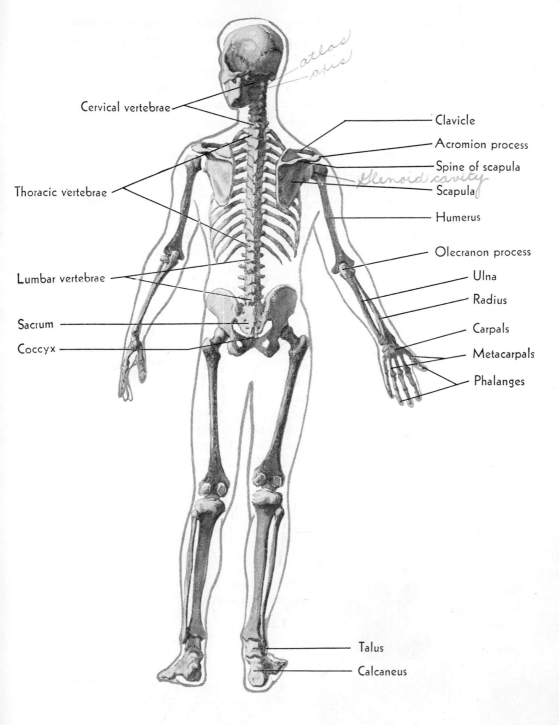

Cervical vertebrae

Thoracic vertebrae

Lumbar vertebrae

Sacrum

Coccyx

atlas
axis

Clavicle

Acromion process

Spine of scapula

Glenoid cavity

Scapula

Humerus

Olecranon process

Ulna

Radius

Carpals

Metacarpals

Phalanges

Talus

Calcaneus

Fig. 5-10. *Back view of the human skeleton.*

replaced by hard bone. The result is a solid, dome-shaped structure that is a highly efficient protective mechanism for the soft brain that lies beneath it. From a purely mechanical standpoint, a rounded surface, such as that of the upper part of the skull, is a better protection against injury than is a flat surface. Not only do blows glance off more easily, but the archlike structure serves to strengthen it. A severe blow sometimes results in a fractured skull. So long as this break is simply a crack in the walls of the cranium, it can be treated as any other broken bone. However, if any part of the bone is pushed inward, the underlying brain tissue may be injured. A depressed fracture of this type usually requires surgical intervention to relieve the pressure on the brain.

The bones of the cranium are the **frontal, parietal, occipital, temporal, sphenoid,** and **ethmoid.** The remainder of the skull is composed of **facial bones** that house the organs of smell, taste, sight, and hearing. The cheek bone may be seen in Fig. 5-11 as the **zygomatic bone.** It joins with the temporal bone to complete the **zygomatic arch.** Certain bones aid in the process of chewing, such as the **mandible,** or lower jaw, and the hard palate (**palatine bone** and part of the **maxilla**) that forms the roof of the mouth. More will be said later about some of these bones, as the individual organ systems of which they form a part are discussed.

Within the bones of the skull are several large cavities in the facial region. These are the **paranasal sinuses** (Fig. 5-11). They are lined by ciliated columnar epithelium and normally drain through small openings into the nasal cavity.

Certain bones of the skull contain small cavities that are sufficiently numerous to give the bone a spongy appearance. This condition is well illustrated by the **mastoid process** of the temporal bone. This lies just behind the ear and may be identified as a slightly raised area.

The vertebral column. The vertebral column (Fig. 5-12) is made up of a series of 33 separate bones, the **vertebrae,** linked by cartilage and ligaments in such

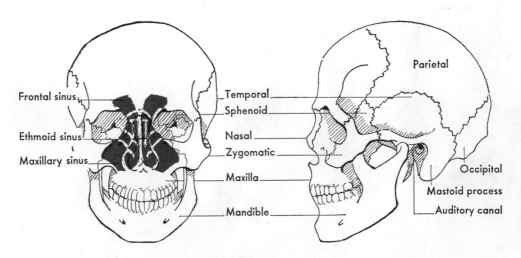

Frontal sinus
Ethmoid sinus
Maxillary sinus

Temporal
Sphenoid
Nasal
Zygomatic
Maxilla
Mandible

Parietal
Occipital
Mastoid process
Auditory canal

Fig. 5-11. *The bones of the human skull. Sinuses are shown in color in the drawing at the left.*

a manner as to permit flexibility of the trunk. It is divided into five regions from top to bottom: (1) **cervical** (neck), (2) **thoracic** (chest), (3) **lumbar** (small of the back), (4) **sacral** (hip), and (5) **coccygeal** (tail). It will be noted that these bones are not in a straight line as seen from the side. The thoracic and sacral curves appear before birth, but the others develop later. The lumbar curvature enables an infant to sit up without support, and the cervical curve appears when he begins to walk. These changes in the curvature of the column represent shifts in the center of gravity of the body.

An individual vertebra, as represented by one from the lumbar region of the column (Fig. 5-13), is composed of three main regions of bone with a centrally placed opening. The large, solid part of the vertebra is the *body,* from the top of which winglike *transverse processes* project to either side. Behind the body of the vertebra is an opening, the *vertebral foramen,* through which the spinal cord passes. The roof of this arch is then completed by the *spinous* and *auricular processes.*

Between the individual vertebrae are the **intervertebral disks** of cartilage which serve as the principal connecting bonds between the vertebrae. Bands of ligaments secure the vertebrae to each other.

The sternum and ribs. The chest region is supported and protected in back by the thoracic vertebrae and in front and along the sides by the **sternum** (breast bone) and the **ribs.**

The sternum consists of a single bone that is divided into three general regions (Fig. 5-14): the upper part, or **manubrium;** the **body;** and a cartilaginous portion, the **xiphoid process.** The general shape of the bone suggested the form of a Roman thrusting-sword, hence the name manubrium (Lat., *manus,*

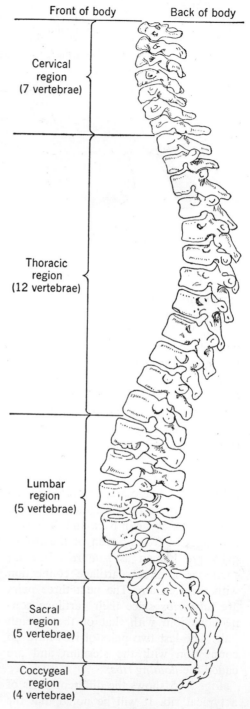

Front of body   Back of body

Cervical region (7 vertebrae)

Thoracic region (12 vertebrae)

Lumbar region (5 vertebrae)

Sacral region (5 vertebrae)

Coccygeal region (4 vertebrae)

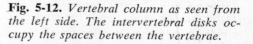

Fig. 5-12. *Vertebral column as seen from the left side. The intervertebral disks occupy the spaces between the vertebrae.*

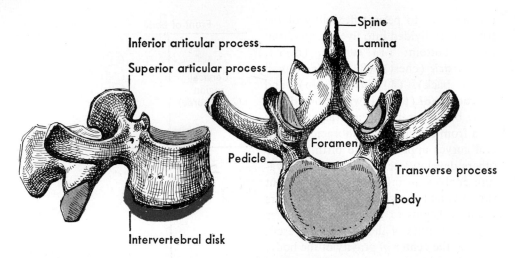

Fig. 5-13. *Lumbar vertebra. Left, as seen from the side; right, from the top.*

hand), for the upper part, which has been likened to the hilt region of the sword. While the two upper parts are quite solid, the lowest is soft and flexible due to the presence of cartilage. Ligaments attach a clavicle (collar bone) to each side of the top of the sternum. To the sides of the breast bone are attached seven pairs of **costal cartilages** (Lat., *costa,* rib), by means of which the ribs are joined to the sternum.

There are normally 24 **ribs** in all human beings. These are curved bones arranged in pairs that articulate with the thoracic vertebrae in back and the costal cartilages in front. Seven of the twelve pairs are known as *true ribs* because each has a direct cartilage connection with the sternum. The next three pairs are *false ribs* since their cartilage connections join with that of the seventh pair. The last two pairs of ribs have no connection with the sternum and are called the *floating ribs.*

Fig. 5-15 shows the different parts of a typical rib. It will be noted that the vertebral end is equipped with smooth surfaces, the *head* and the *tubercle,* which fit into the articular processes of

the thoracic vertebra and permit the rib a slight gliding motion when a person breathes. Between these two surfaces is the neck region, where ligaments are attached to hold the rib securely to the vertebra. The shafts of adjacent ribs are joined by the **intercostal muscles,** the action of which serves to increase and decrease the capacity of the chest cavity during the act of breathing.

The appendicular skeleton. The word "appendicular" refers to a structure one end of which is attached to the axial part of the body while the other is free. Such an organ (e.g., an arm or a leg) is an **appendage.** In the skeleton, these appendages are attached to the axial skeleton by means of a series of bones that form the **girdles**—the *shoulder girdle* (pectoral girdle) and the *pelvic girdle.*

Each shoulder girdle consists of a large, roughly triangular **scapula** (shoulder blade) and a thin, slightly curved **clavicle** (collar bone) (Fig. 5-16).

The broad, flat surfaces of each scapula permit the attachment of muscles which aid in the movement of the arm and which also serve to hold the upper arm bone firmly in place. There is a

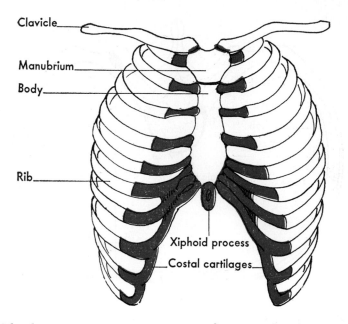

Clavicle

Manubrium

Body

Rib

Xiphoid process

Costal cartilages

Fig. 5-14. *The human sternum as seen from the front. Costal cartilages serve as connections for the ribs.*

prominent shelflike ridge running obliquely across the upper third of the bone on the posterior (back) side. This is the *spine of the scapula,* and it ends in a flattened projection, the *acromion process,* that overhangs the shoulder joint. Beneath this projection is the *glenoid cavity* which articulates with the head of the humerus. The acromion can be felt as a slight bony projection on the upper surface of the shoulder. Articulating with the acromion is one end of the clavicle, the other end of which rests against the top of the sternum. The two collar bones thus serve to brace the shoulders and prevent excessive forward motion. The *coracoid process,* which projects forward, is an attachment for several muscles and ligaments.

The arm. Each arm is divided into four general regions by the principal joints which permit action of these parts. The upper arm extends from the shoulder to the elbow and its skeletal support is supplied by the **humerus.**

The head of the humerus (Fig. 5-16) is smoothly rounded and articulates with the scapula at the glenoid cavity. The opposite surface is somewhat roughened, indicating that muscles and ligaments are attached to it. These help to hold the humerus in the socket. Also, along the shaft of the bone we find ridges and depressions that show where various other muscles are attached to it. (The muscles cannot be seen in the X ray.) At the lower end of the humerus are the areas which serve as the points of articulation with the bones of the forearm. On the posterior surface of the bone just above one of these articular surfaces is a notch or depression into which the head of the ulna fits when the arm is extended at the elbow. This depression is called the *olecranon cavity.*

The skeleton of the forearm is composed of two bones, the **radius** and the **ulna.** The name, radius, is derived from the fact that this bone can be rotated around the ulna, since both of its ends

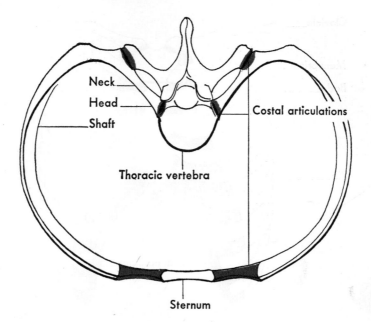

Neck

Head

Shaft

Costal articulations

Thoracic vertebra

Sternum

Fig. 5-15. *Sixth rib, showing its articulation with a thoracic vertebra. Compare the general outline of this type of vertebra with that of the lumbar vertebra shown in Fig. 5-13.*

are flattened and the bone can be moved freely through an arc. This method of articulation permits the hand to be rotated and greatly increases its flexibility. The ulna lacks this ability to rotate. At the upper end of the ulna there is a projection, the *olecranon process,* which fits into the olecranon cavity of the humerus when the arm is extended. This not only prevents a side-to-side motion, but it also serves to stop the backward motion of the arm beyond an approximately straight line. At its lower end, the position of the radius is indicated by a projection just above the thumb side of the wrist, and the corresponding end of the ulna forms an easily felt prominence on the opposite side.

The **wrist** (carpus) contains eight small bones which are held together by ligaments. These **carpal** bones are roughly arranged in two rows and can move on each other in such a manner as to allow flexion of the wrist, but they do not permit a wide lateral (side) movement. We can consider these a complex form of gliding joint. On their inner (*palmar*) surface are attached some of the short muscles that move the thumb and little finger.

The **hand** can be divided into two main sections: the palm of the hand with its five **metacarpal bones** and the five fingers supported by 14 **phalanges** (sing., *phalanx*). Four of the fingers have three phalanges in each; the thumb has only two. Due to the way the muscles and ligaments are attached to these bones, there is very little motion in the palm of the hand. The fingers, however, have great flexibility in a vertical plane. The joints between each phalanx form a hinge that permits the parts of the fingers to be bent. The thumb is more flexible than the other four fingers because the end of its metacarpal bone is more rounded and because it is supplied with muscles that lie

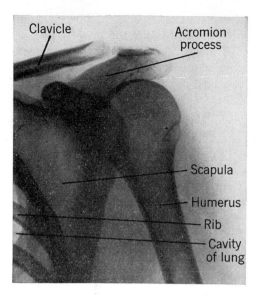

Clavicle

Acromion process

Scapula

Humerus

Rib

Cavity of lung

Fig. 5-16. *X-ray of the left shoulder showing the relation of the bones in this ball and socket joint.*

within the hand itself. These permit the thumb to be brought across the palm of the hand, a condition that does not exist in any other group of mammals except that to which man belongs, the Primates. Occasionally in the hand, and elsewhere, small nodules of bone are formed in the tendons at the region of a joint. These *sesamoid bones* may remain completely separated from the adjoining bony structures or may become attached to them.

The pelvis (Fig. 5-17). In the course of its development, the hip is first formed as six separate bones, three on each side

of the middle line of the body. These are the **ilium, ischium,** and **pubis.** As growth continues, the three bones on each side fuse into a single structure and with the sacrum form a bowl-shaped cavity, the **pelvis,** that supports the viscera (soft organs) of the lower abdomen. Eventually, the two sets of bones form a joint with the pubic bones in front, the **symphysis pubis,** and with the sacrum in back, the **sacroiliac joint.**

One of the more obvious differences between the male and female skeletons is evident in the region of the pelvis (Fig. 5-17). In the male, the angle made by the two pubic bones (**pubic arch**) is more acute than in the female. Also, the height of the male pelvis is somewhat greater than that of the female, although it is not as broad. As a result, the heads of the thigh bones are more widely separated in women than in men. Since the thighs grow toward the center line of the body as they approach the knees, this outward flare at the hips has a tendency to bring the knees of a woman somewhat closer together than is the case in a man.

The leg. The **femur** (Fig. 5-9) is the longest and strongest member of the skeleton. The head of the femur is rounded and smooth and articulates with the ilium at a pronounced indentation in the latter, the *acetabulum,* forming a strong ball and socket joint. The head is set off at an angle of about 125° from

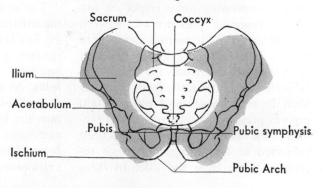

Sacrum

Coccyx

Ilium

Acetabulum

Pubis

Ischium

Pubic symphysis

Pubic Arch

Fig. 5-17. *Human pelvis: male, black outline; female, colored area.*

the main shaft of the bone by a short region, the neck. The weight of the body is thus supported at a point slightly inside of the main axis of the limb. The neck region is a fairly common site of fracture, especially in older persons, in whom it tends to become rather porous and thus weaker.

The internal architecture of the femur follows a very definite pattern. The shaft of the bone is filled with marrow and is almost completely cylindrical in outline. The walls are composed of very compact bone. At the lower end the femur expands to a broad surface to permit articulation with the tibia. In both the lower end of the bone and head and neck regions, the femur shows excellent examples of the application of mechanical engineering principles to bodily structure. The trabeculae in the upper end of the bone grow in curved lines so that they offer the maximum strength to the bone. In this respect they may be likened to girders in a structure that is designed to carry a heavy load. At the lower end of the bone the trabeculae are arranged in parallel, longitudinal walls, thus affording support for a direct downward thrust. While some measurements have been made on the amount of compression the femur can stand before breaking, these have not given uniform results due to the variability in the specimens used and to the methods employed. The results indicate, however, that if a direct compressing force is put on top of the femur, a pressure of between 15,000 and 19,000 pounds per square inch is needed to break the bone. If cylinders are cut from the shaft and subjected to similar tests, fresh bone has been found to withstand over 27,000 pounds pressure per square inch. Fracture of the bone occurs when it has been subjected to a twisting motion or receives a blow from the side. In these circumstances, a few hundred pounds pressure will break the bone.

The lower end of the femur is expanded into a large flattened region, the two sides of which can be felt at the knee joint (Fig. 5-7). This is the point of articulation with the larger of the two bones of the leg, the **tibia.** The **patella** (kneecap) is located just in front of this joint. This large sesamoid bone has developed in the tendon of the principal muscle of the front of the thigh. It is flat and roughly triangular in outline, with the apex of the triangle pointing downward. A ligament attaches it to the tibia. Surrounding the patella are four bursae which serve to cushion the joint.

From the standpoint of comparative anatomy, the bones of the lower part of the leg are comparable to those of the forearm. The **fibula** would correspond to the radius of the arm in position and mode of development, while the tibia can be compared to the ulna. There, however, the similarity stops. Both the tibia and fibula are immovable as far as rotation is concerned. This results in a lower leg that cannot be rotated from side to side in the same manner as the forearm. It increases the stability of the leg as a whole and makes it a more suitable organ of locomotion. The lower end of the tibia forms the projecting ankle bone on the inside of the leg, while the end of the fibula can be felt on the outer side.

The **ankle** (tarsus) is comparable to the wrist, in that it serves as the connecting link between the bones of the leg and the foot. Both the tibia and fibula articulate with a broad-topped tarsal bone, the **talus.** As in the wrist, the movement of the ankle is a sliding motion which permits the foot to be extended and flexed each time a step is taken. The largest bone of the ankle is the heel bone, the **calcaneus.**

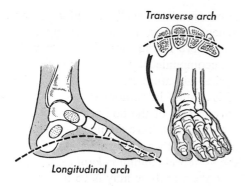

Transverse arch

Longitudinal arch

Fig. 5-18. *Arches of the human foot.*

The foot. There are five **metatarsal bones** in the foot that correspond to the metacarpals of the palm of the hand. Each of these bones articulates with at least one of the tarsal bones, and in some cases, they articulate with other metatarsals. There is one important difference between the palm of the hand and the metatarsal region of the foot: the foot has two main curvatures in its architecture that are lacking in the palm (Fig. 5-18). These curves are the result of the arching of the metatarsals as they join the tarsus. Thus we find that one of these arches is longitudinal in its direction and the other lies perpendicular to it and is transverse. Together they strengthen the foot and give a certain amount of springiness to the stride. Due to any one of a variety of causes, including faulty prenatal nutrition, improper posture, excessive weight, fatigue, or improperly fitting shoes, these arches may be lowered. The result is a "flat-footed" condition which throws unnatural stresses and strains on the muscles involved in walking and may lead to increased fatigue and pain.

The phalanges of the toes are similar in number and relative position to the corresponding bones in the fingers. Four of the toes have three phalanges each; the great toe has only two. Unlike the thumb, the great toe is nonopposable: that is, it cannot be brought across the sole of the foot, although in a young infant it has greater flexibility than in an adult.

DISORDERS OF SKELETAL STRUCTURES

The skeleton, like any other part of the body, is subject to various diseases and injuries. Bone infections may result from invasion by bacteria from some other region where these organisms are the cause of a difficulty quite unconnected with the skeleton. Thus bone infections may develop as a result of badly infected teeth, pneumonia, typhoid fever, or other diseases. Injury to a bone as a result of a hard blow may also serve as a predisposing condition that will be followed by an infection. The general name given to several conditions involving infection of bones is **osteomyelitis.**

One of the more common types of skeletal disorders is **arthritis.** This term is used to include a large number of different conditions in which joints are affected. Arthritis is usually thought of as a disease of the aged, but only certain types, particularly hypertrophic arthritis, occur as a result of aging. The most serious forms of arthritis usually develop between the ages of 25 and 50. Rheumatoid arthritis is a particularly devastating form of the disease. It affects about three times more women than men. The cause is unknown, though emotional factors, infections, metabolic and endocrine abnormalities, and diseases of the nervous system are suspect. In this condition the joints become badly swollen and painful (Fig. 5-19). The pain causes muscle spasm which may result in deformity. As the disease progresses, the cartilage that separates the bones of the joints is gradually destroyed and hard calcium bands fill the spaces.

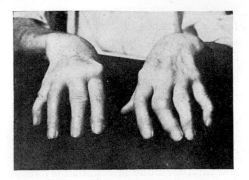

Fig. 5-19. *Rheumatoid arthritis. Note the swollen joints and the muscular contractions of the fingers. (E. R. Squibb and Sons)*

These calcified bands restrict the movement of the joint so that crippling and wasting of the muscles result.

The vertebral column is subject to several conditions which result in an abnormal curvature of the spine. **Scoliosis** is the name given to the side-to-side curvature of the spine. This may arise from an attack of infantile paralysis,

poor muscle "tone," or faulty posture. When it exists, there is usually a lateral curve in the thoracic region which is accompanied by a corresponding opposite curvature in the lumbar region. This results in compression of the ribs on one side of the body, while those on the other side have a tendency to spread apart. Another abnormal condition of the vertebral column is **kyphosis.** In this case the vertebrae may have been weakened by an infection, such as tuberculosis of the bone, and are not able to support the weight of the upper part of the trunk. This results in outward bending of the bones, a condition commonly known as hunchback. A third abnormal curvature is **lordosis,** an exaggerated inward curvature in the lumbar region just above the sacrum.

There are several different types of **fractures** that have been named according to the way the broken ends of the bone behave. The simplest type is known as a *green-stick fracture* because the

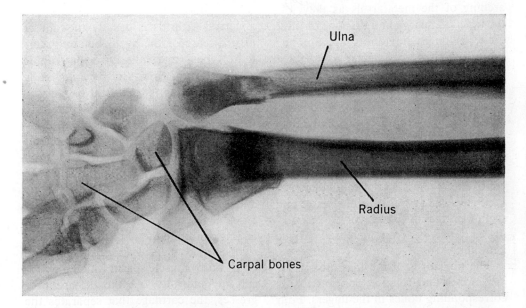

Ulna

Radius

Carpal bones

Fig. 5-20. *A simple type of fracture of both the radius and ulna just above the region of the wrist.*

broken bone does not separate completely but acts like a sap-filled stick, the fibers of which separate lengthwise when it is bent. Green-stick fractures are usually found in young children whose bones still contain flexible cartilage. A *simple fracture* is one in which a bone is broken but the ends do not push outward through the skin. As the X-ray photograph in Fig. 5-20 shows, both of the bones in the left forearm have been broken just above the wrist and the ends have overridden each other. This slipping of the bones over each other may have been the result of the blow or of a contraction of the muscles that pulled the broken bones into that position. The most serious type of fracture is the *compound fracture,* in which the end of the bone protrudes through the skin. This may lead to an infection of the bone or of the surrounding tissues.

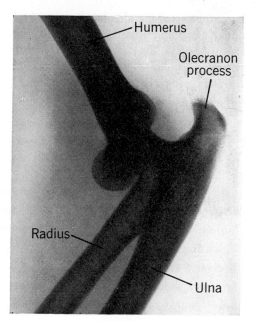

Fig. 5-22. *Dislocation of the elbow. Note the olecranon process projecting away from the bottom of the humerus.*

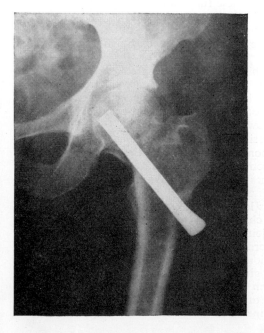

Fig. 5-21. *In this X-ray photograph of a hip fracture, a metal pin has been used to hold the broken bone until it can knit together normally.*

The periosteum and the endosteum play important roles in healing broken bones. After a fracture has occurred, there is an immediate stimulation of these membranes to produce bone-forming cells. In bones of membranous origin, healing occurs as a direct extension of new growth from each side of the break. However, in long bones there is the formation of a fibrous cartilage model to fill the gap, and this model is replaced by bone, as occurs in the initial ossification of long bones. The fibrous connective tissue, cartilage, and new bone form a **callus** or bridge between the broken ends of the bone until healing is complete. In some cases, surgeons use metal pins to hold fractured bones together until they can heal properly (see Fig. 5-21).

A **dislocation** (Fig. 5-22) occurs when a bone is forced out of its proper position in a joint. In the case shown here, the top of the ulna has been pushed out of position. Note the displaced olecranon process, the sharply curved upper part of the ulna.

When a joint is subjected to a sudden, unnatural motion, a **sprain** may result, because of the tearing or straining of the tendons that hold the muscle to the bones, or of the ligaments that connect the bones. This is usually accompanied by acute pain and rapid swelling in the region of the injury.

SPEAKING OF Physiology

Briefly identify each of the following:

bursa	**lamellae**	**sprain**
cartilage	**ligament**	**sternum**
cranium	**medullary canal**	**suture**
dislocation	**osteoblast**	**synovial fluid**
epiphyseal cartilage	**osteocyte**	**tendon**
fibrous capsule	**patella**	**trabeculae**
joint	**sesamoid bones**	**vertebra**

Test YOUR KNOWLEDGE

1. What are the important functions of the human skeleton? Give examples of how specific parts of the skeleton perform these functions.
2. From what two types of tissue in the embryo does the skeleton develop? Approximately when does this development begin?
3. List several minerals necessary in the formation of bone. Which of these are of the most importance?
4. With reference to question 3: after birth these minerals are absorbed from food in the daily diet. How are they obtained by the developing child before birth?
5. The ossification of a long bone, such as the femur, occurs at more than one center. In which part does the fastest rate of development occur? What do we call that part of a bone with the slower rate of development?
6. Briefly describe the method of ossification of a long bone. How does this method differ from that of a flat bone such as those of the skull?
7. Describe the unit of structure of compact bone, the Haversian system.
8. What covers and protects the bones of the body? What part does it play in bone formation?
9. Explain how the bones are used as levers, using examples of body movements other than those mentioned in this chapter.
10. Describe the six types of movable joints. Give at least one example of each and describe the type of movement afforded by each joint used as an example.
11. How does a tendon differ in function from a ligament?
12. What bones make up the shoulder girdle? The pelvic girdle?
13. The skeletal parts of the human arm and leg are quite similar. Explain any *differences* in their structure in terms of their different functions.
14. What is unique about the hand of man and other Primates as compared to that of other animals?
15. What are the functions of the paranasal sinuses?
16. Describe the healing process that occurs after a bone is fractured.
17. Why are pins and plates of metal sometimes used in the surgical treatment of fractures?

See FOR YOURSELF

1. Probably the greatest knowledge of prehistoric man is derived from skull fragments. These fossil skulls have been traced back approximately 500,000 years, and enable scientists to reconstruct man theoretically as he evidently appeared at that time. With the knowledge you can gain from library research, and using the evidence of skull fragments, construct a chart showing the evolution of man. Starting with the Heidelberg jaw fragment, include: Pithecanthropus erectus, Sinanthropus, Pekinensis, Neanderthal, Cro-Magnon, and any others which would give greater meaning to your work. It would be wise to include a time scale and the divisions of the Pleistocene Epoch.

2. Procure from a meat market a meatless leg bone which has been cut longitudinally. Draw and identify the following: compact bone, spongy bone, medullary canal, red bone marrow, yellow bone marrow, foramens, epiphyseal cartilage, periosteum. Describe the function of each part labeled.

3. Procure and mount the skeleton of a small animal. Try to visualize how the structure of the skeleton helped the animal survive in the competitive environment in which it lived.

4. Obtain information about current research on the effects of radiation on bone growth and development. Write a brief summary of this information.

5. Get two similar thin (uncooked) bones from a freshly killed vertebrate. Put one bone in a dilute solution of hydrochloric acid and allow it to stand for a few days. Heat the other bone strongly over a gas flame for about an hour. Record any differences in properties of the two bones after this treatment, and try to explain the differences noted.

6. Prepare an oral or written report on the recommended first aid treatment for fractures, dislocations, and sprains. Explain the physiological reasons for these treatments.

CHAPTER 6

The Physiology of Skeletal Muscle

Without muscles we could not move nor speak nor breathe. Such movement is possible because of the high degree of development in muscle of the contractile quality of protoplasm. When stimulated, the long fibers that make up muscle tissue are able to conduct a wave of excitation along its entire length. The resulting chemical reactions produce a contraction of the fibers, thus transforming chemical energy into mechanical motion.

In any mechanical device that converts one type of energy into another so that work can be done, the energy is changed from an inactive, *potential* form into an active, *kinetic* state. In a gasoline engine, for example, liquid fuel is rapidly oxidized and converted into a gaseous state. This chemical reaction is accomplished by heat generated in the cylinder. The force of expanding gases on the piston pushes it into action. The piston action is then converted mechanically into the motion of the automobile. This is a common example of conversion of one form of energy (chemical) into another (mechanical). The body, however, is more efficient than the gas engine. Nothing is lost. When muscle fibers contract, about 60 percent of the energy used is converted into heat and about 40 percent into mechanical work. The mechanical efficiency of an automobile engine is only about half that of muscle fibers.

Skeletal muscle tissue. Striated muscle tissue makes up about 40 percent of the body weight and is the largest single tissue part of the body. As we learned in Chapter 4, skeletal muscle tissue consists of elongated cells or fibers characterized by striations. This long, slender cell (*muscle fiber*) is ensheathed in a very thin membrane, the sarcolemma (Fig. 6-1). Internally, the fiber is made up of *myofibrils* which lie parallel to each other and run lengthwise in the cell. The striations characteristic of this type of tissue are found on each of the myofibrils. Within them are still smaller filaments, the *micellae,* which are composed of the protein molecules *actin* and *myosin.* These substances play an important part in muscle contraction, as will be seen later. The long muscle fibers are bundled together in groups that are separated from each other by connective tissue called the *perimysium.* The whole muscle is wrapped in another connective tissue sheath, the *epimysium.*

Fine branches of nerves pass to the

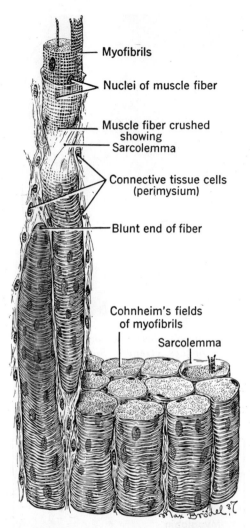

Myofibrils

Nuclei of muscle fiber

Muscle fiber crushed showing Sarcolemma

Connective tissue cells (perimysium)

Blunt end of fiber

Cohnheim's fields of myofibrils

Sarcolemma

Fig. 6-1. *A three-dimensional diagram of the structure of a muscle. Note the relation of the various parts to each other. (Courtesy of Department of Art as Applied to Medicine, John Hopkins Medical School)*

muscles (Fig. 6-2) and spread over the cells, making contact at specialized nerve endings called **myoneural junctions.** A chemical, **acetylcholine,** produced at this junction, transmits the stimulus to the muscle fiber, which then begins a series of chemical reactions that result in contraction. Since all fibers have these nerve endings over their surfaces, and

since the impulse reaches all simultaneously, the entire muscle contracts at the same instant. It would remain in this state of contraction if it were not for another substance, **cholinesterase,** formed by the nerve to neutralize acetylcholine. To get an idea of the rapidity of alternation between these two processes, consider that in the mosquito they occur with each beat of its wings.

Sometimes a normal function can be well illustrated by a condition in which that function goes wrong. **Myasthenia gravis** (meaning "muscle weakness, severe") is a disease in which acetylcholine appears to be blocked at the myoneural junctions. This is thought to be due to an abnormal accumulation of another chemical, possibly a waste product of muscle fatigue. Thus there is abnormally rapid exhaustion of any or all voluntary muscles.

The eye muscles are most frequently affected, causing drooping eyelids and double vision. There may also be difficulty in smiling, chewing, speaking, swallowing, reaching, walking, or even breathing, in severe cases. All of these symptoms are worse with exertion and are somewhat relieved by rest.

Dr. Mary B. Walker, an English physician, noted the similarity of these symptoms to those of persons affected by the South American arrow poison, curare. An antidote for curare was known—neostigmine, which raises the level of acetylcholine by suppressing the activity of cholinesterase. Dr. Walker reasoned that if a patient with myasthenia were given this drug, improvement might result. The effects of the drug are shown in Fig. 6-3.

Patients may take neostigmine and similar drugs by mouth in tablet form, according to their needs. Fortunately, there are no real toxic effects, but if an overdose is taken, unpleasant muscle

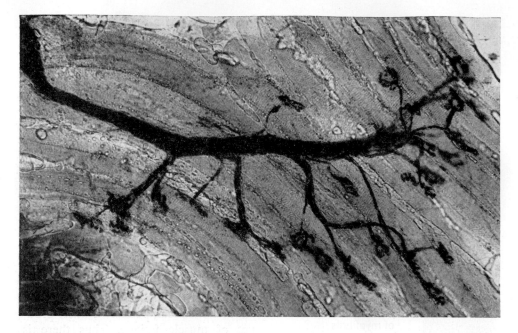

Fig. 6-2. *Distribution of nerve endings over striated muscle fibers. The myoneural junctions are the small bodies at the ends of the nerve branches. (General Biological Supply House)*

twitching, stomach cramps, and diarrhea occur, due to the presence of excess acetylcholine.

Since the discovery of neostigmine, thousands of cases of myasthenia gravis have been found, but many more, especially, milder cases, probably remain undiagnosed.

Chemistry of muscle contraction. Striated muscle tissue consists of approximately 75 percent water, 20 percent protein, and 5 percent minerals and various organic substances. The most abundant minerals in muscle tissue are potassium and sodium, the former being found within the cell itself and the latter in the intercellular fluid. Calcium, phosphorus, and magnesium are also present in significant amounts, and all take the form of chlorides, carbonates, and phosphates. Some of these salts help regulate the osmotic pressure of the cells, and others take an active part in muscle contraction. Most important of the organic compounds are creatine, creatine phosphate, adenosine, triphosphate, and glycogen.

Water	75%
Proteins	20%
Myosin	
Actin	
Myoglobin	
Minerals and organic substances 5%	
Potassium	
Sodium	
Calcium	
Magnesium	
Chlorides	
Carbonates	
Phosphates	
Fats and fatlike	
compounds	
Glycogen	
Lactic acid	
Creatine	
Creatine phosphate	

The table on page 64 shows the approximate composition of muscle tissue.

Analysis of the muscle twitch. The classic method for studying the contraction of a muscle is that of the so-called **nerve-muscle preparation.** The calf muscle from a frog's leg with the nerve intact is usually used with an apparatus like that shown in Fig. 6-4. The upper of the two lines on the drum is a record of a single muscle twitch which results from stimulating the nerve by means of a small electric current.

From the record made on the kymograph, it can be seen that a single muscle twitch is divided into three distinct periods (Fig. 6-5). The electrical stimulus was applied at the point marked "S," and for 0.01 second thereafter no movement was recorded. This is the **latent period,** during which presumably there is a series of chemical and electrical changes within the muscle fibers. The **contraction period** commences with the breakdown of a complex chemical within the fibers. This supplies energy for contraction. The contraction period lasts about 0.04 seconds during a single twitch. When contraction reaches its maximum peak, there follows a 0.05 second **relaxation period.** During the time the muscle is relaxing, the original complex chemical is re-formed from simpler compounds. Besides the energy produced in this reaction, further energy is being supplied by the breakdown of glycogen. These three periods can occur in the absence of oxygen. There follows a **recovery period** during which the muscle is supplied with oxygen for the oxidation of waste products that accumulate during the contraction.

Since the frog is a cold-blooded animal, these measurements are usually made at room temperature (68° F.—70° F.). The latent, contraction, and relaxation periods occur in about 0.1 sec-

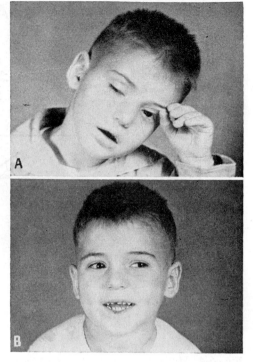

Fig. 6-3. *The dramatic effect of neostigmine. Above, the child is suffering from a severe case of myasthenia gravis. His eyelids droop so that he has to support one to look at the camera. Below, the child is shown 42 seconds after receiving an injection of neostigmine.*

ond, and under the conditions existing in making a kymograph record of a single muscle twitch, the recovery period is approximately one minute in length. The speed of reaction increases as the temperature is raised. In the human body, the effect of temperature is of minor importance because we maintain a fairly constant temperature at which the chemical processes occur with the greatest efficiency. In the human, the total time elapsing during a twitch of a muscle is about 0.001 second.

If a muscle is stimulated repeatedly and with such rapidity that no complete recovery periods are allowed between stimulations, the condition of **fatigue**

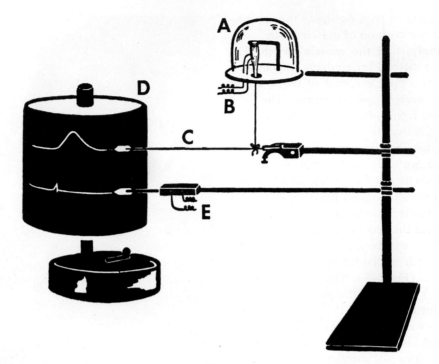

Fig. 6-4. *Method of recording a muscle twitch. The muscle is placed in a moist chamber, A, with proper electrical connections, B, for its stimulation. The contraction of the muscle is recorded by the lever, C, on the smoked paper that covers the drum of the kymograph, D. In the base of the kymograph is a spring-driven motor that will make the drum revolve at a definite rate of speed. The exact instant of stimulation of the muscle is recorded by the signal lever, E, that has been wired into the same circuit as the stimulating electrodes. The writing points scrape the soot off the smoked paper and leave a white record on a black background. (Drawing by P. McC. From Gerard,* The Body Functions, *permission of John Wiley and Sons, Inc.)*

appears. The responses of the muscle to the stimulus become weaker and weaker until they fail entirely (Fig. 6-6). This condition of fatigue will last until the oxidation and removal of wastes has been completed.

A type of prolonged muscular contraction, which differs from the muscle twitch, is the state of **tetanus.** It is obvious that a single twitch of very short duration such as we have considered would not be effective in performing any work nor would it result in coordinated movements. However, if impulses are sent into the muscle at a very rapid rate (20 or 30 per second) the muscle will

contract and remain contracted until the impulses cease. An example of this type of action is found in the motion of closing your hand slowly. Such motion involves a large number of muscle bundles acting together in a coordinated action for a considerable time interval.

Especially involved in muscle contraction are the proteins, actin and myosin, which compose the micellae. There are many theories that attempt to explain the role of these proteins in contraction, and some of the most exciting work in the field of physiology is being done in this area. One of the few things definitely known of this phenomenon is that the

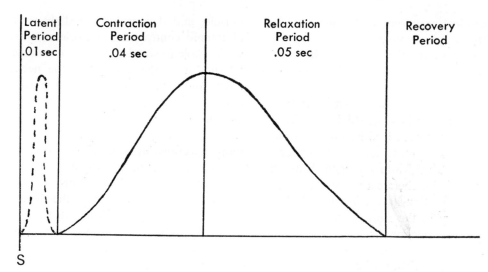

| Latent Period .01 sec | Contraction Period .04 sec | Relaxation Period .05 sec | Recovery Period |

S

Fig. 6-5. *An analysis of the record of a muscle twitch shows that it is divided into three principal parts followed by a period of recovery. Each phase of this process is characterized by definite chemical processes occurring in the muscle.*

combination of actin and myosin, or actomyosin, contracts in the presence of a nonprotein substance, **adenosine triphosphate** (ATP). ATP breaks down into a simpler substance, **adenosine diphosphate** (ADP), by the explosive separation of phosphate. The energy released in this reaction brings about the contraction of the actomyosin. Because of the importance of ATP as an energy source, it must be kept in constant supply. This is done through an intricate series of recombinations involving other nonprotein substances. Thus, resynthesis of ATP is accomplished by the combination of ADP with creatine phosphate

(CP). In this reaction, energy is supplied for ATP formation. CP is resynthesized as a result of a series of reactions that occur when glycogen combines with the phosphate released by the ATP breakdown. A waste product, lactic acid, is also formed.

These complex chemical reactions can occur without the presence of oxygen in the cell, which accounts for the fact that a runner can cover several yards' distance without taking a breath. However, the muscle must recover from its activity and must have the waste products of contraction removed. We have seen that lactic acid accumulates from the initial

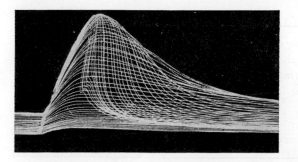

Fig. 6-6. *Fatigue resulting from repeated stimulation of a muscle. Note how the curves become shorter. (From Gerard, The Body Functions, permission of John Wiley and Sons, Inc.)*

chemical reactions, and it must be oxidized and removed. Thus oxygen is needed to rid the muscle of its wastes and to enable the contractile process to continue. One fifth of the lactic acid is oxidized to form water and carbon dioxide, which is removed by the blood. The energy produced by this reaction is used to resynthesize the remainder of the lactic acid into glycogen. With this last step the chemical processes of muscle contraction have come full circle. A summary of the steps involved in these chemical reactions is given in the table below.

The contraction of the muscle is the sum of the contractions of the micellae within the individual fibers. There is a wealth of evidence that actomyosin is the substance that causes this contraction. The principal mystery that muscle physiologists are trying to solve is what happens between the releasing of energy by the ATP breakdown and the action of actomyosin to bring about contraction. There is some evidence that the phenomenon of muscle contraction may involve electronic energy migrations within the muscle fibers. However, the chemical explanation given here is the one now most widely accepted by students of physiology.

Muscle tone. A normal characteristic of all muscle tissue is that it remains in a state of partial contraction at all times. This condition is the result of a constant flow of weak nervous impulses to the muscle, and is considered a slight state of tetanic contraction. Because of this, we are able to stand erect without undue fatigue, since the muscles of the neck, back, and legs are in a state of partial contraction. A good example of how muscle tone affects muscles is seen in the fingers. If you allow your hands to hang naturally by your sides, you will see that the fingers are slightly bent. If the muscles were not constantly receiving a stream of impulses, the hands would be in a flat position with the fingers very loose and relaxed. An unconscious person shows the loss of muscle tone, which is one reason why it is so difficult to carry him in this condition. Normally, when a person is asleep, the tone of his muscles is at the lowest point short of complete unconsciousness.

THE EFFECTS OF MUSCULAR EXERCISE

Increase in muscle tissue. The number of striated muscle cells present at birth is essentially the same as that found in the adult. In other words, muscle cells are unable to reproduce themselves, except for a very short period of time immediately following birth. Thus there must be some other explanation for the increase in muscle tissue. It is true that the nuclei increase in number by a process of simple nuclear division, and that some very few fibers may split, but there is a very small increase in number of cells. Nor do muscle cells have the power

---

(1) ATP $\rightleftarrows$ ADP + phosphate + energy for immediate contraction

(2) ADP + CP $\rightleftarrows$ creatine + phosphate + energy for resynthesis of ATP + ATP

(3) glycogen + phosphate $\rightleftarrows$ intermediate stages $\rightleftarrows$
    lactic acid + energy for resynthesis of CP and ATP

(4) $\frac{1}{5}$ lactic acid + O_2 $\rightarrow$
    carbon dioxide + water + energy for the resynthesis of glycogen

(5) $\frac{4}{5}$ lactic acid + energy $\rightarrow$ glycogen

to replace themselves once they have been lost, except in those cases where a sufficient amount of their substance remains to permit regeneration.

As everyone realizes, continued muscular activity is accompanied by an increase in the size of the muscles that are being used. This enlargement is the result of an increase in the amount of cytoplasm within the individual cells. When any organ increases in size, it is said to **hypertrophy,** and the opposite, **atrophy,** occurs when the organ becomes smaller. Atrophy is seen in those muscles which have not been regularly used, either from a lack of exercise or because of injury to the nerves which control their activity. Muscles affected by paralyzing poliomyelitis frequently grow smaller. Muscle cells are not actually lost, but there is rather a destruction of the nerves in the spinal cord that control their activities. This loss of ability to move brings about a shrinking of the individual fibers in the unused muscles.

During exercise, not only do muscles themselves increase in total volume, but the products they produce cause changes in other organ systems. Respiratory, circulatory, excretory, and nervous systems all respond to the extra demands of the body during moderate or strenuous exercise.

Increase in respiration. We have all experienced the increase in the rate of breathing during exercise. This is the body's attempt to supply oxygen used up in muscle activity. As we learned, some of the chemical reactions that occur in muscle contraction do not require oxygen. But the recovery phase of contraction does need oxygen in order to restore energy-producing substances. Deeper, more rapid breathing helps pay this **oxygen debt** so that continued work is possible. For example, it is possible for a runner to run 100 yards at top speed without taking more than one or two breaths or, perhaps, none. At the end of the race he may fall to the ground completely exhausted. This simply means that he has used up his oxygen supply in the effort of the race and does not have a sufficient amount for the processes of recovery. Prolonged, severe exercise does not have this same effect; the runner in a long race "gets his second wind" by an adjustment of the body to the demands that are made on it.

During severe muscular exercise, the rate of the necessary increase in the rapidity and depth of respiration depends on the amount of exercise taken. Consider what happens when a runner sprints for 120 yards. The following data will show his oxygen requirements at varying rates of speed.

Length of time to finish race	Oxygen requirements	
	Quarts per 120 yards	Quarts per minute
22.6 seconds	1.93	5.35
16.4 seconds	3.25	11.80
14.3 seconds	4.58	19.20
13.0 seconds	7.80	35.39

We have seen that more oxygen is needed during exercise to oxidize the increased amount of lactic acid formed in the cells during muscular contraction. Lactic acid may appear in the blood in quantities twenty times as great as that found when the muscles are normally resting. When this lactic acid is oxidized, the carbon dioxide formed becomes carbonic acid when absorbed into the blood stream. The change in the acidity of the blood has a profound effect on the nervous system, one result being an increase in the rate of breathing.

Changes in the circulatory system. Since it is extremely difficult to make

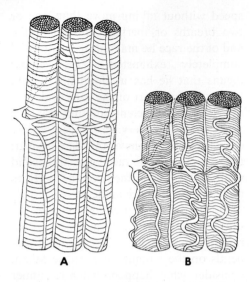

Fig. 6-7. *Diagram of three muscle fibers. In A the fibers are relaxed; in B the fibers have contracted and the capillaries are shown as folded.*

direct chemical analyses of the changes in muscles during exercise, it is necessary to examine the body fluids. Both blood and urine furnish clues to some of the changes that go on in the muscles during exercise. During exercise, there is an increase in the number of red blood corpuscles, the rise being directly proportional to the severity of the exercise. Since the function of these cells is to transport oxygen around the body, the needs of the muscles can thus be met more easily. Two factors probably play a role in this increase in the number of red cells: (1) some may be forced into the blood stream from the reservoirs such as the spleen; and (2) there is a loss of water by sweating and the passage of some of the blood fluid into the tissues, which results in the concentration of the blood solids.

Following severe exercise, such as running a quarter-mile race, we find that the hydrogen ion concentration of the blood drops from a normal pH value of 7.35 to 6.95, indicating a marked shift to the acid side. Ten minutes after the race has been finished, the pH rises to 7.04, showing that some of the substances responsible for the shift have been removed. Four minutes after the race it is found that the lactate—a slightly acid salt of lactic acid—in the blood rises from a normal 5.6 milligrams per cent to 163, but at the end of ten minutes drops to 150 milligrams. The lactate is removed from the blood by the kidneys until a more normal level is reached.

Muscles are richly supplied with capillaries, the smallest types of blood vessels, to insure an adequate supply of blood to these active tissues. This supply is so great that in the gastrocnemius muscle of a cat, for example, there are 2341 capillaries per square millimeter of cross section of the muscle. This will give a surface area of 44.1 square millimeters of capillary surface for each cubic millimeter of muscle—a truly amazing amount of surface. In man, these values are approximately the same. When a muscle is at rest the blood flows through the capillaries at approximately 850 milliliters per minute, but when it is active, the rate is increased to about 6,920 milliliters per minute. The arterioles dilate or contract to give a greater or lesser flow to the capillaries. Since the capillaries themselves cannot contract, the muscle fibers over the surface of which they are spread tend to make the vessels fold on themselves. This is shown in Fig. 6-7.

One special effect of exercise is to assist in the return of the blood and lymph to the heart. The contraction of the muscles of the legs presses on the walls of the veins and lymphatics and drives their contents upward toward the heart. The presence of valves in these vessels prevents the backward flow of the fluids. Many of us have noticed that on long auto rides, or on standing without much movement for long periods, our shoes feel tight and our ankles are swollen. When walking is resumed, this swelling usually disappears as tissue fluid returns to veins and lymphatics and is forced upward through the vessels by the squeezing action of the large leg muscles.

Increase in heart rate. Studies indicate that the rise in the heart rate starts almost at the same moment that the exercise begins. In fact, the first beat after the work has started is shorter than the preceding one. The rate then rises very sharply but soon has a tendency to level off and remain more or less constant during the exercise periods. In trained athletes, the pulse rate following strenuous exercise varies between 126 and 152 beats per minute. After the exercise has stopped, the rate falls back to normal. At first this reduction is quite rapid, but it then drops more slowly. If the work has been severe, the postwork rate may remain above the prework rate for as long as half an hour.

Elevation of the blood pressure. During severe exertion, a person's blood pressure may rise as much as 60 points above his resting rate. Recent work indicates that of the several factors involved, one may be the fact that the drop in the blood pH has a stimulating effect on the nervous system which results in the constriction of some of the larger blood vessels, thus increasing the tension on their walls.

Rise in body temperature. The heat produced during muscle activity is the principal source of heat in the body. Sixty percent of the energy liberated during muscle contraction is generated in the form of heat. During strenuous exercise, the rectal temperature (normal 99.6° F.) rises swiftly to about 100.4° F.

and then drops rapidly back to normal at the end of the work period. If very fine needle thermocouples are introduced into the thigh muscles of men who are pedaling bicycles, the temperatures recorded within the muscles will be about 102° F.

The body has, however, a very complex system of liberating this excess heat over the surface of the body and by way of body wastes, so that the temperature is kept under control (see Chapter 28). There is a particularly interesting safeguard against too great a decrease in the body temperature. If a person is outside on a cold day and is not exercising, he may start to shiver. This phenomenon is simply a series of slight involuntary muscular contractions which raise the temperature by producing more heat in the muscles. The excess heat produced is then distributed through the body by the blood.

Change in the composition of the urine. In the first place, the amount of urine is reduced and does not return to its previous prework level for about an hour and one half to two hours following the stoppage of work. It had been thought that this was due to the control of the nervous system over the flow of blood to the kidneys, reducing their activities. Fairly recent work has shown that this may not be the case and that, instead, the production of urine during exercise may be under some other control. It may be that the increased absorption of fluids from the blood reduces the amount excreted through the kidneys. A second feature is an increase in the amount of acid present in the urine. Because of the amount of lactic and other acids formed during exercise, the acidity of the urine increases sharply following the completion of the work and then drops back to normal quite rapidly as the body relaxes.

SPEAKING OF Physiology

Briefly identify the following:

actomyosin

acetylcholine

adenosine triphosphate

atrophy

cholinesterase

hypertrophy

lactic acid

micellae

muscle fiber

myofibril

oxygen debt

tetanus

Test YOUR KNOWLEDGE

1. Describe the composition of a skeletal muscle fiber.
2. Describe the four stages of muscle contraction, as demonstrated by the muscle twitch. Include in your explanation the chemical processes that occur during the twitch.
3. How is oxygen debt related to muscular activity? How is this debt repaid?
4. By what mechanism is the body able to maintain sufficient muscle tension to stand erect? What is this type of tension called?
5. What is the relation between muscular activity and respiratory rate?
6. How is the composition of the blood altered during muscular exercise? Why do these changes occur?
7. In what way does the muscular system assist in returning venous blood and lymph to the heart?

See FOR YOURSELF

1. Is there any statistical evidence that former great athletes have a greater incidence of heart disease than a sampling of nonathletic individuals? What conclusions would you draw from the results of your research?

2. How could you devise a scale to show the relationship of muscle size to muscular strength? Is there a correlation? What effect does the sex of the individual have?

3. Set up a muscle twitch demonstration as shown in Fig. 6-4, page 66. If you do not have the necessary apparatus, try to improvise apparatus that will achieve similar results.

4. Prepare charts showing the effects of exercise on your own heart rate, respiration rate, blood pressure, and body temperature.

CHAPTER 7

The Action of Some Skeletal Muscles

We have seen that muscle action is the result of chemical processes within the individual muscle cells. A more general consideration of the anatomical location and action of some of these muscles will show how this muscular energy is transformed into mechanical energy in the form of motion.

Muscles are able to move bones because of the location of the muscle attachments. These points of attachment are called the **origin** and the **insertion**. The attachment to the bone that serves as a relatively fixed basis of movement is the origin. The insertion is the point of attachment to the bone which is moved. Most muscles are attached to the periosteum of a bone by means of a tendon; however, some make direct contact with the periosteum, while others are attached by a sheet of heavy connective tissue. The **belly** of the muscle contains the body of the muscle tissue itself. To understand the movement made possible by the action of a specific muscle, it is necessary to know its origin and insertion.

Consider, for example, the action of the **biceps,** a large muscle on the front of the upper arm that can be felt when the arm is bent at the elbow. Because of the placement of its origins, it not only brings about a movement of the forearm in a vertical plane, but also gives it a rotary motion, such as that used with a screwdriver. In Fig. 7-1, we can see that both the biceps and the **triceps** (on the back of the arm) have more than one origin each; the triceps has three points of origin and derives its name from that fact (Lat., *tres,* three + *caput,* head), and the biceps has two. It will be noted that these muscles have several points of insertion, and because of this, complex action is possible.

The action of the biceps and the triceps when the arm is flexed or extended at the elbow illustrates an important characteristic of muscles: most skeletal muscles work in pairs. For each muscular contraction that brings about motion in one direction, there is possible a motion in the opposite direction which depends upon the contraction of the other member of the muscle pair. For example, when you flex your arm, the action is largely the result of the contraction of the biceps muscle. But when you extend your arm, the triceps muscle contracts. These opposing actions are brought about by the so-called **antagonistic muscles.**

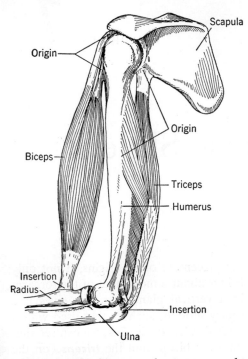

Fig. 7-1. *The biceps and triceps muscles of the arm, showing their origins and insertions.* (*From Miller and Haub,* General Zoology, *Holt, 1956*)

The action of the nervous system in sending contraction impulses to one of a pair of antagonistic muscles, while allowing the other to relax, is termed the **reciprocal innervation** of the muscles.

The action of some superficial muscles. The activities of many of the skeletal muscles pass unnoticed because they lie below the surface of the body. These are known as **deep muscles** to distinguish them from the **superficial muscles** which are responsible for the body's contour and are especially apparent during physical exertion. We will deal here only with those superficial muscles whose action we can readily see in our daily activities (Figs. 7-2 and 7-3).

Your facial expressions are produced by a series of interesting muscles that permit you to frown, smile, raise your eyebrows, squint, and perform a variety of conscious and unconscious facial movements. This is why the facial muscles are sometimes referred to as the "muscles of expression."

The muscle bundles that comprise these are generally not as distinct and separate as those found elsewhere in the body, due to their method of formation and attachment. Around the eyes their arrangement is circular. The **orbicularis oculi** acts as a sphincter muscle to draw the surface of the face around the eye into a circular form and close the lids, as in squinting. Similarly, the **orbicularis oris** allows the lips to be pursed when whistling. Sphincter muscles such as these behave much like a drawstring around the opening of a bag or tube.

A powerful muscle on the side of the face, the **masseter,** is responsible for many of the motions of chewing. Its action may also be noticed during those moments of concentration when unconscious movements of the jaw occur. The masseter functions with the **pterygoideus internus** (the action of which is not visible from the surface of the body) in forming a slinglike structure that holds the lower jaw in place and permits it to move up and down with a slightly rotary motion.

A muscle of the neck, quite obvious when the head is thrown back, is the **platysma.** This muscle has its origin on the upper edge of the **pectoralis major** (described below) and spreads as a broad sheet upward toward the lower jaw. Its action is to draw the outer edges of the lower lip downward, especially when the head is thrown backwards. A runner gasping for air at the end of a hard race will show this muscle clearly.

The most conspicuous muscle on the front and side of the neck is a stout, often prominent band that arises from the inner third of the clavicle and the

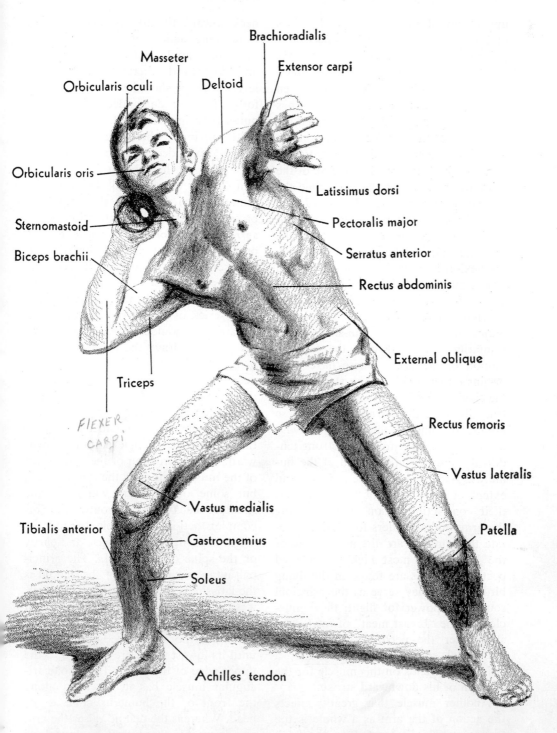

Brachioradialis

Masseter

Extensor carpi

Orbicularis oculi

Deltoid

Orbicularis oris

Latissimus dorsi

Sternomastoid

Pectoralis major

Serratus anterior

Biceps brachii

Rectus abdominis

Triceps

FLEXER CARPI

External oblique

Rectus femoris

Vastus lateralis

Vastus medialis

Tibialis anterior

Gastrocnemius

Patella

Soleus

Achilles' tendon

Fig. 7-2. *The act of throwing an object calls into action the muscles of trunk and legs, especially. Some of the more obvious ones have been indicated in this drawing of a shot-putter.*

upper end of the sternum and passes obliquely over the side of the neck to a point behind the ear. This is the **sternocleidomastoideus** muscle, usually called the sternomastoid. The long name given to the muscle simply indicates that it has two points of origin, the sternum and the clavicle, and that its insertion is on the mastoid process behind the ear. Its action is to bend the cervical region of the spine to one side. At the same time the muscle draws the head toward the shoulder and rotates the chin upward. During this motion, the muscle on the opposite side of the neck from which the flexion is occurring is stretched and stands out like a thick cord.

The front upper half of the chest is covered superficially by the **pectoralis major** muscles, a large fan-shaped pair primarily concerned with the forward motion of the arms. These have their origins on each side of the sternum, on the clavicles, and on the cartilages of the true ribs near the sternum. From these points, the muscle fibers pass fanwise until they converge to form a strong tendon that inserts on the head of the humerus. As a result of the manner and extent of the origins of these muscles, their contracting action tends to bring the arms and shoulders forward and rotate the arms toward the middle line of the body. The most highly developed pectoral muscles are found in the flying birds, which they serve as the principal sources of power for flight; these muscles are the "breast meat" of fowl. In a shot-putter the pectoralis major gives the initial shove to the projectile; a swimmer depends on this muscle for the strength of his downward stroke.

Another muscle that greatly affects the action of the arm as a whole is the **trapezius.** This is located on the back of the trunk and can be seen as a broad sheet extending from the base of the neck toward the top of the shoulder. Contractile action of this muscle will raise the scapula and draw it backward and downward, thereby giving added leverage to the shoulder for the powerful forward thrust demanded of the shot-putter or swimmer. The trapezius is also quite obvious when the shoulder is strongly extended in a downward position such as that shown by a person jumping for a basketball. The opposite (antagonistic) action on the scapula is brought about by the contraction of the **serratus anterior.** This muscle has its origins on the first eight or nine ribs and its insertion on the scapula. Its action is obvious in a person who is required to move a heavy object: the muscle appears as a series of ridges passing obliquely toward the shoulder from the region of the ribs as it draws the scapula forward.

Two other superficial muscles connected with the action of the arm are the **deltoid** and the **latissimus dorsi.** The deltoid forms the triangular pad of muscle which covers the shoulder joint, with the apex of the triangle pointing downward. The contraction of the major part of the muscle will draw the arm upward, but some of its fibers will draw the shoulder backward and outward. This complex action is possible because its origin is partly on the clavicle and partly on the spine of the scapula. The principal antagonistic muscle of the deltoid is the latissimus dorsi. As its name implies, it is the broadest (latissimus) muscle of the back (dorsi). Its origin extends from the sixth thoracic vertebra downward until its lowest fibers are attached to the upper edge of the ilium. This broad triangular muscle has its insertion along the front of the humerus close to its head. Whereas the deltoid raises the arm and draws it forward, the latissimus dorsi pulls it downward and backward. Since the raising and lowering of the arm must

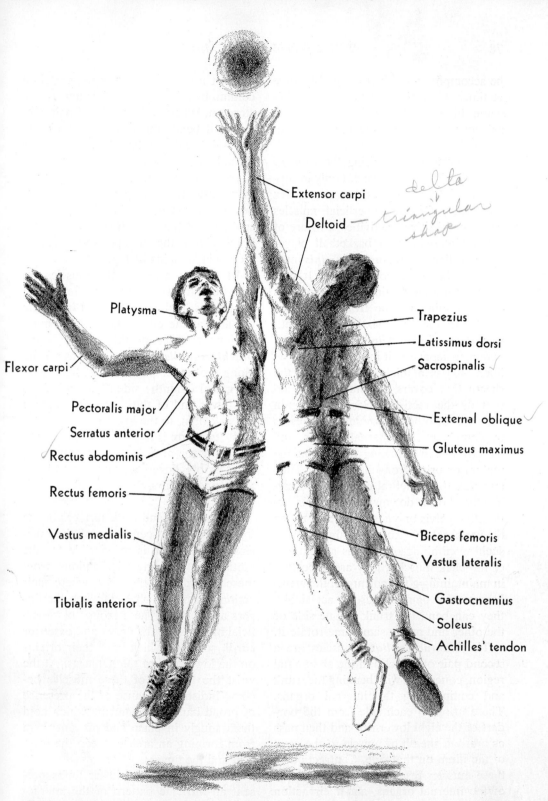

Extensor carpi

Deltoid —

delta
triangular
shape

Platysma —

Flexor carpi

Pectoralis major

Serratus anterior

Rectus abdominis

Rectus femoris —

Vastus medialis

Tibialis anterior —

Trapezius

Latissimus dorsi

Sacrospinalis ✓

External oblique ✓

Gluteus maximus

Biceps femoris

Vastus lateralis

Gastrocnemius

Soleus

Achilles' tendon

Fig. 7-3. *The extension of parts of the body can only be accomplished by the contraction of muscles. Those responsible for these acts show their position as clearly as those that cause flexion.*

be accomplished with considerable force at times, both of these muscles can become highly developed as very conspicuous features of the upper part of the body.

The muscles comprising the front of the abdominal wall serve not only to support the internal organs, but also to flex the trunk. Of the superficial muscles concerned in these activities, two are of special interest. In a basketball player or a wrestler, the **rectus abdominis** muscle may be quite conspicuous. It is a straplike muscle originating on the pubis and extending up the front of the abdomen to the fifth, sixth, and seventh ribs. The midline (**linea alba**) of the abdomen separates it into two parts. The linea alba is a thickened region of the sheath that covers the muscle. The action of the recti muscles, in common with that of other abdominal muscles, is to compress the internal organs and thereby aid in expelling feces from the rectum or urine from the bladder. They also flex the vertebral column by drawing the thorax downward. By their action, the pelvis may also be drawn up on the vertebral column, permitting motions such as climbing. Acting as antagonists of the back muscles, they are important in maintaining good posture. If the members of this pair of muscles act singly, they can bend the trunk to one side of the other and at the same time rotate it.

The **external oblique** muscles are a second pair of muscles in the abdominal region, concerned with bending the trunk and compressing the internal organs. These arise on each side from the borders of the eight lower ribs and then pass as a broad sheath of muscle to the crest of the ilium on that side. Contraction of these muscles results in the compression of the internal organs, and their action can be felt when one coughs or sneezes. When both members of this pair of muscles act together, they flex the vertebral column by drawing the pelvis toward the sternum. When only one of the pair contracts, it bends the vertebral column to the side and rotates it, bringing the shoulder of the same side forward.

In the upper limb, or arm, there are many muscles that play a role in its flexion or extension. We have already spoken of the action of the biceps brachii and the triceps and pictured their relationships in Fig. 7-1.

In the forearm are the muscles responsible for the major movements of the fingers, and some that aid in flexing the arm at the elbow. One of the more obvious muscles of this region is the **brachioradialis** which appears as a band along the upper part of the forearm on the radial (thumb) side. It extends from the lower end of the humerus, where it has its origin, to the lower end of the radius. Its action is to work with the biceps in flexing the arm. When the arm is being forcibly flexed against pressure on the hand, this muscle stands out prominently.

On the front and back surfaces of the forearm can be seen some of the muscles whose action is responsible for the motion of the fingers. Tendons from these extend over the wrist, where their action can be clearly seen when the fingers are moved. These groups of superficial muscles are the **flexor** and **extensor carpi**, some of which have their origins on the lower end of the humerus. At the wrist the tendons of these muscles become indistinct because of the presence of broad bands of ligaments which hold them snugly in place and prevent them from forming an arch between the forearm and the fingers.

The muscles of the lower limbs present an intricate pattern of the interaction of opposing muscle bundles that brings about an integrated motion of the limb. The large muscle at the top of the thigh and covering the hip joint in back is the **gluteus maximus**. This, together with two smaller muscles in the same region, has the action of extending the thigh and rotating it outward.

The muscles of the thigh itself are responsible for many of the more forceful movements required of the body as a whole. You need only watch a person walking to realize some of the roles these muscles play. On the back of the thigh is a large muscle, the **biceps femoris,** which is one of a group of three that are sometimes spoken of as the "hamstring muscles." The biceps of the leg has two points of origin: one on the ischium and the other on the femur. Its principal point of insertion is on the fibula with a small portion passing to the tibia. Its connection with the fibula can be felt as a heavy tendon on the back of the knee toward the outside of the leg. The action of this muscle is twofold: it flexes the leg at the knee and pulls it slightly to the side, and extends the thigh backward and rotates it.

On the front of the thigh are two prominent muscles. One is the **vastus lateralis,** which passes laterally from just above the kneecap across the outer side of the thigh to the pelvis. The second is the **vastus medialis,** which lies slightly inside the middle line of the front of the thigh. Both of these exert a powerful extensor effect on the thigh, and both have their origins on the femur. They have a common tendon which is inserted on the sides and top of the

patella. The action of the individual parts of this tendon can be felt if you swing your leg back and forth over the edge of a chair.

In the leg (below the knee) are two muscles that form the calf of the leg, the more prominent being the **gastrocnemius.** It has its origins on the base of the femur, with its insertion in the heel bone (calcaneus) by means of the heavy **Achilles' tendon.** Closely associated with the gastrocnemius is the **soleus.** This originates on the upper surfaces of the tibia and fibula and its tendon blends with that of the gastrocnemius. The action of both of these muscles is to point the foot downward, and their general form and course can be noted with each step as the heel is raised from the floor in walking.

The front of the leg is characterized by a complex group of muscles, some of which are quite conspicuous in their action, while others show merely as rippling motions under the skin. There is one muscle of especial interest because of its ability to flex the foot strongly at the ankle. This is the **tibialis anterior** which lies just outside of (lateral to) the shin bone. The origin of this muscle is on the front of the tibia and its insertion is on one of the carpal bones. As a result of its contraction, the foot is drawn upward, allowing the weight of the body to fall on the heel. The tibialis anterior is frequently affected by the type of poliomyelitis that injures the nerves controlling the muscles of the front of the legs.

SPEAKING OF Physiology

Briefly identify each of the following:

antagonistic muscles	**flexion**	**reciprocal innervation**
belly of a muscle	**insertion**	**sphincter**
extension	**origin**	**superficial muscles**

Test YOUR KNOWLEDGE

1. When considering the muscular system, why is each muscle (e.g., the biceps or the triceps) considered an organ? Explain.
2. Why do certain groups of muscles work against each other? What do we call these groups and how are they controlled? Give examples, other than the ones mentioned in the text, to illustrate your answer.
3. What muscles of the trunk serve to hold it erect?
4. Why are most of the muscles that move your fingers located in the forearm rather than in the hand?
5. Describe the action of muscles that are used in chewing food or in talking.

See FOR YOURSELF

1. Horsepower equals foot-pounds per minute divided by 33,000 or foot-pounds per second divided by 550. Using the laws of physics, devise a means of measuring an individual's muscular horsepower. You may have to consider the muscles of the arms and legs separately. What horsepower can you produce?

2. What muscular exercise would you devise for the improvement of the following? (*a*) fallen arch of the foot, (*b*) rounded shoulders, (*c*) lordosis, (*d*) abdominal sag.

3. Examine a human skeleton for rough areas on the bones. Most of these rough areas are the points of attachment for skeletal muscles. Try to identify the points of origin and insertion of some of the muscles discussed in this chapter.

4. From a slaughter house or meat market, get a large bone of a freshly-killed cow, sheep, or hog. Identify the tough fibrous tendons by which the muscles of the animal were attached to the bone. Also, get the foot and lower leg of a chicken or turkey. Identify the tendons that are attached to the foot bones and demonstrate (by pulling them) how the action of the muscles is transferred to bones by means of tendons.

The Nervous System

CHAPTER 8

The Structure and General Functions of the Nervous System

CHAPTER 9

The Structure and Functions of the Central Nervous System

CHAPTER 10

The Structure of the Eye and the Physics of Vision

CHAPTER 11

The Physiology of Vision

CHAPTER 12

The Structure and Physiology of the Ear

The Structure and General Functions of the Nervous System

All of the coordinated activities of a many-celled animal are made possible by nervous tissue. As we ascend the scale of animal development from lower to higher forms, the arrangement of this tissue into nervous systems becomes more and more complex. The human nervous system enables us to be aware of our environment, both internal and external. This awareness or perception is dependent upon **receptors,** the nerve cells in the skin and in specialized nervous tissue like the inner ear or the retina of the eye. The receptors are sensitive to specific changes in our surroundings. In the eye and ear, they transform light or sound waves into **impulses,** which are carried, as a kind of electro-chemical charge, along a nerve cell or **neuron** to one or more parts of the **central nervous system,** (the brain and spinal cord).

With the awareness of these impulses by the central nervous system, we are able to adjust to our environment, physically as well as mentally. In addition, this nervous system has the marvelous ability to retain and to organize information for immediate or future use. When called upon to do so, the nervous system responds to the incoming impulses, analyzes information in the light of past experience, and makes an adjustment in a coordinated manner. Thus, the physiological basis for the nervous system involves three specialized characteristics: the ability to receive stimuli, the ability to respond to stimuli (**irritability**), and the process of transmitting impulses to and from the brain and spinal cord (**conduction**).

How the nervous system develops. In a child's development before birth (prenatal), the nervous system arises from a primitive layer of cells called the **ectoderm.** (It is interesting to note that this primitive layer is also responsible for the development of epithelial tissues throughout the body. Therefore the nervous system and epithelium come into existence from the same embryonic layer.)

The nervous system is first seen as a **neural plate** composed of a single layer of ectodermal cells extending along the mid-line of the dorsal surface of the embryo (see Fig. 8-1A). The plate soon becomes thicker at the edges, which then begin to fold upward. As a result, a **neural groove** forms along the center with **neural folds** on each side (Fig. 8-1B). With continued growth, the folds merge and fuse in the center of the groove. The fusion results in formation of the **neural tube.** This eventually sinks below the surface as the ectoderm grows over it to form the skin of the body (Fig. 8-1C).

Except for the cells responsible for olfaction (sense of smell) and certain groups of cranial cells, the entire nervous system of the human body is derived from the neural tube. A portion of the cells of this structure gives rise to certain supporting cells called **neuroglia** cells. The remaining portion develops into true nervous tissue composed of neurons, the structural and functional units of the nervous system.

During the first year of life after birth (postnatal), these neurons no longer have the ability to divide; in fact, many neurons lose this ability before the time of birth.

The forward end of the neural tube continues to enlarge, and eventually develops into the brain; the other end remains proportionately small and develops into the spinal cord.

The central nervous system. As was previously mentioned, the nervous system is a coordinating mechanism. That part of the nervous system directly responsible for coordinating the activities and functions of the human body is the central nervous system, composed of the brain and spinal cord.

Unlike man, the lower animals do not depend entirely upon a central nervous system. For example, the leg muscle of a recently killed frog will contract if the toes are pinched, even though the entire leg is removed from the body. The leg will also attempt to scratch an irritant from its surface. Since the leg has been severed from the body, no connection with the central nervous system is involved in these responses.

In man, no function of the body can be performed independently of some type of control by the central nervous

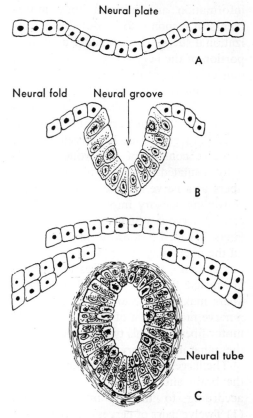

Neural plate

A

Neural fold   Neural groove

B

Neural tube

C

Fig. 8-1. *This series of drawings shows the embryonic development of the neural tube, which gives rise to the central nervous system.*

system; even a simple response to a stimulus involves at least the spinal cord.

A more detailed discussion of the structure and function of the central nervous system will be presented in Chapter 9.

The autonomic nervous system. The activities of the stomach and intestines, of glandular secretions, as well as many other involuntary body functions, are under the control of the autonomic nervous system, which will be discussed in detail in Chapter 9.

The peripheral nervous system. The central nervous system reacts to stimuli from the environment. It analyzes the information and initiates body movements in response to it. But this organizational success is dependent upon that portion of the nervous system which lies outside of the central part and is called the peripheral nervous system.

Basically, the peripheral nervous system is a system of nerves and **ganglia,** which are groups of nerve cell bodies. A nerve consists of numerous individually insulated nerve cell fibers. All the fibers of a nerve may be responsible for conveying sensory impulses toward the central nervous system. Such a group of fibers is called a **sensory nerve.** Again, all the fibers may carry the central nervous system's motor impulses to particular muscle fibers or glands. These nerve fibers make up a **motor nerve.** Finally, a nerve may consist of both sensory and motor fibers. To this type has been given the name **mixed nerve.**

The large nerves directly connected to the brain and spinal cord are grouped according to their point of origin. (1) Twelve pairs of nerves originate from the brain and are called **cranial nerves.** They are motor, sensory, and mixed nerves which emerge or enter through openings at the base of the skull and proceed to or from the point of motor activity or sensory reception. (2) Thirty-one pairs of **spinal nerves** originate from the spinal cord. All of the spinal nerves are mixed nerves having sensory and motor nerve cell fiber components. The cranial and spinal nerves will be discussed in Chapter 9 because of their close relation to the central nervous system.

The branching nerves of the peripheral nervous system terminate in the **special sensory end organs;** those of taste, smell, sight, and sound, and those of the general senses of pressure, touch, pain, heat, and cold. The latter group are often referred to as the *cutaneous senses,* since they are associated primarily with the skin. The special sensory end organs are the receptors which make us aware of changes in our environment.

Receptors are located on the peripheral ends of sensory neurons, or in the various sense organs, such as the eye and ear. They may be naked, free nerve endings (for pain and certain chemical senses); they may contain a light-sensitive chemical which initiates impulses for vision; or they may be specialized nerve endings sensitive to certain stimuli. Receptors vary widely in structure according to the sense they serve and also to their location in the various tissues of the body.

The sense organs responsible for taste are called *taste buds.* They are constructed of epithelial cells and are found predominantly on the surface of the tongue, but may also be found on the walls of the soft palate, the pharynx and adjacent parts (see Chapter 15). Sense receptors for smell are seen in each nasal passage as bare nerve fibers hanging from the roof of the nasal canal (Chapter 19).

As you have probably observed, the sense of taste and the sense of smell are both chemical senses. In other words, this type of receptor is stimulated by a portion of the substance itself in molecular form. It is equally true that those substances that are volatile (for the sense of smell) or soluble (for the sense of taste) will cause greater sensory stimulation than nonvolatile or insoluble substances, such as metals. In terms of the number of different flavors or odors, organic compounds seem to have the greatest stimulatory effect. On the other hand, strong solutions of inorganic substances have a very pronounced stimulatory effect.

The sense organ responsible for vision is the eye. It is able to receive light waves which cause impulses to be conveyed to the brain. There the impulses are recorded, analyzed, and interpreted as vision. The details of the structure of the human eye and the physics and physiology of vision will be covered in Chapters 10 and 11.

Reception of sound, **audition,** is dependent upon the ear and its transmission of impulses to the auditory center in the brain. You will see in Chapter 12 that hearing is one of our most important senses. As a means of communication, spatial understanding, and esthetic satisfaction, the ear has few competitors. To sit before an orchestra and be able to pick out individual instruments or to identify individual voices in a chorus is truly marvelous. It is said that in a completely soundproof room, such as the one on the campus at the University of California at Los Angeles, one can hear the molecules of air striking his eardrum.

Structure and functions of the neuron. We now come to the anatomical basis of all that has been said in this chapter—the neuron, or nerve cell. The nervous system is made up of billions of these highly specialized cells, bound together by a special connective tissue, the neuroglia.

As was mentioned earlier, nearly all of the body's nervous tissue arises from the neural tube early in the embryonic life of the individual. Why these neurons grow and elongate to connect the various sense receptors with the central nervous system, and the central nervous system with the effectors of the body (muscles and glands) is not clearly understood. There is evidence to indicate that the direction of growth is determined by certain biochemical factors appearing along predetermined pathways, but more confirmation is needed to clarify this point.

In the structural make-up of neurons in man and animals, we find three distinct parts: the **cell body,** one or more **dendrites,** and a single **axon.** The latter two parts, which extend beyond the cell body, are collectively called *nerve cell processes* (Fig. 8-2).

The cell body consists of a mass of **neuroplasm** surrounding a nucleus in which is found a nucleolus. Within the nervous system, the shape of the cell bodies varies a great deal: some are round, as in various sensory ganglia; others are diamond or pyramidal in shape, as in the cerebral cortex; yet others may be star-shaped, such as those in various motor neurons (see Fig. 8-3 showing neurons of various types).

The complexity of its internal structures, within the neuroplasm, makes the neuron unique when compared to other cells in the body. Among these cytoplasmic structures are fine fibers running through the neuroplasm. These fibers, called **neurofibrils,** appear to connect the dendrites with the axon. It has been theorized that they are responsible for conveying impulses through the cell body to the axon.

Found also in the neuroplasm are numerous granular structures that absorb basic stains very readily. These structures, which look like the spots on a leopard, are named **Nissl bodies** after their discoverer—Franz Nissl, a German neurologist (1860–1919). The Nissl bodies apparently have a metabolic function in the cell, for they are most evident in a resting cell; but upon continued activity of the cell they disappear. Once they have disappeared, the neuron can no longer carry an impulse, and the cell must rest. As fatigue is overcome, the Nissl bodies once again become evident. This may possibly explain why we tend to lose our power to receive a certain stimulus if that stimulus is constant for a long period of time. When you first enter a room, you may notice

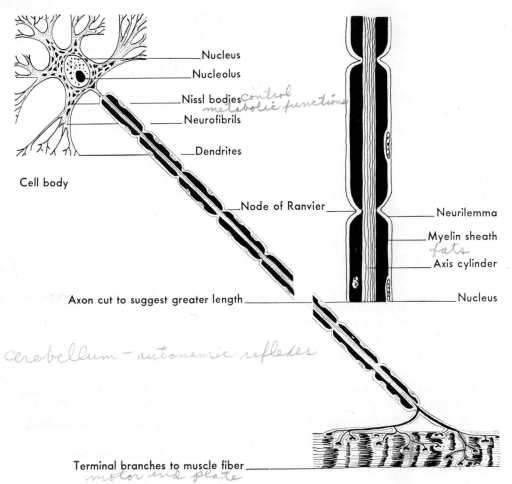

Nucleus

Nucleolus

Nissl bodies *control metabolic functions*

Neurofibrils

Dendrites

Cell body

Node of Ranvier

Neurilemma

Myelin sheath *fats*

Axis cylinder

Axon cut to suggest greater length

Nucleus

cerebellum — autonomic reflexes

Terminal branches to muscle fiber *motor end plate*

Fig. 8-2. *A drawing of a typical neuron.*

a particular odor. After a period of time, you can no longer smell that odor. If you then leave the room and allow the sense receptors in the nasal passages to rest, when you return you will again be conscious of the odor. The Nissl bodies can thus be thought of as small storage batteries, which become discharged with continued use. With rest, there is a recharging of these "batteries."

The nerve cell processes, like the cell body, vary greatly in form (see Fig. 8-3). The dendrite is a branching structure (Gk., *dendron,* meaning "tree"). Its function is to convey impulses to-

ward the cell body, and it is thus referred to as the *afferent* process (Lat., *ad + fero* meaning "carry toward"). The axon is typically long and less branching than the dendrite. It carries impulses away from the cell body and is called the *efferent* process (Lat., *ex + fero* meaning "carry away from").

The number of processes which extend from the body of the cell provide one means of classifying neurons. A neuron may be **unipolar**—consisting of a cell body and a single process. Unipolar neurons are found in lower animals, but are not present in man. In the human

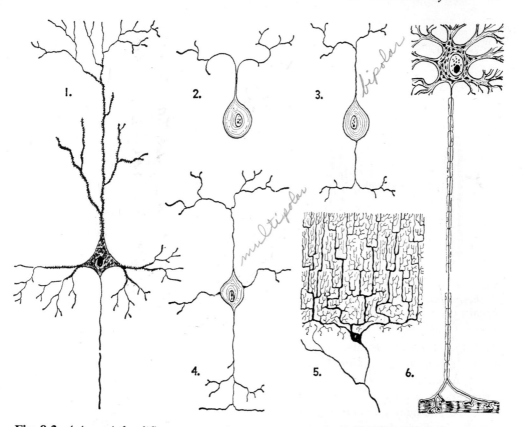

Fig. 8-3. *A few of the different types of neurons: 1, a pyramidal neuron of the cerebrum; 2, a unipolar neuron; 3, a neuron with a short axis; 4, a neuron from the cerebral cortex; 5, a neuron from the cerebellum (Purkinje cell); and 6, a motor neuron from the spinal cord.*

body we find some **bipolar** neurons—made up of a cell body and both a single dendrite and an axon. Most frequently, however, we find **multipolar** neurons—with a single cell body and numerous dendrites plus a single axon (see Fig. 8-3).

Microscopic structure of nerves. As we have seen, the structure called a nerve is actually many nerve fibers (axons, dendrites, or both) bound together. The fine structure of these fibers varies, depending on their function.

The central part of the nerve fiber is called the **axis cylinder.** In peripheral neurons, this cylinder is protected by an insulating covering, the **myelin sheath.**

This is composed of fatty or lipoid substances which give the process a pearly white appearance. Those neurons concerned with conduction within the central nervous system are also covered with a myelin sheath. With the peripheral neurons, they make up the **white matter** of the nervous system. Neurons which lack the myelin sheath, when massed together, appear rather dull and darker than myelinated fibers. Unmyelinated fibers are found in the brain and spinal cord. With the nerve cells and ganglia, they form the **gray matter.**

On all peripheral neurons the myelin sheath is surrounded by an outer covering—the **neurilemma.** It is seen to be

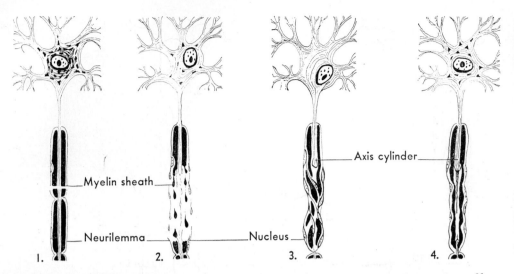

Fig. 8-4. *A series of diagrams to show regeneration of a nerve fiber. 1, the cut nerve fiber; 2, the myelin sheath breaks up into droplets of fat; 3, the myelin sheath and neurilemma begin to form; 4, neurofibrils have begun to sprout from the cut end of the original fiber.*

indented at various points, forming segments much like a chain of sausages. Each indentation is called a **node of Ranvier.** In each of the segments is a nucleus. The neurilemma is important in the repair of any damage to the process. If a peripheral nerve is cut, the section farthest away from the cell body **degenerates** (Fig. 8-4). However, in time, it **regenerates** by means of growth of fibers through the neurilemmal sheaths.

Within the central nervous system, neurons lack a neurilemma and thus are unable to regenerate (repair) if injured. As was mentioned earlier, the cell body cannot reproduce, so that damage to this portion of a neuron is always permanent.

The nerve impulse. It is very possible that many of you have had the experience of driving a car and have been confronted with an emergency situation, such as another car suddenly pulling away from the curb directly in front of you. Then you quickly put your foot down hard on the brake pedal. But there was a lapse of time between seeing the danger and your muscular reaction to

avoid what might have been a disastrous situation. That was your **reaction time.**

How was your brain informed of this sudden problem, and why did your muscles react? For many years, this type of situation perplexed neurologists. Recent knowledge gained from experiments on the neuron indicates that there are both electrical and chemical changes involved whenever you respond to a stimulus.

The passage of the impulse along the nerve was once thought to resemble the flow of an electric current through wires. However, two important differences were observed between the nerve impulse and the current. First, the speed of a nerve impulse (from 1 to 120 meters per second) is very slow when compared to that of an electric current, which flows at a rate approaching the speed of light (299,799,000 meters per second). Second, there seems to be an electrochemical change in the membrane surface of the axis cylinder of the neuron process which, once started, is self-propagating. The nerve itself supplies

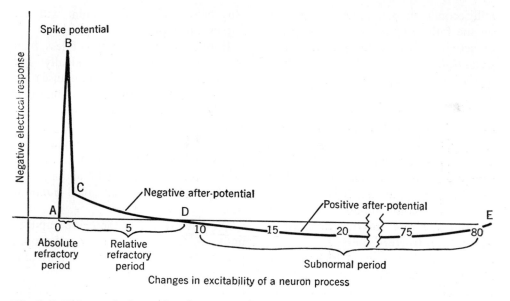

Changes in excitability of a neuron process

Fig. 8-5. *This graph shows the changes in electric potential as an impulse travels through a nerve fiber.*

energy for the transmission of the impulse, whereas the wire is a passive conductor and is dependent on the constant "push" of electrons.

Knowledge of the reaction of the neuron to stimulation has been largely gained through the evidence of **electrical activity.** A great deal of experimentation has been conducted with a highly sensitive galvanometer, an instrument which measures tiny electrical currents. By employing a cathode-ray oscilloscope, which uses a form of TV tube, the electrical effects of a nerve impulse can be observed and recorded. These are seen as very small variations in the electrical potential (voltage).

Nerve tissue is highly developed to respond to stimuli and to conduct impulses. When a receptor responds to a stimulus, such as a mild electrical shock, an impulse is initiated and conducted along the neuron associated with the receptor. In experimentation, one of the electrodes of the galvanometer is placed

in contact with the dendrite receiving the stimulation, and the other electrode is placed on unstimulated (resting) tissue. A characteristic electrical pattern can then be observed, called the **action potential.** The pattern occurs because the point over which the stimulus is passing is negative as compared to the resting tissue. The change in condition can be recorded in the form shown in Fig. 8-5. Starting at point A on the horizontal line (the potential of a resting neuron), the record shows first a sudden rise (A-B), then a quick drop (B-C) which does not quite return to the starting level. This portion (A-B-C) is called the **spike potential,** and lasts about 1 millisecond (1/1000 second). A tapering-off period then follows before the potential returns to normal: the phase C-D, which lasts about 10 to 15 milliseconds. This is the **negative after-potential.** Finally, the electrical pattern dips below the horizontal (D-E) and continues for a period varying from 70 milliseconds to one second, depending on the fatigue of the fiber. This period of activity is called the **positive after-potential.**

Along with these changes in electrical activity occur changes in the ability of the neuron to react to a further stimulus —its excitability. The duration of these changes, also shown in Fig. 8-5, corresponds approximately to the changes in electrical activity outlined above. During the spike potential, it is impossible to send a second impulse through the neuron. We refer to this time as the **absolute refractory period.** It represents a period of recovery for the nerve. During the negative after-potential, if a second stimulus is introduced, a new spike potential develops. It is interesting to note that a new stimulus does not have to be as strong as the first stimulus to produce a comparable effect: in fact, a stimulus weaker than normal can excite the fiber and a new impulse occurs. This period of excitability is called the **relative refractory period.**

During the positive after-potential, a stimulus must be stronger than normal to excite a new impulse; in fact, there is a definite reduction in the ability of a neuron to carry an impulse. This period of reduced ability to carry an impulse is called the **subnormal period.**

Behavior of the nerve impulse. Certain conclusions can be drawn from observation of the way the nerve impulse is initiated and conducted. In some cases the reasons for the observed facts are not clearly understood. How strong must a stimulus be before an impulse is produced? This question brings in a new term—**threshold.** You might think of this in terms of turning on a light. No matter how slowly you throw the switch, you finally reach a point where the electrical contact is made. This point may be called the threshold. Any single stim-

ulus below this critical point will not initiate an impulse.

If two or more stimuli of less than threshold intensity (individually not strong enough to initiate an impulse) are received by a receptor, we may find that the second stimulus will reinforce the first and a third stimulus will add its effect to the second. This continues until the threshold level is reached, and an impulse starts. The effect of adding such subthreshold stimuli is called **summation.**

We have seen that the nerve impulse, unlike the electric current, is self-propagating. That is, its strength remains constant because the nerve itself supplies energy for transmission. The impulse weakens only when a section of the nerve is damaged or weakened. Thus, if a resistance is placed in an electric circuit, the flow of electricity is reduced. However, if we expose a section of nerve to alcohol vapor (which acts like resistance in an electric circuit), we depress the conduction of a nerve impulse through this area, but if it gets through at all, it is as strong beyond the affected section as it was before.

Another aspect of this characteristic of the nerve impulse is that the strength of the nerve impulse carried over a single fiber does not depend on the strength of the stimulus. Once the threshold is reached, the fiber responds to its full capacity. We refer to this factor as the **all-or-none** response or law. The law applies also to the speed at which the impulse is conducted. Different fibers may have different rates of conduction, depending on their size and structure, but each fiber conducts at its own maximum rate, regardless of the strength of the impulse. For example, large fibers covered with a heavy insulating layer (the myelin sheath) will conduct impulses at the rate of 5 to 120 meters per second. Fibers that have a thinner sheath will conduct impulses at a speed of 3 to 15 meters per second. Unmyelinated fibers will carry impulses at the slowest rate—from 1 to 2 meters per second.

We have seen that the changes in our environment are detected by highly specialized nerve endings. Each one is extremely sensitive to a particular type of stimulus and relatively insensitive to others. All receptors have a definite threshold, and must obey the all-or-none law. To that stimulus for which it is specialized—heat, pain, touch, light, taste, etc.—the receptor has a relatively low threshold. To the other stimuli, the particular receptor has a high threshold. It is possible that an extremely intense stimulus might trigger an impulse in a receptor normally insensitive to that stimulus. Thus, the boom of a cannon or a jet plane flying over your head may cause pain in your ears, and though a blow on the eye should be felt and not seen, it may result in the sensation of visible flashes or "stars."

Let us now turn briefly to the evidence of the **chemical activity** of the nerve impulse. Far less is known about this subject than about the electrical activity just described. The lack of information is partly due to difficulty in setting up experiments with the available scientific apparatus. Also, the chemical activities involved are fairly new in theory, so that less research data is available.

Oxygen is necessary to the life of all cells. We know that the rate at which oxygen is used can be correlated to a degree with the cell activity. This has been clearly shown with muscle tissue. The question was asked: "Is this also true for nerve cells?" It was learned that a neuron at rest consumes oxygen at a constant rate, but upon activity—the passage of impulses—there is a sudden increase in oxygen consumption; the higher consumption lasts for a short period of time after the impulse has passed. Furthermore, it was learned that neurons in the peripheral nervous system can accumulate an oxygen debt, similar to that of muscle tissue (see page 69), while those neurons found within the central nervous system cannot operate in the absence of oxygen. The actual chemical changes that occur during the transmission of impulses along a nerve fiber are still not known in their entirety, but as we will see later, much has been learned about them in the past few years.

Neural connections. Thus far, we have been discussing the passage of the nerve impulse along a single neuron. However, impulses must travel over pathways connecting many different neurons. When a receptor is stimulated, the impulse travels along the dendrite (afferent process), through the nerve cell, and along the axon (efferent process). In order to reach the central nervous system, the impulse must be transferred to other nerve fibers. The junction between the axon of one neuron and the dendrite or cell body of the next neuron is called a **synapse.** The term "junction" should not be taken in the literal sense, since there is convincing evidence to show that there is no direct contact between the two neuron processes.

Synapse never occurs between the dendrites of two different neurons, nor does it occur between the two axons of different neurons. In some instances, a number of axons from different neurons will *converge* on the dendrites of a single neuron and in like manner, the axon of one, by means of branches (collaterals), may *diverge* to make synaptic contact with a number of other neurons (see Fig. 8-6).

How the electrical potential (the impulse) jumps the gap at a synapse is not clearly understood, but the most widely

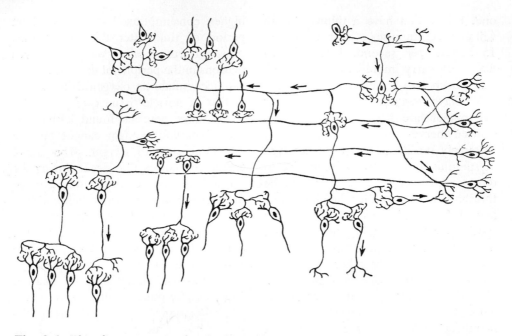

Fig. 8-6. *This diagrammatic sketch shows the complexity of the nerve pathways over which an impulse can travel. The arrows indicate the directions impulses might take from the cells at the top right.*

accepted theory today deals with two chemicals—*acetylcholine* and **cholinesterase**. The action of these chemicals in relation to muscle contraction has been described in Chapter 6 (pages 64–8). It has been learned that acetylcholine is secreted by the unmyelinated end fibers of axons. This substance is a strong nerve stimulator and is produced whenever an impulse reaches the synapse between the axon of one neuron and the dendrites of another. It is believed that acetylcholine is responsible for stimulating the second neuron. This stimulation might continue indefinitely were it not for the action of cholinesterase. As we have learned, cholinesterase, an enzyme also produced by the fibers at a synapse, quickly inactivates acetylcholine. The time it takes for this to occur is less than the absolute refractory period (1 millisecond).

In order that the nerves may continue to transmit impulses, production of acetylcholine must obviously be renewed rapidly after its inactivation by cholinesterase. It has been discovered that this is done by an enzyme, **choline acetylase**, which was found in extracts of brain and nerve tissue.

Dr. D. Nachmansohn has evolved a theory, based on certain recently discovered facts, that would tend to show that both the electrical and chemical theories of nerve impulse transmission may be correct. He has found that the electric organs of the torpedo and electric eel, which can generate up to 1200 volts, produce *several kilograms* of cholinesterase in an hour. This is up to *four times* the weight of the organs themselves. This implies equal production of acetylcholine by these organs, which are believed to have come from muscle endplates that developed this specialized function in the process of evolution.

As acetylcholine is present not only at synapses, but in nerves and brain tissue as well, Dr. Nachmansohn theorizes that this chemical production precedes the electrical impulse. This would mean that the nerve impulse, as well as trans-synaptic transmission, is an *electrochemical phenomenon*. Thus acetylcholine could be considered one of the body's most important chemicals.

SPEAKING OF Physiology

Briefly identify each of the following:

afferent	impulse	postnatal
cutaneous senses	mixed nerve	reaction time
efferent	motor nerve	regenerate
galvanometer	neuroglia	self-propagating
ganglion	peripheral	sensory nerve

Test YOUR KNOWLEDGE

1. Briefly describe the embryonic development of the nervous system.
2. How does the structural path for reflex action of lower animals compare with the reflex path of humans?
3. List and note the function of the various components, i.e., cranial nerves, spinal nerves, etc., which comprise the peripheral nervous system. How does the peripheral nervous system differ from the central nervous system?
4. Briefly describe the method of stimulating the sense receptors of taste and those receptors responsible for our sense of smell. What physical process must precede the stimulation of either of these sense receptors?
5. Why is the neuron classified as the unit of structure of the nervous system? What makes this cell unique when compared to other body cells?
6. How can you explain the fact that with continuous stimulation we may become unaware of a given sensation?
7. What are processes and how do they aid in the classification of various nerve cells?
8. Briefly describe the microscopic structure of a nerve cell process.
9. How do the impulses that travel along a neuron differ from electricity flowing through wires?
10. Which of the following terms in the action potential refer to electrical activity and which refer to the excitability of the neuron: spike potential, relative refractory period, positive after-potential, negative after-potential, subnormal period, absolute refractory period?
11. What is the difference between a subthreshold and a threshold stimulus? What happens if a series of subthreshold stimuli encounter a receptor?
12. As explained in your text, any resistance placed in an electric circuit will reduce the current in the conductor. Does any comparable condition exist in a nervous tissue? Explain with an example.
13. If a stimulus is strong enough to excite a neuron, an impulse is created which travels at maximum speed for the individual neuron. What is this activity called? What happens if the stimulus becomes stronger?
14. Can neurons work in the absence of oxygen? Explain the limitations involved.
15. Describe the body's receptors, including their basic function, general location, and factors which limit their normal activity.
16. What do we call the junction of any two neurons? How does an impulse

move from one neuron to another neuron? What chemical activities are involved? Why is acetylcholine often considered the body's most important chemical?

See FOR YOURSELF

1. Devise an experiment, for classroom presentation, which would show the biological properties of *irritability* and *conductivity*. You might consider that even single-celled animals show these properties. The more complex animals progressively show specialization of parts for receptors, conductors, and effectors. This experiment might involve reaction time of cells, etc.

2. Investigate the vocational opportunities offered in the field of neurology.

3. Study prepared microscope slides of various stages of a vertebrate embryo to see how the nervous system develops from the ectoderm of the embryo.

4. Study prepared slides that show sections of different types of nerve tissue. Try to identify the various kinds of neurons and their cell processes in the sections.

5. Prepare a report on how galvanometers and oscilloscopes are used to study the electrical activity of neurons.

CHAPTER 9

The Structure and Functions of the Central Nervous System

There are millions of miles of wire in the telephone systems of our country. This wire would be useless if it were not connected to central offices where calls could be connected with, and relayed to, their destinations. Similarly, our peripheral nervous systems, with their many miles of nerves and their synapses, would have no value if they were not connected with a central coordinating nervous system.

Since we have already discussed the general structure and functions of the neuron and the peripheral nervous system, we are now ready to study, in more detail, the structure and physiology of the central nervous system: the spinal cord and the brain.

The spinal cord. In the adult, the spinal cord occupies the upper two thirds of the vertebral column within the **neural foramina.** The foramina are the openings formed by the neural arches and the bodies of the vertebrae. You may ask why the spinal cord occupies only two thirds of the vertebral column. The answer lies in the fact that the spinal cord is composed of millions of neurons, all of which lose their ability to divide at the time of birth or even before. The protective vertebrae grow

longer and enlarge faster than the nervous tissue of the cord. In a newborn infant the spinal cord occupies nearly the entire length of the cavity formed by the vertebrae. Continued growth of the vertebrae during childhood results in a spinal column which is longer than the spinal cord.

Starting at the **foramen magnum,** the opening in the skull at the base of the brain, the spinal cord extends downward to the level of the disk between the first and second lumbar vertebrae. In the region of the coccyx and sacral vertebrae, the vertebral canal contains only the spinal nerves as they descend from their origin in the lower portion of the spinal cord. The cord thus has the appearance of being drawn up inside the vertebral canal.

Vital in its functions, and unable to replace itself, the spinal cord has great need of protection from injury. Any injury might permanently destroy the body's ability to coordinate sensory and motor activities. This vital structure is protected in several ways. First, the bones of the spinal column afford the greatest protection. Because the diameter of the spinal cord (about ½ inch) is less than that of the canal in which it is housed, the spine may be moved freely without injuring the cord. Second, the three membranes, collectively called the **meninges,** cover and nourish the spinal cord. The outermost membrane, the **dura mater,** is a tough protective covering lining the vertebral canal. Within this we find the second membrane, the vascular **arachnoid,** whose blood vessels provide nourishment. On the surface of the spinal cord is the thin, delicate **pia mater.** As we will see later in this chapter, the meninges of the spinal cord are continuous with those covering the brain.

Between the arachnoid and pia mater is the **subarachnoid space.** Within this space we find the spinal portion of the **cerebrospinal fluid,** which protects the spinal cord from shocks. This fluid aids in the diagnosis of diseases of the meninges. A sample is taken by a spinal puncture and analyzed for signs of disease bacteria or viruses. In this way such infections as poliomyelitis and meningitis can be detected. Spinal anesthetics are also injected into the subarachnoid space just below the end of the spinal cord, by means of a hollow needle thrust between the lumbar vertebrae.

A cross section of the spinal cord reveals that it consists of two types of nerve tissue. The central portion is darker; its shape is roughly the letter H.

This portion is made up of gray matter. It acts as an integrating center for incoming sensory impulses and outgoing motor impulses. Surrounding the gray matter and rounding out the oval shape of the spinal cord is white matter, composed of sheathed nerve fibers for transmitting nervous impulses to and from the brain.

The four arms of the H formed by the gray matter are called horns. The two to the front are the **anterior horns,** and the two to the rear, the **posterior horns.** These horns give rise at intervals to the **roots** of the spinal nerves, the anterior roots leading *efferent* (mostly motor) fibers from the anterior horns, and the posterior roots bringing *afferent* (sensory) fibers to the posterior horns (Fig. 9-1).

The anterior and posterior roots join a short distance outside of the cord to form a trunk, the spinal nerve, which is a mixed nerve (Fig. 9-2).

The gray matter with its horns divides the white matter surrounding it into three areas or columns, **anterior, lateral,** and **posterior,** on each side of the cord. These columns are made up of bundles of longitudinal nerve fibers called **fasciculi,** or **tracts. Ascending tracts** carry impulses up to the brain, while **descending tracts** carry impulses down from the brain. These tracts are individually

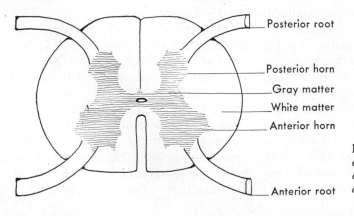

Posterior root

Posterior horn

Gray matter

White matter

Anterior horn

Anterior root

Fig. 9-1. *Diagram of a cross section of the spinal cord, showing the anterior and posterior roots.*

named according to their places of origin and their destinations.

The anterior columns contain descending fibers from the motor areas of the brain (**anterior corticospinal** or **direct pyramidal tracts**), carrying voluntary motor impulses to anterior horn cells, and ascending fibers carrying touch sensations to the brain (**anterior spinothalamic tracts**).

The lateral columns contain the main descending motor tracts from the motor areas of the brain (**lateral corticospinal** or **crossed pyramidal tracts**), as well as ascending tracts carrying sensations of heat, cold, and pain to the brain (**lateral spinothalamic tracts**). Other ascending tracts carry sensations of body position from muscles and joints and receptors in the skin to the cerebellum (**spinocerebellar tracts**).

The posterior columns contain only ascending tracts which carry sensations of touch and "muscle and joint sense," which keeps us aware of the position of our limbs and body even when we are in the dark or have our eyes closed (**fasciculus gracilus** and **fasciculus cuneatus**).

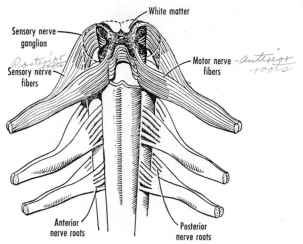

Fig. 9.2. *A section of the spinal cord showing the sensory and motor branches of the spinal nerves.*

The spinal nerves. As previously mentioned, the spinal nerves, numbering 31 pairs, are mixed nerves, combining the anterior, or motor roots, and the posterior, or sensory roots, from the spinal cord. The uppermost eight pairs of the spinal nerves are cervical, the next twelve pairs are thoracic. Then come five pairs of lumbar nerves, followed by five

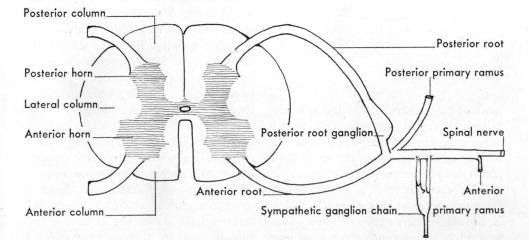

Fig. 9-3. *This diagram shows the relation of the anterior and posterior rami to the spinal cord.*

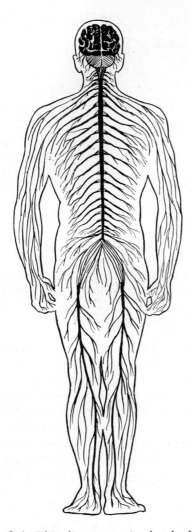

Fig. 9-4. *This diagrammatic sketch shows the relationship of the brain, spinal cord, and spinal nerves.*

cated in the gray matter of the spinal cord (Fig. 9-3).

A short distance from the cord, just outside the intervertebral foramina, the mixed nerve trunk splits, giving off two branches, the **posterior and anterior primary rami.**

The **posterior primary rami** go first to the muscles of the back of the skull and trunk, and their motor fibers supply these muscles. Their sensory fibers then pass through the muscles to the skin overlying the same areas.

The **anterior primary rami** of all except the thoracic area run forward to join in a series of complex nerve junctions called **plexuses,** where they are rearranged and combined to form the final nerves that supply the muscles and skin of the arms and legs. These plexuses are named, according to the areas they supply, **cervical, brachial, lumbar,** and **sacral.** Since the anterior primary rami of the thoracic area run along the lower borders of the ribs, they are called **intercostal** nerves. They supply the muscles between the ribs, the intercostal muscles, as well as the skin over the anterior thorax and abdomen. The general distribution of the spinal nerves is illustrated in Fig. 9-4, which shows the posterior (dorsal) view of the body.

Reflex activity. The term reflex is derived from the word *reflect,* meaning "to turn back." When a receptor is stimulated, as for example, when the finger touches a hot stove—an impulse is carried to the cell body in the central nervous system. The axon of this sensory cell, or **sensory neuron,** contacts the dendrite of a motor nerve cell, or **motor neuron,** which then sends an impulse down its axon to a muscle which lifts the burned finger off the stove. The impulse is thus turned back to a place near where it started. All of this happens in a split second, even before pain, or conscious-

pairs of sacral nerves. The last pair are called coccygeal nerves. The spinal nerves, as you can see, are named according to the regions of the spine from which they emerge. On the posterior root of each nerve is a small swollen area, the **posterior root ganglion,** which is a group of nerve cells supplying sensory fibers to the spinal nerve. Note that the fibers supplied by the anterior root come from motor neurons which are lo-

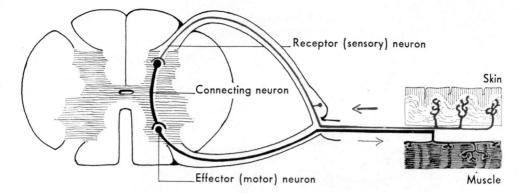

Fig. 9-5. *A diagram to show the nerve pathways involved in a simple reflex arc.*

ness of the situation, occurs. Thus reflexes are involuntary, often unconscious.

Actually, when you touch a hot stove, more than one sensory neuron is stimulated and more than one motor neuron responds, stimulating many muscles to move the entire arm away from the offending heat.

The coordination of sensory and motor neurons involved in a reflex act is known as a reflex arc (Fig. 9-5). Rarely are only two cells concerned, as there is usually a **connecting** (associative) **neuron** within the spinal cord, which connects the **receptor neuron** with the **effector neuron.**

Reflexes are of great protective value, guarding us from harm in many ways, for example, the corneal reflex of the eye, which makes us wink involuntarily when a bit of cinder touches the cornea; sneezing or coughing when an irritating substance gets into the nose or trachea. These acts are effective in promptly ridding the body of harmful foreign materials.

Reciprocal innervation of muscles. When the arm is bent (flexed) at the elbow by the action of the biceps muscle, the triceps muscle, which normally straightens (extends) the arm at the el-

bow, must relax, or the two muscles would be pulling against each other and nothing would be accomplished. The reverse must be true when an attempt is made to extend the arm.

This is accomplished by a process called **reciprocal innervation,** in which cooperation is brought about between the nerves supplying any antagonistic pair of muscles. When one receives an impulse to contract, the other relaxes because it does not receive an impulse to cause contraction. It is therefore **inhibited** at the same instant that its antagonist contracts. Without this reciprocal innervation, coordinated muscular activity would be impossible.

The brain. The adult human brain weighs about three pounds. It occupies the cavity formed by the bones of the cranium and is thus one of the best protected organs in the body. (See Fig. 9-6 and Trans-Vision following page 312.) Further protection is afforded by the continuation of the three membranes of the spinal cord, the meninges. Adherent to the bones of the skull is the dura mater, in between is the arachnoid, and attached to the gray matter of the brain itself is the pia mater. Between the pia and arachnoid, in the subarachnoid space, we find the cerebral portion of

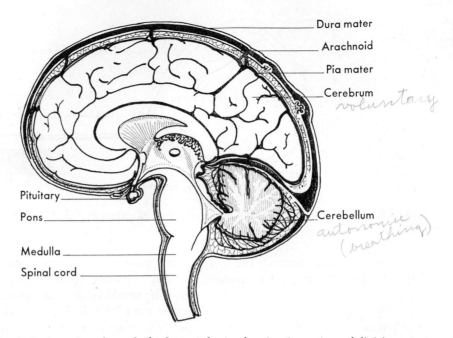

Fig. 9-6. *A section through the human brain showing its major subdivisions.*

the cerebrospinal fluid, so very important in its nutritional and protective function.

Among invertebrate animals, the brain is relatively simple and quite small. In some it is simply a large ganglion that functions as the center of control for sensory activities. On the other hand, the vertebrates all have brains of much greater complexity to control body activities. As we study brains of various vertebrates from fish through mammals, we notice the increase in their complexity (Fig. 9-7). In the higher animals, there is an increase in size and weight of the brain, and also in the brain weight considered in relation to the total body weight. The size of the brain, however, is not the only factor by which to judge its effectiveness. There are several species of mammals that have a brain that is larger in proportion to their body weight than man's, but we do not consider them to be more intelligent. The complexity of the brain, in terms of the number of pathways and centers for the control of specialized functions, is the basis on which its development should be judged. In man this has reached its highest state.

As noted earlier, the human brain is derived from the forward end of the neural tube. This portion of the central nervous system contains the greatest concentration of nervous tissue. In the course of prenatal development, the brain, or *encephalon,* is first seen as three swellings in the neural tube. The smallest of the three is directly connected to the spinal cord and is called the **hindbrain**, or **rhombencephalon**, which later develops into the **medulla** and **pons**. Further up, above the hindbrain, is a larger swelling called the **midbrain**, or **mesencephalon**. The medulla, pons, and midbrain are called the **brain stem**. The **cerebellum** or "little brain" is above the medulla and connected to the pons. The largest portion is the forebrain, or **prosencephalon**, which later divides into the

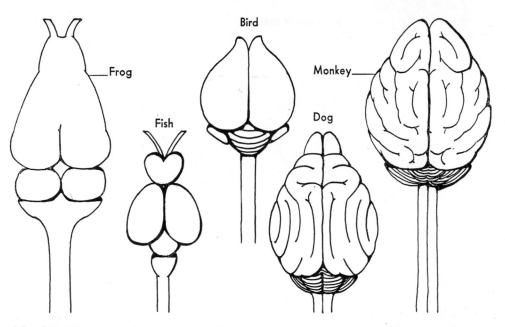

Fig. 9-7. *The outward appearance of several vertebrate brains (not drawn to the same scale). Compare these with the human brain in Figs. 9-6 and 9-10.*

telencephalon, or **cerebrum,** and the **diencephalon,** or **interbrain.**

The medulla. The lowest part of the brain stem is called the **medulla.** In the medulla, as in the spinal cord to which it is attached, the white matter is on the outside, and functions as a pathway for impulses from the higher parts of the brain and from other parts of the body. Also, as in the spinal cord, the gray matter is on the inside. The gray matter of the medulla acts as a coordinating center for incoming sensory impulses and outgoing involuntary motor impulses to the muscles and glands. Certain cells in the medulla's gray matter regulate many vital functions, such as the rate of breathing, heart rate, and circulation of the blood. Disease in this important area, as in bulbar poliomyelitis, can cause cessation of respiration.

The pons. Just above the medulla, the brain stem enlarges because of an increase in bundles of fibers. Some of these come down from the cerebrum and cerebellum. There are also ascending fibers from the medulla, and bundles of transverse fibers partly surrounding the brain stem. This enlarged area is called the **pons.** Many cranial nerves originate or emerge from the brain in the region of the pons.

The midbrain. The highest portion of the brain stem is called the midbrain, which is divided into ventral and dorsal areas (Fig. 9-8). The ventral area is made up of the **cerebral peduncles,** composed mainly of descending (efferent) fibers from the cerebrum. Just above the peduncles are crescent-shaped areas of dark-colored tissue called the **substantia nigra.** This tissue divides the peduncles from the **tegmentum,** which carries ascending (afferent or sensory) fibers to the brain. The tegmentum also contains areas of gray matter.

Above the tegmentum are the **corpora quadrigemina** (four in all; two on each

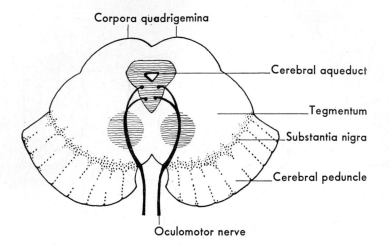

Fig. 9-8. *Section through the human midbrain.*

side), which are important reflex centers that regulate movements of the head and eyes in response to sound and light stimuli. Between, and forming part of these structures, runs the **cerebral aqueduct,** the walls of which are of gray matter containing the nuclei and fibers of the oculomotor nerve.

The cerebellum. The cerebellum is located above the medulla and is connected to the posterior surface of the pons. The internal structure of the cerebellum differs from that of the brain stem, in that its gray matter (**cortex**) is on its external surface, while white matter fills the space inside except for some masses of gray matter, the **cerebellar nuclei.** The largest of these is the **dentate nucleus.** Numerous furrows are located transversely on the outer surface of the cerebellum, increasing the area of the gray matter. The cerebellum has two **lateral hemispheres,** divided by a worm-shaped mid-portion appropriately called the **vermis** (Lat., *vermis,* worm). (See Fig. 9-9.)

Cerebellar functions. The cerebellum is constantly receiving messages concerned with balance, motion, and muscle tone from all parts of the body. When the cerebellum is damaged by disease or tumor, muscular movements become

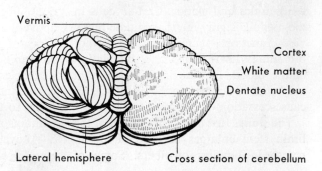

Fig. 9-9. *The cerebellar hemispheres: left, external appearance; right, sectioned.*

jerky, uncoordinated, and unpredictable. Fine movements become impossible. Muscles become weak, tremble severely, and lack tone.

Although motor impulses do not originate in the cerebellum, this structure is responsible for coordinating impulses originating in the highest centers of the brain. Thus muscular activities are smoothly and efficiently controlled. In addition, the cerebellum aids in maintaining the muscular tone and balance of the body. All of these activities are carried on below the level of consciousness.

The interbrain. Between the midbrain and the cerebrum lie two important masses of gray matter, the **thalamus** and the **hypothalamus.** Evidence of their functions has been largely deduced from the symptoms of animals and humans in whom these areas have been injured or diseased.

Injury to the thalamus brings about either increased sensibility to pain or complete unconsciousness. Since the thalamus is primarily a relay station for sensory impulses on their way to the cerebral cortex, injury to it causes a reduction in the appreciation of these stimuli from the opposite half of the body, often associated with spontaneous pain on that side or a perversion of sensation. Thus a stimulus may be unduly painful or may even be pleasant.

Injury to the hypothalamus causes disorders of gastrointestinal functions, temperature control, blood vessel control, regulation of water balance, metabolism, sleep, and emotional response.

If the connections between the cerebrum and the hypothalamus are cut in an animal which is normally vicious, it will become calm and friendly. If, on the other hand, the cerebral cortex is removed in a normally affectionate domestic animal, such as a cat, leaving its hypothalamus unrestrained by controlling impulses, it will become a wild, spitting, bristling creature. This condition, called sham rage, is merely proof that the hypothalamus is a center for primitive emotions such as fear and anger.

The cerebrum. The **cerebrum** is the highest part of the brain, both in its location, and in the type and degree of its functions. It occupies two thirds of the cranial cavity and weighs about two pounds.

The cerebrum is responsible for the highest sensory and motor activities. It is divided by a deep groove, the **longitudinal fissure,** into two **hemispheres.** Covering the outer surface of these hemispheres is a layer of gray matter called the **cerebral cortex.** It has the appearance of a walnut, with many ridges and shallow grooves. Each groove is called a **sulcus** (plural, *sulci*), and the ridge between any two sulci is called a **gyrus** (plural, *gyri*), or, more commonly, a **convolution.** These convolutions result in a proportionately large amount of gray matter.

Each hemisphere is further divided into four lobes. The name of each lobe corresponds to the name of the skull bone adjacent to it. Thus we find the **frontal, parietal, temporal,** and **occipital lobes.** These lobes are divided from each other by two main **fissures,** the **fissure of Rolando** or **central fissure,** dividing the frontal from the parietal lobes, and the **fissure of Sylvius,** dividing the frontal and parietal lobes from the temporal lobe. (See Fig. 9-10.)

The cerebral cortex. Under the microscope, the cerebral cortex is found to be made up of six definite layers from the outside to the center, as in the table on page 104.

The axons of the cortical cells are of three types, according to their destinations and functions: (1) **projection**

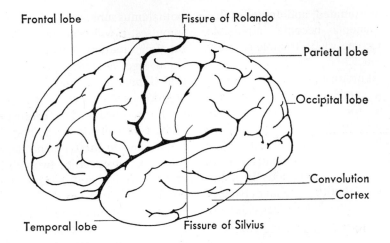

Frontal lobe　　　　Fissure of Rolando

Parietal lobe

Occipital lobe

Convolution
Cortex

Temporal lobe　　　　Fissure of Silvius

Fig. 9-10. *A lateral view of the human brain showing its external features.*

fibers which go to other areas of the nervous system, as from motor (pyramidal) cells to the spinal cord; (2) **association fibers,** which make connections with other neurons of the same hemisphere; and, (3) **commissural fibers,** which connect to neurons in the opposite hemisphere.

1. Molecular	small cells; many fibers
2. Outer granular	tightly packed small cells; few fibers
3. Pyramidal	pyramid-shaped cells, large; many fibers
4. Inner granular	smaller star-shaped cells; many fibers
5. Inner pyramidal (ganglionic)	giant pyramid-shaped cells; more of them found in motor area of cortex
6. Fusiform	tightly packed small spindle-shaped cells

Cerebral function. The functions of the cerebral cortex might be grouped into sensory, motor, and associative activities. The latter group is responsible for the higher attributes of man: intelligence, memory, reasoning ability, emotion, and judgment. All of our senses (smell, vision, hearing, pain, heat and cold, pressure, and touch) have their centers of representation in the cortex. Finally, all voluntary muscle control is under the direction of this portion of the brain.

Associative activities of the cerebral cortex. The frontal lobes were once thought to be the seat of intelligence. However, removal of the human frontal lobes (due to injury or surgical necessity) has shown that an individual can get along quite well without them, except perhaps for some slight loss of ability to form judgments and to assume responsibility.

It is now recognized that no single area of the cerebrum is entirely responsible for total intellectual capacity. However, if an animal's entire cerebral cortex is removed, it will remain conscious, express rage or fear, eat, and respond to loud noises or visual stimuli. Yet it will show no real intelligence, and its emotional reactions (sham rage, for example) will be uninhibited, because lower centers, such as those in the thalamus and hypothalamus, are no longer under the controlling influence of higher brain levels.

Intelligence develops, in part, through storage, in various cortical areas, of impressions received by our special senses (sight, hearing, smell, taste, and touch). These stored impressions are linked by association fibers so that they can, in most cases, be recalled to the conscious level at will, or *remembered.*

Motor activities of the cerebral cortex. It is possible to map accurately the *motor areas* of the cortex by experiments on anesthetized animals, and on humans during brain operations. This is done by applying electrical stimuli to the exposed cortex. It has been found that the motor area (*precentral gyrus*) occupies a long band of cortex just in front of the central fissure (fissure of Rolando) in the posterior part of the frontal lobe. Here the centers for various muscle groups are arranged in reverse order; those concerned with movements

of the jaws and tongue are lowest on the lateral surface of the brain, while those sending impulses to the muscles bending the knees are at the top. Movements of the toes are controlled by areas on the medial surfaces of the hemisphere, in the longitudinal fissure (See Fig. 9-11.)

Sensory activities of the cerebral cortex. Across the central fissure from the motor area, in the front of the parietal lobe, is the **sensory area,** also called the **somesthetic area,** of the cortex. This area receives impulses from receptors of sensations of movement in muscles and joints (kinesthetic sense), of touch, of heat and cold, and, at its lower end, of taste.

Not all sensory impulses are received in the main sensory area. Those for hearing are received in the upper region of the temporal lobe, those for vision in the occipital lobe (inner or medial surface), and those for smell in the anterior pole of the temporal lobe.

Motor pathways from the cerebral cortex. Impulses which govern voluntary muscular movements begin in the pyramidal cells of the motor area of the cortex. The axons of these neurons travel

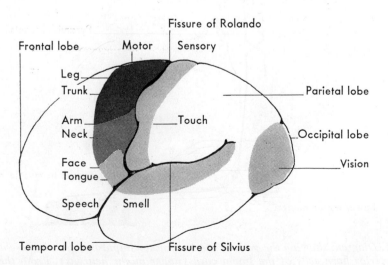

Fig. 9-11. *Diagram to show the functions of the different areas of the cerebral cortex.*

down the pyramidal tracts through a mass of fiber tracts called the *internal capsule,* and through the brain stem to the medulla, where a small number of them continue directly via the anterior columns of the spinal cord to its anterior horn cells (direct pyramidal tracts). However, a large number of pyramidal fibers cross in the medulla to the opposite sides and descend in the lateral columns of the spinal cord (crossed pyramidal tracts), to anterior horn cells.

The pyramidal tracts, which constitute the **upper motor neurons,** join, through synapses, the anterior horn cells of the spinal cord, which then send their axons to their respective muscles. The anterior horn cells with their axons are thus called **lower motor neurons** (Fig. 9-12).

Injury to the motor neurons of the cortex or pyramidal tract fibers, as by a cerebral hemorrhage or stroke, results in a **spastic** or tight muscle paralysis. Because of the crossing of the pyramidal tracts, injury to fibers on one side of the brain causes paralysis on the opposite side of the body, called **hemiplegia.** This is **upper motor neuron paralysis.** In this type of paralysis, the tendon reflexes are overactive, and wasting of the muscles, though it may occur, is not usually severe.

On the other hand, injury to anterior

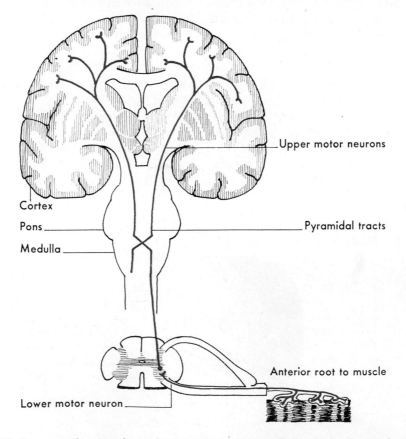

Upper motor neurons

Cortex

Pons

Medulla

Pyramidal tracts

Anterior root to muscle

Lower motor neuron

Fig. 9-12. *Diagram showing the path of cerebral motor impulses from the cerebral cortex to the anterior horn cells of the spinal cord (upper motor neurons). From the anterior horn cells impulses from the anterior root travel to the muscles (lower motor neurons).*

horn cells, as in poliomyelitis, or injury to motor nerves, causes a **flaccid** or "flail-like" paralysis. This is **lower motor neuron paralysis.** In this type of paralysis, tendon reflexes are reduced or absent, and great wasting or atrophy of the muscles usually occurs.

Sensory pathways to the cerebral cortex. Sensory nerve cell bodies, located in the posterior root ganglia of the spinal cord, receive impulses from receptors located all over the body. Axons of cells identified with position, joint, and muscle sense ascend directly in the posterior columns to the medulla. Here they form synapses with cells whose axons then cross the mid-line and ascend through the pons and midbrain to the thalamus. In the thalamus, synapses are formed with cells which then send axons to the appropriate sensory areas of the cortex. Axons of posterior root ganglion cells conveying pain, temperature, and touch sensations form synapses in the posterior horn of the gray matter, cross the mid-line of the spinal cord and ascend the lateral and anterior columns of the white matter to the thalamus, where they again form synapses and project to the parietal cortex. (Fig. 9-13).

The cranial nerves. Nerves arising from the brain are designated *cranial*

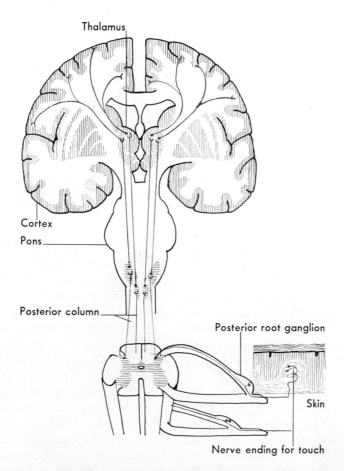

Fig. 9-13. *A diagram of the sensory pathways from the skin to the sensory areas of the cerebral cortex.*

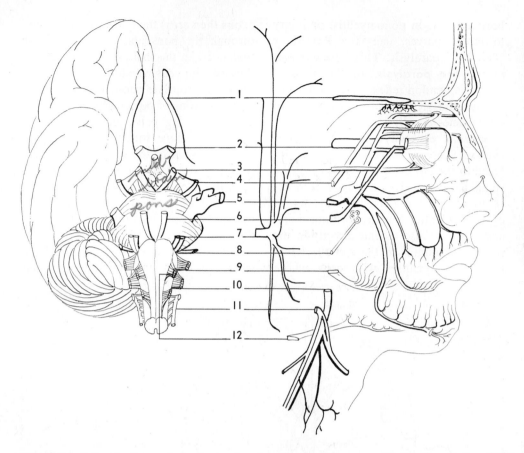

Fig. 9-14. *Left: the base of the brain showing the cranial nerves. Right: the relationship of the cranial nerves to the organs of the head. Refer to the table opposite for details of the nerves and their function.*

nerves. These nerves are numbered according to their point of origin, from above downward (Fig. 9-14). With the exception of the 10th, or ***vagus nerve,*** which supplies the heart, lungs, and abdominal organs as well, these nerves function in the head and neck areas. Some are entirely sensory, some entirely motor; others contain both sensory and motor fibers and still others carry ***autonomic fibers*** to innervate involuntary (smooth) muscles, glands, and blood vessels. The table on page 109 lists the cranial nerves and their functions.

The autonomic nervous system. We now come to another part of the nervous system, one often called the ***autonomic*** or ***involuntary nervous system.*** It is so called because the individual has very little conscious control over the many activities performed by it.

Frequently the autonomic system is considered a part of the peripheral nervous system because of its extensive distribution of nerves away from the brain and spinal cord. However, since there are important direct connections to a part of the forebrain (the hypothalamus) and parts of the midbrain and medulla, as well as the spinal cord, it seems best not to classify the autonomic nervous system directly with any other division

THE CRANIAL NERVES

NAME AND NUMBER	ACTION
1. OLFACTORY (Sensory)	Sense of smell (Chap. 19)
2. OPTIC (Sensory)	Sense of vision (Chap. 10)
3. OCULOMOTOR (Motor)	Movement of extrinsic muscles of the eye except superior oblique and external rectus; through parasympathetic fibers, control of iris constrictor muscles (Chap. 10)
4. TROCHLEAR (Motor)	Movement of superior oblique muscle of the eye (Chap. 10)
5. TRIGEMINAL (Sensory and motor)	Sensation in parts of the face, eyes, nose, teeth, gums, and tongue. (Chap. 15) Movement of muscles of jaw in chewing
6. ABDUCENS (Motor)	Movement of external rectus muscle of the eye
7. FACIAL (Sensory and motor)	Sense of taste in anterior two thirds of the tongue (Chap. 15) Movement of muscles of face, scalp, outer ear, and neck Stimulation of secretion, through parasympathetic fibers, in the sublingual and submaxillary glands
8. AUDITORY (Sensory)	Sense of hearing; balance (Chap. 12)
9. GLOSSO- PHARYNGEAL (Sensory and motor)	Sense of taste for posterior third of tongue; sense of touch and temperature in palate, tonsils, and pharynx Movement of stylopharyngeus muscle in pharynx Stimulation of secretion, through parasympathetic fibers, in parotid gland
10. VAGUS, the "wanderer" (Sensory and motor)	Movement of muscles in larynx and pharynx Movement (autonomic) of muscles of heart (inhibition of heart rate), bronchi, esophagus, stomach, pancreas, gall bladder, small intestine, first third of colon Stimulation of gastric and pancreatic secretions
11. ACCESSORY (Motor)	Movement of trapezius and sternomastoid muscles and, in part, of muscles of larynx
12. HYPOGLOSSAL (Motor)	Movement of muscles of the tongue

of the nervous system, but to consider it a part whose functions are essential to all other parts.

In general, the autonomic nervous system is responsible for the control of our internal environment. The rate of the heartbeat, the peristaltic movements of the stomach and intestinal tract, the response the body makes to temperature changes, the contraction of the urinary bladder—these are under autonomic control. In addition, we have all experienced the dry mouth, the pounding heart, and sweating palms in response to an emergency, as well as the red blush of embarrassment or anger. These are also responses that are under the control of the autonomic nervous system.

Structure and activities of the autonomic nervous system. The cell bodies of the efferent nerves of the autonomic nervous system are located in areas ranging from the midbrain to the sacral division of the spinal cord. The axons of cells within the central nervous system are called **preganglionic fibers,** while the axons of cells lying in ganglia outside of the spinal cord or in or near the muscles or glands innervated are called **postganglionic fibers.**

The autonomic nervous system is divided into two parts, on both anatomical and physiological grounds. They are the **parasympathetic** and **sympathetic** divisions, also called the **craniosacral** and **thoracolumbar** divisions, respectively (Fig. 9-15). The latter terms refer to the location of the cell bodies of each portion in the gray matter of the spinal cord.

The two divisions are largely antagonistic to each other, although they have independent functions as well. If you drive a car with one foot on the accelerator and the other on the brake pedal (as some racing drivers do), you are in a position either to speed up or slow down very quickly. Similar quick changes are achieved by the autonomic nervous system. If you observe the iris of someone's eye you will note frequent changes in the diameter of the pupil. The nerve control of this reaction can be traced to the autonomic nervous system. The craniosacral division is responsible for the contraction while the thoracolumbar dilates the pupil.

Parasympathetic division of the autonomic nervous system. The cranial part of the parasympathetic division takes its origin from cells in the midbrain, pons, and medulla. Four cranial nerves carry autonomic preganglionic fibers. These include the oculomotor (to constrict the pupil), the facial and glossopharyngeal (secretory to salivary glands), and the vagus, which is mainly a parasympathetic nerve (motor and/or secretory to the heart, bronchi, esophagus, stomach, small intestine, first third of the colon, liver, gall bladder, bile ducts, and pancreas).

The sacral part of the parasympathetic division comes from cells in the second, third, and fourth segments of the sacral spinal cord. They leave the cord with the anterior roots, then leave the roots and come together to form the **pelvic nerve,** which supplies motor fibers to the involuntary (smooth) muscle of the lower two thirds of the colon and urinary bladder. The pelvic nerve also sends inhibitory fibers to the bladder and anal sphincters.

Sympathetic division of the autonomic nervous system. The nerve cell bodies of the sympathetic or thoracolumbar division are in the gray matter of the spinal cord, from its first thoracic to third lumbar segments. Preganglionic sympathetic fibers run from these cells down the anterior roots to their junctions with the posterior roots. Here some of them leave, as slender strands called **white rami communicantes,** to join the sympathetic ganglia. The ganglia are arranged as two beaded **cords** for each side of the body, extending from the base of the skull to the coccyx. Those situated along the sides of the vertebrae, the **vertebral cords,** have smaller ganglia than those running down the front of the vertebrae along with the aorta, the **prevertebral** cords. Each ganglion contains

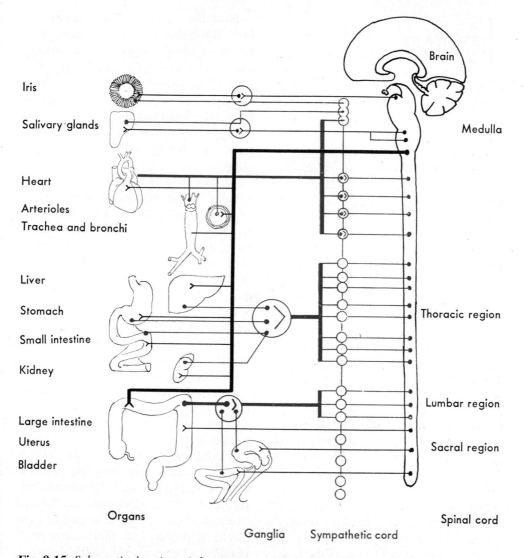

Fig. 9-15. *Schematic drawing of the autonomic nervous system and the organs it supplies. The sympathetic division is in red, while the parasympathetic division is in black. The heavy black line represents the vagus nerve.*

cells with which some of the white rami form synapses, although many white rami send fibers along the cords to higher or lower ganglia.

Axons of cells in the ganglia leave as **gray rami communicantes** to join the spinal nerves, which distribute them to their destinations.

The sympathetic division of the au-

tonomic nervous system sends accelerator nerves to the heart, and vasoconstrictor nerves to the blood vessels of the skin. This system inhibits secretion of salivary and gastrointestinal glands, and inhibits the motility of the gastrointestinal tract and the urinary bladder. It stimulates the production of adrenalin (epinephrin) by the adrenal glands.

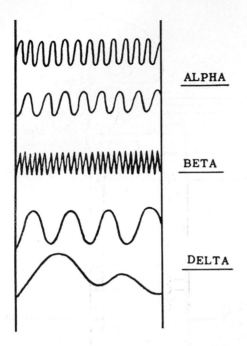

ALPHA

BETA

DELTA

Fig. 9-16. *A reproduction of the alpha, beta, and delta waves from a typical electroencephalogram.*

The sympathetic division is of great importance in preparing the body for action at times of stress. It speeds the heart's action, dilates the blood vessels in the muscles (including the coronary vessels of the heart muscle), and constricts them in the skin. This diverts a greater blood supply to muscles and other vital organs. The sympathetic system also dilates the pupils of the eyes for maximum peripheral vision; quiets the gastrointestinal tract, which is not needed in the emergency; and stimulates the production of adrenalin (epinephrin), from the adrenal glands. This hormone liberates sugar from the liver for immediate use in energy production.

Autonomic chemicals. Until recently, the effects of autonomic nerves on the muscles and glands they stimulate has been thought to be due to the nerve impulses themselves.

Now the parasympathetic nerve endings throughout the body have been found to liberate acetylcholine. Sympathetic nerve endings have been found to liberate adrenalin or substances resembling adrenalin. This has led to use of the terms **cholinergic** for those fibers liberating acetylcholine, and **adrenergic** for those liberating adrenalin-like substances.

It has been known for some time that the liberation of acetylcholine at the myoneural junction brings about initiation of voluntary muscle contraction (see Chapter 6). It has also been discovered that acetylcholine plays some part in the transmission of impulses across both sympathetic and parasympathetic synapses, as well as performing its known function in synaptic and nerve impulse transmission in the rest of the nervous system.

Electroencephalography. As early as 1874, Caton, an Englishman, observed electrical fluctuations from the cortex of animals and believed them to be related to the functional activity of the brain. Not until 1929, however, in the laboratory of Hans Berger, was the electrical activity of the human brain successfully recorded. When electrodes are affixed to the scalp, a record of changes in the electrical potential of the brain can be obtained. These changes appear mainly as sinusoidal waves of varying frequencies (see Fig. 9-16). The alpha waves (8-14 cps) are the predominant wave forms in the relaxed, normal adult. Also present may be beta waves (15-30 cps) which may be exaggerated by certain diseased states and the administration of certain drugs. The slower rhythms, such as delta (.5-3 cps) are seen normally in infants, children, and adolescents, and during sleep, and are also fairly characteristic of diseased states of the cerebral hemispheres, such as brain tumors. Other more specific wave forms, such as spikes and spike wave complexes, are seen in association with epilepsy.

The electroencephalogram has thus become a valuable tool in many of the diseased states which affect the intracranial contents of the nervous system. Electrospinograms and electromyograms, using similar electronic principles, are useful techniques for evaluating normal or diseased states of the spinal cord, peripheral nerves, and muscle.

Conditioned reflexes. The reflexes we have considered thus far are **unconditioned reflexes:** that is, they are present when we are born, and most of them occur even in the lowest animals. They are not altered by, nor do they depend on, past experience. These include such responses as are required for taking food, removing waste, and simple defense from obvious danger.

Any reflex which is modified as a result of experience or training is known as a **conditioned reflex.** The Russian physiologist Pavlov developed methods whereby conditioned reflexes could be studied in animals. For example, he found that food placed in the mouth of a very young puppy which had not been fed before would bring secretion of saliva. This is, of course, an unconditioned reflex. If, however, a bell was rung every time the animal was offered food, eventually saliva would flow every time he heard the bell, even in the absence of food. The puppy was now *conditioned*

to the sound of a bell: that is, he remembered the association between the bell and food. Conditioned reflexes obviously require the participation of the cerebral cortex of the brain.

Sleep: its nature and physiology. The true cause of the phenomenon we know of as *sleep* remains unknown in spite of much intensive research. There are many theories, none of which is immune to challenge. They range from reduced blood supply to the brain to Pavlov's theory of conditioned inhibition of brain activity.

We do know that sleep is necessary for all animals, and that lack of it, especially in younger animals, may lead to death.

During sleep, most of the body's functions are carried out on a greatly reduced level as compared with the waking state. The body temperature may drop as much as one or two degrees, the heart rate may be decreased as much as 40 beats a minute, blood pressure falls, muscle tone and reflexes are reduced or abolished, and the volume of urine production drops. On the other hand, secretion of both perspiration and stomach acid may be increased.

The need for sleep varies for different people, but in general children require more than adults, and aged people require less than younger adults.

Depth of sleep in adults is usually greatest at the end of the first hour, while in children, it again deepens at the end of the sleep period.

SPEAKING OF Physiology

Briefly identify each of the following:

arachnoid	hemisphere	pia mater
cerebral lobes	inhibit	posterior root ganglion
dura mater	longitudinal fissure	reciprocal innervation
foramen magnum	meninges	vertebral foramen

Test YOUR KNOWLEDGE

1. What are the two primary functions of the spinal cord?
2. The spinal cord occupies what portion of the spinal column? Why?
3. Since the neurons which comprise the spinal cord cannot reproduce, protection of this structure is essential. Describe the various ways in which this nerve cord is protected from injury.
4. Where is the spinal fluid located and what is its function? What conditions can be diagnosed from a laboratory examination of this fluid?
5. Briefly describe the appearance of a cross section of the spinal cord.
6. Why are all spinal nerves mixed nerves?
7. Trace the path of a simple reflex arc from a receptor through the spinal cord to an effector. Is this a learned or unlearned response? What is the primary function of reflex activities?
8. Describe the location and function of each of the membranes which comprise the cranial meninges.
9. What differences can one observe when comparing the brain of a simpler animal, such as a frog, with the human brain?
10. Describe the activities of the brain stem of the human brain by considering the following: (*a*) the structure and function of the medulla, pons, and midbrain, (*b*) location, appearance, and function of the cerebellum, (*c*) the activities performed by the thalamus and hypothalamus.
11. What part of the human brain is responsible for the highest motor and sensory activities?
12. How is the surface area of the cerebrum increased without an increase in the total volume?
13. Describe the microscopic structure of the cerebral cortex.
14. Briefly describe the structure of the autonomic nervous system. How can you explain the following statement: "The autonomic nervous system is responsible for the control of our internal environment"?
15. What is an electroencephalograph? What types of information can be obtained by use of this apparatus?
16. How does a conditioned reflex differ from an unconditioned reflex? Give examples of each type.

See FOR YOURSELF

1. Procure a calf's brain from a meat market and locate the surface structures as noted in your text. Can you identify any of the meninges? Note the fissures, convolutions, and various internal ventricles.

2. List 25 different activities performed during a 24-hour period. List these activities as simple responses (reflex or involuntary actions) or conditioned responses (habits). Which of these activities seem to be most common according to your classification?

3. Write a report on how to develop and break habits.

CHAPTER 10

The Structure of the Eye and the Physics of Vision

It has often been said that vision is one of our most cherished possessions, and the human eye is one of the most remarkable organs in the body. Your eyes convert light waves traveling at a speed of over 186,000 miles per second into nerve impulses which are transmitted by way of the optic nerves to the brain. It is in the cerebral cortex of the occipital lobe that these impulses, as a result of the light stimulus, are interpreted as vision.

We often say that we see with our eyes. Actually, the eye is simply a highly specialized receptor, sensitive to light stimuli. We cannot see until impulses from the eye reach the brain. Even though the eye may receive a light stimulus, we are totally blind if the nerve impulse is stopped before it reaches the occipital lobe of the cortex. On the other hand, a visual sensation is frequently reported if the occipital lobes are stimulated by a weak electric current during a surgical operation.

Visual function is much more complicated than the average person realizes. For instance, we have vision in dim light as well as in bright daylight or artificial light; we have black and white vision as well as color vision. We can see objects at a distance as well as close by; we have acute vision of what we look at directly, and hazy vision of the surrounding area. Some of these aspects of vision we will discuss in Chapter 11, but for the present, let us consider the structure of the eye and see how certain aspects of physics apply to its function.

The orbital cavity. Each eye lies within a bony socket, the **orbital cavity.** It is a funnel-shaped depression which is made up of seven different bones. If you look at a human skull, you will see a rather prominent ridge around the anterior surface of each orbital cavity. This protective ridge is made up of three bones: on the upper surface and continuing into the eye socket is the **frontal** bone; the bone forming the medial side and about one half of the lower ridge is the **maxilla;** the lateral portion of this ridge and the outer lower portion is made up of the **zygomatic** bone. Forming the interior walls of the orbital cavity are the **sphenoid, lacrimal, ethmoid,** and a small portion of the **palatine.** These seven bones form a protective, unyielding housing for each eye (Fig. 10-1).

Two openings are found in the bones of the orbital cavity. One of these, the **optic foramen,** the smaller of the two,

115

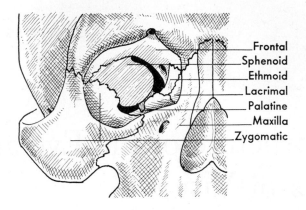

Fig. 10-1. *Bones of the orbital cavity.*

allows both the **optic nerve** and the **ophthalmic artery** to enter the eye. The second opening, the **superior orbital fissure,** provides an entrance for other arteries and veins and the nerves which carry impulses to the muscles that move each eye.

The orbital cavities house, in addition to the eyeball, numerous other structures: the extrinsic eye muscles; the lacrimal apparatus, which is responsible for producing tears; blood vessels; nerves; various tissues called **fascia,** which hold these structures in place; plus a rather heavy padding of fat. This fat tissue cushions the eye itself and thus provides an excellent protective substance which will absorb the shock of a blow on the external surface of the eye. During illness, as fat is used up by the body for energy, the eyes may appear to sink into their sockets and give a person a rather ghostly appearance.

The muscles of the eye. Two groups of muscles operate in the process of vision. One group, the **intrinsic muscles,** is found within the eye. Among these are the muscles of the *ciliary body.* This structure is mainly responsible for the ability of the eye to focus on near or distant objects. The **iris** contains a second group of intrinsic muscles which

control the amount of light entering the eye. We will discuss these muscles later. For the present, let us turn to those muscles responsible for eye movement—the **extrinsic eye muscles.** (See Trans-Vision, following page 120.)

Three pairs of striated muscles are responsible for the movement of each eye. The insertions of these muscles lie along the mid-line, or equator, of the eyeball and their origins, except for one, the inferior oblique muscle, are near the apex of each orbital cavity. Two pairs of muscles in each eye are attached to the eye at right angles to each other and each is called a **rectus** muscle (Lat., *rectus,* straight). Depending upon their position, they are: **superior rectus, inferior rectus, internal rectus,** and **lateral** or **external rectus.**

When the superior rectus muscle contracts, the eye turns upward; opposing this muscle is the inferior rectus, which turns the eye downward. Attached to the inner surface of the eye is the internal rectus, which turns the eye inward. The lateral or external rectus is attached to the outer surface of the eye and turns the eye away from the mid-line of the body.

The remaining two muscles of each eye are set at an angle to the other four. The **superior oblique** is attached to the

Frontal
Sphenoid
Ethmoid
Lacrimal
Palatine
Maxilla
Zygomatic

upper part of the eye and passes through a small ring of bone, called the **trochlea,** located on the upper medial surface of the orbital cavity. After passing through the trochlea, the muscle attaches near the apex of the socket with the four recti muscles. Opposing this muscle is the **inferior oblique.** It arises from the orbital wall of the maxilla and inserts on the under portion of the eyeball. These two muscles act to rotate the eye, probably helped by the recti muscles.

The coordination of the eye muscles is complex. If you look at the eyes of a newborn child, you will probably see that each eye moves independently. As the child grows, the brain becomes more highly developed and the ability to follow moving objects becomes coordinated in both eyes.

Three cranial nerves supply the connection between the central nervous system and the controlled movements of the eyes. The **oculomotor nerve** (third cranial nerve) sends branches to the superior, inferior, and medial rectus, and the inferior oblique. The **abducens nerve** (sixth cranial nerve) supplies the lateral or external rectus. The **trochlear nerve** (fourth cranial nerve) supplies the superior oblique muscle.

As has been mentioned, a nerve consists of many individual neuron processes. That fact is important, considering that the same cranial nerve controls both opposing muscles used in moving the eye upward and downward (the superior rectus and the inferior rectus). In like manner, when the right eye turns outward, the left eye must turn inward and vice versa, in order to keep both eyes properly focused on an object. Higher centers in the brain are responsible for the complexity of coordinated eye movement.

Protection of the eye. Except for the extrinsic eye muscles, the accessory organs of the eye are concerned primarily with protection.

The **eyebrows** protect the eye from small particles falling from above the eye. This skin projection, containing rather short stiff hairs, also shades the eye from bright illumination.

The two **eyelids** are folds of skin which protect the eye by closing over its surface. Sphincter-type muscles, the **orbicularis oculi,** open and close the eyelids. Although they are under voluntary control, their conscious action is not usually fast enough to prevent injury to the eye. The eye is therefore protected by an automatic (reflex) action which closes the lids whenever the eye is liable to be damaged by a blow or by some foreign object. The visual receptors within the eye must detect the approaching object and send impulses to the brain. The brain responds unconsciously, and returns impulses to the muscles which close the eye—all in a fraction of a second.

Attached to the anterior margin of both lids is a row of short curved hairs, the **eyelashes.** Near these protective hairs are oil (or sebaceous) glands which lubricate the hairs. If one of these glands becomes infected, the result may be a *sty.*

Attached to the inner surface of the eyelids and continuous over the surface of the eye is a thin transparent mucous membrane, the **conjunctiva.** When the eyelids close, the conjunctiva attached to the inner surface of the lids comes in contact with that portion of the conjunctiva which is folded back over the surface of the eye. Any inflammation of this membrane is called **conjunctivitis.** A good example of this is "pink eye," a highly contagious infection.

The last protective accessory structure we will consider is the **lacrimal apparatus.** (See Trans-Vision, following page 120.) The production of tears is the responsibility of the **lacrimal gland,** located in the orbital cavity in a slight depression of the frontal bone along the lateral superior wall. The tears produced by the lacrimal gland are slightly germicidal and composed mostly of water with a little salt and mucin. The secretion, which is under the control of the autonomic nervous system, flows from the gland through several ducts to the surface of the eye, where it performs its lubricating function. Most of these tears evaporate from the eye's surface, but those which do not are drained into the nasal cavity by way of two **lacrimal ducts,** located at the inner margin of the eye. These ducts connect to the **nasolacrimal duct** which leads to the nasal cavity. When the production of tears increases, due to pain or some emotional state, the lacrimal ducts are unable to carry away the added quantity, and tears overflow the lower lid.

The structure of the eye. The eyeball is nearly spherical, measuring approximately 24 millimeters (1 inch) in diameter, although the distance from front to back is slightly longer than from side to side. This difference is due to the slight bulge in the front of the eyeball. This region of the eye, the **cornea,** is transparent, while the rest of the eye wall is opaque.

Structurally, the wall of the eye is composed of three layers:

1. The outer layer is called the **sclera** or **sclerotic coat.** It is a grayish-white, tough, fibrous membrane which helps to maintain the spherical shape of the eye. The six extrinsic eye muscles insert onto this layer. The cornea is part of the sclerotic coat. This transparent "window" has no blood vessels to interfere with the transmission of light waves. The cells of the cornea are fed by the movement of tissue fluid through the intercellular spaces. The cornea is supplied with receptors for touch and pain, and is extremely sensitive to any object coming in contact with its surface.

At each margin of the cornea we see the sclera as the white of the eye. This layer has few blood vessels. It may appear inflamed, but this is usually due to the dilation of the small blood vessels within the conjunctiva which covers this portion of the eye, rather than to enlargement of the vessels in the sclerotic coat.

2. The middle layer of the wall of the eye is known as the **choroid** layer. This contains many blood vessels which bring food and oxygen to it as well as to the other coats. It is colored a deep reddish-purple by the presence of pigment granules. This prevents reflection of light within the eye in much the same manner as the black paint within a camera eliminates stray rays of light that would fog the film.

The anterior part of the choroid layer is known as the **iris.** It may be of a blue, brown, gray, green, or black color due to the amount of pigment that is present in it. Structurally, the iris is composed of two distinct layers. The layer toward the back of the eye contains a pigment (melanin) in the form of large granules; the layer in front of this may lack pigment entirely or may contain some pigment in either small or large granules. If there is no pigment present, the light rays striking the iris are dispersed and, the iris appears blue. (By a similar circumstance, certain dark-colored birds seem blue. Actually, such birds are brown, but fine lines on the feathers break up the light and reflect it in the form of blue wave lengths.) If there is a small amount of pigment in the outer layer, the eye appears to be green or gray. As the amount of melanin increases, the depth of color approaches

| Pupil contracted in bright light | Normal pupil opening | Pupil dilated in dim light |

Fig. 10-2. *The reaction of the pupil to light of varying intensity.*

black. The distribution of these pigments is controlled by the genes (Chapter 33) and, therefore, inherited.

Within the iris of the eye are two sets of smooth muscles. The inner set is circular (sphincter) and has the ability to constrict the inner edge of the iris. The second set is perpendicular to the circular muscles. When this set contracts, the inner edge of the iris is drawn open again.

The hole in the center of the iris is the **pupil**. The pupil is not a structure, but an opening in the iris which varies continually as the two sets of muscles vary in contraction. Thus the amount of light which can enter the eye is determined by the size of the pupil. These changes in the pupil are evident as the eye adjusts to variations in illumination. If a bright light is flashed into the eye, the sphincter muscle contracts and the size of the pupil is reduced very rapidly. In dim light the pupil becomes larger (Fig. 10-2).

The muscles of the iris are under the control of the autonomic nervous system through the oculomotor (third cranial) nerve.

3. The innermost layer of the wall of the eye is called the **retina.** It completely lines the inner surface of the eye up to the ciliary body and is composed mainly of different kinds of neurons. The blood supply to this important receptor layer is from two sources: (1) The choroid capillaries supply a small amount of the nutritional requirements; (2) Of greater importance is the **central retinal artery** which spreads throughout the retina. Waste materials are removed by the retinal veins which parallel the arteries.

It is within the retina that we find the neurons responsible for vision. If the cellular structure of the retina is analyzed, it is seen to consist of many layers. Three of these layers contain neurons which are of special importance. The layer closest to the choroid coat is responsible for converting visual light into impulses. These receptors are called **rods** and **cones** because of their appearance. The axons of the rods and cones make synaptic connections with the bipolar neurons in the second important layer, found in the middle of the retina. Finally, the axons of the bipolar neurons form synapses with the neurons in the third important layer, the multipolar **ganglion cells.** The axons of these neurons all pass across the inner surface of the retina and collect in one area at the posterior part of the eye. These axons collectively make up the **optic nerve** which leads to the brain (Fig. 10-3).

From this description of the retina, it should be noted that light must first pass through the ganglion layer of neurons, then the other layers, including the bipolar cells, before they come in contact with cells directly stimulated by the light: the rods and cones. Once these receptors are stimulated, nerve impulses must again retrace the path of the incoming light waves to the ganglionic

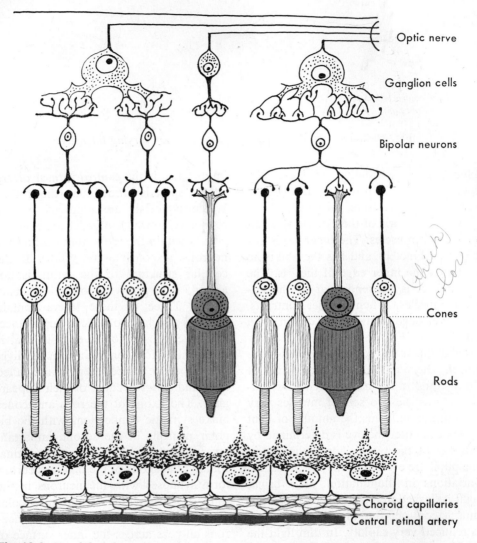

Fig. 10-3. *Simplified diagram of the important layers of cells in the retina of the eye.*

axons before they enter the optic nerve. Such an arrangement of cells is called an ***inverted retina,*** and is typical of all vertebrates.

The rods and cones. These elongated neurons, the rods and cones, are both photosensitive receptors. The rods are more cylindrical than the cones, and measure between 40 and 60 microns in length and about two microns in width (Fig. 10-4). Each cell is divided into an inner and outer segment. In the outer segment we find the chemical responsible for this cell's photosensitivity— ***rhodopsin*** or ***visual purple.*** It is estimated that there are as many as 125 million rods in each retina.

The cones are conical or flask-shaped, with the pointed end toward the choroid layer. Like the rods, these neurons are made up of an inner and an outer segment. In the cones, the photochemical

THE EYE AND EAR
IN ANATOMICAL TRANSPARENCIES

by Mr. ALFRED FEINBERG, Instructor of Medical Art

Department of Pathology, College of Physicians and Surgeons
Columbia University, New York City

As you turn the pages of these "Trans-Vision" dissections, you see deeper and deeper structures of the eye and ear. The right pages are from the outside looking toward the inside of the head; the left pages are from the inside looking out. Many more muscles, blood vessel branches, and nerve branches in the region of the eye and ear are shown than are labeled, so as to stress the functioning structures of the eye and ear. A description of each plate of the eye appears on the text page at the left. The text page opposite the back of Plate 6 describes corresponding plates of the ear. An identification key for the eye appears below and continues on the back of Plate 6, with a similar key for the ear.

Key to the Structures of the Eye

1. Muller's muscle, helps elevate eyelid
2. Levator palpebralis superior muscle, opens eyelid
3. Lacrimal gland, secretes tears
4. Lacrimal artery, to lacrimal gland
5. Lacrimal nerve, stimulates lacrimal gland to secrete tears
6. Superior branch, ophthalmic vein, drains eye socket
7. Annulus of Zinn, fibrous ring, origin of most muscles moving the eye
8. Inferior tarsus, supporting plate, lower eyelid
9. Superior tarsus, supporting plate, upper eyelid
10. Meibomian glands, lubricate eyeball
11. Conjunctiva, mucous membrane of eye
12. Frontalis muscle, assists in opening eye

13. Superior rectus muscle, turns eyeball up
14. Inferior oblique muscle, rotates eyeball toward temple
14A. Tendon, inferior oblique muscle
15. Inferior rectus muscle, turns eyeball down
16. Lateral rectus muscle, turns eyeball toward temple
17. Bulbar conjunctiva, mucous membrane covering sclera
18. Cornea, clear window of the eye
19. Tendon, superior oblique muscle
20. Optic nerve, nerve cable to brain
21. Central retinal artery and vein
22. Choroid, dark pigmented layer, nourishes retina
23. Sclera, white outer layer of eyeball
24. Retina, contains receptor cells and optic nerve

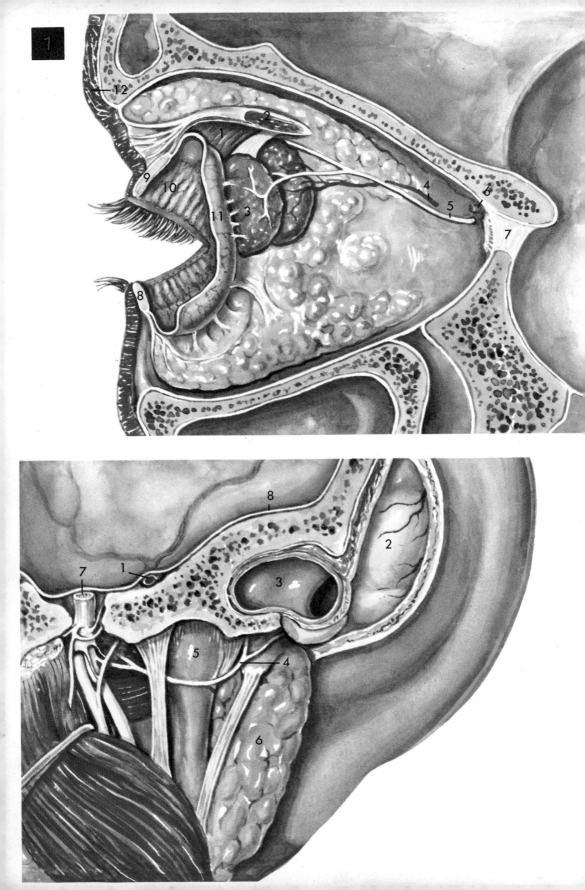

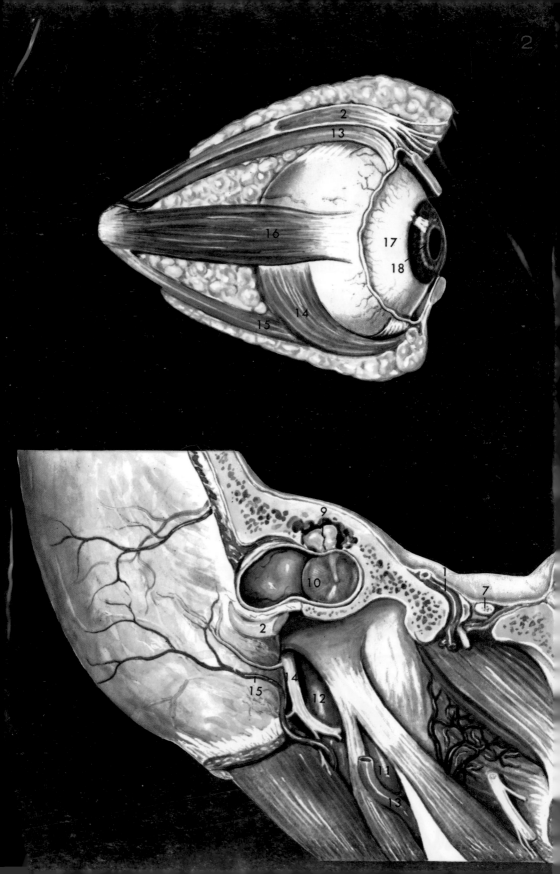

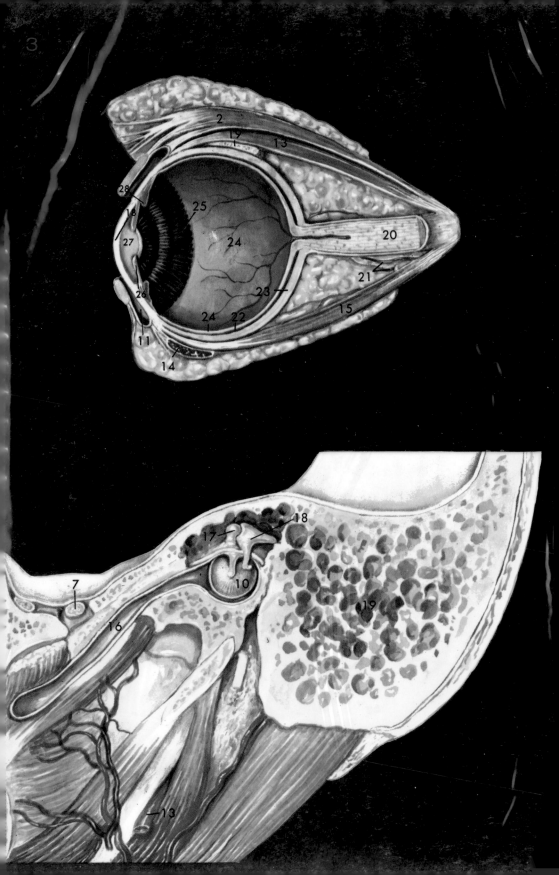

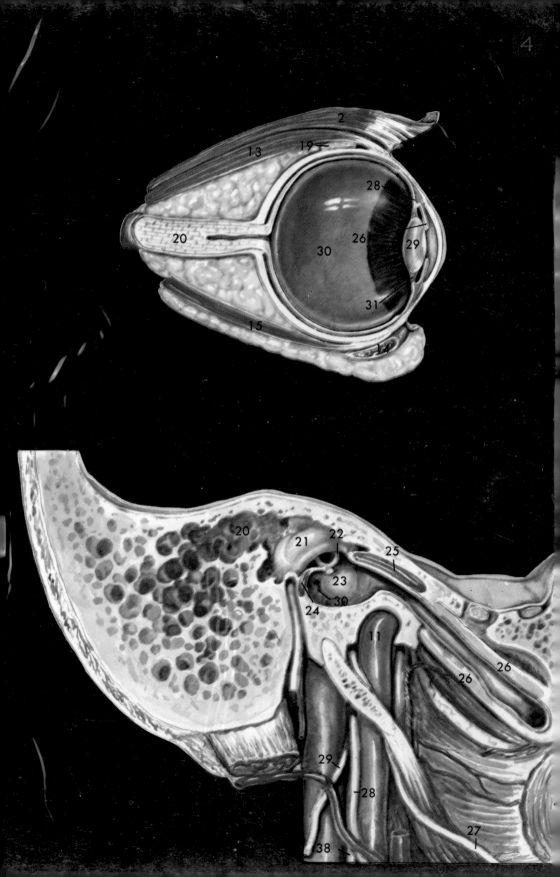

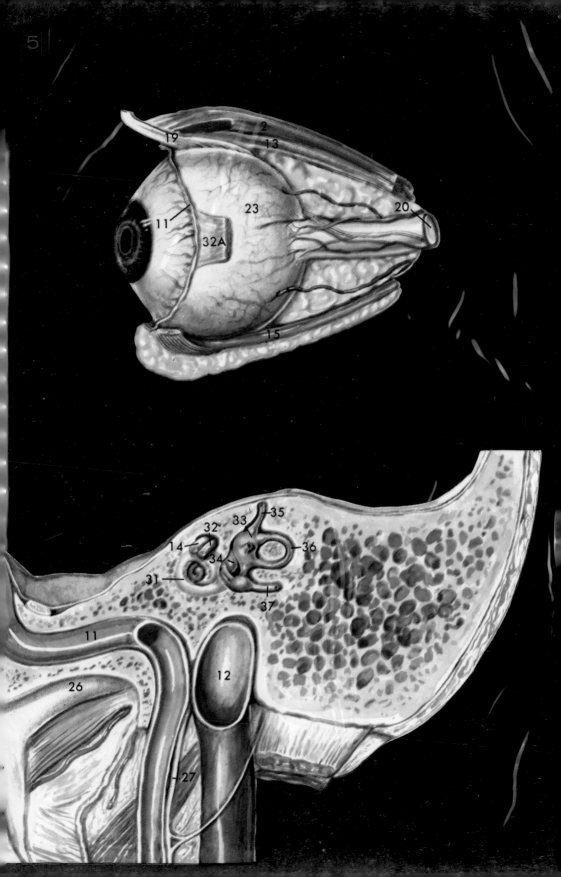

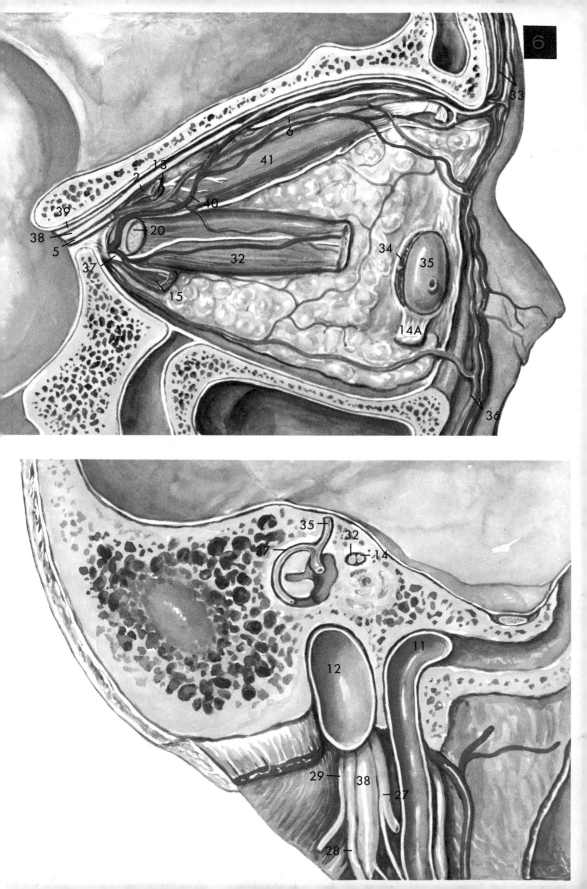

25. Ciliary body, composed largely of ciliary muscle
26. Iris, muscle, dilates and constricts pupil
27. Anterior chamber, between cornea and iris and lens
28. Ciliary muscle, regulates shape of lens
29. Crystalline lens, bends light rays
30. Vitreous body, fills eyeball back of lens
31. Zonule of Zinn, attaches ciliary muscle to lens
32. Medial rectus muscle, turns eyeball toward nose
32A. Tendon, medial rectus muscle
33. Frontal artery and vein, to forehead
34. Orbicularis muscle (lacrimal portion), closes eyelids
35. Lacrimal sac, reservoir for tears
36. Facial artery and vein, to eye structures and face
37. Oculomotor nerve, 3rd cranial nerve, to most eye muscles
38. Frontal nerve, to conjunctiva and upper eyelids
39. Trochlear nerve, 4th cranial nerve, to superior oblique muscle
40. Ophthalmic artery, to muscles, socket, and eyeball
41. Superior oblique muscle, rotates eyeball down and out

Key to the Structures of the Ear

1. Middle meningeal artery, to the dura mater
2. Cartilage of auricle, gives form to external ear
3. External auditory canal, channel through which sound waves travel to ear drum
4. Auriculo-temporal nerve, to external ear, ear canal, and temple
5. Ascending ramus of mandible, upper end of lower jaw bone
6. Parotid salivary gland
7. Mandibular nerve, branch of 5th cranial nerve
8. Dura mater, one of the brain membranes
9. Incus-malleus joint
10. Drum, tympanic membrane, inner end of auditory canal
11. Internal carotid artery
12. Internal jugular vein
13. External carotid artery
14. Facial nerve, 7th cranial nerve
15. Posterior auricular artery, to ear drum, mastoid bone, semicircular canals
16. Eustachian tube, connects middle ear and nasophraynx
17. Malleus, hammer bone of middle ear
18. Incus, anvil bone of middle ear
19. Mastoid cells, spaces in spongy mastoid bone
20. Mastoid antrum, air-filled cavity of mastoid bone
21. Horizontal semicircular canal
22. Stapes, stirrup bone, base of which presses against oval window
23. Promontory, rounded bulge formed by projection of first turn of cochlea
24. Stapedius muscle, moves stapes
25. Tensor tympani muscle, tightens tympanic membrane
26. Cartilage of Eustachian tube, forms lower portion of tube
27. Glossopharyngeal nerve, 9th cranial nerve
28. Hypoglossal nerve, 12th cranial nerve
29. Accessory nerve, 11th cranial nerve
30. Round window niche, membrane-covered opening to cochlea
31. Cochlea, conical, spiral bony labyrinth of inner ear
32. Vestibular nerve, branch of acoustic nerve, to semicircular canals; the balance nerve
33. Utricle, membranous sac in vestibule of inner ear
34. Saccule, membranous sac at base of cochlea
35. Superior membranous semicircular canal
36. Horizontal membranous semicircular canal
37. Posterior (inferior) membranous semicircular canal
38. Vagus nerve, 10th cranial nerve

substance within this outer segment is called **iodopsin.** The nature of this pigment, or pigments, is not clearly understood. The cones measure about 25 microns in length and up to six microns in width. There are only about 7 million cones in each retina, but they are concentrated in the posterior portion of the eye.

The rods have a low threshold of light sensitivity and are thus responsible for vision in dim light. It is also believed that they are insensitive to color. The cones, on the other hand, have a relatively high threshold of sensitivity and are responsible for our perception of color, or **chromatic vision.** This topic will be covered in more detail in Chapter 11.

Other structures of the retina. With the aid of an ophthalmoscope (an instrument which shines a light on the retina and reflects it into the operator's eye) you can see the retinal surface. The most obvious feature on the posterior wall is a yellow disk, known as the **macula lutea.** In the center of this disk is a small area called the **fovea centralis,** the center for distinct and color vision, containing only the cones. The area around the fovea centralis, called the **extrafoveal** or **peripheral region,** contains mainly the rods (Fig. 10-5) for dim or peripheral vision.

Slightly toward the nose from the fovea centralis is a pale area in which blood vessels can be seen entering and leaving the eye. It is in this area, the **optic disk,** that all of the ganglion axons converge. Thus there is no room for the receptors (rods and cones). We have no visual reception in this area, so it is called the **blind spot.**

There are many ways of explaining why we are not conscious of the blind spot, but probably the explanation easiest to understand is that there is an

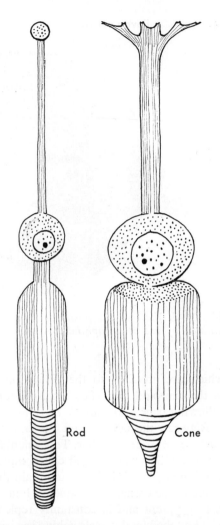

Rod   Cone

Fig. 10-4. *Diagrams of typical rod and cone receptors in the retina.*

overlapping of the retinal images of the two eyes, and what one cannot see, the other eye can.

The lens and associated structures. Just behind the pupil is a transparent cellular body, the **crystalline lens.** This structure is disk-shaped and somewhat elastic. The two surfaces are convex, forming a biconvex lens; but the posterior surface has a greater curvature than the anterior surface. The crystalline lens is held in place by **suspensory ligaments**

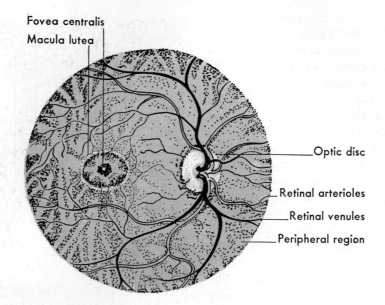

Fovea centralis
Macula lutea
Optic disc
Retinal arterioles
Retinal venules
Peripheral region

Fig. 10-5. *View of the posterior surface of the retina. This part of the eye can be examined by use of an ophthalmoscope.*

which are attached to the ciliary body of the choroid layer. (See Trans-Vision, following page 120, *Zonule of Zinn.*)

Between the cornea and the iris we find the **anterior** chamber. This chamber is filled with a watery fluid called **aqueous humor,** which helps to maintain the shape of the cornea. The aqueous humor is transparent and is constantly replenished by the blood vessels behind the iris.

Behind the lens and suspensory ligaments and within the space lined by the retina is the **vitreous body.** It is a transparent jellylike substance which helps to maintain the spherical shape of the eyeball.

If the amount of fluid in the eye increases, the eyeball becomes very hard because of the increased pressure caused by the fluid. The optic disk is depressed, and there is restriction of the field of vision. This condition is called **glaucoma** and necessitates immediate medical attention. Blindness may result if the internal pressure is not relieved.

The physics of vision. Light is the form of radiant energy which can stimulate the receptors in the retina of the eye. Only through the presence of light are we able to respond visually to our surroundings. The wave lengths of radiant energy capable of producing sight vary from 3.9 ten thousandths of a millimeter to 7.6 ten thousandths of a millimeter. This is often written in **Ångstrom units** (which equal one ten-millionth of a millimeter) as 3900 to 7600 Å (Ångstrom units). These wave lengths are very short and travel at the tremendous speed of 186,000 miles per second.

For all practical purposes, light may be considered to travel in straight lines through a transparent medium of constant density. However, light rays are bent or **refracted** when they pass from one medium to another of different density. This refraction of light is easily seen if a straw or a pencil is put into a glass of water so that it leans against the side of the glass (Fig. 10-6). The object seems to be bent at the surface of the water. It is this refraction that explains why light rays bend as they pass through the cornea and the lens of the eye, and fall as a clear image on the retina. Of the two structures in the human eye, the cornea has the greater responsibility for refraction.

When light passes through a transparent object, the rays will bend both on entering the object and upon leaving it. Just how much the light will bend depends not only on the curvature of the object but also on its density. If a transparent object, such as a lens, varies in thickness, the light rays will bend toward the thicker portion. A lens that has a uniformly curved surface and is thicker at the edge than in the middle, is called **concave**. Parallel rays of light passing through this type of lens will **diverge** or spread outward. If on the other hand, parallel light rays pass through a lens that is thicker in the center than at the edge (a **convex** lens), the rays will **converge** and be brought to a single point or **principal focus** (Fig. 10-7). The distance from the center of the lens to the focal point is called the **focal length** of the lens. If both sides of the lens have a similar curvature, the lens is called **biconcave** or **biconvex** depending upon the location of the thickest part of the lens. Thus the crystalline lens of the human eye is biconvex, even though the posterior surface has greater convexity than the anterior surface.

One of the optical principles of convex lenses is that if the object is further in front of the lens than its focal length, the image focused on a surface behind the lens will be inverted. The image will also be reversed from side to side. This can be seen easily by looking at the frosted plate on the back of a portrait camera. If the camera is directed toward an individual, his image appears upside

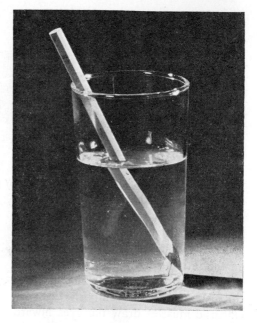

Fig. 10-6. *The effect of refraction. The pencil appears bent where it enters the water. (Charles Phelps Cushing)*

down and reversed in the view plate.

The inversion of the image produced by a convex lens can also be demonstrated by holding such a lens between the eye and an object at some distance from the eye. If you move the lens backward and forward, you will see at one point a clear inverted image of the object. The way in which the visual center of the cerebrum interprets the inversion and reversal of the image produced by the convex lens of the eye will be discussed in Chapter 11.

If a normal eye observes an object at a distance of twenty feet or more, the light rays entering the eye are almost parallel and the resulting image is in focus on the retina. However, if the object is less than 20 feet away, the light rays entering the eye are not parallel. If there were no changes in the eye, the image would be blurred since it would not be focused on the retina. In order to form clear images of objects

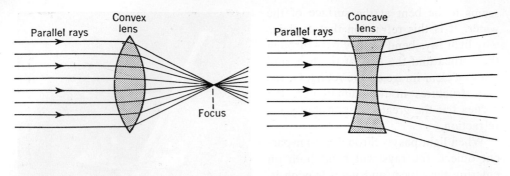

Fig. 10-7. *These diagrams show the effects of concave and convex lenses on the light rays that pass through them.*

nearer than 20 feet, two corrections must be made by the eye to sharpen the image on the retina. First, each eye must turn slightly toward the object. This is called **convergence.** To accomplish this, the extrinsic muscles draw the eyes inward so as to point them directly at the object in view. Second, and of greater importance for sharp focus, the eye must **accommodate.** Many theories have been proposed to explain accommodation, but the one most widely accepted involves contraction of the ciliary muscle, and a resulting change in shape of the lens. As was mentioned earlier, the crystalline lens is an elastic body. If unsupported, it would assume more of a spherical shape than it has when held in position by the suspensory ligaments. When the ciliary muscles are relaxed, the suspensory ligaments exert tension on the lens, thus decreasing the lens's curvature. This is what happens when we look at distant

objects. Since the ciliary muscles are relaxed there is little or no fatigue.

When we must focus on an object less than 20 feet away, the ciliary muscles contract. This in turn decreases the suspensory ligament tension. The lens assumes a greater curvature, thus decreasing its focal length. This brings the image into focus on the retina. If you read a book, or do other close work, you may begin to feel the fatigue of the contracted ciliary muscles after several hours.

The entire process of accommodation is automatic. As the image becomes blurred, when the object changes position within the 20-foot range, sensory impulses are carried to the brain by way of the optic nerves. The brain in turn sends motor impulses by way of autonomic fibers in the oculomotor nerve to the ciliary muscles, which adjust their contraction to bring the image into clear focus again.

SPEAKING OF *Physiology*

Briefly identify each of the following:

ciliary body	**divergence**	**ophthalmoscope**
conjunctivitis	**fascia**	**optic foramen**
convergence	**germicide**	**sty**
cornea	**glaucoma**	**superior orbital fissure**
density	**inverted retina**	**trochlea**

Test YOUR KNOWLEDGE

1. Briefly describe the structure of the orbital cavity. What are the functions of this cavity?
2. In addition to the unyielding bony housing for the eye, how do the following protect it? (*a*) eyebrows, and eyelashes, (*b*) eyelids, (*c*) tears, (*d*) conjunctiva.
3. What is the difference in action of the intrinsic and extrinsic muscles of the eye? Describe the function of each group.
4. The sclera aids in maintaining the spherical shape of the eye. What are some other functions of this layer?
5. What is the function of the iris? To what layer of the eye is the iris attached?
6. What is the primary function of the middle layer of the eye wall?
7. In what layer do we find the visual receptors? Describe the cellular structure of this layer.
8. What is the function of each of the following: (*a*) fovea centralis, (*b*) optic disk, (*c*) suspensory ligaments, (*d*) vitreous body?
9. Describe refraction and use a diagram to show how light is focused on the retina.
10. What is the functional difference between a convex and concave lens? What type of lens is the crystalline lens of the eye?
11. What is the position of the image on the retina? How does the brain interpret this image?
12. What changes must occur in the eye when we view an object that is close to us? How does this differ from viewing distant objects?
13. As light enters the eye, name all of the structures through which the light must pass until the image reaches the retina.

See FOR YOURSELF

1. Show diagrammatically how the human eye resembles a camera. Trace the path of light through each and show how the image is recorded. What advantages does the human eye have over the camera?

2. Determine how the following physical principles are related to the structure and function of the human eye: measurement of the speed of light, units for the measurement of light, law of refraction. What other principles might apply? How?

R - longest, least energy

V - shortest, most energy

CHAPTER 11

The Physiology of Vision

Probably none of our special sense organs has received as much experimental study as the eye. As we have seen in Chapter 10, the anatomy of the visual organs can be fully described to show how the structures within each eyeball form a mechanism which converts light stimuli into sensory impulses for vision. The accessory structures of the eye, except the extrinsic eye muscles that move the eye, are primarily concerned with protection. The optic components of the eye operate on physical principles to refract the light waves to those cells responsible for visual perception. These parts adjust to changes in distance and intensity of illumination. Finally, the photochemical receptors—the rods and cones—convert the radiant energy of light into nerve impulses. Just how the impulses are initiated and how they result in mental interpretation is still not completely understood.

In order to gain a better understanding of the physiology of the human eye, let us now see how these structures operate in the visual process.

Field of vision. We little realize the full extent of our field of vision. When you drive an automobile down the highway, your visual attention is directed straight ahead of you on the roadway. Yet you are still conscious of movement at each side. This *peripheral vision*

does not form a very sharp image, nor is it usually in color, because the associated areas of the retina do not contain cones. Peripheral vision is very important since it enables you to be somewhat aware of what is going on around you without the necessity of constantly turning your head.

You can determine the extent of your own peripheral vision by a simple experiment. Hold both hands together about a foot in front of your nose. Now, while looking straight ahead, move your hands slowly apart and around your head. Continue moving them until you can no longer see them. Most people can see through an arc of about 190°. This area is called your *field of vision.* Your peripheral visual field is highly important in driving a car, in various sports, and in many other activities. A test of a patient's field of vision is helpful in diagnosing certain types of brain tumors.

The retinal image. As we have learned, the image projected onto the retina is inverted and reversed. The visual centers in the brain are responsible for correcting these changes in position. Experiments have been conducted in which special glasses are worn by a subject so that he sees everything reversed and inverted. After a period of time, the brain once again makes the correct adjustment and the subject sees objects in their true position even though he still wears the glasses. When the glasses are removed, everything seems turned upside down and the brain once again has to readjust. This experiment shows the importance of mental interpretation of retinal impulses in visual perception.

Binocular and stereoscopic vision. When we close one eye, the brain receives visual impulses from the other eye only. This is *monocular vision*. Normally, however, the brain receives impulses from both eyes simultaneously. We know that although our eyes are set at a slight distance apart, we do not "see" two separate images, but one single image in which the two are fused. This phenomenon is called binocular vision.

A single impression is recorded in the brain because the two images fall on corresponding points in the retina. To understand this, we must consider the route the retinal impulses take as they move from the eye through the optic nerves to the visual centers in the brain. Impulses follow the **central visual pathways.** As shown in Fig. 11-1, each retina is divided into a nasal or medial portion and a temporal or lateral portion. Due to the reversal of the retinal image, the visual field from a point straight in front of the eye to where the bridge of the nose blocks the view is recorded on the temporal (lateral) half of the retina. The area from straight ahead to the margin of our peripheral view (approximately 95°) is recorded on the medial or nasal half of the retina. If you follow the route of the optic nerves as shown in Fig. 11-1, you will see that the temporal fibers do not cross at the **optic chiasma,** but they join the optic tract on the same side and continue to the visual center in

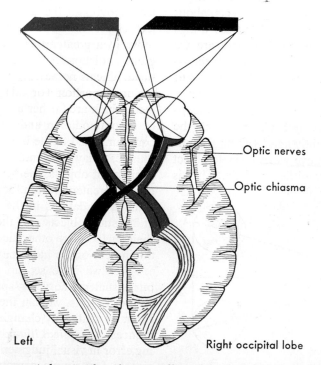

Optic nerves

Optic chiasma

Left
Right occipital lobe

Fig. 11-1. *Diagram of the visual pathways followed by impulses caused by light stimuli from an object on the right (black) and on the left (red).*

that side of the occipital lobe. The fibers from the nasal half of each retina cross at the optic chiasma and enter the optic tract with the temporal fibers from the opposite eye. The terminations of all these fibers form a field of interpretation in one area of the visual center.

You will note from Fig. 11-1 that the image of an object falls on one half of each retina. Impulses from corresponding points on the retinas are carried to the same part of the brain. Thus both images of an object on the right of the viewer are received in the left occipital lobe, and create a single visual impression.

The fact that the eyes can converge on a single point is an important factor in binocular vision (see Fig. 11-2). As an object is brought forward to nearer view, the eyes must turn inward toward each other or the images would not strike corresponding points on the retinas.

One of the remarkable facts about the visual process is that we see things in a third dimension. Not only are we aware of the surface area of objects— the vertical and horizontal planes—but we are also conscious of their volume. We are thus equipped for **depth perception** or **stereoscopic vision**. Since the eyes are set slightly apart (about 64 millimeters), each eye views a single object from a slightly different angle. This is called **parallax.** The left eye sees a little more of the left side of the object than the right eye and vice versa. The images on the retina are not quite identical. However, the visual centers in the brain interpret these images as one that has depth and solidity.

Judgment of spatial relationships. Our judgment of distance is dependent upon many different clues which are interpreted by the brain. An infant will reach for the larger of two colored toys even though the smaller toy is held closer to him. Both seem equally near to his judgment. As we gain knowledge of the size of familiar objects, we use their size as a means of judging their distance. For example, we soon recognize the difference in height between a telephone pole and a mailbox. If we see a telephone pole apparently the height of a mailbox, we know that it is a considerable distance from us. We learn that of two objects moving at the same speed, the object closer to the observer appears to move at a greater speed and to cover a greater distance. We also know that those objects nearest us prevent us from seeing a portion (or all) of those objects which are farther away. The degree of accommodation and convergence, as communicated to the brain from the eye muscles, may also indicate the relative position of objects, the nearer object requiring greater effort in focal adjustment. Finally, gradations in the color of near and distant objects and the shadows on their surfaces are other clues used in our attainment of the judgment of depth.

After we have set up guideposts in our visual memory for spatial relationship of objects, we can then confuse the brain by artificially changing certain references. An **optical illusion** is the resulting error in visual judgment. Figure 11-3 gives a few simple examples of optical illusions.

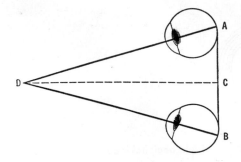

Fig. 11-2. *The action of the eyes in convergence.*

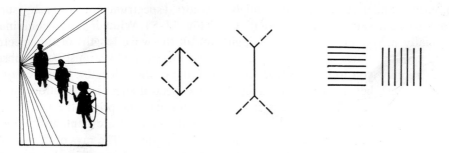

Fig. 11-3. *Three illustrations of optical illusions. Judge the sizes of these figures optically and then measure them accurately.*

Night vision and color vision. The retina of the human eye responds to varying intensities of light, or **achromatic** stimuli, and also to **chromatic,** or color, stimuli. In Chapter 10 we described the structure and location of the receptors responsible for this vision—the rods and cones. Let us now consider the physiological activity of these cells.

The actual process of converting nerve impulses into sight is still a mystery, but many of the chemical changes accompanying it are known. As stated in Chapter 10, the rods are responsible for vision in dim light, and contain the chemical rhodopsin, or visual purple. By extraction of rhodopsin from rod receptors of experimental animals, the molecular make-up of this chemical has been fairly well established. Its molecular weight is over 200,000, and it is composed of a protein combined with **retinene,** a pigment. When rhodopsin is present in the rods, the eyes may be said to show **dark adaptation.**

Rhodopsin is stable in dim light, but when exposed to bright light, it dissociates into protein and retinene. The speed at which this takes place depends upon the brightness of the light and the length of time the rhodopsin is exposed. The resulting protein and retinene is called **visual yellow.** At this point dark adaptation is lost. If the light intensity is

then decreased, the two products recombine and after a short period dark adaptation returns. However, if the bright light continues, there is further breakdown into a protein and vitamin A. This protein is called **visual white** and is apparently insensitive to light. The vitamin A is absorbed by the blood. If at this point the light intensity diminishes, a slower return of dark adaptation occurs as rhodopsin is reformed. Vitamin A from the blood supply to the retina is responsible for this return. (See Fig. 11-4.)

Intense light bleaches rhodopsin very rapidly. Thus, bright light may dazzle the eye and cause pain, but fortunately this pain does not last long. If you have driven an automobile at night, you have had such a reaction to an oncoming car with its headlights on high beam. During the time it takes your eyes to readjust to dark adaptation, your level of visual sensitivity is below normal. It should

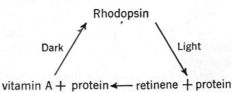

Fig. 11-4. *This diagram summarizes the chemical changes in visual purple on exposure to light and dark conditions.*

be easily understood why this might prove to be a very dangerous situation, especially if you were traveling at high speed. Many states have passed laws which require you to change from high beam to low beam when approaching another car at night. It certainly is the sensible thing to do.

As was mentioned earlier, vitamin A is required in the formation of rhodopsin. If the supply of this vitamin is below normal or lacking in one's diet, dark adaptation occurs very slowly. At night, when light intensities are low, an individual lacking sufficient vitamin A would be nearly blind for a considerable time after a bright light had been shone into his eyes. This condition, called **night blindness** or nyctalopia, can usually be corrected by administration of vitamin A at the rate of 25,000 to 50,000 USP units per day.

We have referred to dark adaptation or **scotopic vision** as that adjustment the eye makes to a low intensity of illumination. Adjustment is made by the reformation of visual purple. In order to allow the maximum available light to enter the eye, the pupil enlarges, or dilates. Vision at night has less detail, and little or no color, depending upon the movement of objects seen. If movement is lacking, objects are seen as large masses with no clear outline.

Light adaptation or **photopic vision** occurs when the eyes are exposed to continued bright illumination such as daylight. Under these conditions, the second type of receptor cell in the retina is used —the cones. When the eyes are light adapted, they see objects in fine detail and in color.

What is the source of light that produces a rainbow? It is sunlight, which is classified as **white light.** If you hold a triangular glass **prism** in the sunlight, you will see a similar arrangement of

colors (spectrum) on a nearby surface (Fig. 11-5). White light is a combination of all the wave lengths of the spectrum, and therefore black must be the absence of these wave lengths. The reason for this spectral effect is refraction. In passing through the prism, the various wave lengths of light are bent unequally and thus separated. The rays of the sun striking droplets of water in the air are refracted and then reflected to produce a rainbow.

It has been stated before (page 122) that the wave lengths responsible for our visual spectrum are from 3900 Å to 7600 Å. From the spectrum shown in Fig. 11-6, it can be seen that any color is actually a name for light of a certain wave length. For example: the label "red" is given to the sensation stimulated by the wave length of about 7000 Å. The other colors range through orange, yellow, green, blue, indigo, and violet—the last with a wave length of 4000 Å. From this list, one should note that the colors in the red end of the spectrum have the longest visible wave length, while those with the shortest wave length fall in the violet end of the spectrum.

Those wave lengths just shorter than our visual spectrum are called **ultraviolet** rays. True ultraviolet rays cannot be seen by the normal human eye, but their presence can be detected when they shine on certain chemicals or rocks that have fluorescent qualities. Exposed

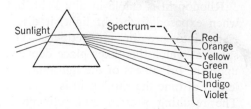

Fig. 11-5. *A prism separates white light into the colors of the spectrum.*

to such rays, the chemical or rock appears to glow or emit its own light.

Wave lengths longer than those within our visual range are felt as heat and are called **infrared.** Photographic film that is infrared-sensitive will take pictures in total darkness. The image on the film results from differences in the amount of heat given off, or reflected, by different parts of the photographed object.

As we know, white light is the combination of all the wave lengths of the visual spectrum. However, it is a fact that if but three of these wave lengths of light are superimposed upon a light

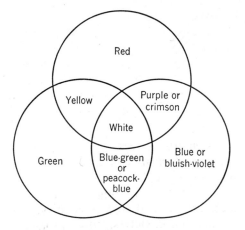

Fig. 11-7. *When the colors of light are superimposed, we get various intermediate colors. The three primary colors of light produce white light when they are superimposed.*

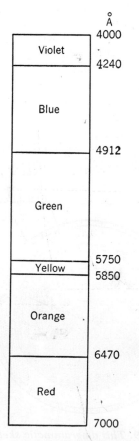

Fig. 11-6. *A graph of the visible spectrum of white light. The distribution of the wave lengths is scaled in Ångstrom units.*

surface, the result is white (Fig. 11-7). The colors used are red, green, and blue-violet. The actual wave lengths of these three colors have been assigned by an international standard: 7000 Å for red; 5460 Å for green; and 4358 Å for blue-violet. We call these three the **primary colors of vision,** or **simple colors.** To this list is often added yellow—5800 Å —since it is very difficult to produce this as a pure color from the combination of any of the above primary colors of light. All of the other colors represent certain combinations of these primary colors and are thus called **compound colors.** The primary colors of *vision* should not be confused with the primary colors of *pigments.* Primary pigment colors are red, blue, and yellow. From these three, nearly all colors can be produced except white and black.

Pigments, that is, the colors we see in objects around us, are dependent on the ability of the surfaces to reflect the various wave lengths of white light. If a surface reflects wave lengths of all colors, it appears white. If it absorbs all of the

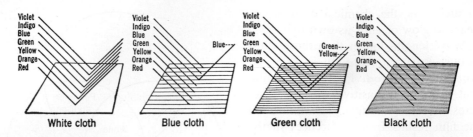

Fig. 11-8. *We see colored objects by the colors that they reflect to our eyes. Other colors of the spectrum are absorbed.*

wave lengths and thus reflects none, it appears black. Between these extremes, a surface may absorb some wave lengths, and reflect one or more of them (Fig. 11-8). The waves that are reflected stimulate the cones of the retina and we say the surface is red, blue, green, etc.

Many theories have been proposed to explain color vision. None of these theories has received complete acceptance, however, since in all certain visual activities remain unexplained. One of the oldest but most widely accepted theories was proposed by Young and Helmholtz early in the nineteenth century. According to the theory, there is a corresponding type of receptor in the retina for each of the three primary colors of light. The three kinds of cone receptors contain different photochemical substances, each chemical sensitive to one of the three primary wave lengths of color.

Impulses are initiated by the decomposition of each photochemical substance within its particular cones. These impulses are transmitted to the occipital lobe of the cerebral cortex by the optic nerves. In the cortex they are recorded as the three sensations: red, green, and blue-violet. It is assumed that there are specific locations in the visual center of the brain for the three primary colors, although there is no experimental evidence of this at present.

To explain the various other color sensations, the theory assumes that if all of the receptors are stimulated at the same time, a visual sensation of white is obtained. Other colors represent varying stimulation of two or more photochemical substances.

It is possible to determine the zones of primary color sensitivity on the surface of the retina by a fairly simple method. A person looks with one eye at a fixed point. Disks of each of the three primary colors are then slowly moved, one at a time, in a circle around his head. He reports when a disk loses color but is still visible as an object. By mak-

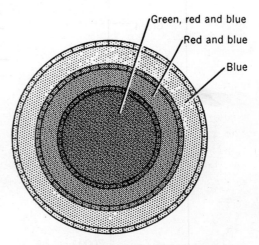

Fig. 11-9. *This diagrammatic sketch shows the comparative areas of the retina that are sensitive to the three primary colors of light.*

ing measurements of his field of view for the three primary colors, it is possible to map his color receptors on the retina. Such a map is shown diagrammatically in Fig. 11-9. The zones of color sensitivity may be thought of as irregular disks superimposed. In the largest area we find cones receptive to blue wave lengths of light. In the area marked red, we find cones sensitive to this wave length as well as cones sensitive to blue. In the area recorded as green, we find an additional type of cone, as well as the other two. Beyond these three zones, there is an area composed predominantly of rod receptors, which will record the various intensities of white. The final peripheral area of the retina is insensitive to any intense light.

It should be noted at this point that as the intensity of white light gradually decreases, for example at dusk, there is a shift from cone reception to rod reception. This shift from photopic vision (cone vision) to scotopic vision (rod vision) is called the **Purkinje shift**. It also occurs when light increases, as at dawn, but in the opposite direction—from rod vision to cone or color vision.

Afterimages. Whenever we see a motion picture, we are actually seeing a series of still pictures flashed on a screen at a minimum rate of 16 pictures, or frames, per second. Because of an afterimage, we are conscious of a single picture in which the objects appear to move. The activity in the photochemical substance within the receptors cannot keep pace with changes in visual stimuli and thus there is a carry-over of visual impressions. If this carry-over is exactly the same as the original stimulus pattern, we say that it is a **positive afterimage**. When you glance at a very bright object, such as an electric light, and then close your eyelids, you are conscious of the same visual image even though the

external stimulus has stopped. If, however, you stare at a colored object for a few minutes and then close your eyes or look at a blank wall of a neutral color, you are conscious of the image, but in the complementary color. Thus, a white figure on a dark background will appear as black on a very light background. A red image will appear to be green, since green is the complementary color of red. This **negative afterimage** is probably due to the fatigue of the originally stimulated receptors.

Characteristics of color vision. There are three qualities of color vision: *hue, saturation,* and *brightness.* **Hue** refers to the sensory response made by the eye to various wave lengths. If the eye is stimulated by light of a wave length of from 6750 Å to 7000 Å, we say that we are looking at red. If light of a wave length of from 5000 Å to 5500 Å enters the eye, we say we are looking at green, and so on. As each black and white key on a piano represents a different note on a musical scale, each wave length within the visible spectrum represents a different hue.

A hue of one single wave length is said to have complete **saturation**. Such a color is seldom encountered in nature, although it can be produced under controlled conditions in a laboratory. The light reflected from the objects around us contains varying amounts of white light. As a pure color is mixed with white light, it becomes less saturated and appears pale, or pastel. Thus pink is a red color of low saturation.

Brilliance or **brightness** is a quantitative factor determined by the intensity or energy of the light waves reflected by a surface. In terms of pigments, we say that brilliance depends on the amount of black added to the color. Navy blue is a color of low brilliance. Of course, the appearance of colored objects is affected greatly by the brightness of the light falling on them. Objects that seem brilliantly colored in bright light will appear darker and duller in color under dim illumination.

Color blindness. We have been speaking of color vision as if all individuals respond equally well to these visual stimuli. Actually, 6 to 8 percent of all males and about 0.4 to 0.6 percent of all females have some defect in color vision. In Chapter 33 you will learn about the heredity of certain defects in color vision.

Deficiency in color perception is called **color blindness.** Persons who have this hereditary condition may be classified in two general groups. One group is totally color-blind, apparently having either no active cone receptors or a defect in the visual center of the brain. This results in lack of ability to distinguish the various wave lengths of light responsible for color vision. Individuals in this group are called **monochromats**—they see objects only in terms of white, gray, and black. A second group, the **dichromats,** may be red-green or blue-yellow color-blind, the latter type being rather rare. In this second group, the defect may be due either to a weakness in the receptors sensitive to red, green, or yellow; or to some neurological change in the complementary relationship of the red-green receptors.

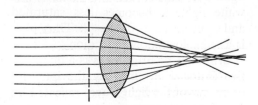

Fig. 11-10. *Spherical aberration of a lens. The vertical dotted line illustrates how the iris cuts off the peripheral rays to reduce the aberration. The diaphragm of a camera serves a similar purpose.*

Individuals are called **trichromats** if they are receptive to all three primaries: red, green, and blue-violet. This is normal color vision. There may be slight deficiency in determining closely related wave lengths of light, but this defect is negligible and certainly causes little hardship.

Visual acuity. Not only are the cones responsible for color vision, but as was mentioned earlier they are concerned with acuteness of vision. **Visual acuity** is the sharpness with which detail is seen. It is often measured in terms of the smallest distance that can be seen between two vertical black lines on a white background.

Many factors influence visual acuity: brightness or intensity of illumination; the size of the objects; the color of the objects; and the retinal area on which the image of the object falls. Certainly if the image falls outside of the fovea centralis, visual acuity is greatly reduced.

Doctors use a simplified visual acuity test when they ask you to read the letters on an eye chart. The **Snellen Eye Chart** contains series of letters, each series having a different standard size. If you can read at twenty feet the line of letters the average person can read at twenty feet, you vision is measured as 20/20 and is normal. However, if your visual acuity is poor, you may only be able to see at twenty feet what the average person can see at 100 feet. Your vision is then said to be 20/100. Many young people have better than 20/20 vision.

Visual defects. We can classify abnormalities of vision into two general groups: (1) defects characteristic of all convex lenses; (2) structural defects of the organs within the eye or of the eyeball itself.

1. Characteristics of all convex lenses. In all convex lenses, rays of parallel light that pass through the outer edge of the lens are refracted more than the rays passing through the center of the lens. This is called **spherical aberration.** It results in a series of focal points rather than the single focal point which is required for acute vision (Fig. 11-10). If the aberration is uncorrected, the central visual field may be in focus, while the perimeter of the image is fuzzy or out of focus.

We correct for spherical aberration automatically by shutting out the rays at the edge of the crystalline lens. This is accomplished by decreasing the size of the pupil, thus allowing only those rays of light in the center of the lens to pass through.

Usually an oculist puts drops into your eyes during an examination in order to dilate the pupils. If the eye is then exposed to intense illumination the effects of spherical aberration are easily noted. The dazzling brilliance is almost painful and visual acuity is low due to the diffusion of focus.

A distortion very similar to spherical abberation occurs because white light rays passing through a convex lens break up into their individual wave lengths. This is called **chromatic aberration.** When the spectral waves of white light pass through a convex lens, the short wave lengths (violet) are refracted or bent more than the long wave lengths (red). In between these extremes, there is a progressive distribution of colors,

Fig. 11-12. *This type of diagram is used to test the eyes for astigmatism.*

like a rainbow. As a result, a halo effect of colors is seen surrounding each image (Fig. 11-11).

To correct this, the sphincter muscles of the iris contract and the pupil is constricted. This shuts out rays that pass through the perimeter of the lens where the greatest amount of aberration occurs. Once again we have sharp color vision without distortion.

2. Defects in eye structure. In scientific instruments, like the microscope or telescope, all of the optic surfaces must be perfectly ground and polished. All of the light waves, either passing through or reflecting from these optics, must reach their predetermined focal point without distortion.

As you know, the optical parts of the human eye (the cornea and the lens) are composed of specialized living cells. A slight irregularity may be the cause of distortion of the cornea or lens. This results in a common eye defect, called **astigmatism.** In this condition, light waves passing through the cornea (or lens) are not all refracted to a single point. There is a distorted image on the retina. Uneven curvature of the anterior surface of the cornea is most common. If the distortion is great enough, eye

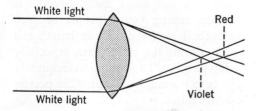

Fig. 11-11. *Chromatic aberration of a lens. Compare this with Fig. 11-5. Why does the lens act like a prism?*

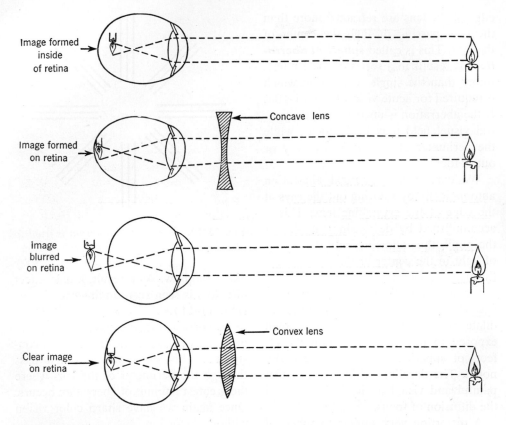

Fig. 11-13. *This series of diagrams shows how lenses can be used to compensate for myopia (above) and hyperopia (below).*

strain and frequent headaches may result.

The eye specialist may use numerous devices to determine astigmatism. One such device is an **astigmatic dial** as seen in Fig. 11-12. It consists of radiating lines or spokes which all have the same width and darkness. A person with astigmatism will see some of these lines more clearly than others, because they are brought to a sharper focus on the retina. Astigmatism can be overcome by the use of eyeglasses with lenses ground to correct for any defects in curvature on the cornea or lens.

A less common eye defect than astigmatism is *myopia.* In myopia (nearsightedness), the eyeball is too long from front to back. Parallel light waves come to a focus in front of the retina and *distant vision* is blurred or out of focus. Rays of light which diverge from *near* objects, with the aid of accommodation, are focused on the retina. Thus a person may be able to read a printed page with little difficulty, but will be unable to read a stop sign one block away. Myopia is common among young people because the eyeball may increase in length too rapidly during the early years, especially during puberty. The condition frequently adjusts to normal by the time the person becomes adult.

To correct myopia, a concave lens which will diverge parallel waves of light is placed in front of the eye. This pushes

about acetate

the focal point back to the retina and results in a clear sharp image of distant objects. Correction for myopia is shown diagrammatically in Fig. 11-13.

If the length of the eyeball is too short, a person can see clearly at a distance but is not able to form a clear image of nearby objects because the image falls behind the retina. In this condition, called **hyperopia** (farsightedness), the lens cannot accommodate enough to produce a sharp image of a nearby object on the retina. However, images of distant objects are focused easily by slight accommodation of the lens.

We correct for hyperopia by the use of eyeglasses having convex lenses which aid the lenses of the eyes in bringing the images of nearby objects to a sharp focus (Fig.11-13).

Nearly all muscles gradually lose some of their contractive power as they age.

This is also true of the ciliary muscles in the eyes. In addition, the crystalline lens loses some of its elasticity with age and is no longer able to assume the maximum convexity necessary for near vision. After about the age of 45 years, there is a decline in the accommodation that can occur in each eye. This condition is called **presbyopia.** An individual finds as he gets older that he must hold reading materials farther and farther from his eyes in order to have acute vision. From this time on, eyeglasses with convex lenses are necessary for reading without discomfort.

A person with myopia may find the onset of presbyopia no disadvantage, and he may never need corrective lenses for reading. Nearly all elderly individuals who can still read easily without glasses show histories of myopia in their younger years.

SPEAKING OF Physiology

Briefly identify each of the following:

Ångstrom unit	optical illusion	prism
chromatic aberration	parallax	scotopic vision
field of vision	photopic vision	spectrum
optic chiasma	presbyopia	stereoscopic vision

Test YOUR KNOWLEDGE

1. Discuss the importance of peripheral vision. How detailed is the visual image in peripheral vision?
2. How does the brain interpret a single image with binocular vision? How is this related to the central visual pathway?
3. By what clues do we judge the distance an object is from us? How is this related to the judgment of size?
4. Discuss the photochemistry of the rod receptors. How does this compare with that of the cones?
5. What is night blindness and how is it related to diet?
6. Describe the visual spectrum and its relationship to color vision. What is the relation of the infrared and ultraviolet waves to the visible color spectrum? How are these waves useful to us?
7. List the primary colors of vision. What experiment could you perform to show that white light is a combination of these primary colors?

8. Discuss the Young-Helmholtz theory of color vision.
9. What is the Purkinje shift?
10. What are the two types of afterimages? What practical application is there for an afterimage?
11. Briefly summarize the three characteristics of color vision.
12. List the various forms of color blindness, noting the colors involved.
13. How do doctors measure the degree of myopia and hyperopia?
14. What is spherical aberration and how does the eye correct for this physical defect?
15. Astigmatism is probably the commonest of all eye defects. What causes astigmatism and how can this condition be corrected?

See FOR YOURSELF

1. Determine the number of students in your class that are color blind. How does the percentage of color-blind individuals in your class compare with national ratings? Test the students for visual acuity. How many have 20/20 vision? How many are better than average? How many need glasses to correct for myopia and are not at present wearing them?

2. Make a report on the various theories of color vision. What are your conclusions?

3. Determine the extent of the peripheral vision of several members of your class, using the method outlined on page 126 of this book.

4. Set up a simple experiment to demonstrate the difference in what you can see using binocular and monocular vision.

5. Demonstrate some optical illusions other than those found in this book.

6. Demonstrate spherical and chromatic aberrations, using ordinary glass lenses. Show how the use of a diaphragm in front of the lens will partially correct these aberrations.

7. Using Snellen Eye Charts, prepare a table showing the visual acuity of several members of your class.

CHAPTER 12

The Structure and Physiology of the Ear

Next to visual perception, hearing is probably our most important special sense. Through sound we have a marvelous means of communication. As children we learn to speak when we hear others speak. Later we construct complicated electrical and electronic devices to span great distances and reproduce sound. Even the micro-voice of satellites and radiations from distant stars can be converted to sounds. Sound enables us to judge the distance of objects and to locate them, even in the dark. We respond emotionally to various sounds: we receive pleasure from music, we are annoyed by a creaking hinge, and we may become frightened by unidentified sounds at night or by unexpected loud noises.

The human ear is responsible for converting sound waves into nerve impulses which result in our sense of hearing. This remarkable auditory structure is divided into the *external ear,* the *middle ear,* and the *inner ear.* Let us now consider the anatomical make-up of each of these three portions and determine the role each plays in the mechanism of hearing. (Note: as you read this chapter, refer to the Trans-Vision of the ear following page 120.)

The external ear. As the name implies, part of the external ear extends beyond the lateral surface of the head. This is the **auricle,** or **pinna.** The pinna has a cartilaginous frame which is covered by skin. It is irregular in shape with several ridges and depressions serving to direct sound waves into the external canal opening. Even though the pinna aids in directing sound waves into the ear, it is not essential to hearing. Below the area of cartilage there is a flap of skin filled with areolar and adipose connective tissue. This part of the auricle is called the **ear lobe** or **lobule,** which may hang free or be attached along the medial edge.

The second part of the external ear is the auditory canal or **external acoustic meatus.** The auditory canal extends about one inch into the temporal bone. The canal, which is open at the auricle to allow sound waves to enter, is closed at the inner end where it meets the middle ear by the **tympanic membrane,** or **ear drum.** This membrane is not clearly visible without special instruments, since the canal is not straight but has an open S-shape.

The meatus is lined with a thin section of skin which adheres to the cartilage

139

and bony framework, and covers the outer surface of the tympanic membrane. Just beneath the skin, in the outer portion of the canal, are numerous wax-producing (**ceruminous**) glands. This wax (**cerumen**) is very sticky. In addition to these glands, we find a few short hairs which point outward. Both the hairs and cerumen help to prevent foreign particles from entering the meatus.

The tympanic membrane, which separates the external ear and the middle ear, is oval in outline and slightly depressed in the center (Fig. 12-1). It measures between 8 and 10 millimeters in diameter and lies at an angle of about 55 degrees to the longitudinal axis of the canal, the lower edge slanting inward.

The middle ear. The second division of the auditory apparatus is the middle ear or **tympanic cavity.** This small air-filled cavity is housed within the spongy portion of the temporal bone near the mastoid process. The bony walls of the tympanic cavity are lined with a mucous membrane similar to that of the nasal cavity. This membrane also covers the inner surface of the ear drum. Between the ear drum and the inner wall of the middle ear we find a chain of three small but exceedingly important bones, the **ossicles** (Fig. 12-1).

Sound waves striking the ear drum are passed along to the inner ear by means of the ossicles, which form a system of levers. The vibrations set up by the sound waves are strengthened as they pass from one to another of the three bones. Thus the vibration of the ear drum is increased tenfold by the time it reaches the inner wall of the middle ear.

The first bone responsible for transmitting the physical vibration of the tympanic membrane is the **malleus** or **hammer.** The handle of this mallet-shaped bone is attached to the inner sur-

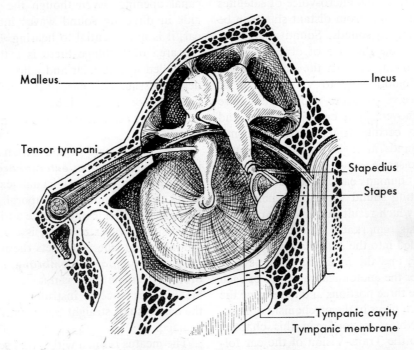

Malleus — Incus

Tensor tympani — Stapedius — Stapes

Tympanic cavity — Tympanic membrane

Fig. 12-1. *Ossicles of the ear showing their relation to the eardrum and other structures within the middle ear cavity.*

face of the ear drum so that the tip of the handle ends at the apex of the membrane. The head portion fits into a shallow socket at the base of the second or middle bone of the three—the **incus,** or **anvil.** There is little individual movement between these two bones because ligaments bind them rather firmly together as a single unit. The long process of the incus comes in contact with the head of the **stapes,** or **stirrup,** the third bone of the three. This articulation is freely movable and results in a rocking action of the stirrup. The base of the stirrup oscillates against the membrane covering an opening, the *oval window,* in the inner wall of the middle ear. It is interesting to note that at birth the ossicles have already reached their adult size and from this time on do not change.

Two small striated muscles are responsible for controlling the extent of movement of the ossicles. Attached at one end to the handle of the malleus near the head and at the other end to the floor of the tympanic cavity, is found the **tensor tympani** muscle. When this muscle contracts, the handle of the malleus is pulled inward, producing a greater tension of the ear drum. (As you remember, the handle of the malleus is firmly attached to the tympanic membrane.) The second muscle is the **stapedius** muscle. It arises near the roof of the cavity and inserts on the posterior surface of the neck of the stirrup. It opposes the tensor tympani muscle.

We said earlier that the middle ear is an air-filled cavity. The tympanic membrane lies between this cavity and the outer air. Equal pressure must be maintained on both sides of the membrane or it will bulge inward or outward. Under such tension, the membrane does not vibrate normally and hearing is impaired. The middle ear communicates with the outer air through the **Eusta-**

chian tube, which extends between the middle ear and the nasopharynx. (See the Trans-Vision following page 120). This tube is about 1½ inches in length and, at the narrowest point, about ⅛ inch in diameter. The pharyngeal opening is oval with the inner edges normally touching. When we swallow or yawn, muscles pull the edges apart and air is allowed to enter or leave the middle ear, depending upon external air pressure. If the entrance to the Eustachian tube is inflamed or congested, as a result of a cold or a sore throat, the edges may not open. Inequalities of pressure are not adjusted and the ear drum cannot move freely. Slight temporary deafness results.

The Eustachian tube is lined with the same type of mucous membrane that is found in the middle ear and in the nasal cavity. Infections in the throat often progress up through the Eustachian tube to the mucous lining of the middle ear. Such infection may then invade the mastoid bone (a portion of the temporal bone) and thus cause mastoiditis. In the past, this condition often required surgical treatment. Today antibiotics are used to control the infection.

The inner ear. Within the inner ear, the third and most important part of the auditory apparatus, we find the receptors that initiate nerve impulses which are interpreted by the brain as sound. The inner ear is divided into three series of fluid-filled tubes or canals, collectively called the **bony labyrinth** (from a Greek word meaning "maze"). The three parts of the labyrinth are the **vestibule,** the **cochlea,** and the **semicircular canals** (Fig. 12-2).

Within the bony labyrinth is a tubular membrane which follows the same shape as the bony canal. This has been called the **membranous labyrinth.** It does not adhere to the bony wall, but is

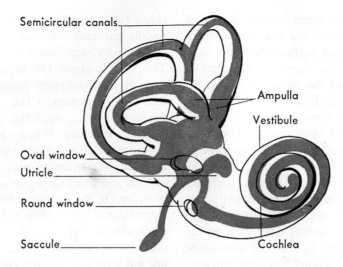

Semicircular canals

Ampulla

Vestibule

Oval window

Utricle

Round window

Saccule

Cochlea

Fig. 12-2. *Structure of the inner ear.*

separated from it by a fluid called the **perilymph.** Within the tubular membranous labyrinth we find a second fluid, the **endolymph.**

The vestibule is connected to the middle ear by the oval window. It acts as an entrance to the other two divisions of the inner ear: the semicircular canals, which are concerned with equilibrium (balance), and the cochlea, in which the sound receptors are found.

The cochlea resembles a snail's shell with its spiral canal making between 2½ and 2¾ turns around a central pillar— the **modiolus.** Within this pillar we find a branch of the auditory nerve (eighth cranial nerve) that is called the **cochlear nerve,** concerned with conducting sensory impulses to the brain for our sense of hearing. Projecting from the central pillar is a small shelf of bone called the **spiral lamina,** which is continuous within the spiral canal and partially divides it in two. Attached to the outer border of the spiral lamina is a thin membrane—the **basilar membrane**— which stretches across to the cochleal wall and completely separates the canal into two passages, except at the apex.

The upper passage is the **scala vestibuli,** and the passage below the lamina and attached basilar membrane is the **scala tympani** (Fig. 12-3). The oval window in the wall between the middle and inner ear communicates with the scala vestibuli. Below the oval window is the *round window,* the membrane-covered opening of the scala tympani.

From the upper edge of the osseous lamina across to the outer edge of the canal above the basilar membrane, extends an extremely thin membrane—the **vestibular membrane,** or the **mèmbrane of Reissner.** This membrane divides the scala vestibuli unequally, forming a small triangular canal, the **scala media.** No direct function has been connected with the vestibular membrane and the resulting scala media (Fig. 12-3).

The sense receptors for sound are found within the **organ of Corti,** which is located on the upper surface of the basilar membrane in the scala media and just lateral to the osseous spiral lamina. The cells of the organ of Corti include a series of columnar epithelial cells out of which small hairlike endings protrude (Fig. 12-3). These *hair cells* lie in two

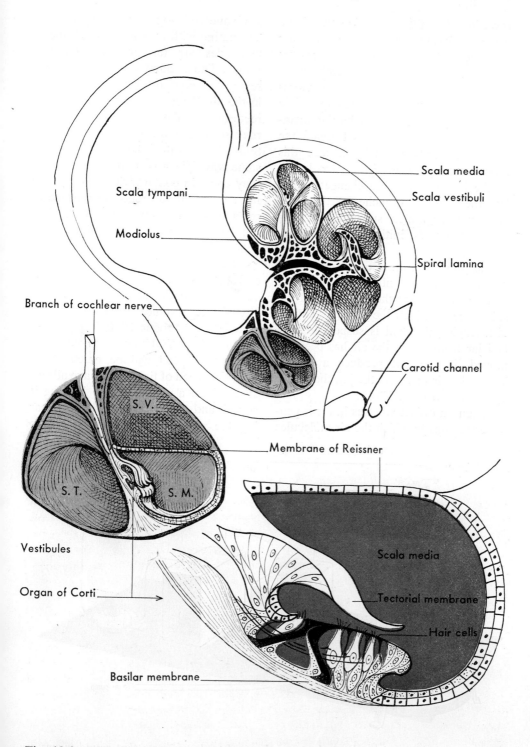

Fig. 12-3. *Diagrams showing successive enlargements of a vertical section through the cochlea.*

rows running the entire length of the canal. Covering these cells is a canopy attached to the lamina which arches over the hair-cell endings; this membrane is called the **tectorial membrane.** As vibrations pass through the noncompressible fluids of the cochlea, the basilar membrane and attached tectorial membrane also vibrate. It is believed that this movement causes changes in the length of the hair cells. These changes stimulate the terminal branches of the auditory neurons which surround the epithelial hair cells, initiating the auditory impulses.

The physical nature of sound. Sound can be produced only when an object vibrates, disturbing the molecules of the substance in which the object is found. If a ringing doorbell is suspended in a bell jar from which the air has been removed, it will not produce a sound. When the air re-enters the jar, the sound can be heard (Fig. 12-4).

When an object vibrates in air it produces regions in which the air molecules are squeezed together (*compressions*) alternating with regions in which the air molecules are farther apart (*rarefactions*). Thus, sound waves are alternate regions of compression and rarefaction in the air. They move outward in all directions like the waves produced by a rock thrown into a quiet pool of water. Sound waves may be reflected in the same way light waves are reflected when they come in contact with a nonabsorbing surface. If the reflecting surface directs the sound waves directly back to the source, we hear the sound as an **echo.**

The speed at which these sound waves travel through various substances will vary according to the elasticity and density of the substance. In air at sea level, sound travels about 1090 feet per second, or about 760 miles per hour. In all cases, the speed will be much slower than the speed of light. You have all seen steam from a whistle before hearing its sound, and smoke of a gun before hearing the report, or the distant flash of

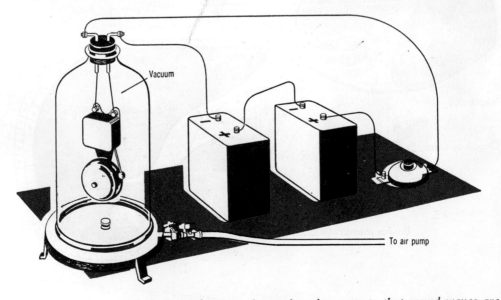

Fig. 12-4. *The apparatus shown here can be used to demonstrate that sound waves are carried by the air.*

lightning before hearing the thunder. The table below illustrates the speed of sound in various substances at 32° F:

Medium	Approximate Speed
Air	1,088 ft/sec
Water	4,750 ft/sec
Wood (oak or maple)	13,125 ft/sec
Iron	16,700 ft/sec
Glass	18,500 ft/sec
Marble	19,500 ft/sec

If we convert compressions and rarefactions into a line graph, as seen on an oscilloscope, we see certain auditory characteristics. The line moves up during the compression phase and downward during the rarefaction phase (Fig. 12-5). The distance it moves up or down is called the amplitude and provides us with the characteristic of **loudness** or **volume.** The higher the curve, the louder the sound.

In determining loudness, we use a comparative scale with the starting point at the threshold of audible sound. The units in the scale are called **bels,** named after the great experimentalist, Alexander Graham Bell (1847–1922). The term **decibel** represents 1/10 of a bel, since the decibel seems to be the smallest unit variance the human ear can distinguish. The following chart indicates the various levels of sound as expressed in decibels:

Type of Sound	Sound Level in Decibels
Threshold of hearing	0
Ordinary breathing	10
Whispering	15–20
Average suburban home	30–40
Automobile	40–50
Conversation	60
Average TV sound system	70
Heavy street traffic	70–80
Elevated trains	90–100
Thunder	110
Threshold of pain	120

The length between one complete compression curve plus the rarefaction curve and the next compression curve gives us the **cycle** of the sound. We call this **pitch,** or **frequency,** usually written as the number of cycles per second or **cps.** As the number of cycles increases, the pitch or frequency becomes higher. When you strike the keys of a piano

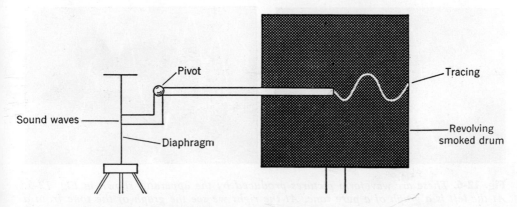

Fig. 12-5. *Apparatus used to produce a graphic record of sound waves. (After Wenger, Jones, and Jones,* Physiological Psychology, *Holt, 1956)*

(moving to the right on the keyboard), each succeeding string vibrates at a faster rate than those before, and thus each note is higher in pitch. As the eye has limits in perceiving light waves (we do not visually respond to ultraviolet nor infrared), so the human ear has two thresholds of pitch. Our ears are unable to respond to sound waves fewer than 16 cycles per second—our low threshold— nor can most people detect sounds of above 15,000 to 20,000 cps—our high threshold. The human ear has its greatest sensitivity between 2000 and 4000 cps.

If several different musical instruments all play the same pitch, it is quite easy to distinguish one type of instrument from another. Most of us can tell the difference in sound between a piano, a clarinet, a trumpet, and a violin. That which gives these instruments their characteristic sound is the *quality* of tone. In describing sound, we may say that a cello is "rich," a trumpet is "harsh," a celesta has a "tinkling" sound, and a bass drum "booms." All of these adjectives are attempts to describe the quality or timbre of the instrument. Graphically, **quality** or **timbre** is represented by the smoothness of the sound wave as seen

in Fig. 12-6. If the line produced is a simple sine wave, or curve, the tone is classified as a **pure tone.** Pure tones can be mechanically produced but they are never found in a musical instrument or in the human voice. If the sound wave produces a curve that contains many smaller deviations, the tone is composed of a number of tones sounding together. We call these overtones or harmonics. If these overtones are produced in a consistent pattern, we usually find the sound pleasing. If, however, the overtones are spasmodic and irregular, we usually classify the sound as a noise. The form of the sound wave determines the quality of the sound.

The physiology of hearing. What happens after sound waves enter the external acoustic meatus and set the tympanic membrane and the chain of middle ear bones in motion? It has already been explained that the base of the stirrup rocks back and forth in the oval window, which is separated from the fluid in the inner ear by a thin membrane. When any part of a confined liquid is subjected to pressure, the pressure is distributed equally throughout the liquid. So, when the base of the stirrup is forced inward, pressure is directed into the scala ves-

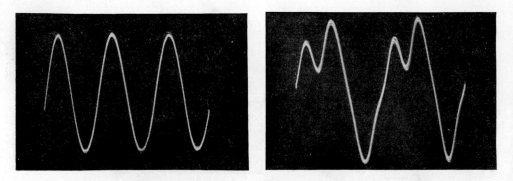

Fig. 12-6. *These are waveform pictures produced by the apparatus shown in Fig. 12-5. At the left is a graph of a pure tone. At the right we see the graph of the tone from a French horn, showing the effect of an overtone (harmonic) on a pure tone. (Hugh Lineback)*

tibuli and the smaller scala media. The fluid exerts a wavelike pressure on certain parts of the yielding basilar membrane, which curves downward, in turn exerting a pressure in the fluid-filled scala tympani. Pressure is directed against the membrane covering the round window, which bulges outward. As you remember, the round window is a membrane-covered opening between the middle ear and the inner ear just below the oval window and at the level of the scala tympani. As the stirrup rocks in the opposite direction (outward) in the oval window, this series of movements is reversed.

The basilar membrane vibrates or curves in sympathy with the various characteristics of sound: amplitude, frequency, and quality of the sound waves. The delicate fibrous membrane is narrower at the vestibular end of the membranous labyrinth within the cochlea and becomes progressively wider up to the apex. It is believed that the higher frequencies result in curves of the basilar membrane near the shorter fibers at the bottom of the cochlea. Lower frequencies are associated with the longer fibers near the apex.

The activities just mentioned briefly describe the **Place Theory** of audition. Impulses are initiated when the receptors of the organ of Corti are stimulated at that part of the basilar membrane corresponding to the pitch. It is estimated that by this mechanism we can distinguish over 10,000 different frequencies or tones. To accomplish this remarkable feat, we have an estimated range of from 15,000 to 30,000 hair cells and resulting fibers in the cochlear nerve for each ear. The resulting impulses travel to the auditory cortex of the brain in the temporal lobe, by way of the eighth cranial nerve —the **auditory nerve.** Many of the fibers that make up this nerve cross to the op-

posite temporal lobe from the ear stimulated.

We have seen how visual judgment of distance is made possible through stereoscopic vision. Similarly, the judgment of direction is possible through binaural (two-ear) perception of sound. Sound vibrations reach one ear before they reach the other, except when we are facing the source of the sound. We are best able to determine the source of sound when the sound originates in front or to one side of us. When the sound is above or behind us, judgment is less accurate. The brain is frequently confused by sound reflections, so we often find ourselves facing a blank wall as we turn toward what we believe to be the source of the sound.

Auditory defects. As we have seen, hearing involves two basic activities: the receiving and conduction of sound waves and the nerve function by which impulses are set up and transmitted to the brain.

If any of the structures responsible for either of these activities fail to function normally, partial or total deafness results. Deafness may thus be caused by conduction failure or nerve failure. Partial conduction deafness may be due to an accumulation of wax in the external auditory canal. While this substance can easily be removed by a physician, your own efforts to remove it may only force the cerumen farther in toward the tympanic membrane. The pressure of the cerumen then interferes with normal vibration. A few of the other forms of partial deafness due to structural defects are thickening of the tympanic membrane, perforated tympanic membrane, adhesion of the ossicles, or loss of elasticity in the oval window membrane. Fortunately, nearly all forms of conduction deafness involving the tympanic membrane or the middle ear can be corrected with an electronic hearing aid. This device may either increase amplitude or give direct bone-conduction.

Of more serious nature is deafness due to nerve deterioration. Many people in heavy industry, such as boiler-makers, are subjected to continuous loud sounds. They frequently develop *tonal gaps* or *islands* which are insensitive to certain frequencies, while bordering areas have greater sensitivity. The explanation seems to be that in these individuals there is usually a separation of the organ of Corti from the basilar membrane at some point.

As an individual ages, there is frequently a gradual decrease in sensitivity in the upper frequency range. In the same way that muscles gradually lose their firmness, the narrower end of the basilar membrane gradually loses elasticity where rapid vibratory activity occurs. There is some question as to the usefulness of hearing aids with high-tone deafness.

Total deafness, without hope of recovery, may result from any of the following causes: destruction of the auditory nerve, destruction of any of the parts of the inner ear mechanism, and failure of the cochlea or its connected nerves to develop properly before birth.

The nonauditory labyrinth and the physiology of balance. We have described in some detail the structure and function of the auditory portion of the bony labyrinth. We must now consider those structures responsible for our sense of balance or equilibrium.

If your body is rapidly whirled around, you become dizzy—that is, you find it difficult to stand upright or walk in a straight line. Two different organs are involved in maintaining proper balance. One is a fluid-filled sac that is divided into two parts, the **utricle** and the **saccule.** The other is a combination of three fluid-filled tubes, the **semicircular canals** (Fig. 12-2).

The utricle and saccule lie within the vestibular portion of the bony labyrinth. The utricle is the larger and is connected to the membranous ducts of the semicircular canals by a number of common openings. The floor of the utricle, called the **macula,** contains two types of modified columnar cells. One kind (hair cells) is made up of neurons which have short hairs extending into the endolymphatic fluid. Intermingled with these hair cells are other supporting cells. Surrounding and covering the hairs of the sensory receptors is a layer of gelatinous material in which are suspended many small solid particles of calcium carbonate known as **otoliths** (otolith means *ear-stone*). When the head is tilted, gravity causes these solid particles to come in contact with the hair cells. These send out impulses which normally enable us to determine the position of the head with respect to gravity.

The nerve impulses from the hair cells are carried through a branch of the eighth cranial nerve, called the **vestibular nerve.** They are conveyed to the medulla and then to the cerebellum where efferent responses result in changing the body position by muscular contraction.

Little is actually known about the function of the saccule. It is innervated by two groups of neuro-fibers from the vestibular nerve. As this structure is closely associated with the cochlea, there is some basis for believing that it may be concerned with hearing rather than balance. It probably involves low frequencies of sound or even the sound sensation of one's own voice. We must not rule out the possibility that the saccule may also have minor functions like those of the utricle, since their internal structures are similar.

Three looped tubes, the semicircular canals, are embedded in the temporal bone anterior and superior to the vestibule. They are about 4 millimeters in diameter and vary in length from 12 to 22 millimeters or about ½ to ¾ inches. The semicircular canals are connected to the vestibule at five points. As seen in Fig. 12-2, two of the canals join to form a common canal which connects with the vestibule. The most obvious structural characteristic of the semicircular canals is the fact that the three loops are situated at right angles (90°) to each other in three different planes. Two of these structures, the anterior canal and posterior canal, are vertical and at right angles to each other. They are also situated at 45° angles to the mid-line of the head. The third canal is horizontal and at a right angle to the two vertical canals.

Within the semicircular canals we find a portion of the membranous labyrinth. As is true of the cochlea, this tubular membrane is filled with endolymph and is held in place by connective tissue and the surrounding perilymph. The diameter of the **semicircular ducts,** as these tubular membranes are called, is about one fourth the diameter of the bony canals which surround them. At the junction to the vestibule, the semicircular ducts join the utricle at the five openings mentioned before.

At one end of each canal, where it comes into contact with the vestibule, there is a swelling or bulging called the **ampulla.** In the ampulla, the semicircular ducts contain a crest-shaped group of hair cells called the **crista acoustica.** These cells can detect changes in acceleration and deceleration. Covering these hairs is a gelatinous substance called the **cupula** into which the hairs protrude. When there is a change in horizontal acceleration, as when we move forward, the endolymph within the ducts presses against the gelatinous cupula which in turn causes the hairs to bend in a direction opposite to the direction of motion. This stimulates the hair cells to produce sensory impulses. The branch of the vestibular nerve which innervates these receptor cells leads to the medulla of the brain. Here it forms synapses with other neurons, some of which carry impulses to the motor nerves that control eye movement. Others carry impulses directly to the cerebellum.

Equilibrium is not classified as one of our special senses, as are vision, hearing, taste, etc., since there is no known anatomical connection with the cerebral cortex. Through the vestibular and semicircular activities we respond to rapid rotation by becoming dizzy. This in turn may involve other side effects. If the rotary movement is accompanied by vertical motion, as is the case when we travel on the ocean, in the air, or in an automobile, we may show symptoms of motion sickness.

During and since World War II, many remedies have been developed to ease or prevent the helpless feeling of motion sickness. Since these drugs have no effect on the frequent changes in body position, it is believed that their action depresses impulses in the vestibular nerve. If these impulses are not controlled, there is a resulting confusion of the balance centers in trying to analyze the constantly changing waves of impulses.

Associated with the function of the semicircular canals and the vestibular apparatus in maintaining equilibrium are the kinesthetic and visual senses which provide clues to spatial and structural position. The resulting response to these sensations involves coordinated muscular activity under the control of the cerebellum which keeps the body in a vertical position.

SPEAKING OF Physiology

Briefly identify each of the following:

anomaly	Eustachian tube	perilymph
bel	incus (anvil)	pure tone
binaural	labyrinth	stapedius muscle
cerumen	malleus (hammer)	stapes (stirrup)
decibel	mastoiditis	tensor tympani muscle
endolymph	otoliths	tonal gap

Test YOUR KNOWLEDGE

1. Explain how the external ear aids in hearing.
2. What structure divides the external ear from the middle ear? How is this structure like a kettledrum in an orchestra?
3. What function do the ossicles perform in the process of hearing? What is unique about their development? Is hearing totally lost if the ossicles are permanently damaged? Why?
4. How do changes in pressure affect hearing? How can these changes be controlled?
5. What covered openings exist between the middle ear and the inner ear? What is the function of each?
6. What are the parts of the bony labyrinth? What type of lining do we find in these structures?
7. Explain how the vestibule and semicircular canals differ from the cochlea in the following ways: (*a*) types of sensation, (*b*) nerve branch innervation, (*c*) sensory center, (*d*) type of stimulus.
8. Briefly describe the structure of the cochlea, giving the function of each part.
9. Where are the sense receptors for sound located? What theory seems best to explain the function of this structure? Why is it difficult to prove this theory?
10. What requirements must be fulfilled before sound can be transmitted?
11. What differences are there between loudness, pitch, and quality or timbre of sound waves? Use diagrams to illustrate your answer.
12. Discuss the thresholds of hearing. How do these thresholds vary with a person's age?
13. What two sensations aid us in maintaining our equilibrium? Which structures are responsible for each of these sensations and how do they function?

See FOR YOURSELF

1. What statistical evidence can you find on the prevalence of deafness in the United States? How does conduction deafness compare with nerve deafness in frequency of cases? What age groups show the greatest occurrence of deafness?

2. Get some advertisements for hearing aids. Analyze the claims of these devices and try to draw conclusions as to their reliability. Write a report on your findings.

3. Devise a simple experiment to determine degrees of deafness. Work with other students to test your experimental device, and report your results to the class.

The Digestive System

CHAPTER 13

Foods: Their Composition and Use

CHAPTER 14

Enzymes and Vitamins

CHAPTER 15

Digestion in the Mouth

CHAPTER 16

Digestion in the Stomach

CHAPTER 17

Digestion in the Small Intestine: The Liver and Pancreas

CHAPTER 18

The Large Intestine

Foods: Their Composition and Use

At first thought it appears hardly necessary to define the word *food,* but there is a surprising amount of misinformation about what constitutes a food. Foods have several characteristics which distinguish them from other materials which we take into the body. In the first place, a **food,** or **nutrient,** must be able to *supply energy* to the body. This must be done without injuring the body in any way. Alcohol, for example, will supply energy, but its side effects are frequently not beneficial. The same may be said for any other substance that is taken in excess. A second characteristic of foods is that they can be used to *increase the amount of protoplasm.* This will result in growth, or in maintenance of the body by replacing the protoplasm that is used up in the normal processes of living. A third requirement of food is that it can be stored and used as a *reserve supply* on which the body can draw in times of emergency. Thus a food may serve as a source of immediate energy or may be temporarily stored for future energy and repair requirements.

GROUPS OF FOOD MATERIALS

Several groups of materials enter into the composition of foods: some of these are relatively simple in their chemical make-up, while others are almost unbelievably complex in structure. Each group has its own particular function in nourishing the body, but these functions are sometimes so interwoven that it is extremely difficult to differentiate between the activities of the various food substances. The principal groups of food materials that are essential for life are:

1. Water: The universal solvent
2. Mineral salts: Compounds of metals with other elements or groups of elements. These may or may not contain the element carbon.
3. Organic nutrients: carbohydrates, fats, and proteins
4. Vitamins

No one group of food materials satisfies all of the requirements of a perfect food because each lacks some property that is essential for complete and proper nutrition. Water, the salts, and the vitamins cannot meet all of the requirements; neither can the organic nutrients supply all necessary substances needed by the body. This chapter will deal with the composition of foods and their uses by the body. The vitamins will be discussed in a later chapter.

Water. This simple compound is necessary for all living organisms: without it plants could not manufacture their food, and animals would be unable to exist. Water is the only fluid which can dissolve the materials present in the human body. It is true that some of the raw materials we consume, such as fats, are insoluble in water; but the activities of the digestive system can change them into materials that either dissolve in water or are carried in water as colloidal suspensions (emulsions). A second function of water and the materials dissolved in it is to maintain the osmotic pressure in the cells. Without enough water the cells would lack food and oxygen, and wastes would collect in them. Water is the carrier of materials between the cells and their surroundings. A third use of water is in the regulation of body temperature through evaporation from the surfaces.

Mineral salts. The term mineral salt can be considered a synonym for inorganic salt because it refers to those substances that lack the element carbon, except in the form of carbonates. These substances play an important role in the regulation of cellular functions: each exerts its own osmotic action, and is able to react with or combine with other compounds to form new materials. Thus the component parts of ordinary table salt, sodium chloride, may later appear as constituents of blood, cell proteins, or sweat.

The table on page 154 gives the functions of some of the more important elements that enter into the formation of these salts.

The presence of inorganic salts in foods is determined either by chemical analysis of the ash obtained by burning the food, or by spectroscopic analysis.

The former method is quantitative, while the latter is most often used to detect small traces of elements that cannot easily be measured by chemical analysis.

Organic nutrients. The organic nutrients are so called because they are carbon-containing compounds which serve as the principal source of materials for energy and protoplasm formation. Of the three classes of organic nutrients, the *carbohydrates* are the simplest. They contain only three chemical elements arranged in a constant relation to each other. The molecules of some of the higher carbohydrates may be extremely intricate, but they all show the same basic structure. The *fats* and *oils* (*lipids*) are more complex because their molecules may contain several different elements in addition to the three in the carbohydrates. Also, these elements do not bear the same exact mathematical relationship to each other that we find in the carbohydrates. The *proteins* are the most complex organic compounds. These compounds are formed into protoplasm and give it those particular characteristics which differentiate it from all other known substances. We will now describe some of the characteristics of each of these classes of organic nutrients.

Carbohydrates. Carbohydrates are defined as chemical compounds, composed of carbon, hydrogen, and oxygen, in which the hydrogen and oxygen are present in the ratio of 2 to 1 (as they are in water). This arrangement of the atoms gives the name carbohydrate to these substances: *carbo-,* referring to the element carbon, and *hydrate* from the Greek word for water.

In a very general way, the carbohydrates can be divided into the *sugars* and *starches.* This is a very loose method of classification because it gives no idea of the complexity of these substances. A few sugars are sweet to the taste, but

ELEMENT	BIOLOGICAL EFFECTS	EXCELLENT SOURCES
Calcium	Building of bones and teeth; aids in clotting of blood; regulation of heart, nerve, and muscle activity; enzyme formation; milk production.	Asparagus, beans, cauliflower, cheese, cream, egg yolk, milk.
Chlorine	Regulation of osmotic pressure; enzyme activities; formation of hydrochloric acid in stomach.	Bread, buttermilk, cabbage, cheese, clams, eggs, ham (cured), sauerkraut, table salt.
Cobalt	Normal appetite and growth; prevention of a type of anemia; prevention of muscular atrophy.	Liver, sea foods, sweetbreads.
Copper	Formation of hemoglobin; aids in tissue respiration.	Bran, cocoa, liver, mushrooms, oysters, peas, pecans, shrimp.
Iodine	Formation of thyroxin; regulation of basal metabolism.	Broccoli, fish, iodized table salt, oysters, shrimp.
Iron	Formation of hemoglobin; oxygen transport; tissue respiration.	Almonds, beans, egg yolk, meat, heart, kidney, liver, soybeans, whole wheat.
Magnesium	Muscular activity; enzyme activity; nerve maintenance; bone structure.	Beans, bran, Brussel sprouts, chocolate, corn, peanuts, peas, spinach, prunes.
Phosphorus	Tooth and bone formation; buffer effects in the blood; essential constituent of all cells; muscle contraction.	Beans, cheese, cocoa, eggs, liver, milk, oatmeal, peas, whole wheat.
Potassium	Normal growth; muscle function; maintenance of osmotic pressure; buffer action; regulation of heart beat.	Beans, bran, molasses, olives, parsnips, potatoes, spinach.
Sodium	Regulation of osmotic pressure; buffer action; protection against excessive loss of water.	Beef, bread, cheese, oysters, spinach, table salt, wheat germ.
Sulfur	Formation of proteins	Beans, bran, cheese, cocoa, eggs, fish, lean meat, nuts, peas.
Zinc	Normal growth; tissue respiration.	Beans, cress, lentils, liver, peas, spinach.

many are tasteless or even rather objectionable in flavor. Starches may be of plant or animal origin but differ from each other by the arrangement of the atoms within their molecules. Sugars are generally soluble in water, while starches are insoluble. This generalized division of carbohydrates into sugars and starches does not take into account a large group of carbohydrates which includes such substances as cellulose, the gums, and agar.

Structurally, we can consider a molecule with the general formula of $C_2H_4O_2$ (glycoaldehyde) as a carbohydrate, but it bears no relation to the subject of nutrition because it does not meet any of the requirements of a nutrient. In fact, no carbohydrate containing less than six atoms of carbon can be used in human cellular oxidations. Our body chemistry is of such a nature that our cells can get energy only from the six-carbon sugars (*hexoses*) and from the more complex carbohydrates which can be converted into hexoses.

The simplest carbohydrates that can meet the needs of the body are those having the empirical formula $C_6H_{12}O_6$. An **empirical formula** is one that shows the number of atoms of each element in a molecule of a compound but does not show the arrangement of the atoms within the molecule. A formula that does show the arrangement is of much value to a chemist. It is called a **structural formula**. Examples of such formulas are shown in Fig. 2-5.

The empirical formula $C_6H_{12}O_6$ represents the basic structure of the carbohydrate used in human nutrition. This substance belongs to the group known as **monosaccharides** because it represents a single (mono-) sugar group (-saccharide). The three principal hexoses in our diet which form the basis of our sugar metabolism are **glucose** (grape sugar or dextrose), **fructose** (fruit sugar or levulose), and **galactose**.

The next more complex group of sugars are the **disaccharides.** These are formed by green plants from the hexoses that are the end products of photosynthesis. They consist of two molecules that have been chemically combined with the loss of a molecule of water, thus:

$$C_6H_{12}O_6 + C_6H_{12}O_6 \longrightarrow C_{12}H_{22}O_{11} + H_2O$$

This type of reaction may be imagined as occurring in the sugar cane or sugar beet. The simple sugars, glucose and fructose, are formed in the plants by photosynthesis. Then molecules of each are joined together to form the principal sugar of commerce, **sucrose.** The same process occurs in grains to form **maltose** (grain sugar) or in cows to produce **lactose** (milk sugar). When any of these sugars is present in food, the digestive system breaks them down into hexoses by a process known as hydrolysis, which reverses the chemical process by which they were formed. Hydrolysis makes the individual hexoses available to the body. In the three principal disaccharides, the process of hydrolysis results in the following chemical changes:

$C_{12}H_{22}O_{11} + H_2O \longrightarrow C_6H_{12}O_6 + C_6H_{12}O_6$	
Sucrose	Glucose + Fructose
Maltose	Glucose + Glucose
Lactose	Glucose + Galactose

Plants and animals are able to recombine the hexoses into higher carbohydrates of extremely complex structure. Such substances may be stored, or used in plants, to give added strength. These materials are called **polysaccharides** (poly- meaning many) and are represented by the starches (plant origin), glycogen (animal origin), and other products such as **cellulose, dextrin,** and **inulin.** The molecules of these substances are so complex (starch has almost 1000 hexose groups) that no attempt is made to write an exact chemical formula for them. The polysaccharides are therefore usually shown by the simplified formula $(C_6H_{10}O_5)_n$, the "n" standing for an unknown number. As in the case of the disaccharides, it is necessary to break a polysaccharide molecule down into its component monosaccharide parts before it can be used by the body. In some cases, starch for example, the structure is so complex that this breakdown cannot be accomplished in a single step. The course of the digestion of starch can be followed experimentally, and changes during the process noted. When a suspension of starch is mixed with a dilute solution of iodine, a dark blue suspension forms. If this suspension is mixed with saliva, the blue changes to red. Then the suspension is dissolved to produce a colorless solution. The red colored stage represents the conversion of the starch molecule into a simpler form, **erythrodextrin,** which is still very complex in structure. This then passes into a colorless form, **achrodextrin,** and then into a disaccharide. In the body, this reduction of starch (our principal source of carbohydrate) requires two different enzymes. More will be said about this later.

As we have just said, starch will turn blue in the presence of iodine; glycogen, on the other hand, gives a mahogany-red color with iodine. These are very simple tests, but the identification of the disaccharides is extremely difficult and requires either special apparatus or more complex chemical procedures. Accurate tests for some dissacharides involve their hydrolysis into their individual hexoses and examination of these in a **polariscope.** This instrument makes use of the fact that the hexoses will rotate a beam of polarized light either to the right or to the left. Since this rotating power is known for each hexose, it is possible to identify the disaccharide that each has been derived from. The monosaccharides themselves can only be distinguished from each other by the use of the polariscope, although they all give certain definite reactions with some copper-containing solutions. The two most commonly used tests for the presence of a monosaccharide employ Fehling's solution and Benedict's solution. Both are prepared by mixing a solution of copper sulfate (blue in color) with a strong alkali such as sodium hydroxide. When either is heated with a solution containing a hexose, its blue color changes to yellow, red, or reddish brown depending on the amount of sugar present. These tests are of great importance from a medical standpoint. Glucose, for example, will appear in the urine of a person suffering from diabetes, and its detection there will aid in the diagnosis.

The carbohydrates play several important roles in the body chemistry. In the first place, their oxidation quickly releases a large amount of energy, so it is no wonder that these materials are stored in nearly all of the tissues of the body except the brain. The liver and muscles are the principal storehouses, although the kidneys also contain a sizable quantity. In a well-nourished individual, glycogen may account for approximately 20 percent of the dry weight of the liver. Carbohydrate (as glucose) is carried by the blood to the liver. Here the mitochondria convert glucose into glycogen. In times of need, the glycogen is reconverted into glucose and enters the blood stream to be carried to those regions where it will be used.

Carbohydrates may also be converted into fats and stored in that form. The

Fatty Acid		Occurrence
Butyric acid	$C_4H_8O_2$	Butter
Caproic acid	$C_6H_{12}O_2$	Butter
Lauric acid	$C_8H_{12}O_2$	Spermaceti, coconut oil
Myristic acid	$C_{12}H_{24}O_2$	Butter, coconut oil
Palmitic acid	$C_{16}H_{32}O_2$	Animal and vegetable oils
Oleic acid	$C_{18}H_{34}O_2$	Animal and vegetable fats
Stearic acid	$C_{18}H_{36}O_2$	Animal and vegetable fats
Cerotic acid	$C_{26}H_{52}O_2$	Beeswax, wool fat (lanolin)

farmer who fattens pigs by feeding them corn, which contains a high percentage of starch, is simply applying this fact in a practical manner. Likewise, people who overindulge in carbohydrates may become overweight by storage of fats.

One of the most important functions of carbohydrates is their action as *protein savers*. Proteins, as we will see later, are essential to the processes of growth and repair of tissue. If the diet consists mainly of proteins the cells must oxidize them to provide energy. If carbohydrates are available, however, these will be oxidized rather than the proteins. Proteins produce as much energy per unit of weight as carbohydrates, but oxidation of proteins for energy would be equivalent to burning the lumber in the walls of a room in order to keep the room warm.

Lipids. The term **lipids** is frequently applied to the fats and their chemical relatives. These include the **true fats,** which are solid at ordinary room temperature (20° C.), and the **oils,** which are liquid at that temperature. The lipids also include waxes and other fat-like substances present in many foods. Some lipids contain nitrogen and thus supplement the proteins in their ability to form protoplasm. Because lipids differ chemically among themselves, they are grouped in three subdivisions: (1) the *true fats,* (2) the *phospholipids,* and (3) the *steroids.*

The molecule of a true fat, like the carbohydrate molecule, contains only the elements carbon, hydrogen, and oxygen, but the two molecules are very different in structure. A typical true fat is beef fat (stearin—$C_{57}H_{110}O_6$). This empirical formula does not show the definite relation of the elements to each other. A molecule of a true fat is formed by the reaction of one molecule of **glycerol** (glycerin—$C_3H_5(OH)_3$) with three molecules of a **fatty acid.** In the case of stearin, the fatty acid is stearic acid. When a fat is digested, its molecules are broken down into glycerol and fatty acids. Some of the common fatty acids are given in the table above.

Many of the fats in our diet contain more than one kind of fatty acid. Since these acids all have distinctive flavors, the mixture of acids gives the food its particular flavor or odor. Butter fat, for example, has the following approximate composition:

Butyric acid	3.0%
Caproic acid	1.4%
Caprylic acid	1.8%
Capric acid	1.8%
Lauric acid	6.9%
Myristic acid	22.6%
Palmitic acid	22.6%
Stearic acid	11.4%
Oleic acid	27.4%

The true fats can be subdivided into two groups depending on the amount of hydrogen that is present in the fatty acid molecule. If you examine the formulae of the fatty acids given above, you will notice that all of them except one (oleic acid) have twice as many hydrogen atoms as carbon atoms. Such acids are called **saturated** fatty acids, while those with a smaller number of hydrogen atoms are known as **unsaturated**. It is possible to convert an unsaturated acid into a saturated one by chemical reaction with hydrogen. This is done on a commercial scale in the manufacture of certain shortening compounds used in baking and in butter substitutes. The process is called hydrogenation.

The **phospholipids** are a group of chemically complex substances that contain nitrogen and phosphorus in addition to the carbon, hydrogen, and oxygen present in the molecules of the true fats. The phospholipids are abundant in brain, heart, kidneys, eggs, soy beans, etc. The best known phospholipid is **lecithin**, a normal constituent of cells. Egg yolk is especially rich in it, and a crude preparation of lecithin can be obtained from that source.

The **steroids** are represented by **cholesterol** $(C_{27}H_{45}OH)$, the best known member of the group. It is normally present in the brain and spinal cord, and plays an important role in the formation of bile by the liver. In some individuals the cholesterol in the liver is converted into hard bodies, *gall stones*. These may cause serious difficulty if they obstruct the flow of bile.

Cholesterol has been given considerable publicity because of its role in one of the most common types of cardiovascular (heart and blood vessels) disease. Deposits of cholesterol may form in the *coronary arteries,* which supply the heart muscles with blood. General hardening of the arteries due to cholesterol deposits may also occur. These deposits gradually decrease the internal diameter of the arteries, permitting less blood to flow to the muscles.

It has been recognized for a long time that overweight people are more prone to cardiovascular disease than those who do not eat fat-producing foods to excess. It has also been observed that in countries where the population eats a large amount of fat, as we do in the United States, the number of deaths from cardiovascular disease is greater than in countries where the average diet contains little fat. The body's supply of cholesterol is not gained solely from dietary sources, as it can be synthesized by various body tissues. However, there is a growing feeling that the presence of a large amount of saturated fatty acids in the diet is responsible for the formation of excess cholesterol deposits in the arteries.

In the process of digestion, the lipids are reduced to glycerol and fatty acids. They are then carried to the cells and stored in the form of fat. Most of our digested fat is oxidized to produce energy. Pound for pound, fats produce more than twice as much energy as either carbohydrates or proteins. The body stores fats chiefly in the vacuoles of specialized cells that make up adipose tissue.

A simple test for the presence of fats is to put the food in question on a piece of paper. If fat is present, the food will leave a greasy spot on the paper. You see an example of this test when you carry doughnuts in a paper bag. Chemical tests for fats are rather complex. First the fats are dissolved from the food by solvents such as ether, chloroform, acetone, or benzine. This is necessary because fats are not soluble in water. Then chemical tests are used to identify the specific fatty acids present.

Proteins. The **proteins**, as has been said, are among the most chemically complex of all of the organic compounds. The molecules of some of these substances are the largest known and have an extremely high molecular weight. Hemoglobin from the blood has a molecular weight of 66,700. (The molecular weight of water, by comparison, is 18.) Actin and myosin have respective molecular weights of approximately 80,000 and 850,000. Other proteins have lower or higher molecular weights, depending on the sizes of their molecules.

In the same way that carbohydrates and fats are made up of simpler compounds, so the proteins are composed of smaller chemical units that are relatively simple. These are the amino acids, of which some 25 have been identified. They all contain carbon, hydrogen, oxygen, and nitrogen: the nitrogen and the hydrogen appearing in the form of NH_2 (the amino group) in the majority of the acids. A few contain sulfur in addition.

The amino acids are not acids in the generally accepted sense of the term; they are more properly called amphoteric or amphiprotic compounds because they have properties which may be either acidic or basic. Thus under one set of conditions they will give a slightly acid reaction, while under another they are slightly alkaline. The reason for this is that each amino acid contains both the NH_2 and the COOH radicals. The amino group has a basic (alkaline) reaction while the COOH (carboxyl group) is acidic.

The kinds of amino acids present in a protein determine its effectiveness and its ability to meet certain requirements

AMINO ACIDS	APPROX. GRAMS PER 100 GRAMS OF DRY PROTEIN				
ESSENTIAL	Gelatin	Casein (milk protein)	Egg white	Pepsin	Insulin
Arginine	8.0	4.3	6.0	1.0	3.4
Histidine	0.8	2.9	2.9	0.8	5.3
Isoleucine	1.3	6.4	7.0	10.8	2.8
Leucine	2.9	7.9	9.9	10.4	13.2
Lysine	4.1	8.9	6.5	1.5	2.4
Methionine	0.9	2.5	5.3	1.7	—
Phenylalanine	2.6	4.6	7.2	6.4	8.3
Threonine	2.2	4.9	4.0	9.6	2.1
Tryptophan	—	1.6	1.2	2.4	—
Valine	2.3	6.3	8.8	7.1	7.8
NONESSENTIAL					
Alanine	10.0	3.8	7.6	—	4.5
Aspartic acid	7.5	8.4	9.3	16.0	6.8
Cystine	0.1	0.4	2.8	2.1	12.5
Glutamic acid	10.8	22.5	16.5	11.9	18.6
Glycine	26.0	2.3	3.6	6.4	4.3
Proline	16.5	7.5	3.8	5.0	2.5
Serene	3.4	6.3	8.2	12.2	5.2
Tyrosine	0.4	8.1	4.1	8.5	13.4

of the body. Since the number of amino acids forming a protein may range from three or four to several thousand, depending on the type of protein, it is obvious that some of the 25 known amino acids will be lacking in some proteins. Other amino acids may be represented several times in the same protein molecule. The table on page 159 shows the amino acid content of several proteins.

It will be noted from the form of the table that the amino acids may be divided into two groups: those that are essential, and those that are nonessential. This simply means that 10 of the amino acids *must* be present in the diet because the body has no way of synthesizing them. The nonessential amino acids are those which the body can synthesize out of other materials that are present in our food; they are just as important as the so-called essential ones for proper body growth and maintenance, but they do not have to be in the diet. For example, a rat kept on a diet in which gelatin is the principal source of protein, will lack tryptophan (see table). The rat will be able to maintain its protoplasm but it will not grow.

The principal use of proteins is to repair and replace protoplasm and to form new living material. Nitrogen is the essential element in the protein molecule. Without this particular element no protoplasm could exist. It is interesting to note that nitrogen makes up about 80 percent of the atmosphere but that we are unable to use this atmospheric nitrogen. We must depend on chemically complex combinations of nitrogen in our food for this vitally important element.

A second use of proteins is to supply energy. There is some doubt as to whether they are oxidized directly or first converted into sugars and fats. If they are oxidized directly, their production of energy is equivalent to an equal amount of carbohydrate. The fuel value of each of the classes of organic nutrients, in terms of the heat they are able to produce when oxidized in the body, is as follows:

1 gram of carbohydrate will yield	4.1 Calories
1 gram of fat will yield	9.3 Calories
1 gram of protein will yield	4.1 Calories

The production of heat in the body is measured in units called Calories (capital *C*) which are 1,000 times greater than the calorie (lower-case *c*) used in the physical sciences. The Calorie is defined as the amount of heat required to raise the temperature of 1 kilogram of water from 15° to 16° C. Since foods must be oxidized to produce energy, any excess food not actually used for energy is largely converted into fats for storage.

Although excess carbohydrates and fats may be stored in the body, there is no provision for protein storage. Therefore, proteins that are not immediately utilized in the formation of new protoplasm are built into the protoplasm of existing cells or are transformed into sugars and fats.

The identification of amino acids is frequently made by a rather interesting process of elimination. There are certain bacteria and fungi whose growth requires one or more definite amino acids. It is possible, therefore, to prepare for them food materials containing the protein to be tested. If the bacteria or fungi fail to grow, we know which amino acids are lacking in the protein.

The presence of a protein in any material can be determined by the **xanthoproteic test.** This consists in heating a food in a solution containing nitric acid. If protein is present, a yellow color develops which changes to orange on the addition of an alkali such as sodium hydroxide.

ᴨ THE DIET

The term **ingestion** is applied to the process of taking solid or liquid foods into the body through a body opening. Some plants and a very few animals absorb prepared food materials directly into their cells, while green plants are able to manufacture their own nutrients. Animals as a group, however, take in complex foods and then break them down into the simpler products that their bodies can use. This second process is **digestion.** The simplified products are then absorbed by the circulating fluid and carried through the body to those areas where they are needed for energy or growth, or are deposited in storage depots. In the first part of this chapter we discussed the role played by each of the nutrients. Now we will try to show how the intake of these nutrients is balanced.

The food requirements of a person vary with his age and size, the amount of work he does, and the climate in which he is living. All of these factors affect the normal, healthy individual. To meet any pronounced change in one or more of them, he has to alter his diet.

For an average person twelve years of age and over a *basic* intake of 2400 Calories per day is considered adequate. This should be supplemented by extra quantities of food to meet the special requirements of various types of work. The suggested additions are as follows:

Type of Work	Addition Per Hour of Work
light	50 Calories
moderate	50–100 Calories
hard	100–200 Calories
very hard	200 Calories or more

These values are based on the needs of a person of average size: for men, a weight of 150 pounds and a height of 5 feet, 7 inches; for women, a weight of 132 pounds and a height of 5 feet, 5 inches. As we will show in a later chapter, most of the body's heat is lost through the skin. If the surface area of the skin is known, this factor can be considered in determining the energy expenditure of the body. The average man has a total body surface area of about 19.36 square feet, while the woman has a surface area of about 17.72 square feet. Persons with smaller surface areas will require a lower basic Calorie intake while those with greater areas will need more Calories.

The diet of a healthy person should include certain general types of foods. Each of these furnishes one or more important food element. A rough grouping of foodstuffs may be made as follows:

MEAT, FISH, and CHEESE supply *proteins. Fats* are also present in varying amounts. Organs such as liver, kidneys, and sweetbreads, as well as shellfish are rich in *minerals* and *vitamins.*

MILK is an excellent source of *proteins, carbohydrates, fats, vitamins, calcium,* and *phosphorus.*

EGGS contain *proteins, fats, vitamins,* and *minerals.*

VEGETABLES and FRUITS are satisfactory sources of *vitamins, minerals,* and *roughage.* Root vegetables and legumes (beans, peas, etc.) contain *carbohydrates* and *proteins.* Raw fruits and green vegetables are needed as sources of *vitamins* and *minerals.*

FATS and SWEETS are sources of *energy-producing materials, fat-soluble vitamins,* and *various fatty acids.*

FOOD VALUE OF SOME OF OUR COMMON FOODS

FOOD	100-CALORIE PORTION MEASURE	DISTRIBUTION OF CALORIES		
		PROTEIN	FAT	CARBO-HYDRATE
Apples	One large	3	5	92
Apple pie	$1\frac{1}{2}$ in. at circumference	3	41	56
Apple sauce	$\frac{3}{8}$ cup	1	3	96
Apple tapioca	$\frac{1}{4}$ cup	1	1	98
Apricots	3 large halves	5		95
Asparagus	20 large stalks	32	8	60
Asparagus soup	$\frac{1}{2}$ cup	17	56	27
Bacon	4 or 5 slices (small)	13	87	
Biscuits	Two small	11	27	62
Banana	One medium	5	6	89
Beans, baked	$\frac{1}{3}$ cup	21	18	61
Beans, lima (buttered)	$\frac{1}{4}$ cup	16	36	48
Beef, Hamburg	1 cake 2 in. diam. $\frac{3}{4}$ in. thick.	38	52	10
Beef, pot roast	Slice $4\frac{3}{4} \times 3\frac{1}{2} \times \frac{1}{8}$	62	38	
Beef, sirloin	Slice $1\frac{3}{4} \times 1\frac{1}{2} \times \frac{3}{4}$	47	53	
Beets, greens	$2\frac{1}{4}$ cups	17	58	25
Beets, fresh	Four 2 in. diam.	14	2	84
Blackberries	$\frac{1}{2}$ cup	9	16	75
Bread, Boston brown	$\frac{3}{4}$ in. slice 3 in. diam.	10	10	80
Bread, graham, w.wh.	$2\frac{1}{2}$ slices $3\frac{3}{4} \times 3\frac{1}{4} \times \frac{1}{4}$ in.	14	6	80
Bread, white	2 slices $3 \times 3\frac{1}{2} \times \frac{1}{2}$ in.	14	6	80
Butter	2 sq. $1\frac{1}{4} \times 1\frac{1}{4} \times \frac{1}{4}$ in.		100	
Buttermilk	$1\frac{1}{8}$ cups	33	13	54
Cabbage, shredded	Four cups	20	9	71
Cantaloupe	One $4\frac{1}{2}$ in. diam.	6		94
Carrots, buttered	$\frac{1}{2}$ cup	4	67	29
Celery	4 cups of $\frac{1}{4}$ in. pieces	24	5	71
Cheese, American	$1\frac{1}{8}$ in. cube	26	74	
Cheese, cottage	5 tbsp.	76	9	15
Cherries, fresh, stoned	1 cup	5	9	86
Chicken, white meat	3 slices $3\frac{1}{2} \times 2\frac{1}{2} \times \frac{1}{4}$	80	20	
Chocolate, beverage (made with milk)	$\frac{1}{3}$ cup	13	49	38
Chocolate cake	$2\frac{1}{2} \times 2\frac{1}{2} \times \frac{7}{8}$ in.	5	41	54
Chocolate nut fudge	$1\frac{1}{4} \times 1 \times \frac{3}{4}$ in. piece	4	36	60
Clams	Twelve clams	56	8	36
Cocoa, beverage (made with milk)	$\frac{1}{2}$ cup	16	44	40
Codfish, creamed	$\frac{1}{2}$ cup	32	46	22
Cod liver oil	1 tablespoon		100	
Cod steak	$3\frac{3}{4} \times 2\frac{1}{2} \times 1$ in. piece	94	6	
Corn bread	Slice $2 \times 2 \times 1$ in. slice	10	24	66
Corn, fresh	$\frac{1}{2}$ cup	12	10	78
Crackers, saltines	Six, 2 in. square	10	26	64
Cream, thick	$1\frac{2}{3}$ tbsp.	2	95	3
Cream, thin	$\frac{1}{4}$ cup	5	86	9

FOOD VALUE OF SOME OF OUR COMMON FOODS (Continued)

FOOD	100-CALORIE PORTION MEASURE	DISTRIBUTION OF CALORIES		
		PROTEIN	FAT	CARBO-HYDRATE
Cream pie	2 in. at circumference	10	37	53
Cup cakes	$\frac{1}{2}$ cake 2 in. diam. 2 in. thick	8	32	60
Custard, boiled	$\frac{1}{3}$ cup	13	44	43
Doughnuts	$\frac{1}{2}$	6	45	49
Eggs, in shell	$1\frac{1}{3}$ eggs	36	64	
Grapefruit	$\frac{1}{2}$ large	7	4	89
Ham, boiled	Slice $4\frac{3}{4} \times 4 \times \frac{1}{8}$ in.	29	71	
Honey	1 tbsp.	1		99
Ice cream	$\frac{1}{4}$ cup	4	63	33
Lamb chops	One $2 \times 1\frac{1}{2} \times \frac{3}{4}$ in.	40	60	
Lettuce	2 large heads	25	14	61
Macaroni and Cheese	$\frac{1}{2}$ cup	7	39	44
Maple syrup	$1\frac{1}{2}$ tbsp.			100
Milk, whole	$\frac{5}{8}$ cup	19	52	29
Milk, skim	$1\frac{1}{8}$ cups	37	7	56
Muffins, bran	$1\frac{3}{4}$ muffins $2\frac{3}{4}$ in. diam.	20	16	64
Oats, rolled-cooked	$\frac{1}{2}$ to $\frac{3}{4}$ cup	17	16	67
Onions	3 to 4 medium	13	6	81
Orange juice	1 cup			100
Oranges, whole	One large	7	2	91
Oyster stew	$\frac{1}{2}$ cup	16	63	21
Parsnips	One 7 in. diam., 2 in.	10	8	83
Peaches, fresh	Three medium	6	3	91
Peanut butter	1 tbsp.	19	69	12
Peanuts, shelled	20 to 24 nuts	19	63	18
Pears, canned	3 halves, 3 tbsp. juice	1	4	94
Peas, green	$\frac{3}{4}$ cup	28	4	68
Plain cookies	Two $2\frac{1}{4}$ in. diam.	6	33	61
Pork chops	$\frac{1}{2}$ chop	32	68	
Potatoes, white	One medium	11	1	88
Prunes, stewed	Two, 2 tbsp. juice	2		98
Raisins	$\frac{1}{4}$ cup	3	9	88
Rice pudding	$\frac{1}{2}$ cup	18	32	50
Salmon, canned	$\frac{1}{2}$ cup	45	55	
Sauerkraut	$2\frac{1}{2}$ cups	25	17	58
Spinach, cooked	$2\frac{1}{2}$ cups	12	8	80
Sponge cake	Piece $1\frac{1}{2} \times 1\frac{1}{2} \times 2$ in.	11	19	70
Squash	1 cup	12	10	78
Squash pie	2 in. at circumference	10	25	65
Sugar, granulated	2 tbsp.			100
Tapioca cream	$\frac{2}{5}$ cup	12	28	60
Tomatoes, whole	2 to 3 medium	16	16	68
Veal cutlets, breaded	$\frac{2}{5}$ serving	30	52	18
Walnuts, English	8 to 16 nuts	11	82	7
Watermelon	Slice $\frac{3}{4}$ in. $\times$ 6 in. diam.	5	6	89
Yeast, compressed	Six cakes	32		68

A balanced diet is one that contains all of the essential food elements in sufficient quantities to supply the needs of the body. As we have said, these needs may vary somewhat, with the result that more of certain nutrients are required at one time and less at another. Protein requirements definitely change during the life of the individual. When he is actively growing, the requirement is higher than it is later in life, because there is a greater demand for the basic materials for protoplasm formation. For example, a child of 3 to 5 years of age will require daily 3 grams of protein for each kilogram of body weight (one kilogram = 1000 grams = 2.2 pounds). Between the ages of 5 and 15, the basic requirement is 2.5 grams per kilogram; from 15 to 17 it should be about 2 grams per kilogram; from 17 to 21 it drops to 1.5 grams; and above 21 it remains at 1.0 gram. During pregnancy the protein intake should be increased from the normal 1.0 grams to 2.0 grams per kilogram of body weight. A list of some common foods and their energy values in Calories is included in the table on pages 162–163.

Raw vegetables should be eaten in moderate amounts only. All plant materials contain cellulose, a complex carbohydrate that cannot be digested. This forms the greater part of the roughage which is essential for the proper elimination of intestinal wastes. However, large quantities of cellulose are very irritating to the lining of the digestive tract. Cooking of vegetables breaks down the cellulose cell walls of plant tissues, thereby freeing some of the nutrients within the plant cells that otherwise might not be digested.

A food is considered to be acid when its oxidation produces compounds such as uric and phosphoric acids. When used in this connection, the word does not refer to the sour flavor of fruits like lemons. Most meats are acid-producing foods, while many fruits are alkaline regardless of their flavor. The reason for this is that oxidation of fruits and vegetables frequently produces salts of magnesium, sodium, and potassium. These eventually combine with other chemicals to produce basic (alkaline) compounds. The flavor of a food does not indicate whether it will have an acid or alkaline reaction in the body.

Physiologically, a distinction can be drawn between appetite and hunger. The former means the craving for a certain food or drink, which can be satisfied quite easily. Appetite is usually based on some previous pleasurable experience. Hunger, on the other hand, is a complex condition that is accompanied by vigorous contractions of the empty stomach, a feeling of emptiness in the abdomen, and a generalized discomfort that cannot be localized in any particular area. It is unwise to confuse these two terms, especially when considering the diet of young children. If appetite is mistaken for hunger, a child may be able to convince his elders that a diet unbalanced in favor of some well-liked item is more satisfactory than one that contains all of the necessary food factors. Hunger is a constant reminder of the primary needs of the body for energy and specific nutrients.

SPEAKING OF Physiology

Briefly identify each of the following:

absorption - *drawing in of food by cell*
adipose tissue - *fatty tissue*
amino acid - *digested proteins*
balanced diet
Calorie - *measuring heat*
carbohydrate *chemical compound* *carbon, hydrogen & oxygen - 2:1*
cholesterol

digestion - *makes food soluble & useable*
disaccharide - *two*
fatty acid
glycerin (glycerol)
hexose
ingestion
lipids

mineral salt
monosaccharide - *one*
nutrient
organic nutrient
photosynthesis
polysaccharide - *many*
roughage

Test YOUR KNOWLEDGE

1. For a substance to be classified as a food, it must meet certain requirements. List these requirements. *P. 152   first column*
2. Why is water considered the universal solvent? *P. 153   first column*
3. Compare and contrast the chemical structure of the three basic organic nutrients: carbohydrates, fats, and proteins.
4. How is it possible for *glusoce, fructose,* and *galactose* to have the same empirical formula and yet show different characteristics?
5. Why must a disaccharide or polysaccharide be broken down (digested) into a monosaccharide before absorption can take place?
6. Of what importance are carbohydrates in the body's chemistry? How are these substances stored?
7. Summarize the characteristics of each of the three principal types of lipids, noting similarities as well as differences.
8. How are fats absorbed, transported, and stored?
9. How is protein different from other organic nutrients in regard to: (*a*) molecular size, (*b*) form absorbed by the blood, (*c*) primary function, (*d*) test for identification, (*e*) method of storage.
10. What are the various requirements which determine our caloric needs? What would represent the normal number of calories for the average high school boy or girl?
11. How does the daily requirement for proteins differ as to age group?
12. What is our major source of roughage? What precautions should be taken in its ingestion?
13. What are the important uses of water to living things?

See FOR YOURSELF

1. What dietary problems would have to be solved by the occupants of the first manned rocket ship to outer space?

2. With the ever-increasing world population, the supply of present-day food resources may become a deciding factor in the survival of man. What resources, yet untouched, might be made available to insure our preservation?

3. Animal life on earth is dependent upon the ability of plants to produce food (sugars, etc.), through the process of photosynthesis. What is photosynthesis? Can this process be carried on artificially? What research has been done in this field and what are some of the problems yet to be solved?

CHAPTER 14

Enzymes and Vitamins

ENZYMES

The growth and activity of every cell in the body is dependent on the presence of a group of chemical compounds, the enzymes. Although it is most convenient to discuss them in this unit, the role of enzymes in living processes is not limited to digestion. Their chemical activities are so varied and complex that enzymes accomplish with ease processes that a chemist can reproduce only with difficulty in the laboratory. From a chemical standpoint, life consists of a series of chemical reactions which are either hastened or retarded by the activities of the enzymes.

An *enzyme* is a complex protein compound capable of effecting a chemical reaction without itself being changed in composition. The chemical name for such a compound is a *catalyst*. Many commercial processes depend on the use of inorganic or organic catalysts to break large molecules into simpler ones. Some of these catalysts are relatively simple compounds while others may be highly complex, but they all differ from enzymes in that they are not produced by living cells. A few industries do make use of enzymes, but in each case it is necessary to grow the appropriate organisms to produce them. Thus the brewing industry makes use of the enzymes of

yeast. Cheese manufacturers use enzymes of molds and bacteria, and farmers use bacterial enzymes in the preparation of silage.

The outstanding characteristic of an enzyme is its ability to bring about a chemical change without itself entering into the reaction. The late Sir William Bayliss once likened the action of a catalyst to that of a drop of oil beneath a metal weight on an inclined glass plate. The oil does not start the weight moving down the plate, nor does it combine chemically with either the metal or the glass. It merely hastens the sliding process.

The action of catalysts can be illustrated by the following simple experiment with cane sugar. A molecule of cane sugar is formed by the combination of two molecules of simple sugars with the loss of a water molecule. This action is carried out in the plant under the influence of enzymes. Now, if we make a solution of cane sugar in water and allow this to stand for a long period of time, water will be taken up by the molecules of the cane sugar and they will break down into the same simple sugars from which the cane sugar was originally formed. The presence of these simple sugars can be detected by Fehling's Test. This chemical change is a fairly slow one involving a period of weeks, but we can obtain the same results in a few minutes by the use of a catalyst. A few drops of dilute hydrochloric acid are added to a solution of cane sugar in a test tube. The solution is then boiled and allowed to cool. When tested with Fehling's solution, it shows the presence of simple sugars. Here the hydrochloric acid is the catalyst and can be recovered unchanged at the end of the experiment. In this case it is necessary to use a strong acid and heat to bring about the change. If, however, we use the enzyme **sucrase,** that is secreted by the walls of the small intestine, we find that the change occurs rapidly without application of heat.

All enzymes that have been isolated and chemically identified thus far are proteins. In many instances these cannot function by themselves but require the presence of some other substance. Some of these accessory materials are relatively simple, like calcium or magnesium ions, while others are highly complex. A good example of the need for these auxiliary materials is found in the action of **rennin,** an enzyme secreted by the stomach of a calf. This enzyme digests the protein of milk (casein), but only in the presence of calcium ions. Since milk normally contains calcium, this process occurs regularly in the calf's stomach. If, however, the calcium is removed from the milk, no digestion by rennin is possible.

Another important characteristic of enzymes is their ability to carry on their activities outside the cells that produce them. Even though they are manufactured by living cells, their structure is such that they do not require the actual presence of protoplasm to make them effective. One of the simplest demonstrations of this characteristic is the effect of saliva on starch. Saliva contains an enzyme which decomposes starch into double sugars. If a starch solution is mixed with some saliva in a test tube, and then placed in an incubator at body temperature, the solution will slowly change from an opaque condition to a clear one as the transformation of starch to sugar takes place. The enzyme in the saliva is **ptyalin.** Its ability to convert starch to a simpler form in a test tube indicates that the presence of living protoplasm is not required to make an enzyme active. The specialized cells in the walls of other digestive organs also form enzymes and liberate these into the alimentary canal where their action takes place.

Enzymes are easily affected by various conditions in their environment. Changes in temperature, acidity, and the accumulation of the products of their activities all have a tendency to influence the rate at which they work.

1. *Effects of temperature.* Temperature plays an important part in the rate at which enzyme reactions occur. The rate of most chemical reactions increases from two to three times with each rise of 10 C. (18 F.) degrees. Enzyme reactions obey this general rule. At 0° C. (32 F.), their action generally ceases, although a few plant enzymes function below this temperature. The rate of activity increases as the temperature rises until heat destroys the enzyme. The destruction of most animal enzymes occurs in the temperature range between 40° and 50° C. (approximately 104°−122° F.). In all animals and plants there is a rather definite temperature at which an enzyme functions most efficiently. This is called the **optimum temperature** for the enzyme. In man, this temperature is approximately 37.5° C. (98.6° F.), as determined by a thermometer placed under the tongue.

Certain light-producing organisms demonstrate the effect of temperature on enzyme action. Whether the light is produced by fireflies, bacteria, or the fun-

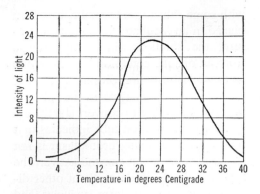

Fig. 14-1. *The effect of temperature on an enzymatic process in light-producing organisms. Note that low temperatures slow down the process, but that light intensity increases until an optimum temperature is reached at about 23.5° C. Beyond this point, higher temperatures retard the reaction. The enzyme is destroyed at about 40° C.*

gus growing on a decaying stump, the process depends on the presence of an enzyme, **luciferase.** A protein, *luciferin,* also must be present. This protein is oxidized in the presence of luciferase to produce the light. As Fig. 14-1 shows, when the temperature of a mixture of luciferin and luciferase is low, the amount of light produced is low. As the temperature is raised, the intensity of the light increases and then decreases until it is totally extinguished. At this point the enzyme responsible for the production of light is destroyed, although the organism may still be alive.

2. *Nature of the substrate.* The term **substrate** describes the material on which an enzyme acts. Enzyme action is highly specific; that is, one enzyme will affect one type of material but not another. In this respect an enzyme is like a key. Many of us carry several keys, each of which will fit a different lock, but none of which will open all locks. The same is true of enzymes: no one enzyme can break down all the molecules of carbohydrates, fats, and proteins which it

encounters. It is necessary, therefore, that there be many enzymes in the body to free the energy from different foods within the cells, decompose complex substances, build up new materials, or speed up oxidation.

To carry the analogy of the lock and key one step further, some enzymes perform like one type of safety deposit box in the vault of a bank. A person cannot open the door of his box unless a bank attendant is present with a bank key that turns the lock part way. After this initial movement of the lock has been made, the person's own key opens the door. One specific enzyme (for example, ptyalin in saliva) will break a complex molecule (starch) into a simpler substance (maltose). It requires the action of another enzyme (maltase) to reduce the maltose to the form of glucose which the body can use.

3. *Effect of pH.* The action of many enzymes depends on the pH of the solution in which they react. A good example of the effect of hydrogen ion concentration is found in the action of ptyalin on starch. In the mouth, ptyalin acts in a solution that has a pH of approximately 6.8 (very close to the neutral point). When the food is swallowed and enters the stomach, it encounters the gastric juice, which has a pH varying between 1 and 3. This greatly increased acidity tends to stop the action of ptyalin and arrest further digestion of starch. In the same manner, the gastric enzyme, pepsin, will act in a highly acid medium, but its activity is stopped when the food enters the small intestine, where the pH varies from about 5 to approximately 8.

4. *Accumulation of end-products.* The materials produced by the activities of enzymes are called their end-products. It is difficult to demonstrate how the accumulation of end-products affects human activities. However, laboratory

experiments with various enzymes have indicated that the rate at which the enzyme activities proceed may be affected.

One of the most carefully studied enzymes is the **zymase** of yeast. This is responsible for the splitting of starch into sugars. Other enzymes then convert sugar into alcohol and carbon dioxide. If the end-product (alcohol) is not removed, its gradual accumulation will slow down the action of the enzymes and eventually bring the process to an end. The most active enzymes of brewer's yeast can therefore produce only 13 to 15 percent alcohol from a grain or fruit substrate before their own products stop their activities.

VITAMINS

Some of the most important and impressive advances in the field of physiology have been made in the study of vitamins. These materials are essential food substances although they contribute no material for production of energy or building of protoplasm. They are required in only minute amounts, but without them the body cannot use some of the foods it takes in or carry on numerous vital functions that are necessary for the maintenance of normal conditions.

The body's need for certain food factors has been recognized for many years, but it is only within this century that we have learned the relation of some of these to specific body conditions. In the sixteenth century, the British sea rover, Richard Hawkins, observed that lemons and oranges prevented the appearance of scurvy among his sailors. About two hundred years later a British physician, James Lind, recommended that the sailors of the Royal Navy be given regular rations of lime juice to stop the ravages of scurvy. This course was adopted and from it arose the nickname of Limey or Lime-juicer for the British sailor.

Beriberi is a vitamin deficiency disease that plagued the people of the Far East. In 1882 Admiral Takaki of the Japanese Navy improved the diet of his men by including a greater amount of meat, barley, and fruit than had been used previously. He held the mistaken idea that beriberi was caused by a diet low in proteins. Five years later, a Dutch physician, Eijkman, discovered that a disease similar to beriberi could be induced in birds fed on polished rice, a staple in the diet of Oriental peoples. He later cured the birds of the disease by feeding them the husks of the rice that had been removed in the polishing process. He formulated the hypothesis that the lack of some factor present in the husks but lacking in the polished grain might be the cause of beriberi. Eijkman's hypothesis aroused the interest of physiologists who were studying the human diet and led to intensive research in the field of food deficiency diseases. In 1911, Dr. Funk developed a general theory to account for these diseases. He used the term *vitamine* as a name for the the factors lacking in deficiency diseases, because his work indicated that they all contained the amino (NH_2) group. It was assumed that this chemical group was characteristic of these vital food factors and essential to their proper functioning. Later work has shown that this is not always true, so the spelling has been changed to **vitamin.**

In the early days of research on vitamins, each of the newly identified factors was designated by a letter of the alphabet. This was not only a convenient method of naming them, but it was also noncommittal about their chemical structure. As the methods of chemistry improved, new information on vitamins was obtained, and the use of letters was found to be inadequate in many cases. Some of the older names have been kept because of their long-established usage, but many of the more recently discovered compounds have been given chemical names.

All of the known vitamins fall into one of two categories: those that are soluble in *oil* and those that are soluble in *water*. The oil-soluble vitamins are known by letters, A, D, E, etc.; while the water-soluble ones are named. An exception to this general rule is water-soluble ascorbic acid, which is still commonly called vitamin C. This difference in the solubility of the vitamins is of considerable dietary importance because it indicates how vitamins will behave when foods are cooked. The loss of oil-soluble vitamins in cooking water, generally speaking, will be less than may be expected of a water-soluble vitamin under the same conditions.

THE OIL–SOLUBLE VITAMINS

Vitamin A ($C_{20}H_{29}OH$). In its pure form, vitamin A is a pale yellow crystalline substance. It is relatively stable in the absence of air, but is rapidly destroyed at high temperatures in the presence of oxygen. This last characteristic explains why some vegetables are almost useless as a source of vitamin A when cooked by ordinary methods in an open pot, but retain their potency when cooked in a pressure cooker.

The principal sources of vitamin A are plants containing **carotene** ($C_{40}H_{56}$). This is a yellowish-red substance that gives a characteristic color to such foods as carrots, pumpkins, sweet potatoes, and butter. Carotene is dissolved in oil in plant and animal products and is the compound from which animals and humans manufacture vitamin A. Any such substance that can be converted into a vitamin is called a **provitamin**. The process involved in the conversion of the provitamin carotene into vitamin A can

be represented by the following equation:

$$C_{40}H_{56} + 2H_2O \longrightarrow 2C_{20}H_{29}OH$$

Actually, the picture is not so simple as this statement makes it appear: the process is complicated by a variety of intermediate steps. The chief organ for accomplishing the conversion is the liver.

The most important function of vitamin A appears to be the maintenance of tissue health. When the vitamin is absent or at a low level in the diet, certain epithelial cells of glands, skin, and mucous membranes are likely to suffer damage. For example, the cells of the tear glands may become affected. The secretion of tears is then suppressed and the surfaces of the eyes become dry and easily infected. This condition is known as **xerophthalmia**. Destruction of the epithelium follows. Scars form over the cornea, often resulting in total blindness (Fig. 14-2).

Night blindness, a more common defect of vision caused by the lack of vitamin A, has been discussed in Chapter 11. If vitamin A is absent from the diet or is present in inadequate amounts, the reformation of rhodopsin cannot occur successfully, and vision in dim light is impaired.

Vitamin A can be stored in quantity by animals and man. Most vitamins are excreted in urine or appear in intestinal wastes if they are in excess of the body's requirements. Excess vitamin A, however, is stored in the liver.

Sources: The common articles of diet that are rich in carotene are all yellow vegetables and the outer leaves of cabbage and lettuce. In addition, green seed foods, such as beans and peas, contain considerable amounts; green peppers, the green stems of asparagus, broccoli, and celery are also good sources. With the exception of yellow corn, all com-

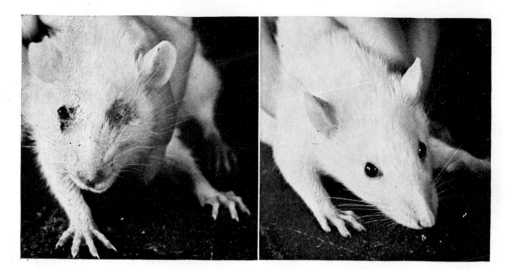

Fig. 14-2. *Left: a rat showing xerophthalmia resulting from serious vitamin A deficiency. Right: the same rat following feeding of sufficient vitamin A to repair the damage. (E. R. Squibb and Sons)*

monly used cereal grains are notoriously low in carotene content. Milk contains variable amounts of carotene and vitamin A, depending on the diet of the cows which produced it.

Oils extracted from the livers of codfish, halibut, and sharks are the main source of the vitamin for medicinal purposes, and a considerable fishing industry has been developed to meet this demand. Animal fats also contain vitamin A, while vegetable oils yield large amounts of the provitamin, carotene. Recently, industrial methods have been developed to extract carotene from alfalfa and carrots.

Vitamin D. The action of vitamin D is primarily to insure the normal development of bone and tooth structure. It increases the absorption of calcium and phosphorus from the food and their retention by the body. It also improves the absorption of phosphorus by the blood in the kidneys. Even if a child receives sufficient calcium and phosphorus in his food, he will not be able to develop normal bones and teeth without vitamin D. In cases of a pronounced deficiency of the vitamin, rickets will develop.

Rickets is characterized by the failure of the bones to add bony material at the epiphyseal cartilages. These remain abnormally large and open. The shafts of the bones may also be affected by the irregular development of bony substance. The result is that the long bones of the legs have a tendency to become bowed and may also be flattened from side to side (Fig. 14-3). Other bones may show deformities, the skull and the ribs being especially susceptible. The liver frequently becomes enlarged, and the teeth either decay early or are malformed.

Vitamin D is often referred to in popular language as the sunshine vitamin. This, of course, does not mean that there is a vitamin in sunlight, but it indicates a relation between the two. The graph in Fig. 14-4 shows that certain wave lengths of the ultraviolet portion of the spectrum are essential to form

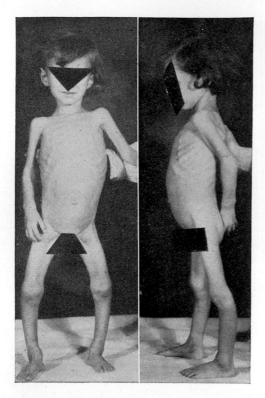

Fig. 14-3. *An advanced case of rickets. At the left, note the enlargement of the joints, the shape of the femur (sickle thigh), and the bowing of the lower leg bones. Some enlargement of the ribs can be seen in this view, but this feature is more evident in the photograph at the right. Advanced cases of this type are becoming rare because of the general improvements in the diets of children. (F. R. Harding, Children's Hospital, Boston, Mass.)*

The action of the ultraviolet light of the sun transforms a substance that is normally present in the skin into vitamin D. This material, known by the chemical name of **7-dehydrocholesterol,** is converted into vitamin D_2 ($C_{28}H_{44}O$). A somewhat similar material, present in plants, is called **ergosterol.** This can be changed into vitamin D_3 ($C_{27}H_{44}O$), which also will prevent rickets.

Like vitamin A, vitamin D is stored in large quantities in the liver and to a lesser degree in the body fat.

Sources: Vitamin D is quite poorly distributed in foods. Aside from fish livers, which serve as the principal commercial sources of vitamin D, its sources are rather limited or seasonal. It is present in small quantities in egg yolk,

vitamin D in the body. The dashed line in the graph indicates that the maximum amount of benefit is obtained from those wave lengths in the neighborhood of 3000 Ångstrom units (Å). It will also be noted that the wave lengths producing the maximum burning of the skin are longer, and nearer the visible end of the spectrum. This means that materials which will prevent sunburn also shield the body from those ultraviolet rays that are beneficial in producing vitamin D.

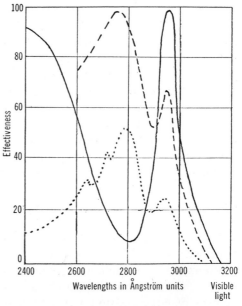

Fig. 14-4. *The effects of various wave lengths of solar radiations outside the visible spectrum. The solid line represents wave lengths most able to cause sunburn; the dashed line, those having the greatest power to prevent rickets; and the dotted line, the wave lengths at which ergosterol is formed in the greatest quantities.*

milk, and milk products. Its presence in milk is determined by the extent to which cows and their fodder have been exposed to sunlight. Thus milk taken during summer months when cattle are in pasture will have a higher vitamin D content than that taken during the winter. Eggs also vary in the amount of vitamin D present in the yolk, although egg yolk may generally be considered a satisfactory source of the vitamin.

Foodstuffs will respond to ultraviolet radiations in much the same manner as the human body does. If foods contain either ergosterol or 7-dehydrocholesterol, light from a carbon arc or a mercury vapor arc lamp will very materially increase the amount of vitamin D in them. Thus, if milk is passed under one of these lamps, the ultraviolet radiations will bring about the conversion of the 7-dehydrocholesterol into vitamin D_2. Such artificially produced amounts of the vitamin allow the processor to label his products as irradiated foods.

Vitamin E. A group of fat-soluble vitamins has been designated by the letter E. Chemically, these belong to a group of organic compounds known as the *tocopherols*. Four of these substances are known to have a vitamin action, but of these, only one, **alpha-tocopherol,** $(C_{29}H_{50}O_2)$ is used experimentally. The name that has been given this group of substances is derived from the Greek word, *tokos,* meaning *childbirth,* because the primary function of the vitamin appears to be closely related to reproduction.

Our knowledge of the action of this vitamin is confined to animals. In rats, mice, chickens, and other animals, the lack of normal quantities of this vitamin in the diet leads to either sterility or the inability of the embryo to reach a stage of development where it can be born alive or hatched. There is no definitely known effect of the absence of this vitamin in humans.

Sources: The chief sources of vitamin E are green leafy vegetables, whole cereals such as oats and wheat, and meat. It is also present in egg yolk.

Vitamin K $(C_{31}H_{46}O_2)$ is the antihemorrhagic vitamin. A disease of chickens in which serious and often fatal bleeding occurred was eventually traced to the absence of fresh green materials in their diet. The addition of alfalfa, cabbage, lettuce, or other green plants arrested the bleeding tendency. It was also shown that the direct cause of the bleeding was an abnormally low amount of a substance, **prothrombin,** which is necessary for the proper formation of a blood clot. Thus it was evident that green foods contain some material that is essential for the formation of prothrombin.

In normal human beings, certain bacteria in the large intestine are able to synthesize vitamin K, which is then absorbed and carried to the liver where prothrombin is formed. The presence of bile is necessary for absorption in the intestine. In cases of jaundice, bile does not reach the intestine, and vitamin K is not absorbed. Until recently, surgeons have hesitated to operate on people who had jaundice because of the possibility of excessive bleeding. This tendency can now be corrected by giving injections of synthetic vitamin K a short time before the operation.

Newborn infants have occasionally died from uncontrollable hemorrhages. Such babies have not received enough vitamin K during prenatal development. If the baby can be helped during the first day or two by injections of vitamin K, he soon acquires the necessary intestinal bacteria to produce the vitamin himself. This prevents further excessive bleeding.

Sources: Vitamin K is distributed

widely in plant foods. It is present in appreciable quantities in the green parts of plants. Fruits, in general, have very little of this vitamin, the one exception being tomatoes. Carrots, potatoes, cereal grains, milk, and eggs are poor sources. Vitamin K is very stable in heat.

THE WATER—SOLUBLE VITAMINS

The Vitamin B Complex. In the early days of vitamin research, a substance was discovered which prevented beriberi in humans. Later work in the field has shown that what was originally

Fig. 14-5. *Above: the pronounced muscular contractions typical of polyneuritis in birds. Below: the same bird three hours after receiving doses of thiamin.* (*From Marsland,* Principles of Modern Biology, *Holt, 1957*)

thought to be a single substance is actually a group of compounds to which the name *vitamin B complex* has been given. Each of the substances composing this group has its own specific action in preventing some deficiency disease. Not all of these materials can be related directly to specific human conditions, but studies of the diet of animals whose food requirements are similar to man's indicate that they play some role in human nutrition. It is known that some of them can be synthesized by bacteria in the intestine and then absorbed. This would greatly lessen the appearance of deficiency symptoms due to their absence from the diet.

Thiamin hydrochloride (vitamin B$_1$) ($C_{12}H_{17}C_1N_4OSHCl$). This vitamin is also known as the *antineuritic vitamin* because its inclusion in the diet will help prevent the appearance of certain types of nervous disorders. If birds are kept on a thiamin-deficient diet, partial paralysis of the muscles may result. This condition is known as polyneuritis (Fig. 14-5). In man, there is retardation of growth, loss of appetite, degeneration of the nervous system, muscular difficulties, enlargement of the heart, and eventual death.

A person's ability to absorb and use this vitamin properly is important. Increased intake of thiamin may be required to offset the effects of diarrhea. Thiamin is often used in cases of severe gastro-intestinal disorders or extensive surgery of the digestive tract. Occasionally beriberi has appeared in people who suffer from tuberculosis, dysentery, or cancer of the liver. Chronic alcoholism may lead to beriberi because the diet of a heavy drinker is often lacking in thiamin.

The staple diet associated with human beriberi is one based on so-called polished grain. In the process of polishing grain, the outer husk is removed and with it goes the thiamin. Thus the ordinary commercial rice is white because the husk has been removed in the process of refining it. The same process is used in making white flour. If polished grains constitute the principal article of the diet, a deficiency in thiamin may result. This deficiency is particularly notable in the Far East, where polished rice is eaten in large quantities. This diet tends to exclude other foods that might replace the thiamin.

Very little thiamin is stored in the body. Some small amounts are normally present in the liver, kidneys, and muscles, but these are quickly used up. Bacteria in the intestine may be able to synthesize thiamin, but not in sufficient quantities to satisfy the body needs.

Sources: Thiamin is found in many foods. Its richest sources are: the husks of grains, wheat germ, milk, potatoes, cabbage, meat (especially pork), eggs, and brewer's yeast.

Vitamin B_1 is easily destroyed by heat. In dry heat there may be a loss of from 10 to 25 percent, whereas cooking in water may dissolve or destroy as much as 50 percent. To meet the body's daily needs, one should drink three glasses of milk per day or have one serving of meat or one egg. Since thiamin can be added to flour, six slices of vitamin-enriched white bread may supply the needed quota.

Fig. 14-6. *Deficiency of riboflavin caused the condition in the chicken at the right. The bird on the left received a diet containing sufficient riboflavin for normal growth.* (*U.S. Dept. of Agriculture photograph*)

Riboflavin (vitamin B₂ or G) ($C_{17}H_{20}N_4O_6$). This yellow compound is quite stable in air. It is not affected by dry heat, but is easily decomposed by exposure to light.

A deficiency of this vitamin results in retarded growth in some experimental animals, such as chickens (Fig. 14-6). In man, a lack of the vitamin causes sores in the region of the lips and corners of the mouth, a scaly skin, increased sensitivity of the eyes to bright light, and the growth of fine blood vessels over the surface of the eyes. The last condition may eventually lead to blindness.

Sources: Riboflavin is quite widely distributed in foods. It is present in milk, eggs, wheat germ, green leafy vegetables, peas, lima beans, and many kinds of meat. The richest sources are pork or beef liver, and brewer's yeast.

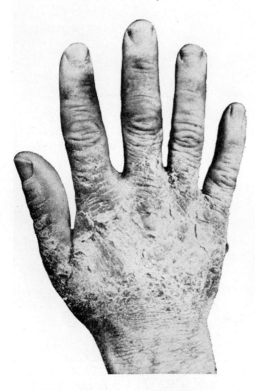

Fig. 14-7. *The skin rash of pellagra.* (*E. R. Squibb and Sons*)

Niacin ($C_6H_5O_2N$) is also known as *nicotinic acid* and the *pellagra preventative vitamin,* in reference to the disease pellagra.

The name *pellagra* comes from words meaning *dry skin,* because this condition is one of the most evident signs of niacin deficiency (Fig. 14-7). The chief features of pellagra are red, dry skin which is irritated by sunlight and heat, and a sore mouth. The nervous system may be affected, resulting in walking difficulties, jerky movements, and finally paralysis.

This disease, like beriberi, is very frequently associated with the overbalance of one staple grain in the diet. In this case it is corn, which is notoriously poor in niacin but is the principal grain in the diet in certain parts of this country. Its low cost, in those regions where corn, cotton, and tobacco are the main crops, accounts for the appearance of the disease among low-income farmers in southern parts of the United States.

Sources: Most meats are well supplied with niacin. Liver, whole wheat, peanuts, and brewer's yeast are especially rich in it. Fresh peas and cabbage are good sources, and many green leaf vegetables contain an adequate amount to prevent the appearance of pellagra symptoms.

Pyridoxine (vitamin B₆) ($C_8H_{12}O_3NCl$). Although it is commonly assumed that man requires pyridoxine, the exact effects of its absence from the diet have not as yet been determined. It is known that many animals do require the vitamin. If rats, for example, are kept on a pyridoxine-free diet, there is a loss of hair from their paws, nose, and ears, with thickening of the ears. Chickens, pigs, dogs, and monkeys also show definite symptoms when the vitamin is absent from their diets.

Sources: This vitamin is abundant in

common foods such as milk, fresh vegetables, whole wheat, and many meats. It is not easily destroyed by dry heat, but readily dissolves when food is cooked in water.

Biotin (vitamin H) $(C_{10}H_{16}O_3N_2S)$. The exact relation of this vitamin to human nutrition in unknown. If rats are kept on a biotin-free diet, they develop severe itching of the skin. Then the hair around their eyes falls out (spectacle eye), and eventually baldness results. In man, skin changes, loss of weight, and muscular pain have been ascribed to a lack of biotin, but there is little conclusive evidence that this is the case.

A biotin-free diet contains raw egg white as the principal source of protein. Raw egg white contains a substance, **avidin,** which combines with biotin and makes it unusable by the body. Cooking evidently changes the composition of egg white so that it no longer will combine with biotin, and therefore the vitamin is available to regulate bodily processes.

Sources: Biotin is present in greatest quantities in liver, yeast, and poultry. It is found in lesser amounts in egg yolk, tomatoes, and carrots. Biotin can be synthesized by some bacteria in the large intestine, which may explain our present lack of knowledge about the importance of this vitamin in humans.

Inositol $(C_6H_6(OH)_6)$. In working on dietary requirements of mice, Dr. Wolley found that his experimental animals failed to grow and lost their hair when fed a diet containing all of the then known vitamins. If, however, he added a relatively simple compound, inositol, to their food, they resumed their growth at a normal rate and retained their hair. The effects of the absence of inositol from the human diet are unknown.

Sources: Inositol is widely distributed in food substances, its occurrence closely

paralleling that of biotin. It is especially prevalent in heart, liver, and kidney.

Choline $(C_5H_{15}O_2N)$. Dr. Best found that the lack of choline in a dog's diet resulted in the accumulation of fat in the liver cells, changes in kidney circulation, and general hemorrhages. If the choline-free diet was continued, dogs developed a condition known as cirrhosis of the liver. Some other investigators in the field have found evidence of the relation of choline to the formation of acetylcholine at the ends of nerves. Currently, little is known about the role of this vitamin in human nutrition, although lack of it causes serious diseases in animals (Fig. 14-8).

Sources: The richest source of this vitamin is egg yolk, closely followed by liver and kidney. It is also present in the germ of cereal grains.

Pantothenic acid $(C_9H_{17}O_5N)$. The role played by this vitamin in human nutrition is unknown. In chickens, its absence results in inflammation of the skin, changes in the spinal cord, and a diseased condition of the eyes. In rats, pantothenic acid deficiency is associated with severe damage to the heart, kidneys, and adrenal glands. There is also a graying of the rat's hair.

Sources: Three rich sources of pantothenic acid are brewer's yeast, liver, and kidney. Other good sources are eggs, sweet potatoes, lean beef, whole milk, and tomatoes.

Para-aminobenzoic acid $(C_7H_7O_2N)$. Little is known about the relation of this substance to human nutrition. It is, however, essential for the growth and reproduction of many bacteria. Also, lack of this vitamin in the diet of black rats causes hair to gray, although there is no proven connection between this vitamin and the graying of human hair.

The drug sulfanilamide contains a chemical group related to one in para-

Fig. 14-8. *The hog at the right was fed a diet deficient in choline. On the left is a hog of the same age that received adequate amounts of choline. (U.S. Dept. of Agriculture photograph)*

aminobenzoic acid. It is thought that although sulfanilamide is useless to bacteria, they absorb the drug because of its chemical similarity to para-aminobenzoic acid. This results in the arresting of bacterial growth and reproduction. Such drugs are termed **bacteriostatic** (the suffix means to stand still) rather than **bacteriocidal** (this suffix means to kill).

Sources: Para-aminobenzoic acid is widely distributed in all plant and animal tissues.

Folic acid ($C_{22}H_{14}N_7O_6$). This vitamin appears to be closely associated with proper blood formation. At one time it was believed to be a specific preventative of pernicious anemia, but investigation shows that folic acid alone is not able to repair the damage this disease does to the nervous system. The chemical structure of folic acid indicates that it is closely related to both para-aminobenzoic acid and vitamin B_{12}.

Sources: Liver, kidney, mushrooms, and yeast are especially rich in folic acid. The word *folic* is derived from the Latin *folium,* a leaf, because green leaves and grass were first recognized as

an excellent source of this vitamin during early experiments.

Vitamin B$_{12}$ ($C_{61}H_{86}N_{14}O_{13}PCo$). This vitamin contains the chemical element cobalt (Co), an infrequent constituent of protoplasm. The exact structure of the molecule has not been determined, but as the tentative formula suggests, it is very complex. In 1926 a substance was found in liver extracts that would cure pernicious anemia. Later this was separated and identified as vitamin B_{12}. Since that time, many sufferers from the disease have been restored to health. The chicken in Fig. 14-9 shows the external effects of deficiency of vitamin B_{12}.

Vitamin C ($C_6H_8O_6$). Vitamin C is now commonly known by either the term **antiscorbutic vitamin** or **ascorbic acid.** The former name is used because this vitamin acts as a specific agent in the prevention and cure of scurvy (scorbutus). For many years this disease was prevalent among sailors and explorers who were deprived of fresh fruit and vegetables for long periods. Scurvy is still common in regions where the diet is limited by custom or occupation, as in isolated fishing villages. There the main article of winter diet is salt or dried fish, because there is no adequate supply of fresh foods. In such places scurvy is known as spring sickness because the symptoms appear in late winter or early spring before home-grown vegetables are available. Strangely enough, farmers may show some signs of scurvy. When vegetables are prepared for home canning by boiling them in open pots, vitamin C is destroyed. If such vegetables are used to the exclusion of fresh ones, the symptoms of scurvy appear. Foods that have been canned commercially by pressure cooking keep much of their vitamin C content.

The absence of vitamin C from the diet will result in fragility of the capillaries and subsequent loss of blood. This condition is due to a weakening of the cement material that holds the endothelial cells together. Tooth structure may also suffer from improper formation and maintenance of the dentine. Also the cementum that holds the tooth in its bony

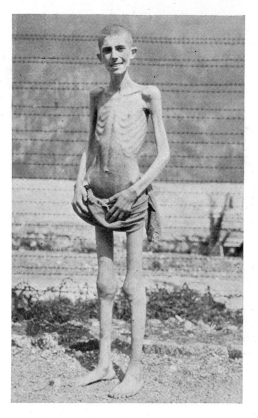

Fig. 14-10. *This inmate of a German prison camp in World War II shows the effects of a near-starvation diet. (U.S. Army photograph)*

Fig. 14-9. *This bird shows the result of a diet deficient in vitamin B$_{12}$. (U.S. Dept. of Agriculture photograph)*

socket weakens and the tooth becomes loose. These effects are accompanied by loss in weight and constant and annoying pains in the joints. Extreme deficiency of vitamin C in the diet may sometimes result in death.

Sources: Vitamin C is found in large quantities in fresh tomatoes, turnips, green leaf vegetables, and the majority of fruits. One of the best sources is the juice of oranges, lemons, and grapefruit. Fresh meats contain vitamin C in moderate amounts. Some animals can synthesize vitamin C in sufficient quantities to be immune from scurvy.

Victims of malnutrition often suffer from a number of vitamin deficiencies simultaneously. Thus it is extremely difficult to identify individually such diseases as scurvy, pellagra, and rickets. Severe cases of malnutrition occurred among American prisoners in German and Japanese prison camps during World War II (Fig. 14-10). It was frequently necessary to feed these men by injection of amino acids, vitamins, and other essential nutrients upon their release from prisons, because their bodies were too weak to digest and absorb food normally. As the men regained strength, they could then return to a normal diet.

SPEAKING OF Physiology

Briefly identify each of the following:

alimentary canal	irradiation	rickets
beriberi	pellagra	scurvy
carotene	pernicious anemia	substrate
catalyst	polyneuritis	vitamin
enzyme	provitamin	xerophthamia

Test YOUR KNOWLEDGE

1. Explain the statement: All enzymes are catalysts, but not all catalysts are enzymes.
2. By considering the following, list the various characteristics that enable an enzyme to function at its optimum rate: (*a*) proenzymes or coenzymes, (*b*) effects of temperature, (*c*) substrate, (*d*) pH, (*e*) accumulation of end-products.
3. Briefly summarize the historical events which led to the discovery of vitamin C and thiamin (vitamin B$_1$).
4. What effect do light, dry heat, moist heat, presence of oxygen have on various vitamins? How can we make allowance for these effects in meal planning?
5. Prepare a chart summarizing the characteristics of vitamins essential to man. Divide the chart into two sections according to solubility. Items to be noted for each vitamin include the following: (*a*) name or letter of vitamin, (*b*) stability, (*c*) principal source, (*d*) importance to man, (*e*) storage in the body, if any, (*f*) results of vitamin deficiency.

See FOR YOURSELF

1. Prepare a hypothetical experiment or participate in actual experimentation to show the effects of vitamin deficiency on certain laboratory animals of your choice. Include the following: (*a*) a statement of the hypothesis or principle you are trying to prove, (*b*) method to be used, (*c*) data to be collected, (*d*) analysis of the data collected, (*e*) correlation of results with research by others in your area of experimentation, (*f*) conclusions, (*g*) final written report suitable for publication.

2. Since enzymes are organic catalysts, they do not enter into chemical digestion of food nor are they changed by it. Find out what happens to enzymes after they have been used.

CHAPTER 15

Digestion in the Mouth

Structures of the mouth. The mouth (Fig. 15-1) is the first part of the digestive system with which food comes in contact. It is bounded above by the *hard* and *soft palates,* on the sides by the *cheeks,* and in front by the *lips.* The *tongue* serves as part of the floor of the cavity. The lining of the mouth is a highly modified type of stratified squamous epithelium. It is similar in structure to the outer skin of the body but lacks the keratin that makes the skin a strongly protective organ. This lining contains nerve endings that respond to pain, pressure, heat, and cold just as the skin does. The mouth, therefore, has a degree of sensitivity that is lacking elsewhere in the digestive system.

The mouth opens into the **pharynx** (Fig. 15-2), a region shared by both the digestive and respiratory systems. The pharynx can be divided into three general parts: the *nasopharynx,* above the opening of the mouth and communicating with the cavity of the nose; the *oral* pharynx, behind the mouth; and the *laryngeal* pharynx, leading downward to the opening of the windpipe. The opening of the nasopharynx is protected by a small flap of tissue, the *uvula,* which hangs from the soft palate into the opening at the back of the mouth (Fig. 15-1). When a person swallows food, this flap is drawn upward and effectively closes

the entrance to the nasal region. The *tonsils* (Fig. 15-1), masses of lymph tissue, lie on either side of the opening, and occasionally other groups of similar cells, the *adenoids,* grow in the nasopharynx. If very large, these may cause difficulty in nasal breathing. The tonsils have pitted surfaces and may easily become infected by the growth of bacteria in the depressions.

The tongue. Not only does the tongue play a primary role in speech, but it also

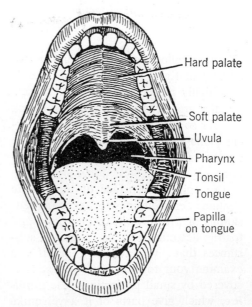

Fig. 15-1. *The mouth cavity showing the opening into the pharynx.*

Hard palate

Soft palate

Uvula

Pharynx

Tonsil

Tongue

Papilla on tongue

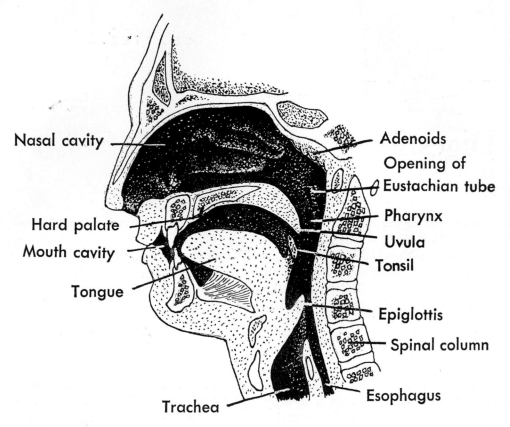

Fig. 15-2. *A longitudinal section through the head showing the mouth cavity and related structures.*

aids in swallowing and contains nerve endings that give us the sense of taste. It is a highly muscular organ; the muscle bundles are arranged in a very complex manner so that they lie in several different planes. The result is that the tongue can be moved in many different directions.

The epithelial surface of the tongue contains nerve endings for receiving sensations of pressure, heat, and cold, and for the detection of those chemical substances that give flavor to food. If you examine your tongue, you will see it is covered by small projections, the **papillae,** which give parts of it a velvetlike appearance. Some of the papillae are very small and inconspicuous, but to-

ward the back of the tongue they become large and are raised above the surface. The sense organs of taste, or **taste buds,** are located in the small depressions in the epithelium of the tongue, and are more heavily concentrated in the areas surrounding the papillae. A substance must be in solution before its flavor can be recognized. The solution passes through the opening of the taste bud (Fig. 15-3) and stimulates the taste cells, giving rise to impulses which are carried to the brain through nerve fibers at the base of the taste bud.

Not all surfaces of the tongue are sensitive to all flavors to the same degree. Taste buds are sensitive to four basic flavors: sweet, sour, bitter, and salt. Taste buds especially sensitive to sweet flavors are located near the tip of the tongue; those for sour flavors lie along the sides. The receptors for bitter flavors are on the surface of the tongue toward the back. Salty flavors are detected by taste buds at the front and sides of the tongue. If these various groups of taste buds are stimulated individually by a very weak electric current, the stimulus will produce in each group the same sensations as a chemical substance of the flavor for which the taste buds are specialized.

Many complex flavors are the result of smelling foods rather than tasting them. Odors are carried to the olfactory nerve endings located in the upper part of the nasal cavity, and we are apt to confuse the odor of the substance with its flavor simply because the material is present in the mouth at the time. You can seldom get the real flavor of a food when you have a heavy head cold. At that time the increased mucus secretions cover the olfactory nerve endings and you cannot detect the odors of the food.

The teeth. Dividing the food into smaller bits is called **mastication** (chewing). This primary function of the teeth

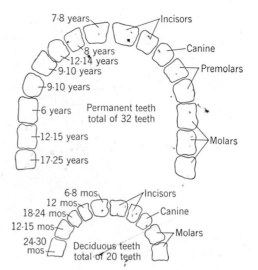

Fig. 15-4. *The types of teeth, their arrangement, and the ages at which they appear.*

is an important one because it increases the surface area of the morsel of food. As a result, the digestive juices can function more efficiently and rapidly than they could if the food were swallowed without being chewed. In man, as in all mammals, there are two sets of teeth: the first begins to appear within a few months after birth and is later replaced by the set that is designed to remain throughout life. This first set of teeth is called the **deciduous** (Lat., *decidere,* to fall down) teeth and is replaced by the **permanent teeth.** Since the deciduous teeth appear early in life, their formation begins some months before birth. The same is true of some of the permanent set: the buds from which they develop are formed in the tissues of the jaws before birth. The approximate ages at which the teeth appear are shown in Fig. 15-4.

When a tooth makes its appearance through the gum it is said to <u>erupt</u>. In the case of the deciduous teeth, this process may cause the young child some pain. It is also usually accompanied by

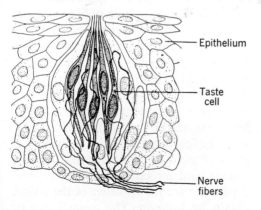

Fig. 15-3. *A taste bud with its nerve connections. The elongated and lightly stippled cells in the taste bud are supporting cells. (From Marsland,* Principles of Modern Biology, *Holt, 1957)*

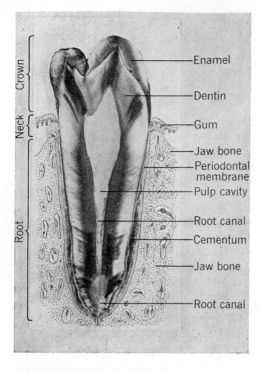

Crown

Neck

Root

Enamel

Dentin

Gum

Jaw bone

Periodontal membrane

Pulp cavity

Root canal

Cementum

Jaw bone

Root canal

Fig. 15-5. *Photomicrograph of a section of a human tooth under polarized light. The surrounding tissues have been sketched in.*

an increase in the amount of saliva formed because of the irritation to the gums and the resulting stimulation of the nerve endings. The eruption of the permanent set, with the possible exception of the last molars, is usually not accompanied by similar discomfort because there is not the same amount of irritation present. These second teeth do not simply push the earlier teeth out of their sockets, as many people believe; as they grow within the jaw, a group of cells, the **odontoclasts,** form in front of the tip of the tooth and dissolve the base of the first tooth. In this respect, the odontoclasts behave much as the osteoclasts do (Chapter 5). Finally, the first tooth is held in place by only the tissues of the gum and final separation from these may occur spontaneously, or the tooth may need a little coaxing.

There are four different types of teeth in the adult set, but only three in the deciduous set (Fig. 15-4). In front, in each jaw, there are four **incisor teeth** with edges adapted for biting. On each side of these is a **canine tooth** with a slightly pointed tip to aid in tearing food, and in back of these are four **premolar teeth**—two on each side. (These are sometimes spoken of as the *bicuspid* teeth because of the presence of two points, or *cusps.*) Since the cusps of the upper and lower teeth mesh when biting, their action is one of cutting or shearing food. There are three **molar teeth** on each side of the jaw behind the premolars. These are characterized by relatively flat surfaces that permit the food to be ground between them. The last of the molars to appear are the *wisdom teeth.* Normally, the total number of permanent teeth is 32, as compared with the 20 in the deciduous set. Occasionally these numbers vary because of the failure of some of the teeth to erupt.

During the formation of a tooth (Fig. 15-5) two separate groups of tissues add to its structure. The **enamel** is formed from **ameloblasts,** specialized types of epithelial cells. At the same time, the **dentin** is formed by **odontoblasts** which are derived from mesenchyme. Both of these regions are formed in a manner that is similar to the formation of bone (Chapter 5). The enamel is laid down in the form of microscopic hexagonal pillars that are held together by a cementing substance. This binding material is attacked first by mouth acids in the initial stage of tooth decay. Acids dissolve the cement and loosen the pillars, making a pathway for the invasion of the softer dentin by bacteria. The enamel covers only the *crown* of the tooth and extends a short distance below the gum line.

The dentin is the somewhat softer part of the tooth that lies below the enamel. It contains a large number of very fine canals, the **dentinal tubules,** which are similar to the small bony tubes in which the osteocytes lie (Fig. 5-5). Within each of these tubules is a cellular process from an odontoblast, the body of which lies against the dentin wall of the **pulp cavity.**

Below the surface of the gum, the tooth is surrounded by the **periodontal membrane,** which supports it in a sling-like manner. The fibers of this membrane are firmly attached by the **cementum,** at one end to the tooth socket in the **jaw bone,** and at the other end to the root. The slinglike arrangement prevents the tooth from being pushed inward by the considerable force exerted on the tooth in chewing. However, in those cases where the teeth do not oppose each other at the correct angle (*malocclusion*), there is a lever action of one tooth against another which pushes the teeth out of their normal position. The abnormal pressure may eventually result in disease of the periodontal membrane. After a tooth has been removed from the jaw, bone fills in the cavity that is created.

The pulp cavity contains the blood vessels and nerves essential for the nourishment of the teeth. If bacteria invade these soft tissues, infection can spread rapidly downward through the **root canal** to the bone. An abscess then forms at the base of the root.

Mastication. Four pairs of muscles are involved in the process of chewing. Because of the manner and place of their origins and insertions, they give to the lower jaw a slightly rotary motion as well as the more obvious up-and-down movement. The lips, cheeks, and tongue also have their roles in the process of mastication. When the teeth come together, the food is squeezed out from between them into the mouth cavity. The lips and cheeks are then drawn inward as the jaw is lowered for the next biting motion and the tongue spreads outward toward the sides. These motions tend to push the food back between the teeth again so that it can be rechewed. The potential force of the muscles responsible for the motion of the jaws is much greater than that actually required to chew the food. By the use of an electronic device, it has been found recently that the incisors can exert a force of between 24 and 55 pounds while the molars can develop forces of between 73 and 198 pounds, depending on the individual. It is not the force of the teeth on the food that is important, but rather the grinding motion mentioned above that serves to break the food down.

An important result of proper mastication of food is the breakdown of the cellulose fibers of plant materials. This allows the digestive juices to act on parts of the food that would otherwise be inaccessible because of their enclosure by cellulose walls. Persons who have lost their teeth or are equipped with poorly fitting dentures sometimes suffer from nutritional disorders because they cannot chew their food sufficiently. On the other hand, excessive chewing of food, as some food faddists recommend, has no special merit.

Salivary glands. The process of mastication is helped by the saliva, which is formed in and secreted by the **salivary glands.** This fluid plays several roles. It softens and lubricates the food mass, which can then be more easily chewed and swallowed. It also dissolves some of the food so that it can be tasted. Saliva partly digests the starch in foods. In addition, saliva washes the teeth, helps neutralize mouth acids, and keeps the inside of the mouth flexible and moist. This last function of the saliva is especially important for speech.

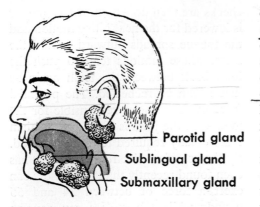

+ Parotid gland

Sublingual gland

Submaxillary gland

Fig. 15-6. *A diagram of the location of the three pairs of salivary glands.*

The three pairs of salivary glands (located on either side of the mouth) empty into the mouth by separate ducts. In Fig. 15-6, the **parotid gland** may be seen lying just in front of and slightly below the level of the opening of the ear. These are the largest of the glands and the ones that usually become enlarged during an attack of mumps. Below it and near the angle of the lower jaw is the **submaxillary** (submandibular) **gland,** and under the side of the tongue is the **sublingual gland.**

The saliva-forming cells are at the ends of small branches leading off from the main duct. They are a compound type of gland composed of serous and mucous cells (Fig. 15-7A). When the gland has been inactive for a time, the cells become filled with granules (Fig. 15-7B) which disappear after a period of activity (Fig. 15-7C). This indicates that the materials in saliva, other than water, are formed as solid substances within the cells and then converted into a fluid that can pass through the cell membrane, and thence by ducts into the mouth.

Saliva is a mixture of different chemical compounds, the composition changing as the activity of the gland increases or decreases. It has an average pH value

of 6.7, which means that it is slightly acid in its reaction. Normally, the saliva contains about 99 percent water. In this are dissolved minute traces of several different salts of sodium, potassium, and calcium, as well as organic materials like the enzyme ptyalin. Mucin also forms a part of the saliva. The fact that there is a very high percentage of water in the saliva indicates that the glands are a storage depot for this fluid. All of us are acquainted with the fact that if we become excessively thirsty, our mouths become dry. This is the result of water being withdrawn from the glands in order to replenish some of the fluid that has been lost from the blood by

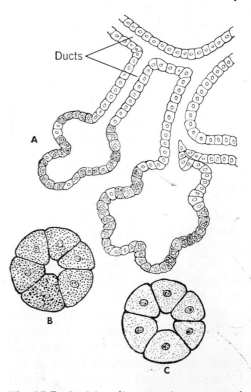

Ducts

A

B

C

Fig. 15-7. *At A is a diagram of a compound gland. The darker cells are those that secrete. At B is a group of cells following a period of inactivity. At C is shown a group of cells after a period of active secretion. Note the difference in the number of granules in B as compared with C.*

sweating, or as a result of strenuous physical exertion.

The secretion of saliva is entirely controlled by the nervous system. As we have pointed out in an earlier chapter, this secretion may be the result of a conditioned reflex brought about by the sight, smell, or even the thought of food. There is also a simple reflex secretion of saliva when food is placed in the mouth, especially if the food is in small particles, as is the case when it is thoroughly chewed. These small particles stimulate nerve endings in the mouth, and in solution also stimulate the taste buds. Through fibers of the autonomic nervous system, there is a dilation of the blood vessels passing to the glands, and saliva is produced. The daily flow of saliva in a normal individual amounts to between 1 and 1.5 quarts. Much of this saliva is produced during periods when there is no food in the mouth.

Digestive action of ptyalin. Food remains in the mouth for such a relatively short time that little digestion can occur there. Nevertheless, the action of the enzyme ptyalin should not be underrated. Ptyalin can decompose starch into simpler products, the dextrins, and break off some of the disaccharide maltose. Although little of this activity occurs in the mouth, digestion of food by ptyalin may continue in the stomach. The ball of food (*bolus*) does not break up immediately upon reaching the stomach, so digestion by the action of ptyalin may continue for as long as half an hour. Eventually, the acid in the gastric juice will stop this digestion, but by then, as much as 75 percent of the starch of potatoes and bread may have been broken down. The digestive process in the small intestine completes the breakdown of carbohydrates by the action of numerous enzymes. This will be discussed in detail in Chapter 17.

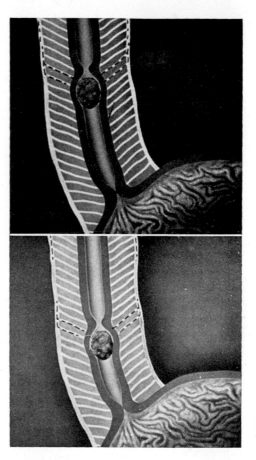

Fig. 15-8. *These two diagrams show the passage of a bolus of food through the esophagus. A series of nerve impulses (black dotted lines) causes the muscles (white diagonal lines) to contract in succession so as to force the food toward the stomach. (Encyclopaedia Britannica Films)*

Deglutition. The act of swallowing (*deglutition*) is a complex one involving many of the muscles that form the walls of the mouth and pharynx. It is usually started as a voluntary process, but shortly becomes involuntary as the food comes under control of the smooth muscles of the esophagus. When we swallow, the tip of the tongue arches slightly and starts to push the food toward the back of the mouth. Then a wave of muscular contraction passes over the tongue which forces the food against the hard palate. At the same time, the uvula and soft palate close the opening to the nasopharynx, preventing food from going into that region. Once the bolus reaches the pharynx, involuntary control takes over the process. As the food moves backward and downward, the soft palate is drawn slightly down, just as the **larynx** (*voice box*) is drawn upward toward the **epiglottis** (the covering of the opening of the windpipe). As added insurance against the entry of food into the respiratory system, the nervous impulses responsible for breathing stop so that it is almost impossible to breathe and swallow at the same time. Action of the involuntary muscles sends the bolus down the **esophagus** to the stomach.

The series of involuntary muscular contractions that move food along the digestive tract is known as **peristalsis** (Fig. 15-8). These contractions appear in back of the bolus and push it forward. At the same time, the muscles of the walls of the esophagus in the region of the food and preceding it relax, thereby relieving pressure on the bolus so that it can go forward. Solid food of an average consistency requires between five and six seconds to pass along the ten inches of the esophagus. When the peristaltic wave reaches the stomach it stimulates the **cardiac sphincter** valve that guards the upper end of this organ. The opening of this valve allows food to pass from the esophagus into the stomach.

When fluids are drunk, they pass quickly through the slightly dilated esophagus and outrun the peristaltic wave. They then collect at the cardiac sphincter and are able to enter only after the wave of muscular contraction has reached that point. If, however, there is a rapid succession of swallowing movements, as in drinking a glass of water, the sphincter may remain open. The fluid then passes directly from the esophagus into the stomach.

The esophagus is covered by a tough protective tissue. Beneath this are two layers of muscle fibers, the outer of which runs longitudinally (lengthwise) and the other in a circular direction. It is through the alternating contraction and relaxation of these two layers that the peristaltic wave is set up. Internally, the esophagus is lined by a mucous membrane that is held loosely to the circular muscles by connective tissue. The mucous secretion of the lining serves as a lubricant.

SPEAKING OF Physiology

Briefly identify each of the following:

adenoid	enamel	soft palate
bolus	epiglottis	papilla
canine	incisor	peristalsis
crown of tooth	laryngeal pharynx	premolar
cuspid	larynx	root of tooth
deciduous teeth	mastication	salivary gland
deglutition	molar	taste bud
dentin	nasopharynx	tonsil
dentition	hard palate	uvula

Test YOUR KNOWLEDGE

1. Describe the process of swallowing. At what point does voluntary control end and involuntary control take over?
2. In the digestive system, what is the difference between a primary organ and accessory organs? Give examples of each.
3. Is the *uvula* a part of the hard palate or soft palate? What function does this structure perform?
4. What is tonsillitis? What treatment is often used for its relief?
5. List and describe the four basic functions of the tongue.
6. The sense of taste and the sense of smell are concerned with the same type of stimuli. Why do we frequently confuse the two senses?
7. Digestion is both a chemical and a mechanical process. The mouth is largely responsible for which one of the two? Explain the reason for your answer.
8. When we say an infant is "cutting" his baby teeth, what is actually happening? How are these temporary teeth removed to make room for the permanent teeth?
9. What is tooth decay? How is it prevented?
10. Describe the muscular process of mastication.
11. What are the functions of saliva and how does its composition aid in performing these? How is the secretion of saliva controlled?
12. A dry soda cracker will begin to taste sweet after it has been chewed for a long period. Explain why.

See FOR YOURSELF

1. Prepare a report on the advantages and disadvantages of a career in professional dentistry. Interview your family dentist or obtain literature from the American Dental Society on dentistry as a career.

2. Show how a conditioned reflex can be established in an animal, using the production of saliva as the basis of your experiment. Can this conditioned reflex be established in humans?

3. Look up the meaning of the following classifications of animals: herbivorous, carnivorous, omnivorous. Find out how tooth structure is related to the general diet of each type of animal.

4. Find out how cases of malocclusion are corrected. What dental specialty deals with such problems?

CHAPTER 16

Digestion in the Stomach

Structure of the stomach. The human *stomach* lies to the left of and just below the diaphragm, as shown in the Trans-Vision insert which follows page 312. Actually the shape of the stomach is highly variable, depending on several factors. As the X-ray photograph in Fig. 16-1 shows, the stomach is J-shaped in

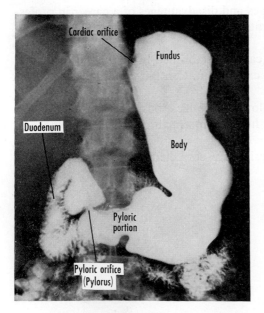

Fig. 16-1. *X-ray photograph of a normal stomach showing the various regions. Beyond the stomach can be seen a small section of the duodenum, filled with a barium compound which is fed to a person before X-rays are taken to make the organs opaque. (Dr. John A. Campbell)*

the living individual, with the upper portion considerably greater in diameter than the lower end. If a thin person is standing, the stomach becomes quite elongated, but if he lies down, the organ becomes shorter although it retains its general J-shape. The amount of food present in the stomach will alter its shape, as will the effect of the pressure of the intestines that lie below it. It is therefore impossible to say that the stomach has a definite shape in the same way that other organs of the digestive system retain their form.

The esophagus opens into the stomach at the **cardiac orifice** (Fig. 16-1). The outlet of the stomach is at the **pyloric orifice** or **pylorus,** which connects with the **duodenum** of the small intestine. The stomach is divided into three general parts: the **fundus,** which is the rounded upper portion; the **pyloric portion** at the lower curve of the J; and the **body,** which lies between these two regions.

The outside layer of the stomach is a thick serous coat which is continuous with the **peritoneum,** the membrane that lines the entire abdominal cavity. At various points, the peritoneum grows forward and surrounds the organs of the abdomen, holding them, as it were, in a sling. From the larger, or left, curve of the stomach (*greater curvature*), this membrane grows downward to form the

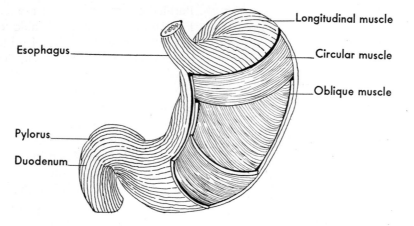

Fig. 16-2. *The structure of the stomach showing its muscular coats.*

greater omentum which hangs like an apron over the front of the intestines. It contains large deposits of fat. Three layers of smooth muscle line the walls of the stomach (Fig. 16-2). As in other organs of the digestive tract, there are layers of both circular and longitudinal muscles, but in addition, the fundus and part of the body contain an inner layer of oblique muscle tissue. The inner lining of the stomach is a mucous membrane, the **gastric mucosa**, which lies in folds called the **rugae** (see Fig. 16-3).

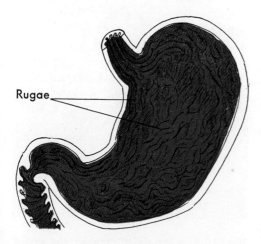

Fig. 16-3. *A section of the stomach to show the mucous lining and the rugae.*

When the stomach is distended with food, these folds stretch so that the interior of the stomach is quite smooth. The capacity of the stomach is 1 to 1.5 quarts.

The gastric glands. The gastric mucosa contains the long tubular **gastric glands** that secrete the **gastric juices** used in digestion. It has been estimated that some 35,000,000 of these glands line the normal stomach. As Fig. 16-4 shows, they contain three principal types of cells: (1) *parietal cells* which secrete hydrochloric acid; (2) *chief cells of the body of the gland* which secrete pepsinogen; and (3) *chief cells of the neck* which secrete mucin.

Hydrochloric acid. The gastric juice is the most acid fluid of the body. This characteristic is due to the presence of hydrochloric acid, which in a concentrated form will destroy tissue. In the concentration in which it is present in the gastric juice (about 0.6 percent) it does not affect the normal, living stomach in this way. Following death, the mucous lining of the stomach is rapidly destroyed, so there is evidently some protective agent present in the living organ that prevents destruction of the tissue. It has been suggested that protection

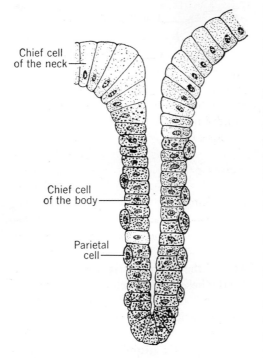

Chief cell of the neck

Chief cell of the body

Parietal cell

Fig. 16-4. *Diagram of a gastric gland showing the three principal types of cells.*

is afforded by the salts of sodium and potassium, especially when they are combined with chlorides and bicarbonates. The range of acidity of gastric juice is from a pH of 1.7 to 0.3.

The HCl functions in several different ways during gastric digestion. In the first place, its presence is necessary for the formation of pepsin from the proenzyme, pepsinogen. Secondly, pepsin is unable to act in the digestion of proteins unless the gastric contents remain acid. A third activity of the HCl is to destroy bacteria that might have entered with the food. This action is so efficient that the material that leaves the stomach is virtually sterile under normal conditions. A fourth property of hydrochloric acid is that it dissolves some of the salts in the food we eat.

Pepsin. The active enzyme of the stomach, pepsin, digests proteins only.

Purified crystals of pepsin are shown in Fig. 16-5. This enzyme is able to break down the large molecules of proteins into simpler molecules which, however, are still too large to enter the blood stream. These intermediate products, the **proteoses** and **peptones,** are groups of amino acids that have been separated from the original protein molecule. This preliminary action of pepsin converts the insoluble forms of protein into soluble compounds which pass into the small intestine for final digestive processes.

For many years, a second protein-splitting enzyme was thought to be present in the human gastric juice. This enzyme was called **rennin** and was considered to act only on the protein of milk, **casein.** Now it is known that this enzyme does not exist in humans, although it may be present in the stomachs of other young mammals, especially calves. The action of rennin is truly amazing. One part of the enzyme is able to convert

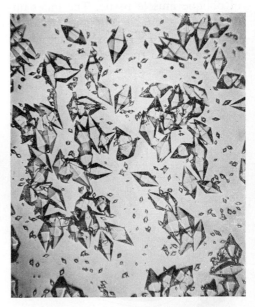

Fig. 16-5. *Crystals of pepsin, the active protein-digesting enzyme of the gastric juice. (John H. Nothrop)*

4,550,000 parts of milk into a curd in approximately 10 minutes at a temperature of 40° C. and a pH value of 6.2. Its action hastens the digestion of milk because it changes a liquid form of the protein into a solid form and thereby permits the digestive enzymes to function more effectively on it. Pepsin has a similar action on the milk we drink. It is able to convert 800,000 times its own weight of milk protein into a curd under the same temperature and time conditions. The fact that the pH value of the human stomach is considerably below that necessary for the proper function of rennin is a strong argument against the presence of this enzyme in our digestive system. Commercially, rennin is used extensively in the manufacture of cheese and milk desserts.

Gastric lipase. Another enzyme in the stomach about which there has been much debate among physiologists is **gastric lipase.** This has the ability to break fats down into fatty acids and glycerol. There appears to be a small amount of this enzyme formed in the stomach, but its action is very weak because it is destroyed when the acidity of the stomach becomes higher than 0.2 percent. The extent to which it affects fats is unknown, but any action it might have would occur early in the digestive process and in connection with the breakdown of fats such as those found in milk and ice cream.

Phases of gastric secretion. The quantity of gastric juice produced during an average meal is about 1 to 1.5 pints. The secretion of gastric juice is partly under nervous control and partly under the control of a chemical regulator belonging to the group of secretions known as **hormones.** We will discuss these in Chapter 31, but you should know that hormones are formed by ductless glands that secrete directly into the blood stream. Hormones are then absorbed by the cells of the body from the blood.

The sight, odor, taste, or even the thought of food will start the activity of the gastric glands. This is the **psychic phase** of gastric secretion. In this respect the glands are showing the same type of conditioned reflex that the salivary glands exhibit under similar stimuli. The gastric juice produced in this phase is rich in pepsin, which has been called appetite juice. When food is introduced experimentally directly into the stomach, without the influence of sensory stimuli, secretion is only three-fourths normal. The question then arises as to what type of mechanism continues the secretion of gastric juice in sufficient quantities to complete the digestion of the meal. Nervous stimulation caused by the presence of food in the stomach is not the answer, because when all gastric nerves are cut, secretion is hardly affected.

Experimental animals were used to work out the problem of how digestion continues after the psychic phase has stopped. The cardiac end of the stomach was tied off while these animals were under anesthesia, and salt solution was introduced into the cavity of the stomach through a tube placed in the pyloric portion. After an hour the solution was removed and tested for the presence of hydrochloric acid and pepsin. None was found. However, if small bits of the lining of the pyloric portion were ground up and an extract of this injected into the stomach's blood supply, pepsin and hydrochloric acid both appeared in the salt solution. This indicated that some chemical substance present in the extract of the pyloric lining was responsible for the stimulation of the gastric glands and the formation of more gastric juice. Later work has confirmed this idea. It is now believed that the presence of food in the stomach stimulates the formation of the hormone of **gastrin,** which is discharged into the blood stream. Carried by the blood, gastrin arouses the gland cells to further activity. This phase of secretion is called the **gastric phase.** Gastrin belongs to that group of hormones known as **secretagogues** because of their ability to stimulate secretion in a gland. We will have occasion to refer to some more of these in the next chapter.

Stomach movements. If a small rubber balloon is swallowed and then inflated in the stomach, a record can be made of the intensity and frequency of the movements of the stomach under various conditions. Such records are made with the aid of a kymograph similar to that used to record a muscle twitch. An apparatus of this type shows that when the stomach is empty, hunger contractions occur at irregular intervals. These contractions may be of sufficient intensity to arouse hunger pangs. It was thought at one time that when a person was suffering from these hunger pangs, the sight, odor, or thought of food would increase the contractions of the stomach. However, recent work on gastric motility has shown that the opposite is true. The stomach slows down in anticipation of the food it is to receive.

From X-ray studies of the stomach during digestion it is seen that the fundus plays the role of a reservoir for the reception of food from the esophagus. Fig. 16-6 shows a series of waves passing over the pyloric end of the stomach; note how the body and the fundus show little activity. A succession of slower waves gradually passes the food from the fundus and body of the stomach toward the pylorus, where the food is churned into a thick liquid state called *chyme.* As the stomach empties, it again resumes its J-shape.

The passage of food from the stomach to the small intestine is controlled by the peristaltic rhythms of the stomach muscles and by the consistency of the stomach contents. The presence of food in the first part of the small intestine (duodenum) causes a slowing down of the gastric peristaltic movements, and the pyloric valve remains closed. Experiments have demonstrated that the pyloric sphincter closes when solid particles touch it. These are moved back into the pyloric portion for further liquefaction. Only when the food mass is converted into chyme is it allowed to pass through the pyloric sphincter.

The length of time food normally remains in the stomach is determined by the nature of the material. Foods that are rich in proteins remain longest in the stomach and produce the high acidity necessary for the action of pepsin. Thus, meats may stay from three to four hours. Foods with high carbohydrate content, such as many fruits and vegetables, leave the stomach within 1.5 and 2 hours. Cereal foods have an intermediate position. The difference in emptying time for these various foods is probably related to the length of time required to liquefy them. Carbohydrates and fats are more easily reduced to a semifluid state than are proteins; thus they can be released from the stomach into the duodenum sooner.

Very little material is absorbed into the blood stream through the walls of the stomach because most foods have not been decomposed into sufficiently simple materials to permit this. Some water, glucose, a few salts, and alcohol are the principal materials passing through the stomach membranes into the blood stream.

Vomiting. Under certain conditions, the normal path of the peristaltic waves of the stomach is reversed and vomiting occurs. This process is controlled by a nerve center lying in the medulla oblongata of the brain. The stimuli capable of affecting this response may arise from several different areas, the back of the mouth and the pharynx being especially sensitive to stimuli that give rise to vomiting. This explains why the process can be started by tickling the back of the throat. The lining of the stomach and especially the duodenum are so highly sensitive that vomiting may be initiated by emetics such as strong salt solutions and mustard in warm water. Rhythmic stimulation of the semicircular canals as the result of the motion of a ship, an airplane, or a swing may cause a person to vomit.

The movements involved in vomiting are primarily those of the abdominal muscles. The feeling of nausea that precedes an attack is accompanied by an increase in the amount of saliva. This is swallowed and, with air that is also gulped down, causes a distension of the lower end of the esophagus. The stomach is pressed against the diaphragm and the force required to eject the material from the stomach is then supplied by

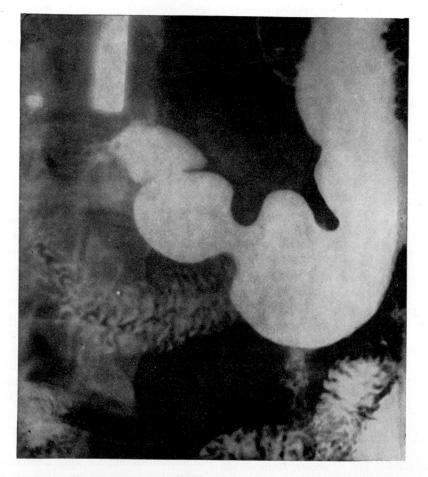

Fig. 16-6. *X-ray photograph of the stomach showing a wave of muscular contraction passing over it. The white object at the left is a metal rod which shows the location of the backbone. (Courtesy Roentgenology Staff, Billings Hospital)*

the contraction of the abdominal muscles.

Psychosomatic influences. Since the movements of the stomach are closely controlled by the nervous system, it is not surprising that a person's emotional outlook may be reflected in the way his stomach behaves. If a person is of a calm disposition and does not permit small annoyances to bother him unduly, his stomach will probably respond in a normal manner. On the other hand, if he tends to be emotionally upset, his stomach will reflect his attitude.

A very graphic demonstration of this control of the nervous system over the activities of the stomach was made by two New York doctors, Wolf and Wolff. A patient had swallowed some boiling

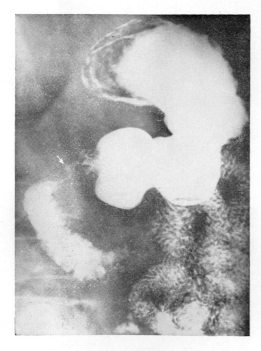

Fig. 16-7. *The arrow shows the location of a duodenal ulcer. Note that the fundus of the stomach is almost empty. Some of the barium compound has left the stomach and is seen in the intestine below the stomach. (Dr. John A. Campbell)*

hot chowder when he was nine years old. The scar tissue that formed over the burned area closed off the esophagus, and it was necessary to make an opening through the abdominal wall directly into the stomach so that he could feed himself. Such a permanent opening is called a *fistula*. Through this opening the doctors were able to observe the action of the stomach on various types of food as well as its behavior in states of emotional stress. When the patient reacted to a situation with fear, the gastric mucosa became pale and the normal movements of the stomach were reduced or stopped entirely. If, however, he became angry and showed resentment toward a situation, the mucosa responded by becoming filled with blood and turning a bright red color. The motions of the stomach were also greatly increased in rate and force. There was an increase in acid production. These findings bore out observations made in 1833 by an Army surgeon, Dr. William Beaumont, on Alexis St. Martin, a man who had been wounded in the abdomen and had developed a fistula.

Continued attacks of indigestion may reflect both emotional and physical problems. Some serious diseases produce symptoms which may be confused with those arising from simple indigestion. Stomach or duodenal ulcers, cancer of the stomach, and some types of liver diseases may be the underlying causes for these symptoms.

People who are under constant emotional strain of one type or another may succumb to ulcers because of the increased motility of the stomach, accompanied by the appearance of an excessive amount of hydrochloric acid. If this condition of hyperacidity continues, the normal defenses of the stomach or duodenal linings are broken down and irritation develops. There are two regions where ulcers most frequently appear: in the region of the pylorus and in the duodenum (Fig. 16-7). A change in the emotional outlook of the person is the best cure for this condition. During the period of recovery, an ulcer victim should have a diet that is sufficiently soft to prevent further irritation. Also, since the symptoms of an ulcer are relieved by the presence of food in the stomach, the patient is usually directed to take at least six light meals per day instead of the usual three.

Unfortunately, many deaths each year are caused by stomach cancer (Fig. 16-8). Many of these are undoubtedly unnecessary. Often people do not heed the preliminary symptoms. The cause of stomach cancer is unknown, but if it is detected early enough, the chances for complete recovery are increasing each year. The treatment for gastric cancer usually involves removing the stomach. Since quite a few people are now living normal lives without benefit of a stomach, the organ is obviously not indispensable. However, early treatment is imperative. If a gastric cancer is not recognized and treated in its early stages, cells from it may enter the blood stream and

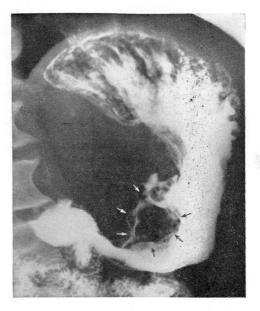

Fig. 16-8. *An X-ray photograph of a gastric cancer. The extent of the cancer is indicated by the arrows. (Dr. John A. Campbell)*

be carried to other regions of the body where they can continue to grow and produce more cancers in other places. This passage of cancer cells from one region to another by way of the blood is known as **metastasis.**

SPEAKING OF Physiology

Briefly identify each of the following:

cardiac sphincter	gastrin	pepsin
duodenum	HCl	peritoneum
fundus	hyperacidity	pyloric sphincter *keeps food from going into small*
gastric lipase	metastasis	pyloric portion *intestine*

near pyloric valve

Test YOUR KNOWLEDGE

1. Why is it difficult to describe the shape of the stomach?
2. Describe the structure of the stomach wall. How does this differ from other regions of the digestive tract?

3. Gastric juice is the second digestive juice which comes into contact with food. Describe its characteristics and composition. What tissues produce the substances which compose the gastric juice?

4. What is the effect of gastric juice on saliva? Does any digestion of carbohydrates occur in the stomach?

5. What specialized functions does the hydrochloric acid of the stomach perform?

6. Describe the chemical phases of digestion that occur in the stomach.

7. What did the two New York doctors, Wolf and Wolff, learn from their observation of their patient? How are the results of these observations of value in understanding digestive processes?

8. How does merely seeing or smelling food bring about the production of gastric juice?

9. Briefly describe the causes, symptoms, and treatment for stomach and duodenal ulcers.

See FOR YOURSELF

1. What was the scientific significance of Dr. William Beaumont's experiments on Alexis St. Martin, "the man with a window in his stomach"? (1833)

2. Determine the effect of intravenous feeding on the normal activity and function of the stomach.

3. Prepare a report on Ivan Pavlov's research on the mechanism of secretion in the stomach. Describe his research methods and the conclusions he reached.

4. Visit your doctor or your local hospital to find out how barium compounds are used to obtain X-ray photographs of the digestive organs. Write a report on your findings.

5. Report on the mechanism of a stomach pump and on how this device is used.

6. Get some rennin and pepsin and demonstrate their effects on various protein foods.

7. Get the stomach of a freshly-killed mammal from a slaughter house. Dissect it and examine its structure to identify its parts. Scrape the stomach lining and mix the scrapings with water. Filter this mixture and test the filtered liquid on some protein foods to see the action of any enzymes that may be present.

CHAPTER 17

Digestion in the Small Intestine: The Liver and Pancreas

Once the food material (chyme) is released from the stomach, it is subjected to a variety of changes during its passage through the small intestine. The relation of the various organs responsible for these changes can be more clearly understood with the help of the Trans-Vision following page 312, and the longitudinal section as shown in Fig. 17-1. Reference should be frequently made to these drawings to clarify the concepts in the following discussion.

The great length of the small intestine, some 23 feet, is evidence of its importance in the digestive process. From the small intestine digested material is absorbed into the blood stream for distribution through the body.

Food material passes from the stomach through the pyloric sphincter into the **duodenum,** which is the first part of the small intestine. The name of this region is derived from the Latin word, *duodeni,* meaning "twelve each," because it was originally identified as being as long as the breadth of twelve fingers (about 10 inches). The duodenum curves upward, forming a horseshoe shape around the head of the pancreas. Its diameter, slightly greater than that of the remainder of the small intestine, is about one

and three-fourths inches. Structurally, it is quite inflexible compared to the rest of the small intestine and lacks their supporting membranes.

The second section of the small intestine is the **jejunum,** which measures about 9 feet in length. The third region, the **ileum,** is about 13 feet long. Total length of the small intestine may vary from the average of 23 feet to between 15 and 31 feet. The difference has no apparent relation to the age, height, or weight of the individual.

The jejunum and the ileum are both supported by thin, strong membranes which are the outgrowths of the peritoneum. These **mesenteries** not only support the folds of the intestine, but they also hold the numerous blood vessels and nerves that pass to and from it. Unlike the duodenum, the jejunum and ileum both have considerable freedom of movement and shift their positions as a result of changes in posture and of the peristaltic activity of the intestine.

For a full understanding of the digestive processes that occur in the small intestine, it is necessary to consider two important glands that pour digestive juices into the duodenum. These are the liver and the pancreas.

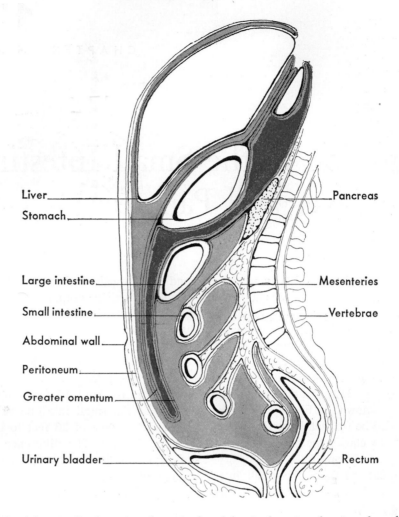

Fig. 17-1. *A longitudinal section through the abdominal cavity showing the relation of the mesenteries and the peritoneum. Some of the organs, such as the pancreas, are at first covered by the peritoneum, but this later disappears.*

THE LIVER

The *liver* is the largest gland in the body and weighs between two and one-half and three and one-half pounds. It lies in the upper right quarter of the abdominal cavity and occupies a major part of that region, with the left lobe projecting downward over part of the stomach. There are four lobes in the liver; two of these can be seen from the front and the other two, much smaller lobes, are visible on the back surface. Under the large right lobe is the pear-shaped *gall-bladder,* the lower margin of which projects slightly below the edge of the lobe. In consistency, the liver is a soft solid of reddish-brown color that is easily broken and cut. The entire liver is surrounded by a serous coat and a thin fibrous coat, but the peritoneum covers only part of it.

Structure of the liver lobule. Internally, the liver is divided into *lobules,* each one to two millimeters in diameter (1 millimeter = 0.039 inch). These, in turn, are made up of **cords of liver cells** that radiate out from a **central vein** in an irregular manner, the columns frequently joining each other. Each cord consists of two adjacent rows of cells (Fig. 17-2). Within these cells take place the many chemical activities that make the liver an intricate laboratory concerned with digestion and metabolism.

Our chief interest here is the function of the liver in secreting bile. The other important liver functions are discussed later in this book.

Portal circulations. The blood supply of the liver is an extensive one. The **portal vein** (Fig. 17-3) brings blood to the liver from the gastrointestinal tract, the pancreas, and the spleen. A relatively small **hepatic artery** also carries to it blood rich in oxygen. The portal vein, once it enters the liver, breaks down into small branches which form a network around the lobules. These branches, joined by capillaries of the hepatic artery, give rise to the **sinusoids** (Fig. 17-2) which pass between the cords to enter the central veins. The central veins of several lobules join and eventually form the **hepatic veins,** which conduct the blood from the liver on its way to the heart.

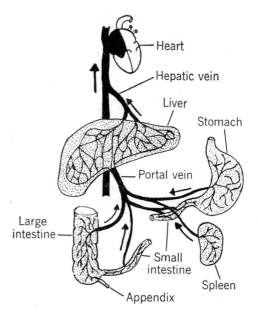

Fig. 17-3. *Diagram of the general distribution of the portal vein. It arises as capillaries in the digestive organs and flows to the liver, where it again breaks down into capillaries. Generally, veins arise from capillaries and flow to the heart without forming another set of capillaries.*

The sinusoids are unusual parts of the circulatory system in that their capillary-like walls are so extremely thin and irregular that the blood is often in direct contact with the cells. This permits an easy exchange of material between the cells and the blood.

Bile ducts. The liver cells obtain from the blood the materials needed to form **bile,** which is collected in minute **bile vacuoles** within the cells (Fig. 17-4). These empty their secretions into the *bile capillaries* (Fig. 17-2), which pass between the two layers of cells that make up the cords. The bile capillaries run together to form increasingly large ducts and these eventually leave the liver as the **hepatic ducts.** The bile passes from the hepatic ducts through the **cystic duct** into the gall-bladder where it is stored

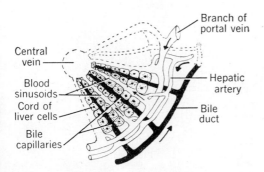

Fig. 17-2. *A diagram of a section of a liver lobule. The central vein carries blood away from the blood sinusoids.*

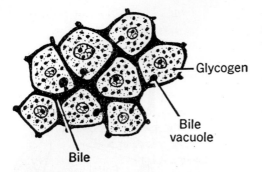

Fig. 17-4. *Diagram of liver cells showing bile formation. Glycogen is stored as granules in the cells.*

until needed for the digestive process. When food reaches the small intestine, the gall-bladder contracts, expelling bile which flows through the cystic duct into the **common bile duct.** As Fig. 17-5 shows, this duct is joined by the **pancreatic duct** at a common opening in the duodenum about three inches beyond the pylorus.

When food is not present in the small intestine, the bile is kept from flowing into the duodenum by a sphincter valve at the opening of the duct into the intestine. Closure of this valve and the resulting pressure changes cause the bile in the ducts to back up into the gall-bladder to await the digestive requirements of the duodenum.

There is a curious anatomical feature found in the cystic duct of the mammal group to which we belong, the Primates, and to no other. The mucous membrane lining this tube is folded in a series of spiral ridges that make the duct quite rigid and prevent its collapse or distension as the pressure in the gall-bladder changes when a person stands or lies down. The ridges, known as the **spiral valves of Heister** in honor of the man who discovered them, are probably a response to the upright method of locomotion that characterizes the Primates.

The composition of bile. Bile, though it contains no enzymes, plays a highly important role in the digestion of fats. The most important constituents are three substances, of which the first two are responsible for the characteristic color and action of the bile. These are: (1) *bile pigments,* (2) *bile salts,* and (3) *cholesterol.*

Human bile is a yellowish-orange fluid that owes its color to two different bile pigments: **bilirubin,** a red compound, and **biliverdin,** which is green. In man, bilirubin is the chief pigment of bile; biliverdin is only the product of oxidation of bilirubin. These pigments are formed as a result of the breakdown of the blood's red pigment, **hemoglobin.** This worn-out hemoglobin is broken down into bilirubin in various organs and tissues, such as the spleen, liver, connective tissue, and bone marrow. The iron content of hemoglobin is extracted for storage in the body, and the bilirubin is carried into the portal circulation and thence to the liver cells. In the liver, the cells that effect the conversion of hemoglobin are the specialized **Kupffer cells** which lie in the walls of the sinusoids. The bilirubin passes from these cells di-

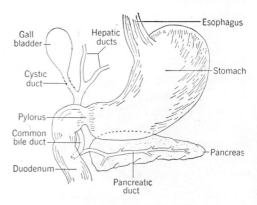

Fig. 17-5. *Diagram showing the relation of the liver and the pancreas to the small intestine.*

rectly into the nearby liver cells which form the bile.

Within the small intestine, the bilirubin undergoes further chemical changes and is converted into **urobilinogen,** a yellowish substance that accounts for the yellow color of the **feces** (intestinal wastes). Some of the urobilinogen is absorbed through the walls of the large intestine and is returned to the liver for reuse.

In the formation of bile the liver exhibits both a secretory and excretory activity. A **secretion** may be defined as a product of cells that is used by the body in its performance of a definite function. As we will see shortly, the bile aids in the digestion of fats, and it can thus be considered a secretion. An **excretion,** on the other hand, is a substance that the body eliminates as a waste material. In this capacity the liver plays an excretory role because it gets rid of worn-out hemoglobin and other products, all of which could cause damage to the body if they were permitted to accumulate.

Digestive action of bile. The bile salts are **sodium glycocholate** and **sodium taurocholate.** These are the constituents of bile concerned with the digestive process. Just as we use soap and water to wash grease off our hands, the digestive system uses these salts as a detergent to surround droplets of fat with a layer of "soap" so that the droplets do not fuse together again. By separating fats and oils into very small droplets of this type, an emulsion is formed. The breaking of the large droplets of oil into tiny droplets greatly increases the surface area of the oil so that it can be subjected more completely to the action of the digestive enzymes. This action occurs in the small intestine, as will be discussed later. A second function of the bile salts is to make water-soluble those fatty acids that

do not readily dissolve in the intestinal fluids. A third function of these salts is to activate the enzyme lipase produced by the pancreas (and, to some extent, the lipase produced by the stomach). After their use in the digestive process, about 90 percent of the bile salts are reabsorbed by the portal circulation and returned to the liver for reuse.

Jaundice. We have not discussed cholesterol in connection with the digestive action of bile because its purpose is not known. Possibly it aids the bile salts in the emulsification process. However, most of our knowledge of biliary cholesterol is concerned with its role in gallbladder disease. In the bile ducts and gall-bladder this material may collect in the form of solid masses, **gall stones,** which may block the ducts and seriously interfere with the normal secretion of bile. This condition results in jaundice. The whites of the eyes and the skin become slightly yellow due to the accumulation of bilirubin in the blood. The feces are pasty-colored as a result of the absence of urobilinogen. Jaundice due to gall stones is the most common type and is known as **obstructive jaundice.** Another type results from a viral (virus) infection of the liver cells which reduces the liver's capacity to secrete bile. The viral type (**infectious hepatitis**) is highly contagious and can be transmitted by contaminated food or water. **Serum hepatitis,** another viral type, may be transmitted by blood transfusions in which the organism is present in the transfused blood.

Other functions of the liver. The formation of **glycogen** from glucose is an important function of the liver. A sample of blood taken from the portal vein following a meal rich in carbohydrates is found to contain a great deal of sugar. On the other hand, a sample of blood taken at the same time from some other part of the circulatory system shows a much smaller rise in sugar content. Since the blood from the digestive system flows through the liver, it is evident that the liver can regulate the amount of sugar in the general circulation. If this condition did not exist, great waste of this energy-producing food would result. The kidneys would then remove the excess and give rise to a condition of **glycosuria,** or sugar in the urine. After a period of fasting, blood from the portal vein contains very little sugar, but the amount in the general circulation remains at about its normal level. This is because the liver has converted some of its stored glycogen into glucose needed to keep the normal general level.

There is one normal condition with which the liver cannot cope. Following a meal in which excessive amounts of carbohydrates have been eaten, the blood and urine of a normal individual may show an increase in glucose. This simply means that such large quantities of sugars or starches have been ingested that the liver cannot take care of all of it.

As we shall see in a later chapter, the glands that produce hormones also play a role in maintaining the sugar content of the blood. *Adrenalin,* a hormone secreted by the adrenal glands, will increase the conversion of glycogen into glucose to meet the demands of an emergency. *Insulin,* on the other hand, prevents too rapid hydrolysis of glycogen and also promotes the storage of glycogen in the liver and its utilization in the muscles.

Deamination is a highly important function of the liver. Following a meal rich in proteins, a very high concentration of amino acids is found in the blood of the portal vein. In the liver, these acids are removed and the carbon, hydrogen, and oxygen are split off from them to form other compounds, especially glycogen. The amino parts (NH_2) are then converted into **urea** which is the principal nitrogen-containing waste of the body. The urea enters the circulatory system and is carried to the kidneys, from which it is excreted in the urine. In order for this process of deamination to occur in the liver, it is necessary for a special amino acid, **argenine,** to be present. This receives the amino groups and converts them into urea.

Another liver function takes place in the Kupffer cells of the sinusoids. These cells take in the droplets of fat that appear in the blood in a form too large to permit their passage through the cell membranes. The Kupffer cells chemically change the fat into a form that the liver cells can use, but just how these transformations occur is not clearly understood.

THE PANCREAS

The **pancreas** is an elongated, somewhat triangular gland, the *head* of which lies in a loop of the duodenum to the right of the pylorus (Fig. 17-5). The remainder of the gland extends to the left for about 5½ or 6 inches and tapers gradually to a narrow tail region. The microscopic structure of the compound gland shows that it is similar to the salivary glands: it is a **racemose** type of gland, the subdivisions resembling a bunch of grapes.

The pancreas contains two types of grandular tissue (Fig. 17-6). One type predominates and is the source of pancreatic juice. Isolated groups of cells, the **Islands of Langerhans,** produce **insulin,** a hormone which plays an important role in carbohydrate metabolism.

The secretion of pancreatic juice and bile is not a nerve reflex activity, but is under the control of secretagogues similar to that controlling the secretion of gastric juice. If all the efferent nerve to the gall-bladder and the pancreas are cut, there is little reduction in the amount of digestive juices entering the intestine. As soon as the chyme passes from the stomach into the duodenum, the cells of the latter produce two hormones: **cholecystokinin** and **secretin.** Both secretagogues enter the blood stream, but their actions are highly specific. Cholecystokinin stimulates only the gall bladder, causing the muscles of its walls to contract. This expels bile into the ducts and thence into the duodenum. Secretin stimulates only the pancreas in its production of juices.

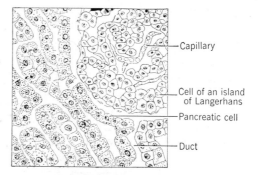

Fig. 17-6. *Diagram of pancreatic structure. The cells that secrete pancreatic juice are quite granular compared to those of the Islands of Langerhans.*

The pancreatic juice flows through the **pancreatic duct** to join the bile in the common bile duct as it enters the duodenum. The juice is alkaline, with an average pH value of 7.5 which may increase to 8 as the rate of secretion gains. As a result of this alkalinity, the pancreatic juice stops activity of the acidic gastric juice, and digestion of the chyme in the intestine proceeds under entirely different chemical conditions than those found in the stomach.

The pancreatic enzymes. The main digestive enzymes of the pancreatic juice are **trypsin, steapsin,** and **amylopsin.** There are two other enzymes, **chymotrypsin** and **carboxypeptidase,** that play minor roles in digestion. Trypsin (pancreatic *protease*) is an enzyme that digests proteins; steapsin (pancreatic *lipase*) acts on lipids; and amylopsin (pancreatic *amylase*) affects carbohydrates. The italicized names in parentheses are general terms designating the function of each enzyme. A protease is any enzyme that will digest a protein; a lipase will digest fats and oils, and so forth. You will note that many of the names of enzymes end in "-ase." This suffix was adopted by chemists to designate an enzyme, just as "-ose" designates a carbohydrate. (Some of the digestive

enzymes that were identified before this modern method of naming enzymes was adopted retain the old "-in" suffix. Thus we have ptyalin, pepsin, and amylopsin.)

In the intestine, the proenzyme, **trypsinogen,** which is formed in the pancreatic cells, is changed into trypsin by the action of an intestinal enzyme, **enterokinase.** Trypsin can act on raw proteins, just as pepsin does in the stomach, but if the protein has been cooked, or has already been acted on by pepsin, trypsin is more effective. As stated in Chapter 16, in the stomach the proteins are broken down into proteoses and peptones by the action of pepsin. Trypsin reduces these molecules to simpler chains of amino acids, the *polypeptids.* Chymotrypsin continues the breakdown of the polypeptids into still simpler chains. Carboxypeptidase acts on these smaller polypeptids to reduce them to dipeptids (two amino acids). The final breakdown into single amino acids takes place by the action of enzymes in the intestinal juice.

Chymotrypsin also has a forerunner, **chymotrypsinogen,** which is converted into chymotrypsin by the action of trypsin. Chymotrypsin curdles milk with

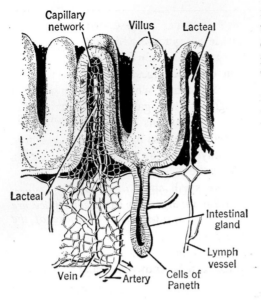

Fig. 17-7. *A section through the intestinal mucosa. Note the structure of the villi and of the intestinal glands.* (*From Johnson, Laubengayer and DeLanney,* General Biology, *Holt, 1956*)

about the same effectiveness as pepsin, so that any milk that has escaped action in the stomach will be digested in the small intestine.

The ability of steapsin (the pancreatic lipase) to digest fats is remarkable; an extremely small amount of the enzyme is needed to bring about normal digestion of fats in the intestine. If the pancreas is removed from an experimental animal so that steapsin is lacking, the amount of fat excreted in the feces is greatly increased. However, if only a small piece of the pancreas is allowed to remain, little fat is lost. Steapsin acts on the fats that have been emulsified by the bile salts and changes them into fatty acids and glycerin, the forms in which fats can be absorbed.

The amylopsin of the pancreas is sometimes referred to as the pancreatic ptyalin because its action so nearly parallels that of the saliva. Much more rap-

idly than ptyalin does, amylopsin is able to break down the starch molecule into dextrins and split off the maltose, but it is unable to carry the reduction farther. These complex carbohydrates cannot be absorbed directly by the blood but must await reduction into hexoses by the intestinal juices.

THE INTESTINAL JUICE

The cells of the intestinal walls produce a digestive fluid that is quite distinct from either bile or pancreatic juice. It is formed by special cells lying at the bottom of the simple tubular glands that dip below the surface of the intestinal lining. These glands, the *crypts of Lieberkuhn,* are scattered quite generally over the inner surface of the intestine between the villi (Fig. 17-7). At the bottom of each gland are cells that contain large granules in their cytoplasm. These are the *cells of Paneth* which produce the enzymes of the intestinal juice. Along the sides of the glands are cells that show mitotic figures indicating rapid division. This condition has given rise to the belief that these dividing cells are able to move toward the surface and replace those cells of the lining of the intestine that are worn away by the normal activity of the organ.

The intestinal enzymes. Digestion of the chyme is completed by the intestinal enzymes. Thus far, the digestive enzymes—with the exception of steapsin—have only reduced the foods to intermediate products which cannot be absorbed because of the size of their molecules. Therefore, to render the foods suitable to pass into the blood stream, these more complex substances must be further reduced. The *intestinal juice* contains six enzymes that bring about this final reduction: *erepsin* (currently known to be more than one enzyme, i.e. *aminopeptidase* and *dipeptidase*), **maltase, su-**

crase, **lactase,** and **lipase.** (The juice also contains enterokinase which, as we have seen, activates the pancreatic trypsinogen into the active enzyme trypsin.)

Erepsin completes the digestion of proteins by splitting the remaining polypeptids into their component amino acids. It is in this form that they are finally absorbed into the blood stream.

Since the action of ptyalin and amylopsin on carbohydrates is relatively slight, the major responsibility for carbohydrate digestion falls to the intestinal enzymes. Maltase converts maltose into glucose which can be absorbed. One of the principal carbohydrates in our diet, sucrose (table sugar) remains unchanged until it encounters the intestinal enzyme, sucrase, which breaks it down into glucose and fructose. Milk has a special carbohydrate, lactose, which can only be digested by lactase in the small intestine, where it is converted into glucose and galactose. In the meantime the dextrins have been further reduced to maltose by the continued action of amylopsin, although little is known about the steps in this process.

The small amounts of lipase are important in digestion of fats and oils. It functions in addition to the steapsin of the pancreas.

The action of the various digestive juices can be shown as follows:

MATERIAL(S) DIGESTED	PLACE OF DIGESTION	DIGESTIVE JUICE	ENZYME	MATERIAL(S) FORMED	MATERIAL(S) ABSORBED
Starch	Mouth and stomach	Saliva	Ptyalin	Dextrins Maltose	None
Starch	Small intestine	Pancreatic juice	Amylopsin	Dextrins Maltose	None
Dextrins Maltose	Small intestine	Intestinal juice	Maltase	Glucose	Glucose
Sucrose	Small intestine	Intestinal juice	Sucrase	Glucose Fructose	Glucose Fructose
Lactose	Small intestine	Intestinal juice	Lactase	Glucose Galactose	Glucose Galactose
Fats and oils	Stomach	Gastric juice	Lipase	Fatty acids Glycerin	Fatty acids Glycerin
Fats and oils	Small intestine	Bile	None	Emulsions of fat	None
Emulsified fats and oils	Small intestine	Pancreatic juice	Steapsin	Fatty acids Glycerin	Fatty acids Glycerin
Emulsified fats and oils	Small intestine	Intestinal juice	Lipase	Fatty acids Glycerin	Fatty acids Glycerin
Proteins	Stomach	Gastric juice	Pepsin	Proteoses Peptones	None
Proteoses Peptones	Small intestine	Intestinal juice	Trypsin Chymotrypsin Carboxypeptidase	Polypeptids	None
Polypeptids	Small intestine	Intestinal juice	Erepsin	Amino acids	Amino acids

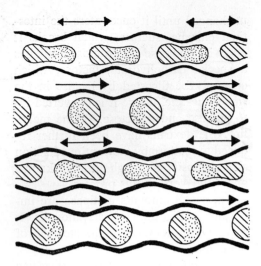

Fig. 17-8. *Segmental action of the small intestine. This mixes the food materials and constantly presents new food surfaces for the action of the digestive juices.*

MOVEMENTS OF THE INTESTINES

The structure of the walls of the small intestine is much the same as that of the other digestive organs. On the outside is a serous coat which is surrounded by the mesenteries. Inside this is a layer of longitudinal muscle fibers, and then a layer of circular muscles. These muscle layers, which are responsible for the movements of the intestines, are attached to the mucosa by a submucosa of connective tissue. The mucosa contains the intestinal glands and the food-absorbing mechanisms.

In the small intestine the partly digested food is subjected to three different types of intestinal movement. First, by **peristaltic contraction** food is moved along the tube at a fairly constant rate of about three inches in eight or nine minutes (Fig. 15-8). This motion, however, follows a spiral course and makes a complete revolution in about every 10 or 11 inches of its forward progress because of the slightly spiral arrangement of the longitudinal muscles. A second type of motion, **segmental action** (Fig. 17-8), appears as the food flows along but does not help it in its forward progress. This action constricts the tube every few seconds, thus churning its contents so that a new surface is constantly being presented to the digestive juices. A third type of movement is the **pendular movement,** in which separate sections of the intestine are involved. The muscular coats contract in such a manner as to hurl the contents from one end of the loop to the other by a pendulum-like motion, thus mixing the food with the digestive juices. As we shall see shortly, there is another type of motion in the intestine: that of the swaying villi. These tiny fingers stir the fluids and the chyme into a more thorough mixture.

In Chapter 4, we discussed some of the properties of smooth muscle tissue. Not only does smooth muscle move more slowly than striated muscle fibers, but it is capable of remaining contracted for longer periods of time. It can also contract to a greater degree without suffering permanent injury. These characteristics make the smooth muscle tissue admirably suited to its function in the intestines. As a moving force in the digestive system, a wave of contraction passes over these muscles. The violence of the contractions is evidenced by the fact that the walls turn pale in the area of the contraction as the blood is squeezed out of the tissues momentarily. Another characteristic of the muscle is its ability to contract rhythmically as a result of the steady flow of nervous impulses to it. Cardiac muscle can also contract in a rhythmic manner, but it does this without nervous stimulation; if skeletal muscles contract in this way, they do it for only a short time before becoming fatigued. Smooth muscle cells are also more sensitive to mechanical and chemical stimuli than either skeletal or cardiac muscle cells. Thus the mere presence of food in the digestive system starts their contraction and maintains it. These intestinal movements mix the chyme with the digestive juices and also aid in absorption of the end-products of digestion.

As indicated in Chapter 9, the autonomic nervous system controls the movement of the smooth muscle of the digestive tract.

ABSORPTION OF NUTRIENTS FROM THE INTESTINE

Both the mucosa and submucosa of the small intestine are thrown into a series of **circular folds** that greatly increase the surface area of the intestine. They form permanent and rather hard ridges that do not disappear when the intestine becomes distended with food. In the lower right-hand corner of the X-ray photograph shown in Fig. 16-6, the edges of some of these folds can be seen clearly because they contain barium compounds.

Over the surface of the circular folds are small fingerlike projections which extend into the opening of the intestine. These are the **villi** (Fig. 17-9). They are so small that they can barely be distinguished by the naked eye, but they give the lining a velvety appearance. Smooth muscle tissue in their walls enables the villi to move with a swaying motion or to stretch or shorten slightly. This movement continually exposes new surfaces over which the digested materials can be absorbed.

The structure of the villi is shown in Fig. 17-7. The outer surface of a villus is composed of a single layer of epithelial cells, while inside there is a network of capillaries and a branch of a lymph vessel, the **lacteal.** Through the outer layer of cells pass the digested proteins, carbohydrates, and fats.

Fig. 17-9. *A photomicrograph of the lining of the small intestine, showing the villi. (From Marsland,* Principles of Modern Biology, *Holt, 1957)*

The lacteals contain an emulsion of fats. How fats get into the lacteals in this form has been the subject of much research. We know that the emulsified fats are broken down in the intestine into fatty acids and glycerin, which enter the villi. Apparently these substances recombine to form fats after they pass through the cell membranes of the villi. The emulsion gives a milky appearance to the fluid in the lacteals. (The word "lacteal" mean milky.) This theory also accounts for the **chylomicrons,** extremely minute droplets of fat, that may be found in the blood stream following a meal that contains a normal amount of fat.

Water, glucose, and amino acids are absorbed by the blood capillaries of the villi and carried to the liver and thence into the general circulation. Part of the fats are carried to the liver through the portal circulation and part enters a lymph vessel, the **thoracic duct,** from which it finally enters the blood stream. The thoracic duct empties its contents into the left subclavian vein in the region of the shoulder after being joined by other lymph vessels. The return of some fat particles to the blood stream in this manner accounts for the presence of the chylomicrons in the blood.

SPEAKING OF Physiology

Briefly identify each of the following:

bilirubin	duodenum	ileum
biliverdin	gall bladder	islands of Langerhans
chyme	gall stone	jaundice
common bile duct	glycogen	jejunum
cystic duct	glycosuria	lacteal
deamination	hepatic duct	villus (i)

Test YOUR KNOWLEDGE

1. List and describe the functions of the peritoneum. What other names are applied to portions of this membrane?
2. Describe the circulatory supply of the liver. Why must the liver have an extensive blood supply?
3. What are the functions of the gall bladder?
4. Under what conditions will a normal individual show a positive sugar urinalysis test? How does the body correct this condition?
5. What are the composition, function, and source of the bile?
6. What part does the liver play in the distribution and assimilation of proteins?
7. Describe the secretory and excretory functions of the liver.
8. How are the liver and pancreas stimulated to secrete bile and pancreatic juice, respectively?
9. What change in pH occurs as the chyme passes from the stomach through the small intestine? What effect does this change have on enzyme action?
10. How are fats absorbed and distributed? Where are they stored?
11. What functions are performed by the intestinal juice?
12. Describe the three principal types of movements occurring in the small intestine.
13. What part of the nervous system is responsible for the muscular activity that occurs throughout the digestive tract?

See FOR YOURSELF

1. With the aid of the digestion chart in this chapter, show how the following breakfast would be digested by considering these points: (*a*) Where does the breakdown of each organic nutrient occur? (*b*) What enzymes are involved for each breakdown? (*c*) Does the digestion of each take place in an acid or basic medium? (*d*) What are the final products formed? (*e*) How are the final products absorbed? (*f*) For what purpose are the final products used?

Menu to be considered: 1 glass of orange juice, 1 boiled egg on white toast, 2 pieces of lean bacon, 1 cup of coffee without sugar or cream.

2. Devise an experiment which demonstrates diffusion and osmosis to a class of students. How are these two processes related to the absorption of food in the digestive organs?

CHAPTER 18

The Large Intestine

Structure of the colon. The large intestine, a tube approximately five feet long, forms about one fifth of the total length of the intestinal canal. At the point where the small intestine enters it, the large intestine is approximately 3 inches in diameter, but from this point on, it tapers finally to little more than an inch. The large intestine forms three sides of a square beginning at the lower right-hand quarter of the abdomen. From the **caecum**, it passes upward along the right side of the abdominal cavity to form the **ascending colon**. The **transverse colon** crosses toward the left side of the body at about the level of the third lumbar vertebra, rising slightly before turning downward. The part that passes downward along the left side is the **descending colon** (see Trans-Vision). This third part makes a sharp S-shaped curve, known as the **sigmoid colon**. The rectum is continuous with the sigmoid colon; its adjoining **anal canal** eventually opens to the exterior at the **anus.**

The differences between the small and large intestine are more than a matter of size. Externally, the small intestine has a relatively smooth surface. This is not true of the large intestine. While it contains the usual four layers of tissue, the layer of longitudinal muscle tissue does not completely surround the intestine,

but is confined to three narrow bands placed almost equidistant from each other. These long strips of muscle pucker the wall of the intestine into pouches, called the **haustrae** (sing., haustra). Unlike the circular folds of the small intestine, the haustrae involve all the layers of the colon. These segments can be clearly seen in the X-ray photograph of the large intestine, Fig. 18-1. The cells that

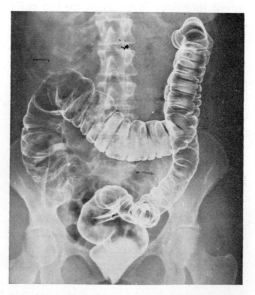

Fig. 18-1. *An X-ray photograph of the large intestine. The haustrae are clearly shown. At the lower part the sigmoid colon and the rectum are filled with the barium compound. (Dr. Eugene Ahern)*

211

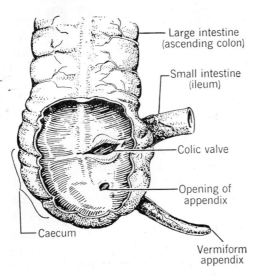

Fig. 18-2. *Junction of the small and large intestine. Note the sacklike nature of the caecum.*

line the colon do not secrete digestive enzymes. Intestinal glands are present, but they secrete mucus. There are no villi. The opening between the large and small intestines is guarded by the **colic valve.** This sphincter controls the passage of the intestinal chyme. Below the colic valve is a blind pouch, the caecum. In a few individuals the caecum may be conical or pyramidal in shape, but the average appearance is that shown in Fig. 18-2. Just beneath this colic valve is the vermiform (wormlike) **appendix** which projects into the abdominal cavity. This may vary in length from three quarters of an inch to almost eight inches, but its average length is slightly over three inches, and its diameter approximately that of the little finger.

As far as has been ascertained, the appendix plays no role in the process of digestion. Being a blind sac, it fills easily but empties sluggishly so that materials may remain in it for unusually long periods. Hard or rough substances may irritate the inner walls of the appendix, making it a favorable place for the

growth of bacteria. An inflammatory infection of the walls (*appendicitis*) results (Fig. 18-3).

Water absorption. The material that enters the caecum is, at least theoretically, lacking in usable nutrients. These have all been digested and their products absorbed during their passage through the small intestine. There are, however, still some substances that the body can use and that the large intestine will retrieve before the waste materials are eliminated. As the contents of the small intestine enter the caecum, they are in a very liquid state. Because water accounts for a large percentage of the total fluids of the body, its loss would represent a serious depletion of fluid reserves. One of the principal functions of the large intestine is to recover this water so that the body's reserves are not lowered.

The large intestine's capacity to absorb water is very great. Some people who suffer from constipation have the idea that their condition can be helped by drinking large quantities of water to make the evacuation of the bowel's content easier. Even though a person drinks as much as three quarts of water per day above his usual intake, there is no indication that the nature of the feces is changed or that constipation is relieved.

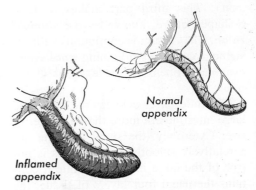

Fig. 18-3. *These diagrams compare the normal appendix with one that is infected.*

This additional water is absorbed through the walls of the large intestine, and the amount of urine formed and excreted is proportionally increased.

Bacterial action. Throughout the entire life of the individual from a few hours after birth until death, the large intestine contains bacteria. These enter with ingested food, and although many are destroyed by the action of the digestive juices, a sufficient number escape and find their way to the large intestine where they multiply rapidly and in huge numbers. Without these bacteria, life would be impossible.

Bacteria in the large intestine are largely harmless to man. They act on the undigestible materials and break some of them down into gases, acids, amines, and other waste products. Some of these products of decomposition are excreted through the intestinal tract. Potentially toxic (poisonous) materials are absorbed and are carried by the portal vein to the liver for **detoxification.** Special enzymes produced by the liver cells convert these toxic substances into nontoxic materials which are excreted by the kidneys. This process of detoxification is one of the chief functions of the liver. The poisons of the body are thus kept from reaching a dangerous level in the circulation.

Formation of the feces. After the absorption of water from the contents of the large intestine, bacterial action changes the consistency of the intestinal contents from a liquid to a semisolid state, the **feces.** A part of the contents of the feces are bacterial; the other substances are waste products brought by the blood, the products of bacterial action in the intestine, many inorganic salts, mucus, and the undigestible components of food, such as cellulose. Cellulose, as we have seen, is the fibrous part of plant food that is undigestible by man.

It forms a small percentage of the feces and contributes to its bulk. This bulk stimulates the lining of the intestines and induces peristalsis. Fruits and vegetables provide this type of roughage necessary to a balanced diet.

Movement of the colon. There is considerable question as to just how the colon moves its contents along its tube. No frequent, rhythmic peristalsis or other movement has been observed except in the transverse colon, where there are slow, weak accordion-like movements of the haustrae rather than actual peristalsis. At certain intervals two or three times in 24 hours, **mass peristalsis** occurs in the large intestine. This massive movement often sweeps through the entire length of the colon, pushing the feces before it. These waves are sometimes preceded by peristalsis in the small intestine and by the taking of food into the stomach. The sigmoid colon, which serves as a storehouse for the feces, becomes filled so that during a wave of mass peristalsis the feces may enter the rectum. The lower end of the rectum is equipped with stiff longitudinal folds of tissue that lie just beneath the lining mucosa. These delay the further progress of the contents into the **anal canal.** Nervous stimuli are set up which result in **defecation,** or the act of excreting intestinal wastes through the anus. This process is voluntarily controlled by the action of two sets of sphincter muscles which surround the anus. In an infant, the ability to control the act of defecation is lacking, but with patient training it can be established.

Constipation is a condition in which normal, regular defecation is lacking. The feces are retained within the bowel for a longer than normal period of time. This permits continued bacterial activity with production of large amounts of gas. During longer retention in the intestine, the feces lose more water, forming a very solid mass difficult to evacuate. Ignoring the desire to defecate at the habitual time is often the beginning of constipation. Otherwise, if a normal person follows a well-balanced diet and takes a moderate amount of exercise, there are few physiologic grounds for constipation. Sometimes a person becomes "bowel conscious" and worries about his inability to have bowel movements at regular intervals. The individual may seek aid from laxatives which eventually reduce the muscle tone of the bowel so that he becomes more and more dependent on them. Thus habitual use of laxatives may replace the normal functions of the large intestine. For people whose activities and diet are limited by conditions such as long periods of illness, the use of laxatives is required, but healthy individuals seldom have a need for them. The regularity of bowel movements varies from two or three a day to one every other day, depending on individual differences.

SPEAKING OF Physiology

Briefly identify each of the following:

anal canal	**colic valve**	**feces**
caecum	**defecation**	**mass peristalsis**

Test YOUR KNOWLEDGE

1. Why can the vermiform appendix become easily infected?
2. What are the three major divisions of the large intestine?
3. What similarities and differences exist between the structure of the small intestine and that of the large intestine?
4. What are the primary functions of the large intestine?
5. What part do bacteria play in the activities of the normal large intestine?
6. What is the purpose of roughage in the diet?
7. What is constipation?
8. What is the process of detoxification? Where does it occur?

See FOR YOURSELF

1. With the aid of a microscope, observe prepared slides of the following: stomach, duodenum, ileum, colon. What similarities and differences can you note in each of the above? Draw each of the above to show these characteristics.

2. By using library research or interviewing your family physician, write a report on a disease directly associated with the large intestine, i.e. colitis, appendicitis, diverticulitis.

3. Make a comparative study of the various treatments for constipation. Describe the physiologic action of each and explain how habitual use of these aids can be harmful.

The Respiratory System

CHAPTER 19
The Respiratory Structures and the Mechanics of Breathing

CHAPTER 20
The Physical and Chemical Processes in Breathing

CHAPTER 21
Artificial Respiration and Phonation

The Respiratory Structures and the Mechanics of Breathing

Respiration is a combination of two distinct processes, one mechanical, the other chemical. *External respiration* is a mechanical process controlled by the pressure of the atmosphere and the action of certain body muscles. Its function is to bring air into the lungs where oxygen is absorbed by the blood and to remove gaseous wastes brought from the body by the blood. In one form or another, all animals and plants carry on external respiration, exchanging their waste products for the usable materials present in the environment. While the methods may vary widely, the fundamental principles are the same. *Internal respiration* is the exchange of oxygen and carbon dioxide between the body's cells and the fluids which circulate around them. The cells obtain energy for their chemical activities by oxidizing nutrients. The waste products of this oxidation, carbon dioxide and water, are picked up by the blood and returned to the lungs for removal. Chemically, these are highly complex reactions in which numerous enzymes present in the cells act on various substrates.

In a way, external respiration may be compared to the action of a bellows. As the bellows is expanded, the cavity within it becomes enlarged so that the internal air pressure is less than that of the surrounding air. The outside air therefore rushes in to equalize the air pressure, thereby inflating the bellows. If the handles of the bellows are then pressed together, the inside volume is reduced and the pressure within becomes greater than that of the outside air, so that the air within is forced out. The difference in air pressure between the outside and the inside of the bellows is the essential principle of the breathing movements.

STRUCTURE OF THE RESPIRATORY SYSTEM

The nasal cavity. The first part of the human respiratory system with which air normally comes in contact is the *nasal* (nose) *cavity,* whose inner walls are folded into three ridges on each side— the *nasal conchae* or *turbinate bones.* Like the rest of the lining of the nose, the conchae are covered by a layer of mucous membrane that is richly supplied with blood. As Fig. 19-1 shows, the air passes over the series of ridges, the arrangement and relationship of which are evident in the diagram of a vertical section through this region (Fig. 19-2).

216

This folding of the inner surface of the nasal cavity is of great importance, because here the air is *warmed* (by the blood), *moistened* (by the mucus), and *cleansed* of small particles of dirt which are drawn in with the air. This last function is carried on by the sticky mucus which traps the particles. Small hairs are located in the front of the nostrils, and they aid in preventing larger bits of dirt from entering. By the time the air reaches the lungs it is saturated with water vapor cleaned, and warmed to body temperature.

The nose cavity is divided internally into two smaller cavities by a wall, called the **septum.** The external openings of these two cavities are called the **nostrils.** The cartilage of the outer nose is firmly attached to the **nasal bones** that make up the bridge of the nose. The conchae are located on the walls of the nasal bones. In the covering of the uppermost

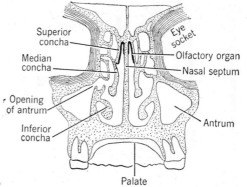

Fig. 19-2. *A vertical frontal section through the nasal cavities to show the arrangement of the nasal conchae. (The antra are paranasal sinuses which have no respiratory function.)*

of these three ridges (the *superior concha*) we find the nerve endings for the sense of smell (*olfactory sense*). The cells which receive olfactory stimuli are elongated and supported by larger cells. Their free ends have hairlike projections against which the air brushes as it flows along the nasal passage (Fig. 19-3).

Although our olfactory sense is poorly developed as compared with that of some animals, we still have a remarkable ability to distinguish odors even when they are present in surprisingly small concentrations. Next to sight, smelling is our most acute sense; and it is possible that proper training would greatly improve it. We can detect the odor of ethyl alcohol in a concentration of approximately 0.0000003 percent by weight, but it must be present in about a 14 percent solution before we taste it, and between 25 and 50 percent before it produces a burning sensation on the lining of the mouth.

The pharynx. From the nasal cavity, the air enters the **pharynx.** This is the region in the back of the mouth which serves as a passageway for both food

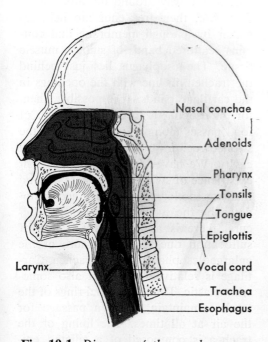

Fig. 19-1. *Diagram of the nasal passages showing the relation of the nasal conchae and the air passages.*

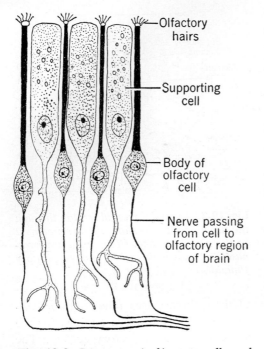

- Olfactory hairs
- Supporting cell
- Body of olfactory cell
- Nerve passing from cell to olfactory region of brain

Fig. 19-3. *Diagram of olfactory cells and supporting structures. The nerve fiber from each olfactory cell joins with others to form the olfactory nerve, which carries impulses to the olfactory center in the brain.*

and air. The pharynx is the site of extensive growth in the early embryo. From its walls develop a fingerlike projection that later divides into two parts and gives rise to the lungs and the passages leading to them. Also, from this area develop masses of lymphatic tissue which become the **tonsils** and **adenoids**. The lower end of the pharynx ends at the **glottis**. This is the opening into the windpipe, or **trachea**. The glottis is a narrow slit, with its long axis lying in a front-to-back direction. In men, this opening is about 23 millimeters long; in women, somewhat smaller, being 17 to 18 millimeters long. Around the rim of the glottis are the vocal cords, whose vibrations produce the sounds we make. More will be said about sound production and speech in Chapter 21.

The larynx. The glottis opens into a roughly triangular chamber, the **larynx,** or voice box. The apex of this triangle points forward and may be quite conspicuous in some men. It is commonly called the *Adam's apple.* The walls of the larynx are composed of plates of cartilage derived from the embryonic structures called the **pharyngeal arches.**

The trachea. Below the larynx is the trachea. This is a tube, about four and one-third inches long and from three-quarters to one inch in diameter. It is usually larger in males than in females. The trachea is not a perfectly round tube, being slightly flattened along the rear surface. Its walls are composed of alternate bands of membrane and cartilage, the former supporting and holding the cartilage in place (Fig. 19-4). The bands of cartilage may be either horseshoe shaped, almost completely encircling the trachea, or short, passing only part of the way around the tube. In either case, their free ends are held together by a tough membrane that contains scattered bands of smooth muscle tissue. The esophagus lies just behind the trachea, in line with the openings in the cartilage bands. It is possible, then, for the esophagus to swell as a bolus of food passes along it, so that part of the swollen region projects into the tracheal cavity. We have all had the unpleasant experience of swallowing a mass of food that was too large to be easily accommodated by the esophagus. When this occurs, there is a momentary feeling of suffocation due to the pressure of the enlarged esophagus on the trachea. Cartilage is relatively firm, but also somewhat elastic. Thus the partial rings of the trachea maintain an open passage for the air at all times. The lining of the trachea is composed of a ciliated epithelium in which are goblet cells that secrete mucus. The function of the cilia is to carry small particles of dirt from the lungs upward to the mouth or nasal cavity so that they can be eliminated.

Structure of the lungs. The lower end of the trachea divides into two parts, the **bronchi** (sing., *bronchus*). They are similar in structure to the trachea in that their walls are strengthened by cartilage rings and they are lined by ciliated epithelium. The bronchi divide many times, spreading through the substance of the lungs like the branches of a tree. Their finer divisions are called **bronchioles.** Eventually the ends of the finest twigs open into the **air sacs**, from the walls of which protrude the **alveoli** (sing., *alveolus*). As shown in Fig. 19-5, the walls of these structures are one cell thick in most places, and a network of capilla-

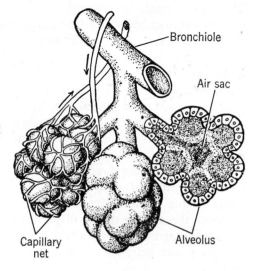

Fig. 19-5. *Diagrams of air sacs. At the left, capillaries are shown covering the alveoli. In the center is an air sac with protruding alveoli. At the right the air sac is shown in cross section. (From Whaley, Breland, Heimsch, Phelps, and Rabideau,* Principles of Biology, *Harper & Bros., 1954)*

ries passes over their surface. Through the thin walls of the alveoli and the capillaries, the gases in the air and the blood are exchanged. The blood supply to the lungs is so extensive that these vessels contain approximately one quarter of the body's blood at any one moment. If it were possible to spread out all of the internal surfaces of the lungs to form a single sheet of tissue, they would cover an area of about 1,100 square feet.

The texture of the lungs is similar to that of a sponge with very fine openings. In the walls of the air sacs are blood vessels and strands of smooth muscle fibers. The sac is lined by a layer of epithelium so extremely thin that it was not known to exist until 1953, when photographs taken with an electron microscope showed its presence. The finest branches of the bronchioles, less than 1 millimeter in diameter, lack the rings of cartilage that are characteristic of the larger tubes.

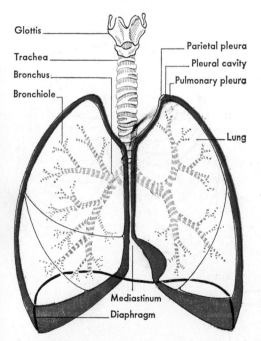

Fig. 19-4. *Diagram of the lungs and associated parts. The size of the pleural cavity has been exaggerated, since the space between the pulmonary and parietal pleurae is very slight. The only place where there is an appreciable separation of the two layers is below the lungs.*

These fine vessels may therefore occasionally constrict and shut off the passage of air to some small areas of the lungs.

The subdivisions of the lungs, the **lobes,** are shown in the Trans-Vision following page 312. Each lung is covered by a membrane, the **pleura,** made up of tough endothelial cells. The pleura is composed of two layers. The **pulmonary pleura** completely covers the lungs, dipping between the lobes. The outer layer, the **parietal pleura,** forms the lining of the chest cavity and continues over the surface of the diaphragm. Each lung, therefore, lies in a two-walled sac. Since the lungs almost completely fill the thoracic cavity, the space between the two layers of the pleura is negligible. This potential space, called the **pleural cavity,** is moistened by a thin film of

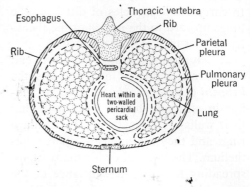

Fig. 19-6. *A cross section through the chest cavity to show the relation of the various structures. The space between the pleurae has been exaggerated in this diagram.*

serous fluid which prevents the pleurae from rubbing together when the chest moves with each breath. If this **pleural fluid** increases as the result of a local

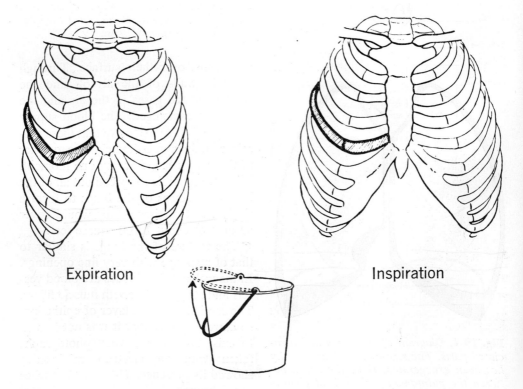

Fig. 19-7. *The movement of the ribs is quite similar to that of the handle of a bucket. In both cases there is an outward and an upward movement. (Drawn by E. M. from Gerard, The Body Functions, 1941, by permission of the John Wiley and Sons)*

infection, the distressing symptoms of *pleurisy* may appear. Although small, the pleural cavity is of great importance in breathing.

The interpleural space, containing the heart, large blood vessels, nerves and other structures of the thoracic cavity, is called the **mediastinum** (Fig. 19-4). The relationship of the main structure is shown in Fig. 19-6.

Mechanics of breathing. The process of breathing is quite distinct from the chemical reactions of internal respiration. Breathing is a purely mechanical act that can be divided into two stages: the intake of air into the lungs, called **inspiration,** and the passage of air out of the lungs *(expiration).* Inspiration is the more active of the two processes because it requires the contraction of more muscle bundles than expiration. The latter is largely the result of relaxation of muscles and the return of the viscera (soft organs) to their original position. With each breath of air that we inhale, we expend considerable energy in the form of muscular contraction. Exhala-

tion, being more passive, requires less energy.

When we inhale, the muscles that play the major roles are those attached to the ribs (**intercostal muscles**), and the **diaphragm.** Other groups of muscles also help in the process, but their actions are not so pronounced. The intercostals are divided into two groups: the **external intercostals** and the **internal intercostals.** The fibers of these muscles pass at an angle of almost 90° to each other. The external layer lifts the ribs upward and thereby increases the volume of the thoracic cavity during inhalation (Fig. 19-7). The inner layer draws the adjacent ribs toward each other and reduces the size of the thoracic cavity during exhalation. In the process of inhalation the sternum rises as the ribs rise. At the same time the dome-shaped diaphragm (see the Trans-Vision) drops to a flatter condition as its muscles contract. This motion of the diaphragm results in pressure on the viscera of the abdomen, which is transmitted to the front muscular walls so that that they protrude

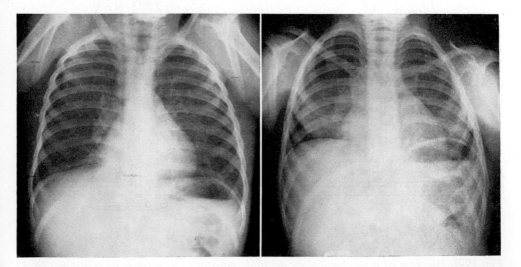

Fig. 19-8. *X-ray photographs of the lungs during inspiration (left) and expiration (right). Note the differences in position of the diaphragm and the clavicles. (Dr. John A. Campbell)*

slightly. The result is a marked increase in volume of the thoracic cavity, as is evident by comparing the X-ray pictures in Fig. 19-8.

The classic method of demonstrating the mechanics of breathing is by means of an apparatus shown in Fig. 19-9. Here we have a glass bell jar in the top of which is a cork with a glass tube passing through it. The tube acts as the trachea, and divides into two branches, representing the bronchi. At the end of these branches, thin-walled toy balloons are fastened to represent lungs. A rubber sheet, fitted with a device to pull it downward, is stretched over the bottom opening of the bell jar to represent the diaphragm.

This apparatus has several limitations as a model. First, the walls of the bell jar are rigid, whereas the walls of the chest are moved by the intercostal muscles. Second, the stretched rubber diaphragm is flat, while the normal human diaphragm is dome-shaped in its relaxed position. However, this model is very useful in explaining the mechanics of breathing. The balloons alternately inflate and deflate as the rubber diaphragm is pulled down and released; just as our lungs inflate and deflate following the movements of the muscular diaphragm. Inflation results from a decrease in air pressure within the cavity of the bell jar (or the chest) as the diaphragm is pulled down. Deflation occurs when the diaphragm is released (relaxed), increasing the air pressure within the cavity. If the diaphragm is pushed up into the cavity of the jar, the balloons will deflate still more because of the further increase in air pressure within the bell jar. We might compare this to our forceful exhalation of air, using the abdominal muscles to press the diaphragm further up into the chest cavity.

Pressure of gases is generally measured by the height of a column of mer-

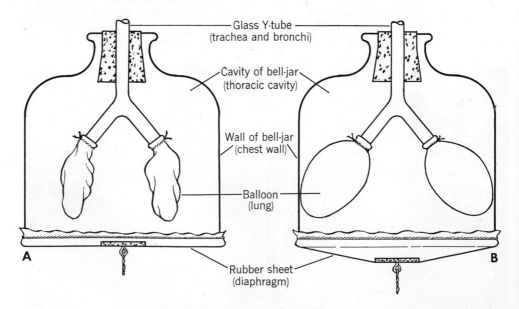

Fig. 19-9. *Diagram of a mechanical model to demonstrate the process of breathing. In A the balloons (lungs) are collapsed because of the relaxation of the rubber diaphragm. In B the balloons are inflated because the volume of the cavity in the bell jar (chest cavity) has been increased.*

cury (chemical symbol, *Hg*) that the gas will support. If we fill a long glass tube, sealed at one end, with mercury and invert it in a dish of mercury (Fig. 19-10), the liquid in the tube drops to a point where its weight is balanced by the pressure the air exerts on the surface of the mercury in the dish. Such an instrument is called a **barometer.** At sea level, the height of the column of mercury, measured from the level of the mercury in the dish, is 760 millimeters, or 30 inches. This is taken as the standard pressure of air at 0°C. (32°F.). However, at a higher elevation, the height of the mercury column drops because the pressure of the air constantly decreases with elevation. We will discuss the importance of this effect on breathing later, but it should be clearly understood now that standard air pressure is the weight of a column of mercury that can be supported by the air pressure at sea level.

In the process of inhalation, pressure within the chest cavity decreases by only about two millimeters of mercury. This slight change of pressure is sufficient to cause air to enter the lungs. Exhalation produces a much greater pressure within

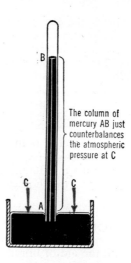

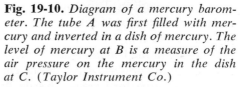

The column of mercury AB just counterbalances the atmospheric pressure at C

Fig. 19-10. *Diagram of a mercury barometer. The tube A was first filled with mercury and inverted in a dish of mercury. The level of mercury at B is a measure of the air pressure on the mercury in the dish at C. (Taylor Instrument Co.)*

the chest cavity. Due to relaxation of the elastic diaphragm, the pressure of the abdominal viscera, and the lowering of the ribs, a pressure of about four millimeters of mercury is built up within the thorax. This forces air out against the normal atmospheric pressure.

SPEAKING OF Physiology

Briefly identify each of the following:

Adam's apple	**conchae**	**pharyngeal arches**
atmospheric pressure	**glottis**	**pleurisy**
bronchus	**nostrils**	**pulmonary pleura**
cilia	**parietal pleura**	**septum**

Test YOUR KNOWLEDGE

1. Explain this statement: All animals that breathe have respiration, but not all animals that have respiration breathe.
2. Describe the functions of the nasal mucous membrane. What effect would removal of the turbinate bones have on these functions?
3. How does the sense of olfaction compare in acuteness with the various other special senses of the human body?

4.   What is the common name for the pharynx? Discuss the embryological signifi-
      cance of this structure.
5.   What are the function and importance of the cartilaginous rings in the trachea
      and bronchial tubes? What infections are often centered in these tubes?
6.   What type of respiration is illustrated by the exchange of gases between the alve-
      oli and the capillary network that covers them?
7.   Describe the muscular activities involved in breathing.
8.   What two cavities does the diaphragm separate? How is this dome-shaped muscle
      controlled?
9.   Why is mercury used in the construction of a barometer? Could any other sub-
      stance be used? Explain.
10.   How great a difference must exist between atmospheric pressure and the pres-
      sure within the thoracic cavity in order for us to breathe?

See FOR YOURSELF

1. With the aid of library research and statistical evidence prepared by various
agencies (American Tuberculosis Association, American Cancer Society, and numerous insurance agencies), plot a graph showing the incidence of pneumonia, tuberculosis and lung cancer. Starting at the turn of the century, show the death rate
percentages in the United States due to the above causes, and continue with five-year
intervals to the present. Mark on the chart where great advances have been made in
medical research to decrease this death rate, i.e. antibiotics, radioactive isotopes,
drugs for tuberculosis, etc. Did these discoveries change the curve of your graph?
What can you predict about the future?

2. Get sheep lungs with trachea attached from a butcher shop. Examine the
various structures noted in your text: trachea, bronchi, bronchioles, lobes of the
lungs, various blood vessels, pleurae (if any are present). How does their structure
fit them for their function as described in your text?

3. Devise and construct a working model to demonstrate the process of breathing. Construct the model to show the movement of both the diaphragm and the
chest wall.

CHAPTER 20

The Physical and Chemical Processes in Breathing

The atmosphere. The atmosphere we live in is a mixture of gases rather than a chemical compound. The gases in the air are not combined with each other, nor is their proportion definite and unchanging. The proportions of the various gases in the air differ from one locality to another; over cities or volcanoes, the amount of some substances may be very high, while over the open sea or grasslands and deserts these same compounds may be in low concentrations or entirely absent. The wind flow in a certain locality may bring in traces of unusual gases. The water content of air is also variable from place to place. If moisture is present in large quantities at any given temperature, it may produce a fog, or, if other substances are also present, a smog. Air composition is therefore usually stated in terms of dry air and the measurements are made in a place that is not subject to local pollution. The following table gives the composition of air at sea level when the various factors that may contaminate it have been excluded. Any mention of the water vapor in air has been purposely omitted from the table because its percentage varies greatly.

Nitrogen	78.03%
Oxygen	20.99%
Argon	0.94%
Hydrogen	0.76%
Carbon dioxide	0.03%
Neon	0.0012%
Helium	0.0004%
Xenon Krypton	traces

The gases that are important in respiration are **oxygen, carbon dioxide,** and **water vapor** (omitted from the foregoing table). Although nitrogen constitutes the major part of the air we breathe, it plays no part in respiration, nor do the other gases listed. These elements combine with other substances with great difficulty and are therefore termed **inert.**

Each of the respiratory gases acts independently in the body according to the laws of chemical and physical behavior. A knowledge of the *Gas Laws,* a series of statements about the behavior of gases, is therefore helpful in the study of respiration. The mathematical formulations of these laws are of great value in physiological research.

The Gas Laws. The first of the Gas Laws that affects respiration is that of *Avogadro* (1776–1856). This states that equal volumes of all gases at the same temperature and pressure contain the same number of molecules. It has been found that at standard pressure (760 millimeters of mercury) and temperature (0°C), one molecular weight in grams of any gas will occupy a volume of 22.4 liters, the size of a cube which is 11 inches on each side. The average pressure of air at sea level is 1033.3 grams per square centimeter, or about 15 pounds per square inch.

The second Gas Law is *Boyle's Law*. This states that when a gas is subjected to pressure, its volume decreases inversely with the pressure. If the pressure on 100 milliliters of gas is doubled, the volume is reduced by one-half. If the pressure is tripled, the volume is reduced to one-third. The law is named for the English physicist, Robert Boyle (1627–1691), who discovered and stated this relationship.

The third Gas Law that affects respiration is *Charles' Law* (Jacques Charles, 1746–1823). This law states that the volume of a gas changes in direct proportion to changes in temperature. That is, all gases expand at the same definite rate when warmed, and contract when cooled.

Charles' Law explains why inhaled air must be warmed before it can enter the blood efficiently. If the air in the lungs is at a lower temperature than that of the blood, the movement of the molecules is too slow for them to be readily absorbed into the blood. When molecules move rapidly, the gas expands in volume and thus spreads out over a greater area. The activity of the molecules of a gas in the lungs, therefore, hastens their absorption into the blood.

The fourth Gas Law that is important in respiration is *Dalton's Law of Partial Pressures*. This states that each gas in a mixture exerts its own pressure in proportion to the percentage of its occurrence in the total volume of the gas. Thus, at sea level, the volume of oxygen present in the air of average composition is approximately 21 percent. Hence, oxygen will exert only 21 percent of the total pressure of the air. If we rise to an altitude of 12 miles (63,360 feet), the percentage of oxygen is reduced to about 18 percent of the total volume of the air and will therefore exert a pressure that is 2 to 3 percent below that at sea level. This means that the molecules of oxygen are so widely separated that they are unable to exert adequate pressure on the cell membranes and therefore cannot enter the blood in sufficient numbers.

The fifth Gas Law that plays an important part in the entrance of gases into the blood is known as *Henry's Law*. This states that a gas is dissolved by a liquid in direct proportion to its partial pressure, provided that it does not react chemically with the liquid. Henry's law is important to the understanding of the physical processes in breathing, since all gases that pass through the cell membranes in the lungs must first be dissolved in the cell fluids and in the thin film of fluid that covers the inner surface of the lungs.

Gases of low molecular weight are absorbed into the blood less easily than those of higher molecular weight. For example, a molecule of hydrogen with a molecular weight of 2 is absorbed less easily than a molecule of oxygen with a weight of 32. Carbon dioxide, with a molecular weight of 44, enters the fluid of the blood (plasma) more readily than oxygen. On the other hand, nitrogen (molecular weight = 28) is present in the plasma of the blood in much larger quantities than its weight might indicate because it is four times more common in air than oxygen. The total amount of oxygen absorbed by the whole blood is much greater than the amount dissolved in the plasma. Oxygen combines easily with hemoglobin, and the red blood cells are constantly taking up oxygen from the plasma. Since nitrogen does not combine easily with any of the components of the blood, it is carried as a dissolved gas in the plasma. Knowledge of the solubility of the various gases in the blood is necessary in aviation and deep-sea diving as will be made clear later in this chapter.

The relative solubility in whole blood of the three important gases is shown below in terms of volume percent.

Oxygen	0.23
Carbon dioxide	3.00
Nitrogen	0.80

It is important biologically that the solubility of these gases at low temperatures is considerably greater than at high temperatures. This explains why minute plants flourish in the colder waters where carbon dioxide is more readily available for the process of photosynthesis. These plants, in turn, attract the great whales that use them as their principal food.

Lung capacity. The capacity of the lungs increases from birth to adulthood. The following table shows human lung capacity at various age levels in terms of liters of air (1 liter = 1.056 quarts).

These figures are averages, since it is evident that people with larger chest cavities will have larger lung capacities than those with smaller chest cavities. For example, data for males, age 25, show extremes of 4.3 to 9.0 liters. Figures for women of the same age group vary from

Age 6	1.6	liters
10	2.5	liters
18	5.9	liters
25	6.4	liters (males)
	4.3	liters (females)
45	5.9	liters (males)
	4.3	liters (females)
65	5.6	liters (males)
	3.9	liters (females)

3.1 to 5.4 liters. The greater average size of the male chest cavity explains the differences in lung capacity between adult men and women.

In the process of normal breathing, a surprisingly large quantity of air is exchanged between the body and its surroundings. When resting, the average adult male exchanges about 8.4 liters of air per minute, while an adult woman exchanges about 4.5 liters. By comparing the values for adults with those for a newborn child, we see the effect of the size of the lungs on the amount of air inhaled and exhaled. In a newborn infant in a resting condition (asleep), there is an average exchange of only 0.72 liter per minute.

The moving body of air at each normal breath is called the *tidal air,* or **tidal volume.** If a person inhales as deeply as possible, he can draw in about 6 times as much air as he does on a quiet breath. This forced inhalation constitutes the *complemental air,* or **inspiratory reserve volume.**

A forceful expiration which follows a normal inspiration will expel an additional quantity of air constituting the *supplemental air* or **expiratory reserve volume.** Even after the supplemental air has been expelled from the lungs, there is always about 1 liter to 1½ liters of air remaining. This is called the *residual air,* or **residual volume,** and will remain until such time as the chest cavity is opened so that the pressure within is equal to that of the surrounding atmosphere. Even when this apparently last remnant of air has been removed, there is a very small amount of gas still clinging to the walls of the bronchioles and alveoli. This is termed the *minimal air,* and is scarcely measurable in volume.

The usual method of measuring the capacity of the lungs is by a simple device called a **spirometer** (Fig. 20-1). This consists of a can, or jar, inverted within another container which is filled with water. The inverted can has a valve to allow all the air to escape from it as it sinks to the bottom of the outer container. After the valve has been closed, air can be forced into the inner container through a tube which opens above the level of the water in the outer vessel. As the air fills the inner container, it rises because its weight is counterbalanced by appropriate weights in the supporting columns. The height to which this inner container rises is measurable evidence of the volume of air that it contains. If a person, therefore, breathes into a device of this type, his **vital capacity** can

be determined. This represents the sum of his tidal, complemental, and supplemental air, and amounts to about four liters for a male of average size and physical fitness. If we consider this in relation to the body surface area of such a person (see the chart in Fig. 29-5) it is equal to about two liters per square meter (1 square meter = 1.196 square yards = 10.76 square feet) of body surface for women and 2.5 liters per square meter for men. A well-trained athlete will average about 2.8 liters per square meter of body surface.

During the time when air is in the lungs, a change occurs in its composition. Some of the oxygen that enters the lungs combines chemically with the hemoglobin of the blood to form *oxyhemoglobin.* Likewise, some of the carbon dioxide that has been formed by cellular oxidations leaves the blood and enters the air sacs. We can therefore expect to find a difference in the composition of the inhaled air as compared with that expelled on a normal breath. This is shown in the following table:

	Inhaled air	Exhaled air
Nitrogen and other inert gases	79.02%	79.07%
Oxygen	20.94%	16.03%
Carbon dioxide	0.04%	4.40%

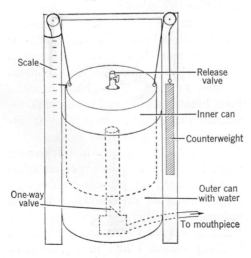

Fig. 20-1. *A spirometer. Its operation is explained in the text.*

Scale — Release valve — Inner can — Counterweight — One-way valve — Outer can with water — To mouthpiece

Control of breathing. The rate at which we breathe is controlled by two different factors: one of these is a *neural* (nervous) control, while the other is *chemical* in nature. Both of these may operate simultaneously, but each is independent of the other. The neural control of the respiratory movements is the result of stimuli affecting the **respiratory**

center in the medulla of the brain, while the chemical control depends on a change in the pH of the blood which also stimulates the neurons in the respiratory center.

Neural control was first demonstrated by Galen in the First Century A.D. He showed that a center in the lower brain was responsible for this activity. More modern experiments carried out under very rigorously controlled conditions have shown that Galen was essentially correct in his conclusions.

Located near the upper part of the medulla is an island of cells that constitutes the respiratory center (Fig. 20-2). The exact location of this region has been well established by experiments using electrical and thermal (heat) stimuli. A slight stimulus of any nature applied to the center causes the rate of respiration to increase or decrease. It is thought that the center is actually composed of two distinct regions, one that controls inspiration and one that controls exhalation.

Two nerve pathways are concerned in control of the breathing process. One follows the **phrenic nerves** to the diaphragm and the intercostal muscles. This pathway consists largely of motor fibers, although there are sensory fibers that carry impulses to the respiratory center. The other pathway transmits afferent impulses along the vagus nerves from the lungs, skin, nose and larynx, and abdominal organs. Thus, many different stimuli from various regions of the body help to regulate the breathing process.

Stimuli that arise in the surface membranes of the body can change the breathing rhythm in several familiar ways. The prick of a pin or a sudden drenching with cold water makes a person gasp. Irritation of the nasal membranes or the larynx results in a sneeze or a cough. Likewise, a thought, sight,

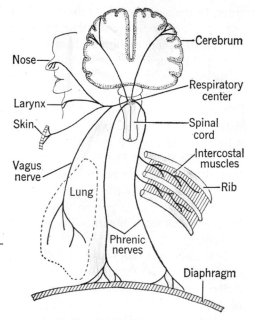

Fig. 20-2. *The nerve pathways involved in the control of respiration.*

or a sound may bring about a change in the respiratory rate. We have all gasped in surprise. It is also possible to alter voluntarily the rate of breathing by holding the breath. All of these stimuli arise either in body surfaces or in the cortex of the cerebrum.

Impulses that normally regulate the rhythm of breathing travel along branches of the vagi to the lungs. As the lungs expand, nerve endings in their tissues are stimulated and set up impulses that pass to the respiratory center. Here these impulses initiate a series of stimuli that eventually pass along the phrenic nerves and their branches and cause the diaphragm and external intercostals to relax. At the same time, the internal intercostals contract and the ribs are drawn back to their resting position. When complete exhalation has occurred, the process is reversed and inspiratory impulses travel to the diaphragm and external intercostals, causing them to contract. In the action of these muscles during breathing, we have another example of reciprocal innervation such as that illustrated by the biceps and triceps.

Respiration is chemically controlled through the carbon dioxide in the blood. When the blood passes through an active tissue it picks up carbon dioxide and other products of the oxidations occurring in the tissues. The increase in carbon dioxide stimulates the respiratory center, which is richly supplied with blood vessels. Thus a person who is doing strenuous work breathes deeply and rapidly.

It is easy to demonstrate the effect of carbon dioxide on the rate of respiration. After you have determined the number of breaths (inhalations) you take per minute, inhale deeply eight or ten times, or until your fingertips tingle. Then observe the second-hand on a watch and note how much time elapses between your last deep breath and your next normal inhalation. If you do this carefully, you will find that the necessity to breathe has been delayed by four or five times its normal rate. Thus if you find that you normally breathe 15 times per minute (four seconds between each inhalation), you may not require another breath for 20 seconds following your last forced inhalation. In an experiment, a person who inhaled pure oxygen to rid his blood of carbon dioxide was able to hold his breath for 21 minutes before the accumulation of carbon dioxide in his blood forced him to exale. (Do not experiment with deep breathing more than a few seconds at a time, as dizziness and cramps may result.)

Effects of changing atmospheric pressure. Some of the effects of changes in atmospheric pressure have been mentioned previously. It must be remembered that man is best adapted to air pressure at sea level. If he ventures far

above or below this level, he must provide his own atmosphere to approximate that to which he is accustomed.

On the surface of the earth at sea level, the body is subjected to an air pressure of approximately 15 pounds per square inch. Since a man of average size has approximately 2,864 square inches of body surface, the force exerted by the atmosphere reaches the total of 42,960 pounds. Under ordinary circumstances, this is simply a mathematcal curiosity because the external force is equalized by a corresponding one within the body cells. We are, therefore, not conscious of this tremendous weight. But for some people who may be subjected to rapidly decreasing pressure, these figures have a very real significance. If the pilot of an airplane is not provided with a pressurized cabin or pressure suit, he may experience considerable discomfort and danger if he ascends too rapidly, because the internal pressure cannot decrease as fast as the external pressure. Gases in the digestive tract and other body cavities expand (Boyle's Law) to a degree that results in acute pain and even disability.

As we ascend into the atmosphere, the weight of the column of air above us gradually decreases (Fig. 20-3). This not only has an effect on the internal pressures, but it has a drastic effect on our breathing. We frequently hear that a person at a high altitude has difficulty in breathing because there is not enough oxygen. To a certain extent, this is correct. It would be necessary, however, to ascend to an altitude of over 12 miles before the oxygen content of the air dropped much more than two percent; this would not be more than the decrease normally found in a stuffy room occupied by several people. Unless proper precautions against pressure changes are taken during an ascent to the height of

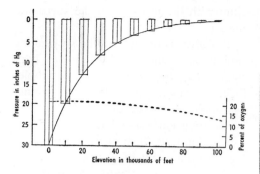

Fig. 20-3. *The relation of altitude to air pressure and the amount of oxygen in the atmosphere.*

dicates the increased efficiency of the circulatory system under unusual conditions:

Elevation in feet	Millions of red blood corpuscles per milliliter
Sea level	4.93
5000 feet	5.02
10,740 feet	5.82
14,800 feet	6.46
17,500 feet	7.37

12 miles, a person will collapse regardless of the oxygen content of the atmosphere.

The primary reason for such a collapse is that a point is reached during the ascent when negative pressure cannot be established in the thoracic cavity. The atmospheric pressure decreases until it equals that of the thoracic cavity when the lungs are expanded; hence, no air can be inhaled. This leads to decreased oxygenation of the blood, known as **anoxia**. The decrease in pressure produces anoxia in another way as well. At any altitude, the partial pressure (Dalton's Law) of oxygen is 20.94 per cent of the barometric pressure. The result is that as we ascend above the surface of the earth, the molecules of oxygen exert less pressure on the walls of the alveoli and, therefore, do not enter the blood stream as effectively.

People who live at high altitudes have become adapted to their environment in two ways. In the first place, their thoracic cavities are larger than those of persons living at lower levels. Secondly, the number of red blood corpuscles is greater insuring adequate storage and transportation of oxygen around the body. The following table shows the effect of altitude on the number of red cells and in-

The above data apply to residents at these various elevations. People who are visitors at high elevations may increase their red cell count by as much as 500,000 per milliliter of blood during a stay of less than two weeks. A return to sea level results in a reduction in the number of red corpuscles.

Anoxia is a condition that may occur in circumstances other than those associated with altitude. Drowning results in the failure of the blood to absorb a sufficient amount of gaseous oxygen. Electric shock and certain drugs depress the rate of breathing to a point where the body suffers from a lack of oxygen. Certain gases, such as carbon monoxide (CO), combine easily with hemoglobin and deprive it of its ability to carry an adequate amount of oxygen to the tissues. If the normal breathing mechanism fails, various manual and mechanical methods may be used to insure receiving the minimum amount of oxygen necessary to maintain life. Some of these methods will be discussed in the next chapter under the heading *Artificial Respiration*.

Rapid changes in pressure may have other dangerous effects besides anoxia. When the body is exposed to pressures that are higher than normal and is then decompressed rapidly, a condition may arise that is known by a variety of names, such as: *caisson disease, diver's palsy,* the *bends,* or the *chokes.*

Divers are the people most liable to suffer from rapid decompression. They work in rubber suits in which the internal pressure balances that of the surrounding water. For each 33 feet the diver descends below the surface of the sea (34 feet in fresh water), his body is subjected to an increase in pressure of 1 atmosphere. Therefore, as he descends, the pressure of the air surrounding his body is increased to permit freedom of movement and prevent his being crushed by the pressure of the water. Of the three important atmospheric gases in air, nitrogen is most affected by the increased pressure. The oxygen in the air is being constantly used up, the carbon dioxide passes out of the body in the exhaled air, but the nitrogen is neither used nor expelled. It therefore enters the plasma of the blood in such quantities that the blood nitrogen is in constant equilibrium with the nitrogen in the surrounding air.

If a diver is brought to the surface too rapidly after this equilibrium has been established, the nitrogen forms bubbles in his tissues in much the same manner as bubbles of carbon dioxide appear in a bottle of carbonated drink when the cap is removed. In both cases, the bubbles are the result of a sudden decrease in pressure on the liquids. X-ray photographs of victims of caisson disease show that the gas collects first in the spaces surrounding the joints. In severe cases (sometimes fatal) extensive bleeding occurs in the brain and spinal cord. The treatment for persons suffering from this disease is to put them into a chamber that can be pressurized to a level equal to that under which they had been working. Very slow decompression will then return the internal pressure to normal levels. Skin divers who descend to great depths under water must also allow time for decompression as they rise to the surface in order to prevent the bends.

SPEAKING OF Physiology

Briefly identify each of the following:

air or atmosphere	**caisson disease**	**Henry's Law**
anoxia	**Charles' Law**	**oxyhemoglobin**
Boyle's Law	**Dalton's Law**	**water vapor**

Test YOUR KNOWLEDGE

1. What is the importance of Avogadro's Law to the process of breathing? Keeping this information in mind, how could man survive in outer space? Does any other Gas Law apply to this problem? If so, explain.
2. Explain why carbon dioxide is carried by the liquid portion of the blood (plasma) while oxygen is transported by the hemoglobin within the red blood cells (erythrocytes).
3. What differences would be noted between the lungs of a child that died a few hours after birth and a child that was dead at birth (stillborn)?
4. Over which of the following volumes of air do we have *no* voluntary control: tidal, complemental or inspiratory reserve, minimal, supplemental or expiratory reserve, residual?

5. What correlation is there between vital capacity of the lungs and the total surface of the body? How does this vary in men and women?

6. Describe the neural control of respiration. What types of external or internal stimuli affect the respiratory rate?

7. Explain why changes in the pH of the blood affect breathing.

8. Which of the following has the greater significance to a pilot flying at 18,000 feet elevation: the decrease in oxygen content of the air, or the change in atmospheric pressure? Explain.

9. When a person goes from sea level into the high mountains, he must become acclimated if he expects to do any physical activity. What does this involve and why is it so important?

10. What precautions should skin divers observe when swimming under water with a breathing apparatus to avoid difficulty from pressure changes?

See FOR YOURSELF

1. Select a number of students in your class who vary in size and weight. See if you can determine whether there is a relationship between chest size and vital capacity of the lungs. You will need a cloth measuring tape and a spirometer apparatus. Measure each student for: tidal or normal breathing, deep inhalation for complemental air; deep exhalation for supplemental air. Measure for complete vital capacity of the lungs. What conclusions can you draw from your investigations?

2. Using library research and other sources of information, can you find evidence that changes in atmospheric pressure influence the emotional health of an individual?

3. Construct a chart to show how each of the Gas Laws affects the physiological functions of the human body.

4. Consult physics and chemistry texts to find the mathematical equations for the Gas Laws mentioned in this chapter. Explain these equations to the class.

5. Prepare a report on current research into the problems of respiration at high altitudes and in outer space.

look up caisson

CHAPTER 21

Artificial Respiration and Phonation

ARTIFICIAL RESPIRATION

In Chapter 19 we discussed the relationship of air pressure to breathing. We pointed out that each breath we take is the result of a change within the thoracic cavity which either reduces the air pressure below that of the surrounding atmosphere or raises it. When the pressure is reduced, air is drawn into the lungs. It is expelled when the internal air pressure rises. The motions which bring about these changes result, normally, from the contraction of muscles, but they can also be duplicated mechanically when the muscles fail to act. A device called the *iron lung* (Fig. 21-1) has been developed to produce forced breathing over a long period of time. In this apparatus the air pressure on the outside of the body is alternately increased and decreased by means of an air pump. These changes in pressure compress the chest cavity and then enlarge it so that air is forced out of the lungs and then drawn in. The iron lung is of inestimable value in cases of anterior poliomyelitis in which the respiratory muscles are affected.

Artificial respiration is used to aid people who have breathing difficulties or to revive those who have stopped breathing. The process can be carried on by a variety of methods without the aid of complex machines. In all manual procedures, however, the underlying principle is the same: the chest cavity is first compressed so that air is forced out of the lungs, and then allowed to return to its normal size.

In all instances of stoppage of breathing, it must be remembered that complete lack of oxygenation of the blood for more than four or five minutes may result in permanent injury or death. If artificial respiration is required, it should be started immediately and continued for as long as necessary. Occasionally, victims have been saved from death by continued manual artificial respiration over a thirty-hour period. Thus it is evident that once started, the process should be continued as long as there is the faintest hope for revival. In a few cases victims have been revived even after they had been pronounced dead by qualified physicians.

Causes of respiratory failure. We are very apt to think of artificial respiration only in terms of drowning, but there are other conditions which call for this procedure. Electrocution, the use of certain

234

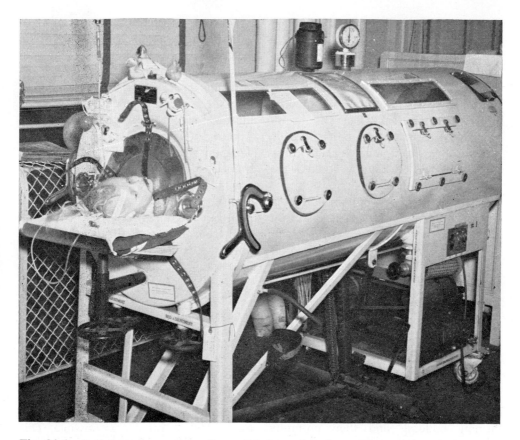

Fig. 21-1. *A victim of anterior poliomyelitis in an iron lung. The motor and pump that regulate the rate of breathing are below the tank and to the right in this picture. The ports along the side permit a nurse to examine the victim within the iron lung. (National Foundation for Infantile Paralysis)*

drugs which depress the nervous impulses passing to the respiratory muscles, poisonous gases such as carbon monoxide, or mechanical obstruction of breathing by the clogging of the respiratory passages—all call for artificial respiration.

One of the most common causes for the failure of respiratory movements is carbon monoxide poisoning. This gas is produced whenever a carbon-containing substance is incompletely oxidized. Under this condition, each atom of carbon combines with only one atom of oxygen. Carbon monoxide has the ability to combine with the hemoglobin of the blood 210 times more easily than oxygen. This means that the hemoglobin molecules that have combined with carbon monoxide are unable to accept oxygen and the cells of the body are therefore deprived of this substance. The carbon monoxide-hemoglobin compound (COHb) is also quite stable chemically so that the carbon monoxide is not readily given off in the lungs.

Carbon monoxide is odorless, tasteless, and slightly lighter than air. The exhaust from an efficiently operating automobile engine contains about 6 percent of this gas, but while the engine is warming up, the amount is much higher. Some fuel gases contain between 30 and 40 percent carbon monoxide. To avoid accidental gas poisoning by the odorless carbon monoxide, producers of such fuel gases frequently add to them an odorous substance so that consumers can more easily detect gas leaks. There is no appreciable percentage of carbon monoxide in natural gas, so it is much safer to use for heating and cooking purposes in the home, and in industry.

The early symptoms of poisoning from carbon monoxide are nausea, disturbed vision, and headaches. Later, behavior may become irrational. These symptoms may not be readily recognized since they are the same as those often associated with the stuffiness in poorly ventilated rooms. The mental disturbance moreover, may appear some time after a person has been removed from the poisonous atmosphere. A classic example of this mental reaction is the case of the man who very thoughtfully thanked his rescuers for removing him from the burning building and then promptly knocked one of them unconscious.

The length of time a person is exposed to carbon monoxide is as important as the amount of gas present in the atmosphere. An exposure for two hours to air with a concentration of 0.075 percent carbon monoxide would be as dangerous as an exposure of one hour to 0.15 percent or 0.3 percent for half an hour. A person at rest can withstand a 50 percent saturation of the blood by the gas before collapsing, but if he is exercising, the limit is about 30 percent. This difference is the result of the increased consumption of oxygen during exercise and the more rapid rate of absorption of carbon monoxide. A person may sit quietly in a room containing a small percentage of carbon monoxide, and then collapse suddenly when he gets up to try to open a window.

Methods of applying artificial respiration. Artificial respiration should be started immediately, whenever a person becomes unconscious because of obstruction in the respiratory tract, or because of the depression of the nerve stimuli that activate the respiratory muscles. Time is of the essence. Linesmen who work on high-voltage electric cables are trained to begin artificial respiration on any fellow worker who receives a severe electric shock. They even apply the process to the victim while he is being lowered from the top of the pole that supports the cables, so that no time is lost in restoring his normal respiratory movements.

Artificial respiration can be applied by the primitive but still effective method of breathing into an infant's mouth or by complex mechanical devices such as resuscitators and iron lungs. In the final analysis, neither the method nor its exact application counts as heavily as the fact that respiratory exchange must be established as rapidly as possible. This is particularly true when the respiratory failure is sudden, as in cases of electrocution or drowning. It is, of course, greatly to the advantage of the victim to have artificial respiration applied efficiently because the resumption of normal breathing will then occur more rapidly.

Various methods of artificial respiration have been devised during the last sixty or seventy years. The earliest of these, the **Sylvester method,** was developed to revive miners who had been overcome by poisonous gases. Today, many agencies are working to improve methods of artificial respiration, the American Red Cross being among the leaders. The methods may be roughly divided into two groups: those involving the use of mechanical devices and those depending on manual methods. In the

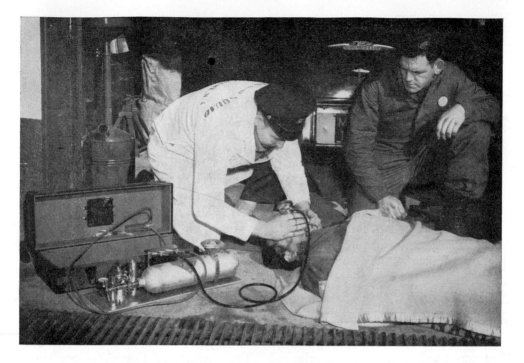

Fig. 21-2. *A resuscitator is used here to revive a victim of carbon monoxide poisoning. Resuscitators are valuable also in cases of drowning, electric shock, and other conditions of suffocation. (Stephenson Co.)*

former belong the iron lung, the inspirator, the resuscitator, and the inhalator. We have already described the action of the iron lung. The *inspirator* was a device in use some years ago, consisting of a mask that was placed over the face of the victim. Through the mask, compressed air was pumped into the lungs and then withdrawn. While the theory on which this machine was based was a good one, its operation depended on a well trained operator. In the hands of a poorly trained person, it proved highly dangerous because of the great force it exerted on the thin-walled air sacs.

The *inhalator* is not, strictly speaking, used for artificial respiration. It is a device to supply oxygen to persons who are still breathing, but with considerable difficulty. The victim inhales oxygen from a tank through a mask that covers his mouth and nose. The more modern inhalators, known as the demand type, allow oxygen to flow only as the victim inhales. Older types permitted a wasteful flow of oxygen during the exhalation period also.

Devices for artificial respiration are constantly evaluated. The late Professor Yandell Harrison of Yale University was convinced that the addition of carbon dioxide to the oxygen inhaled was highly beneficial in maintaining normal respiration. He therefore urged that five to seven percent of pure carbon dioxide be added to the oxygen to stimulate the respiratory center of the medulla to greater activity. Re-evaluation of this procedure during World War II showed that in many instances this was harmful, so the procedure has been generally abandoned except in one case. This exception is in the case of carbon monoxide poisoning. Here the administration of carbon dioxide is of advantage because it competes with the carbon monoxide in combining with hemoglobin.

Modern _resuscitators_ work on the same principle as the inspirator, except that they are fitted with complex pressure reduction valves that automatically produce a positive pressure of five to eight millimeters of mercury for inhalation and a similar negative pressure for exhalation. The resuscitator is equipped with one or more tanks of pure oxygen under a pressure of about 1500 pounds per square inch and is able to apply resuscitation for periods of from 20 minutes to an hour or more, depending on the size of the tanks and the pressure within them (Fig. 21-2).

Manual methods of restoring breathing may be divided into three principal procedures: (1) those that depend on the movement of the abdominal viscera to increase, or decrease, the capacity of the thoracic (pleural) cavity; (2) the methods that depend on the compression of the thoracic cavity to force air out of the lungs and then rely on the natural elasticity of the respiratory muscles to bring air into them; and (3) a combination of the two methods.

The first procedure can be illustrated by **Eve's technique,** which was developed by a British surgeon just before World War II. The victim is strapped to a board that is pivoted so that a seesaw movement can be obtained. The abdominal viscera are forced against the diaphragm as the head is lowered. As the head is raised, the viscera move downward and permit an increase in the chest cavity. The alternate compression and relaxation of the diaphragm results in forcefully expelling air from the lungs and then permitting it to re-enter. This method of artificial respiration exchanges about 235 milliliters (about 1½ pint) of air on each motion. Its advantage is that an operator can continue the process without becoming unduly fatigued. One major disadvantage is that it requires a special apparatus that is not always easily available.

The second procedure used in artificial respiration depends on the compression of the rib cage to force air out of the lungs. Release of this pressure allows air to enter the lungs because the ribs, their attached muscles, and the diaphragm, are elastic and have a tendency to return to their resting state. The thoracic cavity is therefore increased in size as soon as the pressure is released.

The best known method of artificial respiration was developed by Dr. Shafer and is called the **Shafer prone method,** in which the victim is laid face down. The operator then straddles one leg of the victim and presses on lower ribs. The force used is approximately 40 pounds and is released after about two seconds. A period of two to three seconds is allowed before pressure is again applied. This resting period allows air to enter the lungs. Approximately 185 milliliters of air is exchanged between the lungs and the surroundings on each cycle. This method is very fatiguing for the operator, so that other trained people must be available to take over when needed. The Shafer method has been credited with saving more lives than any other method of artificial respiration.

The third procedure for artificial respiration relies on a combination of the two previously mentioned. It may be classified as a push-pull procedure. Pressure is applied to the rib cage and then an additional movement is added to enlarge the chest cavity. The **back pressure-arm lift method** was devised by Hilger Nielson, a physical education specialist attached to the Danish army. His

Fig. 21-3. *The Nielson method of artificial respiration. In performing this, the victim is placed in a prone position with his elbows bent and his cheek on the back of his hands. The operator then kneels with his hands on the victim's back so that the heels of the hands are just below a line running between the armpits, as shown in the top drawing.*

The operator then rocks forward, keeping his elbows straight, until his shoulders are directly over his wrists. He exerts a force of about 40 pounds when in this position. This is the compression stage.

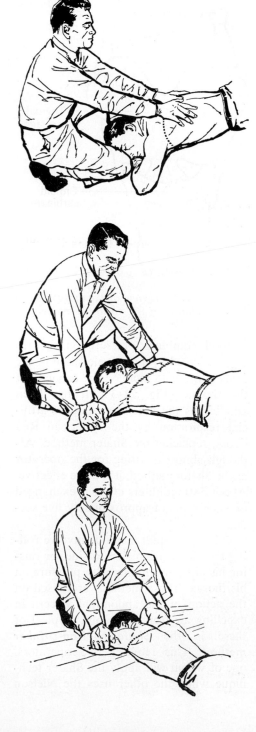

Expansion of the lungs is brought about as the operator rocks backward to his original position and slides his hands along the victim's upper arms until he can grasp the elbows. This is shown in the middle drawing.

He then lifts the elbows and draws them toward him in a continuous motion as he leans back. This is shown in the lower drawing. The arms are lowered to the ground and the cycle is repeated.

The compression and expansion should be carried out 12 times per minute with about an equal amount of time devoted to each part of the cycle. The release period should be as short as possible. A uniform pressure and motion should be used so that the method will be as nearly like normal breathing as possible.

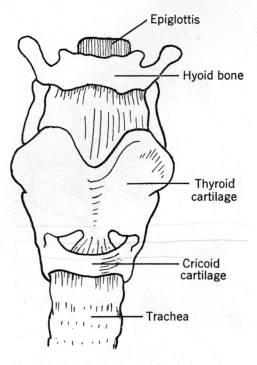

Fig. 21-4. *A front view of the larynx showing the relation of the various cartilages.*

method combines pressure on the rib cage followed by a slight elevation of the arms in order to increase the capacity of the thorax (Fig. 21-3). It has been adopted as the official method of artificial respiration by the American Red Cross, replacing the Shafer method. Although almost as tiring for the operator as the Shafer method, it is more effective. About 580 milliliters of air is exchanged on each cycle of approximately five seconds.

Other push-pull methods involve rolling the victim from side to side, or raising his hips, alternating with pressure on his thorax. These methods are based on the action of the abdominal viscera in expelling air from the lungs. Typical of these is the **Shafer-Nielson-Drinker method.** This requires two operators, one of whom will apply the Shafer technique while the other uses the Nielson

method. The one who is applying the Shafer method is then required to roll the victim gently on his side to obtain an added advantage from the movement of the viscera. This method is reported to exchange about 575 milliliters of air on each cycle.

PHONATION

Organs of phonation. Man and other mammals can produce sounds because they have a special organ of **phonation** (sound production), the larynx. Among all of the mammals, the giraffe alone lacks a larynx. We might consider that the larynx of this animal has been sacrificed in favor of a tremendously long neck.

As we have said previously, the walls of the larynx are composed of cartilages derived from the arches that supported the pharyngeal pouches of the early embryo. The largest of these cartilages are the **thyroid** and **cricoid cartilages.** The thyroid cartilage is formed by two separate plates that meet on the mid-line of

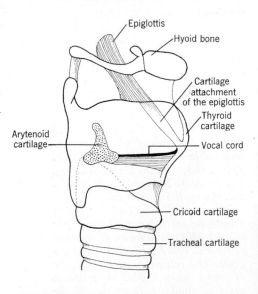

Fig. 21-5. *A side view of the larynx with the thyroid cartilage shown as though it were transparent.*

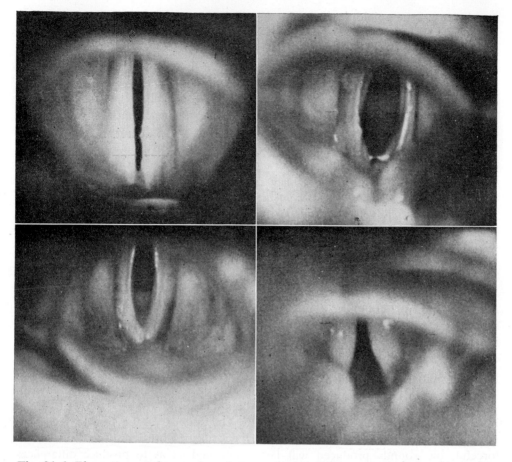

Fig. 21-6. *The action of the vocal cords in producing different types of sounds: top left, a falsetto note; top right, a loud, low-pitched tone; bottom left, a loud high-pitched tone; bottom right, whispering.* (*From the film* High-speed Motion Pictures of the Human Vocal Cords, *produced by Bell Telephone Laboratories*)

the neck to form a prominent structure somewhat like the prow of a ship (Fig. 21-4). Its movement can be seen and felt during the act of swallowing, as the muscles that are attached to it bring it upward to aid in preventing food from entering the trachea. These two cartilages form the so-called Adam's apple which is so much more prominent in men than in women. In males, the larger size of the larynx results in a deeper pitch of voice. As boys mature, the larynx grows larger, producing a lowering of the pitch of the voice. In girls, the enlargement of the larynx does not occur, and their voices remain high pitched.

The cricoid cartilage is shaped somewhat like a signet ring with the thickened area pointing toward the back of the trachea. It lies below the thyroid cartilage, and is connected with it and the lower part of the trachea by means of membranes.

There are seven other cartilages connected with the larynx. Two of these are the **arytenoid cartilages** that are attached to the **vocal cords**. Another is the attachment of the epiglottis to the front wall of the thyroid. These cartilages are shown in Fig. 21-5.

Attached to the inner walls of the larynx, at one end by the arytenoid cartilages and at the other by membranes, are the vocal cords (Fig. 21-6). The space between them is the opening of the glottis. When these cords are in a neutral position, as they are during quiet breathing, the glottis is somewhat triangular in shape with its apex pointing forward. The shape of the glottis can be changed, however, and these changes result in the different qualities of the voice.

Characteristics of human sounds. Three characteristics of sound (Chapter 12) are important in speech. *Loudness* (volume, or amplitude), is the result of changing the force with which air is expelled from the lungs when the vocal cords are held in the proper position to produce sound. You need only try to speak on an inhalation to realize that the sounds are quite indistinct; clear speech is possible only on an outgoing column of air. If, then, the exhalation is very forceful, the sounds produced will be much louder than when the vocal cords are not subjected to strong and violent passage of air.

A second property of sound is its *pitch*. The pitch of the voice changes as the vocal cords increase or decrease in length because of the tension exerted on them by the arytenoid cartilages. The vocal cords behave very much like a violin string, which emits a low pitch when it is relatively relaxed, but a high pitch when drawn taut. In males, the vocal cords behave very much like the G string on a violin. Even though they are drawn as tight as possible, their upper range of pitch cannot equal the high notes produced by women, which might be likened to the tone of the E string of a violin. In either the violin or the vocal cords,

the smaller and shorter the vibrating string, the higher the note it will produce.

A third characteristic of the voice is its *timbre,* or *quality*. This is a complex aspect of speech in which harmonics (overtones) are formed as a result of vibrations occurring within the cavities of the nose, throat, and thorax. A violin and a cello differ in tone because of their variation in size and in the resonating qualities of the woods used in making them. Just so, the various cavities of the body give a quality to the human voice that is quite separate from that produced by the vocal cords. If the larynx, chest cavities, and sinuses are large, the pleasing quality of the voice is increased. In trained singers, the harmonics that develop in these cavities give particular qualities to their voices that distinguish them from untrained singers. It is only by rigorous training that the full value of the resonating chambers of the body can be attained.

The sounds of the human voice are the result of vibrations of the vocal cords controlled so as to produce differences in pitch and volume. Variation in pitch is limited by the size of the vocal cords. Those of a man are between 0.8 and 1.0 inch long, while those of a woman average about 0.7 inch in length. Since this fundamental difference exists, the pitch of the male voice is somewhat lower than that of a woman.

It is possible, however, for both sexes to alter the length of the cords by voluntarily controlling the movement of the arytenoid cartilages. This conscious contraction and relaxation of the vocal cords results in the range of a person's voice. In a few individuals this may extend over three or four octaves on the musical scale. Only with special training can these limits be exceeded. Based on the rate of vibration of the cords, the ranges of human voices may be classified as follows:

	Vibrations per second
Bass	80–250
Baritone	100–350
Tenor	125–425
Contralto	150–500
Mezzo-soprano .	200–650
Soprano	250–750, or higher

The individual speech sounds are the result of the action of the tongue, teeth, and lips, and the partial closing of the glottis. In making the sounds of the various vowels, the tongue and the lips play the major roles. The back of the tongue may be elevated in forming some sounds, while the front may be active in making others. Thus, in making the sound of *ee* (as in ch*ee*se), the front part of the tongue is slightly elevated and the lips drawn back. To sound the letter *u* (as in r*u*le), the lips are pursed and the back of the tongue raised.

In the formation of consonants, the lips, teeth, and tongue are important. As you say the letters *p* or *b,* you notice that the sound is made by the sudden opening of both lips. The difference between the *p* and the *b* depends on the position of the vocal cords. The *b* is *voiced;* that is, it has tone produced by vibration of the vocal cords. The *p* is *voiceless.*

Other consonants in which the lips and teeth are used are *f* and *n*. Various combinations of sounds result from different positions of the organs in the mouth region, or from the regulation of the rate at which air is expelled. In some instances a nasal tone is produced by the passage of the column of air through the nose. Thus a word like *sing* has a nasal quality that can be easily detected if the nose is held while the word is being pronounced.

SPEAKING OF Physiology

Briefly identify each of the following:

carbon monoxide   **iron lung**   **resuscitator**

inhalator   **oxygenation**   **saturation**

inspirator   **phonation**   **voice range**

Test YOUR KNOWLEDGE

1. The iron lung has saved thousands of lives. What is the principle behind the operation of this apparatus?
2. Why is speed so essential in starting to give artificial respiration to restore breathing? How long should artificial respiration be continued on the victim?
3. List as many different ways as you can for administering artificial respiration. For each method, note the advantages and disadvantages.
4. Of the various manual methods listed in your text for restoring breathing, which method exchanges the greatest amount of air? Why is this knowledge important?
5. What characteristics of carbon monoxide make it so deadly? What are the symptoms of carbon monoxide poisoning?
6. Describe the structure of the larynx.
7. Why does an adolescent boy's voice change?

8.   Why is it easier to talk when air is exhaled than when it is inhaled?
9.   On a piano, changes in pitch are produced by striking different strings. How is man able to change pitch in speech? What differences are there between the voice of a man and that of a woman?
10.   What is the function of the resonating chambers in speech? What happens when one has a cold?
11.   Explain how an understanding of the mechanics of normal breathing should make it easier to perform artificial respiration.

See FOR YOURSELF

1. Describe the procedure you would use to instruct other students in one of the manual methods of artificial respiration. A course in American Red Cross first aid would be most helpful in answering this problem.

2. Visit the rescue squad of a fire department and have them demonstrate their equipment for artificial respiration. Why is it necessary to have specially trained operators? Write a report describing your visit.

3. Borrow some tuning forks from your science or physics instructor. By comparison with the tones of the tuning forks, prepare charts of the ranges of tones that you and your classmates can produce. Compare these charts with the one on page 243.

4. Make a simplified working model of an iron lung. Demonstrate its operation to your class.

5. Get the larynx of a mammal from a slaughter house. First identify its external features. Then dissect it to show the internal features. Compare it with the illustrations of the human larynx on pages 240 and 241 of this chapter.

The Circulatory System

CHAPTER 22

The General Functions of the Circulatory System

CHAPTER 23

The Solid Parts of the Blood

CHAPTER 24

Plasma, Hemorrhages, and Transfusions

CHAPTER 25

The Structure and Action of the Heart

CHAPTER 26

The General Plan of Circulation, the Spleen, and Lymph

The General Functions of the Circulatory System

Body fluids. The fluids of the body, other than those secreted by definite glandular structures, fall into one of two main groups: those that comprise the **blood,** or **intravascular fluids** (*intra,* within and *vascular,* vessels), and those that are outside the main circulatory system, the **extravascular** (*extra,* outside) **fluids.** The latter may be further subdivided into two groups: the ones that are contained within the cells (**intracellular fluids),** and those that bathe the cells (**extracellular fluids**). These latter supply the cells with materials that are carried to them by the blood. Since the blood does not come into direct contact with each individual cell of the body, it cannot supply all cells directly. There must, therefore, be some intermediate substance to carry materials between the blood and the cells. The extravascular fluids are also responsible for removing waste materials from the cells.

General functions of the blood. The blood is a circulating tissue. The blood cells are the solid parts of blood, while the fluid in which they float, the **plasma,** serves to convey the cells around the body. Both the cells and the fluid play very distinct and individual roles in the distribution of materials. The solid parts

of blood are primarily responsible for the transport of gases, protection against invasion by foreign bodies, and prevention of excessive loss of blood when blood vessels are broken. The fluid part carries dissolved materials which nourish the cells or are the waste products of their metabolic activities.

The functions of the blood are closely tied to the functions of all the organ systems. The blood *transports* all materials that are required by the cells or discarded by them. As we have seen (Chapter 20) the gases concerned in respiration are carried by the blood. Oxygen is carried from the lungs to the cells in chemical combination with hemoglobin, while carbon dioxide is also transported in this manner, although most of this gas is carried dissolved in the plasma.

Foods that have been rendered soluble by digestion are absorbed into the plasma and are thus transported around the body. In a similar manner, soluble wastes are removed from the cells and carried by the plasma to those organs where they can either be eliminated or changed into compounds that are useful for other purposes. (Unit 7) The glands that manufacture chemical regulators of bodily functions (hormones) empty their secretions directly into the blood for transportation around the body in the plasma. (Unit 8)

Maintenance of water content of the tissues is one of the principal functions of the circulatory system. If the water content of a particular region of the body is lowered as a result of increased chemical activity, the blood makes up this deficit. It then draws on reserve supplies of water to maintain its own fluid nature. We have all had the experience of a dry mouth following some unusual exertion. The salivary glands are one of the principal water-storage depots in the body, and the blood draws extra fluid from them to replenish its supply.

The blood, as a whole, helps to *maintain body temperature.* If some tissue, such as muscle, is very active, the increased rate of oxidation occurring in it raises its temperature. Continued exposure to high temperature has a serious effect on enzymatic reactions in the cells. It is therefore essential to bring the temperature of the tissue to a normal point as rapidly as possible. Thus any increase in the activity of a tissue is also accompanied by an increase in the circulatory rate so that the blood passing through it is heated. This excess heat is then given off over the surface of the body, through the lungs, or by excretions.

Protection against disease is another important function of the blood. This is accomplished by the white cells, or *leukocytes,* in one of two ways. First, some leukocytes are able to engulf bacteria and other foreign bodies that have succeeded in penetrating the surface covering. Secondly, still other types of white corpuscles have the ability to manufacture chemical substances to destroy bacteria or to neutralize the toxins (poisons) produced by invading organisms.

The *acid-base equilibrium* of the blood is maintained by the action of bicarbonates and phosphates which neutralize the usually small amounts of acids or alkalis that the blood absorbs.

The composition of blood. A person weighing 150 pounds has approximately five liters of blood. The exact amount of blood in the body cannot be determined with accuracy, since the blood is normally contained within vessels that have a total length of almost 100,000 miles. Many of these vessels are of microscopic diameter, so it is obvious that there will always be some blood adhering to their walls. Measurements of the quantity of blood in the circulatory system must be carried out by indirect methods. In health, the quantity of blood in any individual varies only slightly from time to time, the total volume making up about nine percent of the total body weight.

Blood is approximately 55 percent fluid and 45 percent solid matter. Although both the parts of the blood will be discussed in detail in later chapters, a brief statement of the function of each is helpful here.

Plasma. The plasma contains the following materials in solution:

1. Water makes up about 92 percent of the total volume of plasma.

2. Fibrinogen is a protein that is essential for the formation of a blood clot. Plasma from which fibrinogen has been removed is known as **serum.** Thus far, approximately 60 different *plasma proteins* have been identified, and several have been isolated in their pure form.

3. Inorganic salts. These relatively simple compounds are obtained from foods. Some of their ions act as buffers in helping to maintain the acid-base equilibrium of the blood.

4. Nutritive materials are absorbed from the digestive system. The monosaccharides, fatty acids, glycerin, and amino acids are all dissolved in the plasma.

5. *Hormones, vitamins,* and *enzymes* are present in minute quantities. Some of these enter the blood in specific organs, while others originate in various tissues scattered in many places throughout the body.

6. *Waste products.* Each cell of the body may be considered a complex chemical factory that manufactures substances necessary for its own existence. The blood carries the waste products of cell activity.

The solid parts of blood. Floating in the plasma are the following solid cellular structures:

1. *Red blood corpuscles* (erythrocytes). When fully developed, these can hardly be considered true cells because they lack nuclei and therefore are unable to reproduce. Their function is to transport gases around the body. Each contains a minute amount of hemoglobin which gives blood its characteristic red color.

2. *White corpuscles* (leukocytes). These corpuscles do not contain hemoglobin and are therefore almost colorless. They engulf and destroy invading bacteria and other foreign particles. Some, also, are responsible for the destruction of worn-out red corpuscles.

3. *Blood platelets* (thrombocytes). These are the smallest of the blood solids. Although we know little about their structure and origin, we know they play an important role in the formation of a blood clot.

The average composition of the blood is summarized in the table at the right.

The circulatory system. Among animals, the general pattern of the circulatory system falls into one of two categories: it is either an open system or a closed system. The *open circulatory system* is present only in those animals that lack a backbone (invertebrates). The *closed system* is found in some inverte-

---

BLOOD PLASMA
Males: 54% by volume
Females: 58% by volume
pH: 7.3 to 7.4 at 38° C.

RED BLOOD CORPUSCLES
Males:
46% by volume
5,400,000 per cu. mm.
Hemoglobin: 15.6 gm. per 100 ml. of blood
Oxygen capacity: 20.9 ml. per 100 ml. of blood
Females:
42% by volume
4,900,000 per cu. mm.
Hemoglobin: 14.2 gm. per 100 ml. of blood
Oxygen capacity: 19.0 ml. per 100 ml. of blood

WHITE BLOOD CORPUSCLES
6,000 per cu. mm. of blood

PLATELETS
250,000 per cu. mm. of blood

---

brates, but it is the only type present in vertebrates.

In the open circulatory system the blood is not always confined within blood vessels. After having been forced out from the heart through vessels, the blood leaves them and passes among the tissues, returning to the heart as a result of the contraction of muscles of the body. In the closed type of circulation, blood never normally leaves vessels to flow among the tissues. In humans, as in other vertebrates, blood is forced *outward* from the heart through **arteries** which become increasingly smaller as they branch out among the tissues. These finer branches which retain the principal characteristics of the arteries are known as **arterioles**. Eventually, these branch further to become tubes whose walls are

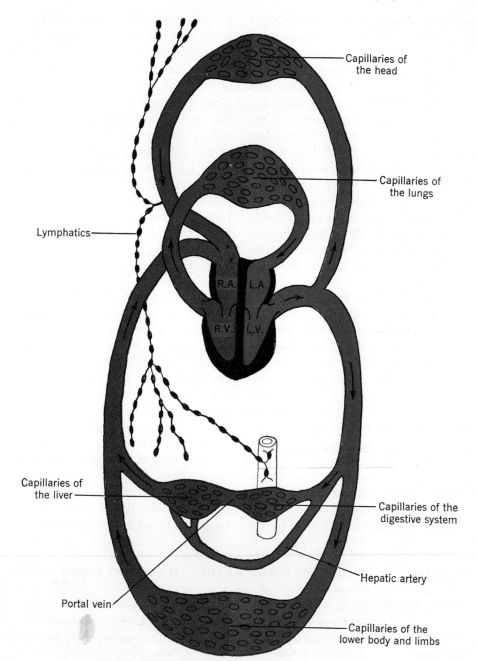

Capillaries of
the head

Capillaries of
the lungs

Lymphatics

R.A. L.A.

R.V. L.V.

Capillaries of
the liver

Capillaries of the
digestive system

Hepatic artery

Portal vein

Capillaries of the
lower body and limbs

Fig. 22-1. *Diagram of the circulatory system showing the path of the blood through the principal regions of the body. Note that the blood passes through the heart twice during each complete circuit of the body. The vessels in the dark red portions of the diagram carry deoxygenated blood; the bright red vessels carry oxygenated blood. The portal vein is an exception to the general rule that veins lead back to the heart from the capillaries. This vein leads from the digestive organs to the liver, where it breaks down into capillaries again.*

composed of only a single thickness of endothelial cells, called **capillaries.** These extremely small vessels pass between cells, or layers of cells, bringing blood into intimate contact with the cells and allowing materials to be easily exchanged. The capillaries then join together to form larger tubes (**venules**) with thicker walls. These become increasingly larger as they are joined by others. Finally, the **veins** are formed, which *return* the blood to the heart.

The **heart** is a muscular pump that is responsible for forcing the blood around the body. It is four-chambered, divided into distinct right and left halves. Each half is composed of an **atrium** (auricle) and a **ventricle.** The former is the receiving chamber for the blood as it enters the heart. The latter is a highly muscular chamber from which blood is forced out through the arteries. Blood in the right side is *deoxygenated* and is pumped only to the lungs. The left side contains *oxygenated* blood that is pumped throughout the body.

The blood must pass through the heart twice in making a complete circulation of the body. For example, if we follow a drop of blood from the time it leaves the wrist in a vein until it returns to the same spot, we will find that it has passed into the right side of the heart and from there to the lungs. In the lungs it gives off carbon dioxide, takes on a supply of oxygen, and then returns to the left side of the heart. From here it is forced out along arteries that eventually bring it to the capillaries of the hand. These then unite to form veins and the blood arrives at the point from which it started. As Fig. 22-1 shows in a diagrammatic fashion, the blood goes through a long and twisted path in its passage around the body. Later we will find out something about these pathways and the way the blood travels through them.

A diagrammatic representation of some of the vessels of the lymphatic system is shown in Fig. 22-1. The vessels of this system will be described in Chapter 26. They drain waste materials from the tissues and return them, with the fluid in which they are dissolved, to the blood stream by way of the veins. As we will explain later, there is a constant passage of fluid from the blood to the tissues. Unless this fluid is returned to the blood, the body suffers seriously from the loss of an important transporting medium.

The table below summarizes the principal materials that are exchanged between the blood and the tissues:

MATERIAL	ENTERS THE BLOOD AT THE	LEAVES THE BLOOD AT THE
Oxygen	Lungs	Cells
Carbon dioxide	Cells	Lungs
Food	Digestive organs	Cells, for use or storage
Inorganic salts	Digestive organs	Cells or as excretory products
Hormones	Endocrine glands	Cells
Water	Digestive organs	Cells
	Cells	Skin, lungs, kidneys
Organic wastes	Cells	Excretory organs
Erythrocytes	Bone marrow	———
Leukocytes	Bone marrow, lymph tissue	———
Platelets	Bone marrow	———

SPEAKING OF Physiology

Briefly identify each of the following:

arteriole	extracellular	intravascular
artery	hormone	serum
atrium (auricle)	inorganic	toxin
buffer	intracellular	ventricle

Test YOUR KNOWLEDGE

1. In simple animals (paramecia, hydra, and jelly fish) there is no circulatory system as we know it. Why then must there be a circulatory system in more advanced animals, such as man?
2. Why is blood classified as a circulating tissue?
3. List the various functions performed by blood. How is each related to the activities performed by the various other body systems?
4. Why is it difficult to measure accurately the total volume of blood in the human body?
5. What are the advantages and/or disadvantages of an open system of circulation as compared to a closed system?
6. Why is the heart considered a double pump?
7. In what ways does the blood in one side of the heart differ from that in the other side?

See FOR YOURSELF

1. Select an invertebrate animal that has a typical open circulatory system and prepare a schematic drawing to show how blood moves through the animal's body. Compare the open system with a typical closed system, as seen in Fig. 22-1.

2. Using library references, trace the historical discoveries of such men as Galen and William Harvey, which led to the knowledge that blood makes a complete circuit of the body within a closed system of vessels. Prepare an oral or written report.

3. Study with a microscope a portion of the urinary bladder of a freshly killed frog (kept moist with saline solution) to see capillary architecture and circulation.

The Solid Parts of the Blood

The solid parts of the blood; the erythrocytes, leukocytes, and platelets, have a common origin. Most of these are formed in the marrow of certain bones, although two types of white corpuscles are produced by the lymphatic tissue. Of all of the blood solids, only a few of the white corpuscles are able to reproduce themselves. It is therefore necessary for the cells of the body to replace those solid parts that become worn out and are removed from the circulation. It is one of the primary functions of bone marrow to meet this constant demand for new blood solids.

Functions of the marrow. The marrow of bones is of two different types: **red marrow**, containing large amounts of blood, and **yellow marrow.** The latter serves as a depot for the deposition of fat throughout the life of the individual. In the early stages of embryonic development it may aid in the formation of blood cells. Red marrow is confined to certain bones such as those of the cranium, ribs, and sternum, the bodies of vertebrae, the bones of the pelvis, parts of small bones, and the ends of long bones. All other marrow cavities contain yellow marrow, which may, in case of severe damage or loss of the red marrow, revert to its embryonic function of producing blood cells.

Within the blood-forming tissues of the marrow appear large, primitive cells that contain distinct nuclei. These are known as the **reticular cells.** The process of division and differentiation by which these cells develop is shown in Fig. 23-1. Note that the reticular cells give rise to an intermediate form, the **myeloblasts,** that eventually forms the red cells, most of the white corpuscles, and the platelets. The last are formed from a special type of cell that arises from the myeloblast and is known as a **megakaryocyte.**

During the changes that occur in these cells of the red marrow, the future erythrocytes lose their nuclei, and the leukocytes develop cytoplasmic structures that will later differentiate them into their various types. When blood cell formation is occurring in the marrow, the blood vessels in which the cells form are temporarily closed off from the general circulation. Within these tubes the cells pass through their various stages. When the blood cells have become mature, the vessels open and discharge their contents into the general circulation.

Red corpuscles (erythrocytes). Mature red corpuscles normally lack nuclei, the chromatin material having been lost before the cells entered the blood stream. The **reticulocytes,** which make up from one to three percent of the erythrocytes in the blood, contain a material that may represent the remnants of the former

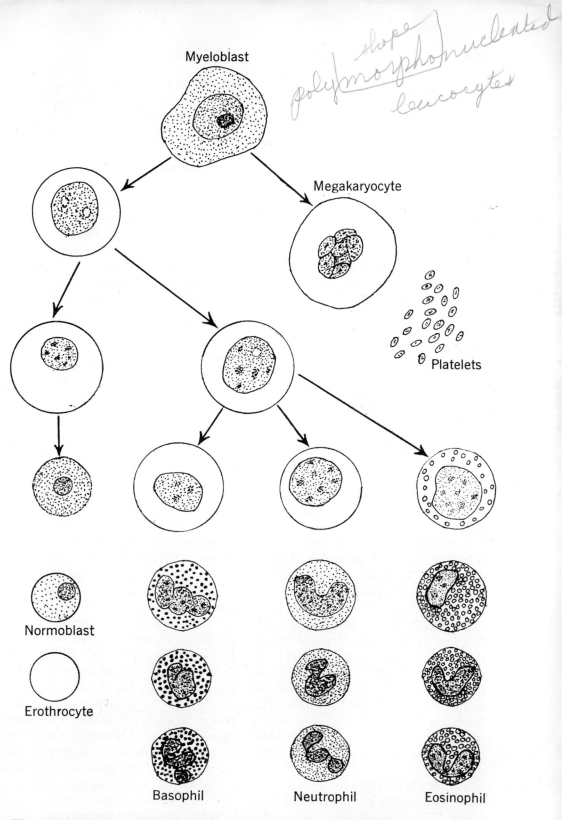

Myeloblast

polymorphonucleated leucocytes

Megakaryocyte

Platelets

Normoblast

Erothrocyte

Basophil   Neutrophil   Eosinophil

Fig. 23-1. *Diagrams showing the development of the various solid structures of the blood from the myeloblast.*

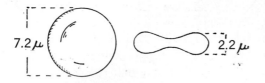

Fig. 23-2. *Outline and dimensions of a typical red blood corpuscle.* (*From Mars-land,* Principles of Modern Biology, *Holt, 1957*)

nucleus. A normal red blood corpuscle is round in outline when viewed from above. If taken from an artery and examined in a fresh film, it may appear yellowish red, but if it has come from a vein, the color will tend toward a yellowish green. Blood owes its typical red color to the presence of large numbers of these cells; the individual corpuscles in fresh blood do not have a distinctly red appearance.

A red blood corpuscle (Fig. 23-2) has an average diameter of 7.2 microns (1 micron = 0.0001 millimeter), and it is usually described as a biconcave disk, because it is thicker along the margins than in the middle. At the margin, the cell measures about 2.2 microns in thickness, but the center is only approximately half as thick. This inequality in thickness causes red blood corpuscles to appear doughnut shaped when viewed from above. The shape of these cells is of great importance from the standpoint of their function. It has been calculated that if the red corpuscle were a spherical body with a diameter of 7.2 microns, its surface area would be 163 square microns and its volume 197 cubic microns. The biconcave disk form, however, gives it a surface area of 302 square microns while still retaining its volume of 197 cubic microns.

The membrane that surrounds the corpuscle is complex; it is made up of three layers. On the outside is a protein layer three or four molecules in thickness.

Within this is a layer of lipid molecules. The innermost layer is composed again of protein molecules. Within this envelope is a mixture of hemoglobin, salts, and other substances that transports gases and maintains osmotic pressure in the cell.

Hemoglobin is composed of a protein, **globin,** and an iron compound, **hematin.** A hematin compound, **hemin,** is easily obtained from blood. If a drop of blood is heated with a drop of glacial-acetic acid, long brown needles of hemin are formed. This is considered a reliable test for the presence of blood. Globin and heme combine in the bone marrow before cells are released into circulation.

Hemoglobin is a remarkable substance in two respects. In the first place, it is able to change from the deoxygenated to the oxygenated state in a remarkably short period of time—about 0.01 second. Secondly, it is able to retain its oxygen content until such time as it comes in contact with a tissue that is suffering from oxygen want. Only under this condition does the hemoglobin release its supply of oxygen. It has been calculated that if the blood lacked hemoglobin, a person of average size would require approximately 75 gallons of circulating fluid to dissolve sufficient oxygen to supply the needs of the cells. The reason for this is that oxygen dissolves in plasma at sea level only to the extent of 1.23 milliliters per 100 milliliters of fluid. In the presence of hemoglobin, full saturation of the blood with oxygen results when 20.5 milliliters of oxygen is present in each 100 milliliters of blood, since each gram of hemoglobin will combine with 1.34 milliliters of oxygen. This gives a ratio of one part of oxygen dissolved in the plasma, as compared with 192 parts combined with hemoglobin.

White corpuscles (leukocytes). These are somewhat larger than erythrocytes.

They range from one and one-quarter to two times the diameter of the red cells. The leukocytes can move independently. Whereas red corpuscles must be carried by the plasma and cannot change their shape except as they are squeezed in passing through very small vessels, the white corpuscles are capable of changing shape when the proper chemical stimulus is applied. They can move out from the blood stream by passing between -the endothelial cells that comprise the walls of the capillaries. In this respect, they resemble the single-celled animal, *Ameba*. In both, the cytoplasm flows toward a stimulus. An ameba, for example, will move toward a source of food or oxygen by an oozing, flowing movement that is generally believed to be caused by a change in the surface tension of the cell membrane on the side toward the stimulus. The same general movement is found in white corpuscles.

These cells are able to change their shape in such a manner that they can escape from the capillaries. It is thought that they are able to penetrate the capillary walls by dissolving the cement substance that holds the endothelial cells together.

The diagram in Fig. 23-3 shows how leukocytes pass through a capillary wall toward a stimulus, represented by a small wound that has allowed bacteria to gain entrance through the skin. The bacteria produce various chemical substances (toxins) which are the products of their metabolic activities, and which act as stimuli for the leukocytes.

One of the first results of the presence of foreign materials in tissue is the dilation (enlargement) of the capillaries in the area. As a result, more blood enters the tissue and there is a corresponding rise in the local temperature. Also, with the increased blood flow, more white corpuscles are carried to the area. We do

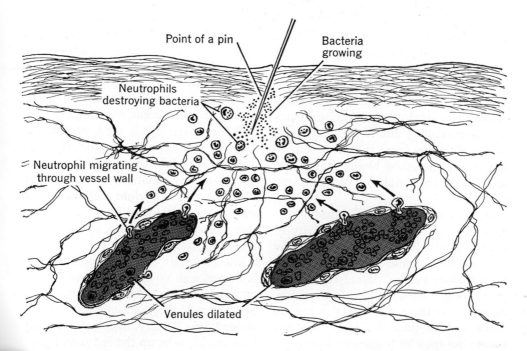

Fig. 23-3. *Diagram showing how neutrophils move from the blood vessels to attack invading bacteria.*

not yet know what mechanism stimulates the production of a larger number of leukocytes or attracts them to a specific region of the body. On arrival in the infected area, the white corpuscles pass between the cells of the capillary walls and move toward the invading bacteria. As they approach the bacteria, the cells send out projections that surround and engulf the bacteria. Once inside the leukocyte, the bacterial cell is digested and rendered harmless. This process is known as **phagocytosis** (Greek, *phagein,* to eat; *cyton,* cell), and any cells that perform this function are called **phagocytes.** The number of bacterial cells that a single leukocyte ingests may be greater than its digestive capacity. When this occurs, the leukocyte dies. Its remains, plus the active white cells and invading bacteria, are the material commonly known as **pus.** As pus collects in the tissue, materials produced by the bacteria cause a breakdown of the surrounding tissue. An abcess then develops as a wall of tissue is formed around the area by specialized white cells known as **fibroblasts.** Meanwhile, more blood is carried to the area with resulting redness. The nerve endings of pain are also stimulated. The signs of an infection, therefore, are *swelling* due to the accumulation of fluids, *redness* and *heat* as a result of the increased blood supply and *pain* caused by stimulation of the nearby receptors.

In addition to engulfing invading organisms, another phagocytic activity of the white cells is their ability to destroy red cells that cannot function normally. Erythrocytes become damaged as they pass through the smallest blood vessels, especially if these are in active muscle tissue. Indeed, there is evidence that red corpuscles may be broken up into small fragments as a result of the activity of a muscle. These damaged cells, or their parts, are engulfed by some of the white blood cells. The regions where this destruction of red cells occurs most actively are the spleen, red bone marrow, liver, and certain lymph glands. The digestive activities of the leukocytes break down hemoglobin into globulin and heme. The latter is further reduced to **hemotoidin,** which is then transformed into bilirubin by the liver. Another product of this decomposition is **hemosiderin,** which may be stored as an iron compound for later conversion into hemoglobin by steps that are not thoroughly understood at present. The rate at which the red cells are destroyed is almost unbelievable; it is estimated that there are an average of 3,500,000,000 red corpuscles consumed per kilogram of body weight each 24 hours. Of course, there is a corresponding production of cells by the bone marrow. If an excess of erythrocytes is injected into the blood stream, they are rapidly removed until the count returns to a normal level. This indicates that the number of erythrocytes is kept at a fairly constant level, but the mechanism which accomplishes this is not known.

The types of white corpuscles can be identified by different methods of staining. If a mixed dye is used, certain cellular structures take up the different components of the dye in a definite manner. The most commonly used stain for blood smears is **Wright's stain.** It is a mixture of **methylene blue** (a dye that stains alkaline materials) and **eosin** (a bright red stain that has an affinity for acidic materials). When a blood smear is stained with Wright's stain, the nuclear materials of the cells are colored blue and any acidic cytoplasmic granules are stained red. The erythrocytes, since they lack nuclei, take up the red stain lightly and appear as pink objects. On the other hand, the white corpuscles show a

cleus that is stained deep blue. Some of these cells may contain relatively large cytoplasmic granules that stain red, others may have granules that are blue, while other cells may not show any large distinct blue or red inclusions. In some of the leukocytes, the cytoplasm shows no staining reaction whatever. Thus these cells may appear red, blue, an intermediate shade or almost transparent when stained.

On the basis of their staining reactions, white blood corpuscles are classified as follows:

1. Neutrophils. In these cells the cytoplasm is stained a very light red, due to the presence of extremely small granules. The particles are not distinct under the high power lens of a microscope and may appear as either blue or red. The nucleus is large and forms several distinct lobes. Occasionally neutrophils are mistaken for the cell type that is described next, because of their light red staining reaction. The neutrophils are the cells that are primarily responsible for the destruction of bacteria.

2. Eosinophils. These leukocytes have large granules in their cytoplasm that stain a bright red with eosin. Their name is derived from the fact that they have an especial affinity for this dye (Greek, *eosin + phileo,* I love).

3. Basophils are white cells that absorb methylene blue in their cytoplasmic granules. These cells therefore contain large numbers of small blue particles in the cytoplasm.

4. Lymphocytes are formed by lymph tissue. They may be differentiated from other forms of white corpuscles by the fact that their cytoplasm is only slightly granular and does not absorb dyes in the same manner as the others. The lymphocytes are quite easily distinguished by the fact that they have a large, single nucleus. There are two general types:

one is as large as the average neutrophil, while the other is somewhat smaller.

5. Monocytes are similar to the lymphocytes in appearance. The large nucleus is indented somewhat. Monocytes are primarily concerned with the destruction of bacteria and red corpuscles.

In health, the leukocytes have a fairly stable ratio in the blood. Their average percentages of the total number of white cells is as follows:

Neutrophils	67.0% of white cells
Eosinophils	3.0% of white cells
Basophils	0.5% of white cells
Monocytes	7.0% of white cells
Lymphocytes ...	22.5% of white cells

If the total white cell content exceeds 10,000 per cubic millimeter of blood, the condition is known as *leukocytosis;* if it is below 5,000 cells per cubic millimeter, it is called *leukopenia.* From the medical standpoint, these variations in the white cell count are very important. They often supply clues in diagnosis of infectious diseases. Various types of invading organisms affect the numbers of different types of white corpuscles. In *pneumonia,* for example, there may be more than 100,000 cells per cubic millimeter of blood, while in *typhoid fever* the count may drop below the normal range. In worm infections, especially in *trichinosis,* the number of eosinophils increases, as it does in *asthma* and other allergic conditions. In *malaria,* the monocytes increase in number and, since they are phagocytic, may frequently contain some of the pigment from the malarial organism in their cytoplasm. Strenuous exertion or severe emotional disturbance may send the white cell count to 35,000 per cubic millimeter. This condition is known as **physiologic,** or **activity, leukocytosis.**

Blood platelets. These are the smallest of the solid parts of blood. In a fresh preparation of blood, they have an oval outline and appear as individual structures. In a dried smear, however, the platelets appear round and are clumped together in small groups. As Fig. 23-1 shows, they arise from a breaking down (fragmentation) of the megakaryocytes that are formed in the red bone marrow. Various theories have been advanced to explain where this disintegration occurs: some investigators are of the opinion that it takes place in the lungs, while others believe is occurs in the bone marrow.

The number of blood platelets is difficult to determine with accuracy, since it varies in different regions of the body, and under varying physiological conditions. The normal range is between 200,000 and 400,000 per cubic millimeter of blood, with the figure 250,000 an average value. In the next chapter we will discuss the role of the platelets in the clotting of blood, since they are most concerned with this process.

Abnormal conditions affecting the blood. Deficiency in the number of red cells is called *anemia*. Studies of this abnormal condition have contributed greatly to our knowledge of blood formation. From a physiological standpoint, anemia results from one of the following principal causes: an acute or chronic loss of blood (hemorrhage) which reduces the number of red corpuscles; the excessive destruction of red corpuscles, as for example in malaria; or the improper formation of hemoglobin or red cells by the body. Regardless of the immediate cause of anemia, there is always a lack of hemoglobin with a corresponding deficiency in the oxygen supply of the body.

Anemia may result from a sudden loss of blood caused by a severe wound, or perhaps the donation of blood at a blood bank. Immediately following loss of blood, the arterial vessels constrict and thus reduce the flow of blood through them. Fluid from the tissues then passes into the blood vessels, restoring the normal blood volume. Approximately forty-eight hours after the loss, many immature red cells appear in the blood stream along with an excess of leukocytes. This indicates that the red marrow has been stimulated to increase its production of blood cells.

A chronic loss of blood caused by hookworm infection may result in a prolonged recovery period after the worms have been killed. The total loss may be considerable, since there are usually a great many hookworms embedded in the mucous lining of the intestinal wall and using their host's blood as food. Not only do these parasites cause an actual decrease in the blood supply, but they also produce toxins which impair the body's ability to regenerate new cells.

A second type of anemia results from the destruction of red corpuscles caused by the ingestion or absorption of poisonous chemicals, or of toxins produced by bacteria that have penetrated beyond the first lines of defense. Lead poisoning, an occupational disease, often results from carelessness in the use of substances containing lead. A house painter, for example, may not wash his hands thoroughly before eating. In this case, minute traces of lead may be ingested. Spray painters may also inhale lead particles. Over a long period of time, these small quantities of lead accumulate in the red marrow of the bones and destroy some of the blood-forming cells. The blood hemoglobin is thus reduced. In severe cases of lead poisoning, enough of the metal may accumulate in the bones to be detected by means of X rays. An early symptom of lead poisoning is the appearance of a dark blue line in the gums just above the teeth. This *lead line* is caused by the deposition of lead sulfate in the walls of the capillaries. In cases of lead poisoning, the red corpuscles show a blue mottling when they are stained because lead salts in their cytoplasm are able to absorb the methylene blue of the stain.

Certain bacteria may invade the blood stream and cause decomposition of the red corpuscles, with resulting anemia. Such an invasion is usually termed **septicemia.** Once bacteria or other invading organisms have succeeded in passing the defensive lines of the skin, the white cells, and the antitoxins, their spread throughout the body is relatively easy. Bacteria and other organisms (popularly known as *germs*) may occasionally destroy red cells. A good example of this is seen in the malarial organisms, which kill large numbers of erythrocytes in the course of their reproductive cycles. Bacteria may also produce toxins, which have a much more rapid and drastic action because they chemically affect the cellular envelopes of the corpuscles and destroy the hemoglobin.

A third type of anemia results from improper formation of red corpuscles. This is the result of either an *inherited* defect in the blood-forming tissues or an *acquired* inability to form blood in a normal manner. An example of the former is the condition called **sickle cell anemia.** This occurs almost exclusively among Negroes and is characterized by red cells that are curved so that they resemble sickles. If the number of affected cells is relatively low, there are no outward symptoms evident, although the cells can be identified in blood smears. In severe cases, however, the red cells are rapidly destroyed and jaundice develops as a result of the accumulation of decomposed hemoglobin in the blood stream. There is an accompanying loss of the oxygen-carrying capacity of the

blood. A somewhat similar condition, known as **Cooley's anemia,** occurs among members of the Mediterranean peoples. **Familial hemolytic jaundice** results from an abnormal activity of the spleen which makes the red cells fragile, so that they break up easily and release their hemoglobin into the blood. Removal of the enlarged spleen usually cures this disease.

Another type of anemia caused by improper formation of blood cells is **pernicious anemia.** In this disease, the blood is characterized by the presence of abnormally large and misshapen erythrocytes. Each of these, however, contains an amount of hemoglobin that is consistent with its size, so the onset of this disease is very difficult to diagnose. In the early stages, a person appears to be quite healthy and of a normal color, because the hemoglobin content of the blood is adequate. However, if the disease progresses without being identified, death usually results. Until a relatively few years ago, victims of pernicious anemia usually died within a few months. Then a group of physicians found that an extract of liver would prolong the patient's life. Later research showed that the active principle in this liver extract was vitamin B_{12}. The disease is believed to be caused by absence of a factor in gastric juice that aids in the absorption of the vitamin. Vitamin B_{12} is most effective when injected.

Iron-deficiency anemia is of rather frequent occurrence in growing children. This is caused by the absence of an adequate amount of iron in the diet, with the result that there is insufficient hemoglobin in the red corpuscles. Since iron is a common element found in the majority of plant foods, a well-balanced diet should prevent this condition. It is rather interesting to note that the minute amount of copper found in most plant foods aids in the absorption and utilization of iron by the body. Copper is usually considered a violent protoplasmic poison in high concentrations, but its presence in concentrations such as those found normally in plants is evidently essential for the formation of hemoglobin by animals.

Leukemia is a blood disease that is usually fatal. It is so named because the blood may show a whitish color caused by the presence of an excessively large number of leukocytes. In extreme cases of this disease, the number of white cells may equal or surpass the number of erythrocytes. There are several well-recognized types of leukemia: some are *acute* in the sense that they develop rapidly and run their course quickly; others are said to be *chronic* because their action is slower and may have little effect on the victim over a period of many years. Unfortunately, acute types of leukemia are more frequently found among children and young adults.

An excess of leukocytes in the blood may replace the erythrocytes to the extent that the blood can no longer carry the needed oxygen to the tissues. It may also detract from the ability of the bone marrow to produce more red cells.

Today there is increased interest in leukemia because it has been discovered that the disease can be caused by excessive exposure to X rays and the radiations from radioactive elements. At present research workers cannot agree on the exact relationship between the amount of radiation exposure and the occurrence of the disease. However, it has been proved beyond any doubt that exposure to these penetrating radiations can cause increased production of leukocytes in the body.

SPEAKING OF Physiology

Briefly identify each of the following:

abscess	leukemia	pus
acute infection	leukocyte	radioactive
biconcave	leukocytosis	reticular cell
chronic infection	leukopenia	septicemia
erythrocyte	phagocyte	thrombocyte (platelet)

Test YOUR KNOWLEDGE

1. Describe the location and functions of each type of bone marrow.
2. Trace the developmental cycle of erythrocytes, noting the cytoplasmic changes that occur.
3. Why is the typical biconcave shape of erythrocytes more advantageous than a spherical shape?
4. Describe the formation and importance of hemoglobin. What happens when this substance is lacking in our blood?
5. Of what importance is the fact that leukocytes are motile? How is this movement accomplished?
6. How do white blood cells combat infection?
7. What are the symptoms of a skin infection?
8. Classify the leukocytes as to: (*a*) staining reactions, (*b*) function, (*c*) relative number per cubic millimeter of blood, (*d*) source.

9. What happens to the hemoglobin when red blood cells are destroyed?

10. Of what importance to a doctor is the knowledge of a patient's white blood cell count?

11. What are the three basic causes of anemia? List the various kinds of anemia that are associated with each cause.

See FOR YOURSELF

1. Obtain a prepared slide of human blood fixed with Wright's stain. Using the high power lens of a microscope, locate one or more examples of each kind of white blood cell. Make a drawing of each type of cell using colors that duplicate what you observe. How do cells you have seen compare with the written description in your text? Compare the human blood slide with a prepared slide of frog blood. Which of the cells are similar? How do the red blood cells compare with each other?

2. Prepare a written or oral report for your class on one of the following blood disorders: leukemia; infectious momonucleosis; pernicious anemia.

3. Get permission to visit a hospital laboratory so as to learn how blood counts are taken. Report on how this is done and on how a doctor may use blood counts for diagnostic purposes.

4. Demonstrate the test for blood, as mentioned on page 254 of this book, by heating a drop of blood with a drop of glacial acetic acid. Examine the crystals of hemin under the microscope. Discuss some possible uses of this test for blood.

CHAPTER 24

Plasma, Hemorrhage, and Transfusion

Plasma is the highly complex part of blood which carries on most of the functions of the circulatory system. Basically, it is a water solution of various substances which also contains a suspension of other materials. Since some of these materials are colloids, the plasma acts in many ways like a colloidal suspension. When separated from the corpuscles, plasma is a yellowish straw-colored fluid.

The composition of plasma is not constant. It varies from person to person and also within any one person from time to time, depending on the materials that are added to it or withdrawn from it by the various activities of the body. Following a meal, for example, it contains an increased amount of nutrient materials. On the other hand, after a period of strenuous exercise, plasma contains wastes that the blood has removed from active tissues. Thus from one moment to the next, plasma reflects the different physiological states of the body. This makes the exact analysis of its composition impossible. The table at the right shows its average composition.

Fibrinogen and the clotting of blood. The plasma protein responsible for the clotting of blood is believed to be formed in the liver, but the exact steps in its production are not clearly understood. It is a substance of uniform chemical composition with a molecular weight of approximately 500,000, which indicates its complex nature.

Several chemical reactions occur during *coagulation,* the formation of a blood clot. The exact steps of the process are not definitely known, and several theories have been advanced. An explanation of each of these may be found in advanced texts in medical physiology. While there is some difference of opinion on the reactions involved, there is

Water	92%
Blood proteins	7%
Fibrinogen	
Serum albumin	
Serum globulin	
Other organic substances ..	0.136%
Nonprotein nitrogen (urea)	
Organic nutrients	
Inorganic ions	0.931%
Calcium, Chlorine	
Magnesium, Potassium,	
Sodium, Bicarbonates,	
Carbonates, Phosphates	

also agreement on the fundamental processes that occur.

All the tissues of the body contain a substance that hastens the coagulation of blood. This material, **thromboplastin,** is produced whenever a tissue is injured. Therefore, when blood comes in contact with cells that have been cut or otherwise injured, thromboplastin initiates the formation of a clot.

Two other materials in plasma are necessary to enable the thromboplastin to function. One of these is *calcium* and the other is *prothrombin.* The reaction that occurs when these three materials combine can be shown as follows:

Thromboplastin + calcium +
$$\text{prothrombin} \rightarrow \text{thrombin}$$

The fact that calcium ions are required for the completion of this process is well illustrated by the effect of their removal from the blood. When a physician takes a sample of blood from a patient for examination, he adds a solution of sodium oxalate to it. This prevents the blood from clotting before he has an opportunity to examine it, because the calcium ions unite chemically with the oxalate to form a compound (calcium oxalate). Thus the calcium is not available for the coagulation process.

The second step in the formation of a clot involves the reaction between the thrombin and the fibrinogen. Again, the exact steps involved in this process are not clearly understood, but the process may be represented as follows:

$$\text{Fibrinogen} + \text{thrombin} \rightarrow \text{fibrin}$$

The fibrin threads produced by this reaction form the basis of the clot. They are actually minute white strands of material which trap the corpuscles until an efficient block has formed across the opening to stop the flow of blood.

The platelets were formerly thought

to be the principal source of thromboplastin. Recent research has thrown some doubt on this supposed function of platelets, since they appear to contain too little thromboplastin to account for the rapid coagulation of blood. Since they are extremely fragile objects, they break up on slight contact with a foreign body. In breaking up, they release a substance, *cephalin,* which apparently aids in the formation of thrombin, but its exact action is not known.

Clotting of blood is affected by physical factors. A surface that can be wetted by water solution hastens the process, while one that prevents molecules of water from clinging to it retards clotting. For example, if blood is carefully removed from a vessel, so that it does not come in contact with injured tissues, and then placed in a clean glass tube, a clot will appear in a short time. If, however, the inside of the tube is coated with a layer of paraffin or wax (which the blood cannot wet), the clotting time will

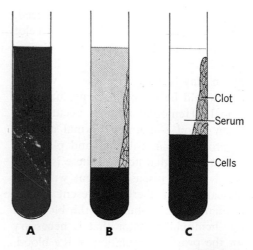

A   B   C

Fig. 24-1. *The clotting of blood. Freshly drawn blood is shown in tube* A. *In* B *some of the cells have settled and a clot is forming along the side of the tube. In* C *most of the cells have settled and the clot is fully developed, leaving the clear serum. A few cells are trapped in the clot.*

be greatly prolonged. Temperature also affects the rate of clotting. At a relatively high temperature, blood will clot easily, while at a temperature such as that found in a refrigerator, blood will remain fluid for a long time. There appears to be a rapid destruction of the blood platelets on contact with a rough surface.

The importance of a rough surface and its physical effect on the clotting of blood is seen whenever a tissue is cut. Since all tissues are wettable by blood, the cut surface itself aids in the formation of a clot. The process can be hastened by placing a piece of gauze or other cloth with a relatively rough surface over a wound. This further stimulates the formation of a clot.

A study of the blood defect known as **hemophilia** has shed some light on the structure of plasma and the possible function of some of the blood proteins in the process of coagulation. Hemophilia is an inherited condition in which the power to produce a sufficient amount of thromboplastin is greatly reduced. The result is a failure of the blood to clot within a normal period of time. Consequently, people suffering from this condition may bleed to death from wounds that would be minor for a normal individual. Hemophilia may occur even when blood contains a normal amount of prothrombin, calcium, and platelets, so it appears that none of these is implicated in this disease. Recent work has indicated that there is present in the normal serum globulin of the blood an anti-hemophilic factor that is necessary for the proper coagulation of the blood. Experimental evidence of this has been obtained by injecting small amounts of normal serum globulin into persons suffering from hemophilia. This temporary measure causes the blood of the victim to clot faster, but it does not change his

hereditary characteristics, with the result that the person can still transmit the defect to his or her offspring.

The fact that blood does not normally clot in the blood vessels has been attributed to a substance known as **heparin.** This was first isolated from the liver but was later found to be present in other organs. At present it is obtained from the lungs of slaughtered animals in sufficient quantity to supply commercial needs. Under normal conditions, heparin is not present in the blood in sufficient quantities to be detectable as an anticoagulant.

Blood clots called **thrombi** (sing., **thrombus**) occur occasionally in blood vessels. If they become too large, they seriously hamper the flow of blood through a vessel. Thus the passage of blood to a region of the brain or to the muscles of the heart may be affected, resulting in *thrombosis*. In such cases, doctors frequently use an anticoagulant such as heparin. Another drug that is being currently used to reduce a thrombus is **Dicumarol.** This compound was first isolated from sour clover fodder that was found to be the cause of hemorrhages in cattle who suffered minor cuts. Vitamin K, which is essential in the formation of prothrombin, counteracts the action of both heparin and Dicumarol.

Plasma proteins. The plasma proteins (other than fibrinogen) are classified as either **globulins** or **albumins.** These terms are used to designate certain types of protein molecules, and there are many individual examples of each. Both of these types of proteins are widely distributed in plant and animal tissue. A good example of an albumin that is not a constituent of blood is the white of an egg, while a globulin is present in the yolk of an egg. The *serum* albumins and *serum* globulins can be separated from the plasma when the fibrinogen has been removed.

Of the two, serum albumin is the more plentiful. Its principal function is to control the osmotic pressure of blood. As blood flows through the capillaries into the tissues, its osmotic pressure is highest just after the capillary branches from an arteriole. From that point onward through the capillary, the osmotic pressure decreases. The result of this gradient in pressure is that materials (food and oxygen) leave the blood early in its passage through the capillary. Then other materials pass into the blood as the capillary joins others to form a small vein (venule). Under normal conditions, the blood proteins do not pass through the capillary walls because of the relatively large size of their molecules. However, since they are colloidal materials, they can give up, or take up, water-soluble substances, and thereby control the osmotic pressure within the vessels.

If there is a decrease in serum albumin, fluids leave the blood throughout the entire length of the capillaries. When this condition arises, the surrounding tissues become filled with fluid and become enlarged. Such a condition is known as **edema.** Certain types of **nephritis** (kidney disorder) result in the removal of abnormally large amounts of protein from the blood with resulting edema. Also, some types of heart disease are accompanied by edema of the ankles and feet, especially in the morning after the body has been inactive during sleep.

The serum globulin also helps in the maintenance of osmotic pressure, but it has other functions to perform. Whether the structural unit of serum globulin is a single large molecule or a combination of molecules has not been definitely established. Under certain laboratory conditions, it is possible to obtain several different substances that show characteristic features. These may, however, be parts of a compound that has been broken down chemically, rather than members of a physical combination which have been separated.

Among the substances that have been extracted from serum globulin is **gamma globulin.** In this substance are the antibodies that protect a person against invasion by bacteria and viruses. For example, if a person has had measles, he has in his blood certain chemical materials which combat another attack of this disease. These materials are present in the serum globulin as definite antibodies: substances that neutralize the effects of a future invasion of the body by the same organism. Since the lymphocytes are the source of serum globulin, they are believed responsible for production of antibodies. It is possible by modern medical techniques to separate some of these antibodies from the serum globulin and to use them to give temporary immunity to a person who has been exposed to a specific disease. The injection of such antibodies either prevents the disease or renders an attack less severe than it might have been without this protection. Among the types of antibodies are the *antitoxins,* which combat the *toxins,* or harmful substances, produced by bacteria.

Physiological shock. This condition is caused by a painful injury, extensive burns, or severe loss of blood. Regardless of its cause, it results in a decreased volume of circulating blood and a reduction in blood pressure. There are two stages in this process. The first, known as *reversible shock,* is characterized by constriction of the small vessels which forces blood into the larger arteries and veins. The recommended first aid procedure for this stage of shock takes into consideration the decreased blood flow through the smaller vessels. The injured person is kept warm and the feet and legs are slightly elevated (8 to 12 inches) in order to insure a better flow of blood to the head and chest regions. This aids in increasing the amount of blood passing to the brain and assures a better supply to the heart.

The second stage of physiological shock, *irreversible shock,* is the result of rapid dilation of the smaller vessels. This greatly increases the area that must be supplied with blood, and blood pressure within the arteries drops. Blood fluids rapidly filter out of the vessels into the surrounding tissues and the volume of the blood is reduced to dangerously low levels. This collapse of the circulation is usually fatal.

Some evidence points to the presence in blood of two substances that bring about these reactions. The constriction of small vessels that occurs in cases of reversible shock is evidently due to the presence of a material formed in the kidneys. This stimulates the smooth muscle fibers in the walls of the vessels. The irreversible condition is brought on by the presence of a second substance, formed in the liver. Its action is antagonistic to that of the kidney secretion, and results in the relaxation of the muscle fibers, so that blood can pass into the smaller vessels. In reversible shock, the skin is pale and there may be profuse sweating, but this is reversed when the second stage is reached. In this condition the skin is flushed, due to the presence of an increased amount of blood in the surface vessels.

The acid-base equilibrium of blood. One of the factors in maintaining a constant internal environment in which the cells can function normally is the control of the amount of acids and alkalis present. Metabolic processes are constantly forming acid waste materials. Some of

these are strong acids which, if allowed to accumulate, might kill the cells. The blood normally keeps the amounts of these substances within limits that will permit the cells to function properly. Except under abnormal conditions, such as those arising during disease, the pH of the blood remains at an almost constant level.

There are three factors which help the blood to maintain its pH value: (*1*) the action of buffers in the blood; (*2*) the excretion of carbon dioxide by the lungs; and (*3*) the excretion of fixed acids by the kidneys. This last method is illustrated by the excretion of uric acid, a process that will be discussed in a later chapter.

A buffer system in a solution makes possible rapid adjustment to the addition of acid or base. If the solution contains chemical elements which enter easily into compounds to form weak acids or salts, these elements "cushion" or buffer the effects of acid or base that enters the solution.

In the table on page 262 there is a list of some of the more common inorganic substances in plasma. They include chemical elements such as sodium and potassium, which may be combined with bicarbonate ions to form such compounds as sodium bicarbonate ($NaHCO_3$). Other compounds of the elements include carbonates and phosphates. These compounds act as buffers by changing their composition rapidly in response to the amounts of hydrogen (H+) or hydroxide (OH−) ions in the blood. Thus, for example, an alkaline substance will be neutralized by the weak carbonic acid in the blood. Bicarbonates in the blood will react with acids to neutralize them. Under normal conditions, therefore, the pH of the blood is maintained at a level of 7.4 by these chemical reactions.

In addition to the inorganic materials present in the plasma, the blood proteins also act as buffers. As we have pointed out, proteins are highly complex compounds containing different components which can ionize in aqueous solutions. These components react to shifts in the blood pH in much the same way as the inorganic compounds. These reactions result in the return of the pH of the blood to its normal level.

The exchange of oxygen and carbon dioxide in the tissues involves constant changes in the acidity of hemoglobin. The compound *oxyhemoglobin* is relatively acid. When blood containing a large amount of oxygen in the form of oxyhemoglobin passes along a tissue that is deficient in oxygen, hemoglobin changes chemically to release oxygen, allowing it to diffuse toward the tissue. The hemoglobin thus becomes more alkaline and accepts the carbon dioxide that the tissue has formed. This is carried to the lungs where the conditions are reversed. Here the blood encounters a region that is rich in oxygen, and hemoglobin once more becomes more acid as it accepts the oxygen while giving up the carbon dioxide it has taken on in the tissues. These reactions are buffeted principally by the presence of bicarbonates in the plasma and the red cells.

As we know, blood in active tissue absorbs an extra amount of carbon dioxide resulting from oxidation in the tissue. This compound combines with water in the plasma to form carbonic acid. When blood carrying excessive amounts of carbon dioxide passes through the respiratory center of the medulla, the center is stimulated and the rate of respiration increases. The excess carbon dioxide is thus removed, and does not affect the pH of the blood.

Hemorrhage. Any undue loss of blood from the circulatory system is a **hemorrhage.** This loss may be external as a result of a wound, or internal. The latter may be caused by a serious puncturing wound, an infection, or the eroding action of an ulcer, which allows blood to flow into some body cavity.

The amount of blood lost in a hemorrhage determines the effect on the body. A person may lose a pint of blood (approximately 10 percent of the total volume of blood) without any ill effects beyond a general weakness for a day or two. On the other hand, if the loss amounts to about 35 percent, serious damage may result, while a 50 percent reduction in volume is usually fatal. If the loss is small, as is the case in the donation of a pint of blood, the body restores the fluid in a period of six to eight hours, and the red cells are brought to normal within about two weeks. White cells are restored more quickly. In fact, following the loss of blood there is a slight leukocytosis, but this disappears rapidly and the number of white cells returns to normal within a short time. If more than a pint of blood is lost, the return of the plasma and solids to a normal condition requires a proportionately longer period of time.

The physiological effects of hemorrhage fall under two headings. If the loss of blood is sudden and extensive, the quantity of fluid is reduced to a point where the heart can no longer pump it around the body efficiently. This loss is indicated by a sudden drop in blood pressure. Because of this decrease in volume of blood the tissues begin to feel the effects of the lack of oxygen. The nervous system responds to the emergency, constricting the cut or broken ends of the vessels in order to reduce the flow of blood from them. Elsewhere in the body the smaller vessels are also constricted. This results in a slower flow of blood due to friction of the blood cells against the walls of the vessels.

With the decrease in the blood pressure comes an increase in the rate of the heart beat, but since there is less blood flowing, the pulse may be weak or apparently absent. There is also an increase in the rate of respiration as the body attempts to compensate for the lowered supply of oxygen going to the tissues. Increases in heart and respiratory rates are important indications of internal hemorrhages. There may be few signs other than these of the loss of blood into a body cavity. Hemorrhage is usually accompanied by signs of physiological shock.

Various artificial methods are used to stop the flow of blood from an open wound or to compensate for the deficiencies arising from a hemorrhage. These are grouped under two headings: those that stop the flow of blood by mechanical means, and those that replace various parts of the blood.

Methods of stopping external loss of blood are as follows:

1. The application of some rough material directly over the wound. The American Red Cross recommends this as the primary method to be used in stoppage of bleeding. Surgical gauze or a piece of cloth will hasten the formation of a clot, since a rough surface favors the destruction of the platelets.

2. The application of pressure to the principal blood vessel that leads to the wounded area. This will stop the flow of blood through the vessel. Such pressure should be applied to an artery between the wound and the heart. On the other hand, if a superficial vein has been cut, pressure may be applied to the vein on the side away from the heart, since veins are returning blood to the heart. Pressure on the gauze or cloth directly over the wound is helpful. To prevent severe loss of blood from an artery, pressure should be applied at the appropriate *pressure point,* where the artery lies close to the bone. The location of the pressure points may be found in any first aid textbook. It is obvious that the only arterial pressure points of importance to the first aider are those where the arteries lie close enough to the surface of the body to make practical the use of external pressure.

3. The use of a mechanical device to put pressure on the principal arteries supplying an injured region. Such a device is called a **tourniquet** and usually consists of a piece of cloth that can be drawn tightly around a limb so that little blood will pass to or from the region below the point at which it is applied. To be effective, a tourniquet must compress all of the major vessels in the area in which the hemorrhage occurs.

A tourniquet should be used with *extreme caution,* since the reduced blood supply to the tissues may cause **gangrene.** This serious condition results when large numbers of cells die because they cannot get nutrients or dispose of accumulated wastes. Leading first aid authorities now recommend that amateurs should *not* apply a tourniquet, except as a last resort in cases where medical aid is not quickly available. Furthermore, they state that a tourniquet, once applied, should only be loosened by a physician or some other medically trained operator. This recommendation is important, since the premature loosening of a tourniquet may result in additional loss of blood. It may also allow toxic wastes from injured tissues to spread to other parts of the body. Medical authorities are agreed that it is safer to risk loss of a limb through continued application of a tourniquet than to risk possible death of the victim by loosening it.

Methods that can be used to combat both internal and external loss of blood may be summarized as follows:

1. Injection of a saline (salt) solution is used to replace the fluids that have escaped. The fluid injected is a sterile water solution of 0.9 percent sodium chloride (table salt) and other salts that do not affect the red corpuscles adversely by changing the osmotic pressure. Although quite popular at one time, this procedure has been found to be inefficient and is used now only in cases of extreme emergency. Sodium chloride molecules are too small to be retained within the blood vessels and rapidly pass to the surrounding tissues resulting in edema. This method, therefore, does not permanently increase the amount of blood fluid.

2. Solutions containing molecules of larger size have been tried with varying degrees of success. Such materials are called *plasma expanders* because they artificially replace the colloids and salts of the lost blood fluid. The larger molecules prevent the loss of fluid to the tissues that accompanies the use of a saline solution. Gum acacia, isinglass, and gelatin have been used. Current research includes a study of the effectiveness of complex polysaccharides, such as dextrin, and certain plastics, such as polyvinyl pyrrolidone (PVP).

3. Human serum and plasma can be dehydrated and preserved for relatively long periods of time. When sterile distilled water is added to them, they can then be used to replace lost blood. The value of these substances in caring for wounded soldiers was dramatically illustrated during World War II when they were used widely for the first time and were responsible for saving many lives. Since both of these substances contain the blood proteins, loss of water to the surrounding tissues is greatly reduced.

Of the two, blood plasma is the more frequently used because of its ease of preparation and the presence of a normal amount of fibrinogen, which is essential in the normal process of coagulation.

4. The most successful method of combating excessive loss of blood is by transfusion of whole blood into the circulatory system of the victim. It is obvious that whole blood is, in most cases, superior to any blood substitute, or fraction of blood. Recovery is hastened to a marked degree. One essential precaution must be observed in making a transfusion of whole blood: the blood of the donor and the recipient must be the same in type.

Blood typing. All human beings may be classified in one of four general blood groups, according to the nature of certain proteins in the plasma and red blood cells. The blood of the recipient and the donor in a transfusion must be of the same type, or a serious reaction occurs between the protein outer layer of the red corpuscles and the plasma protein of the antagonistic type of blood. The corpuscles become "sticky," and tend to clump together in groups. This clumping is called **agglutination.** The plasma proteins concerned in agglutination are called **agglutinins,** while those in the walls of the corpuscles are known as **agglutinogens.**

The blood type of each person is designated as *A, B, AB,* or *O,* depending on the kind of agglutinogen present in the red corpuscle. This system of nomenclature was suggested by Dr. Lansteiner of the Rockefeller Institute for Medical Research in New York. He also found that there were two types of agglutinins in plasma. These he called *a* and *b* (or alpha and beta). If a person, for example, belongs to blood group *A,* his serum contains agglutinin *b*. Since *b* is a protein that is antagonistic to the erythrocyte protein *B,* transfusion from a *B* individual to an *A* individual would result in the agglutination of the *B* type of red cells. Likewise, a *B* individual has *a,* the anti-*A* protein in his plasma, with the result that he cannot receive blood from a person belonging to Group *A*. If agglutination occurs, the masses of clumped corpuscles may be sufficiently great to block the flow of blood through the capillaries. Also, there is a possibility that these agglutinated corpuscles might interfere with the functioning of the kidneys by accumulating in the kidney tubules, thereby preventing the flow of urine.

To prevent transfusion of blood that is not *compatible* (of the same group), the blood of the donor and the recipient must be properly classified. This is usually done by testing the blood with serum of known blood type. A sample of the blood is diluted, and a drop of the serum is added. If the two are incompatible, the mixture becomes speckled as though with grains of red pepper. Thus, if agglutination occurs with Type A serum, but not with Type B, the blood is classified as Type B. As a safeguard, the blood of the recipient and the donor may be *crossmatched* before transfusion. The blood of each person is tested with the serum of the other.

The following table summarizes the distribution of the *A* and *B* agglutinogens and the *a* and *b* agglutinins. It also shows what types of blood are compatible with each other and may be used in transfusions.

The terms *universal donor* and *universal recipient* are frequently applied to members of Groups *O* and *AB,* respectively. In cases of emergency, Group *O* blood can be transfused into most people without ill effects. Although the plasma of this type of blood contains both *a* and *b* agglutinins, it does not cause agglutination when transfused. The reason for this is not clear. Even if one quart of blood is used in the transfusion, the recipient's blood is not affected. Also, since Group *O* corpuscles lack agglutinogens, they will not clump in the presence of either *a* or *b* agglutinins. In a like manner, a person with Group *AB* is a universal recipient because his blood lacks any agglutinins which affect the corpuscles of the donor. Although the corpuscles of a member of this Group contain both *A* and *B* agglutinogens, they usually do not clump together.

The distribution of blood groups varies considerably among the races and peoples of the world. Blood group is an inherited characteristic. The table on page 271 shows how the different groups are distributed among a few peoples.

There are several other proteins in the blood which may bring about agglutination under certain conditions. The most important of these is the **Rh factor,** which, like the blood type, is an inherited characteristic. In the United States, approximately 85 percent of the people have the Rh factor, and are said to be

Blood Group	Corpuscles contain agglutinogen	Serum contains agglutinin	Can give blood to	Can receive blood from
A	A	b	A, AB	O, A
B	B	a	B, AB	O, B
AB	AB	No agglutinins	AB	A, B, AB, O
O	No agglutinogens	a, b	A, B, AB, O	O

Rh positive (Rh+). The Rh factor is not active until an Rh− person has been given a transfusion of blood which is Rh+. An anti-Rh agglutinin may then form in the blood of the recipient, so that a later transfusion of Rh+ blood results in agglutination. Testing for the Rh factor is done in much the same manner as for the general blood type, as described earlier.

Occasionally, damage to a child's blood occurs before birth as the result of the presence or absence of the *Rh* factor. If the father of a child is *Rh+* and the mother *Rh−*, the child may be *Rh+*. Normally, the blood of mother and child are not mixed, but in some cases bits of the child's blood cells enter the mother's blood stream. The mother then develops an antibody against the *Rh* factor. The antibody is seldom strong enough to affect the first child, but its concentration is increased in later pregnancies. This seriously affects the child, which develops **erythroblastosis fetalis,** a condition characterized by severe anemia and jaundice. If the child lives to be born, the condition is treated by means of numerous transfusions by which the child's blood is replaced with Rh+ blood. The antibodies are thus removed. Blood from female donors is most effective. Why this sex difference in the blood types exists is an unanswered question, but experience has shown it to be the case.

Statistically, about 12.7 percent of marriages should pair an *Rh* positive man with an *Rh* negative woman. The number of women showing sensitization to the *Rh* positive factor is, however, only 1/25th of the theoretically possible number. One factor that may account for the nonappearance of erythroblastosis fetalis among the children of such mating is that in most cases, the antibody does not reach a critical concentration in the mother's blood.

	O	A	B	AB
U.S.A.—white	45.0%	41.0%	10.0%	4.0%
U.S.A.—Negro	49.3%	26.0%	21.0%	3.7%
Swedish	37.9%	46.7%	10.3%	5.1%
Japanese	31.2%	38.4%	21.8%	8.6%
Hawaiian	36.5%	60.8%	2.2%	0.5%
Chinese	30.0%	25.0%	35.0%	10.0%
Australian aborigine	53.1%	44.7%	2.1%	0.0%
North American Indian	91.3%	7.7%	1.0%	0.0%

SPEAKING OF Physiology

Briefly identify each of the following:

anticoagulant	hemorrhage	pressure point
cephalin	heparin	serum
dicumarol	nephritis	thromboplastin
edema	physiological shock	thrombus
gangrene	plasma expanders	tourniquet

Test YOUR KNOWLEDGE

1. Briefly describe how the physical and chemical activities in the coagulation of blood are affected by the following factors: (*a*) type of surface on which clot forms; (*b*) effect of temperature on the rate of coagulation; (*c*) function of thromboplastin; (*d*) method of producing thrombin; (*e*) effect of thrombin on fibrinogen.

2. Why does the blood of a person suffering from hemophilia fail to clot? What can be done for these people?

3. Why is vitamin K administered to patients prior to surgery?

4. How does the body use serum albumin in controlling osmotic pressure?

5. Of what importance is gamma globulin in combating infection?

6. What happens to the body in physiological shock? What is the difference between reversible shock and irreversible shock?

7. How is the pH of the blood maintained?

8. What effect does the pH have on the respiratory function of blood?

9. How does the body overcome the loss resulting from the donation of a pint of blood to a blood bank?

10. What changes occur in the circulatory system to combat external hemorrhage? How can we assist the body in this effort?

11. How does the treatment for internal hemorrhage differ from that used for external hemorrhage?

12. Why is it necessary to know a patient's blood type and *Rh* classification before a blood transfusion is given? By what procedure are these determined?

13. Explain the terms universal donor and universal recipient with respect to blood type.

14. Why is the *Rh* factor important in prenatal development?

See FOR YOURSELF

1. Try to find research on the presence of blood factors and blood types in mammals other than humans. Is it possible to use the blood of other mammals in human blood transfusion?

2. What historical connection is there between the blood defect of hemophilia and the decline of certain royal families in European countries? Write a report on your findings.

3. Find out what steps are recommended in first aid textbooks for the treatment of physiological shock. Explain how each step aids the body in recovery from shock.

4. Simple equipment may be obtained from good biological supply houses which will enable you to type the blood of members of your class.

CHAPTER 25

The Structure and Action of the Heart

Structure of the heart. The human **heart** is a four-chambered, muscular pump that owes its unique ability to contract rhythmically to the presence of *cardiac muscle tissue*. As can be seen from the Trans-Vision insert between pages 312 and 313, this organ lies behind the sternum and within the mediastinum (cavity between the lower halves of the lungs). About two-thirds of its bulk lies to the left of the middle line of the body, with the *apex* located between the fifth and sixth ribs (Fig. 25-1). In an adult male of average size, the heart is about 4.7 inches long, 3.3 inches wide at its greatest breadth, and 2.4 inches in thickness. Very roughly, these dimensions correspond to the size of the person's clenched fist. In men, the heart weighs from 9.9 to 12 ounces, while in women it is between 8.1 and 9.9 ounces in weight. As people grow older, the average size and weight of the heart increases more rapidly in men than in women. Before birth, we have approximately the same number of muscle cells in the heart that we will have throughout the remainder of our lives; any increase in the size of the organ as we grow is due to an increase in the size of the individual cells. As the heart grows, the cells add new cytoplasmic material so that their diameter increases to 2.6 times their original size.

The heart is divided into two distinct halves by a muscular wall, the **septum**. Before birth, however, and for a brief time afterwards, these halves are connected by a small opening through the septum, called the **foramen ovalis** (oval window). This allows blood to flow directly from the right side of the heart to the left side without going through the lungs, since in the fetus the lungs have no oxygenating function. Shortly after the time of birth this opening closes, thus separating the two halves of the heart. From this time on, the *right* half receives only blood that *contains reduced (deoxygenated) hemoglobin,* while the *left* side receives only blood *containing oxygenated hemoglobin.*

The heart lies within a double-walled sac, the **pericardium,** whose lower margin is anchored to the diaphragm with fibers extending to the inner surface of the sternum. Above the heart, it surrounds the bases of the large blood vessels. It is composed of a tough, fibrous outer part, the *fibrous pericardium,* and a thin inner layer, the *serous pericardium.* Although a space theoretically

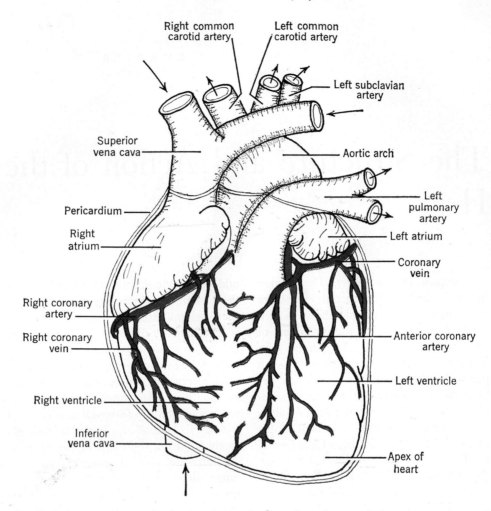

Fig. 25-1. *Front view of the human heart showing the relation of the various parts and the origin of the great vessels. The coronary circulation supplies the heart with blood.*

separates these two layers, it is nonexistent because of the presence of the **pericardial fluid.** This fluid prevents the two layers from rubbing against each other. Thus the heart is separated from the rest of the thoracic cavity, enclosed in a sac that serves as a protection against mechanical injury.

Each side of the heart is divided into two chambers. Those at the top of the heart are called the **atria** (sing., **atrium**), and below them are the **ventricles.** As Fig. 25-2 shows, the openings

between the atria and the ventricles are guarded by **atrioventricular valves,** which prevent blood from passing back into a chamber. The valve between the right atrium and the right ventricle is the **tricuspid valve,** this name having been given it because it has three points or cusps of attachment on the floor of the right ventricle. The opening between left atrium and the left ventricle is controlled by the **mitral (bicuspid) valve.**

The sequence of heart action, called the *cardiac cycle,* may be said to have

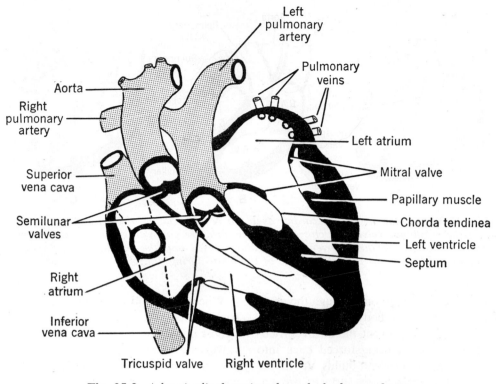

Left pulmonary artery

Pulmonary veins

Aorta

Right pulmonary artery

Left atrium

Superior vena cava

Mitral valve

Papillary muscle

Semilunar valves

Chorda tendinea

Left ventricle

Septum

Right atrium

Inferior vena cava

Tricuspid valve   Right ventricle

Fig. 25-2. *A longitudinal section through the human heart.*

three stages, as shown in Fig. 25-3. Blood enters the atria through the **pulmonary veins** and the **superior and inferior venae cavae.** The latter drain the head, neck arms, and thorax, and the trunk and legs, respectively.

The walls of the atria are relatively thin and weak because these chambers simply receive blood from the veins and pass it into the ventricles. While the atria are filling, the valves between them and the ventricles remain open so that there is a continuous flow from the veins through the atria into the ventricles. As the ventricles fill, pressure builds up within them. When the blood in the ventricles begins to close the tricuspid and mitral valves, the muscles in the walls of the atria contract to force all the blood that remains in them into the ventricles. For the brief time of the contrac-

tion there is no blood in the atria, since the pressure within them is greater than the pressure in the veins entering them.

As the ventricles fill with blood, they become distended. Then a wave of muscular contraction sweeps over them, beginning at their lower ends and moving upward toward the atria. This not only closes the atrioventricular valves, but also forces blood out of the ventricles through either the **pulmonary artery** or the **aorta.** The blood flows from the right ventricle through the pulmonary artery and its branches to the capillaries in the lungs. Here the blood exchanges its carbon dioxide for oxygen. The blood containing oxyhemoglobin then returns through the pulmonary veins ·to the heart, entering the left atrium. Then it passes the mitral valve into the left ventricle. When the ventricle contracts,

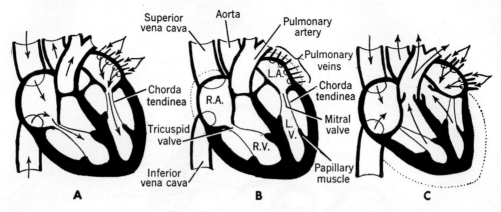

Fig. 25-3. *The sequence of the cardiac cycle. In A the atria and the ventricles are filling and the semilunar valves are closed. In B the atria are contracting. In C the ventricles are in systole with the atrioventricular valves closed and the semilunar valves open. The dotted lines show the relative size of the heart during diastole.*

the blood is forced out through the aorta to all parts of the body except the lungs.

In order to prevent the atrioventricular valves from being forced back into the atria as pressure builds up in the ventricles, their lower surfaces are anchored to the walls of the ventricles by strong elastic tendons, the *chordae tendineae*. The lower ends of the chordae are attached to the *papillary muscles* in the walls of the ventricles. When the ventricles are filling, the papillary muscles contract and draw the valves downward so that the blood can pass freely. As the wave of contraction passes over the ventricles, these small muscles relax, allowing the pressure of the blood within the ventricles to force the valves closed. If any injury to the valves occurs, the efficiency of the heart is lowered, since part of the blood flows back through the valves. The atrioventricular valves are surprisingly tough structures; with each normal contraction of the ventricles they must withstand a pressure of approximately four and one-half pounds per square inch of surface. During violent exercise, this pressure may exceed seven pounds per square inch.

When the blood leaves the right ventricle, it passes through the **semilunar valves** into the pulmonary artery. These valves are pressed against the sides of the artery by the force of the ventricle's contraction. As the ventricle relaxes, the back pressure of the blood in the pulmonary artery forces these valves closed. This prevents blood from passing back into the ventricle. A similar set of semilunar valves controls the flow of blood from the left ventricle into the aorta.

Characteristics of the cardiac cycle. The period of the filling of the atria and the ventricles is spoken of as their **diastole.** This is a period of relaxation in which the chambers become distended. This is followed by a period of active contraction, or **systole,** which is marked by a shortening of the muscle bundles. If we take as a basis for our observations a heart beating at the rate of 70 times per minute, the duration of these phases is as shown in the table on page 277.

A study of this information shows that the heart is not a constantly moving organ. Since both atria fill with blood at the same time and contract simultaneously, they have a moderately long pe-

Atrial diastole	0.7 second	(period of filling)
Atrial systole	0.1 second	(active contraction)
Ventricular diastole	0.5 second	(period of filling)
Ventricular systole	0.3 second	(active contraction)
Quiescent period for entire heart	0.4 second	

riod of relaxation. The same is true for the ventricles. Of course, if the heart rate is increased above 70 beats per minute, the time intervals are correspondingly shortened. The differences in times required for the atria and ventricles to fill and contract are directly connected with the amounts of muscle present in the walls of these chambers.

There are three characteristics of a single cardiac cycle that must be kept in mind: the *origin* of the beat which results from the contraction of the cardiac muscle fibers in a coordinated and rhythmic manner; the *rate* at which the beat occurs and the various factors influencing it; and the *rhythm* the atria and the ventricles show during a single beat. The last two are under the control of nervous impulses and will be discussed shortly.

In order to understand the fundamental processes underlying the beat of the heart, it is helpful to examine briefly the structure of the hearts of some of the lower vertebrates such as the frog and the turtle. In both of these animals there is a special chamber, separate from the atria, into which the venae cavae empty. This chamber is the **sinus venosus** (Fig. 25-4). In the course of the evolutionary development of the mammalian heart, it has become incorporated into the walls of the right atrium as a small structure known as the **atrial appendage**, which still retains one of the characteristics of the sinus venosus. If the beating heart of a frog is examined closely, it is seen that the wave of contraction that sweeps over it has its origin in the sinus

venosus. In the human heart a group of nerve cells, comparable to those that initiate the beat of the frog's heart, is located in the atrial appendage near the opening of the superior vena cava into the right atrium. These nerve cells form a very distinct area that can be isolated and stimulated artificially. When heat or an electric current is applied to them, the rate of the heart beat increases. If they are cooled, impulses flow more slowly and there is a corresponding decrease in the heart rate. This island of nerve tissue is known as the **sinoatrial node.** It is sometimes referred to as the *pacemaker* of the heart.

When the heart beats, a wave of nervous excitation from the sinoatrial node spreads out over the walls of the atria,

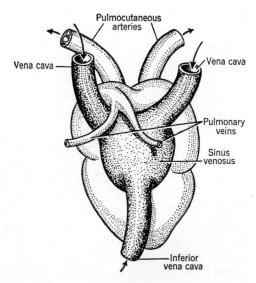

Fig. 25-4. *The dorsal surface of a frog's heart showing the sinus venosus.*

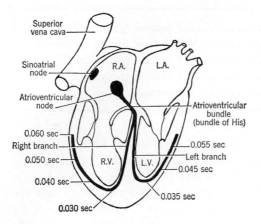

Fig. 25-5. *The conducting pathways in the heart. The times indicated along the branches of the atrioventricular bundle show the rate of the passage of the nerve impulse.*

causing their muscular layers to contract. This forces blood from the top of the chambers downward toward the atrioventricular openings. As the wave of nervous impulse approaches the junction between the atria and the ventricles, it is collected into another group of nerve fibers that make up the **atrioventricular** (A-V) **node.** From this, other fibers pass into the septum of the heart to form the **atrioventricular bundle.** This is also known as the *bundle of His,* in honor of the man who discovered it. The bundle then divides into a right and left half. Nerve impulses pass along these to the apex of the heart and stimulate the muscle fibers in this region first. As Fig. 25-5 shows, the nervous impulse then passes upward along the walls, the time intervals for this passage being indicated in the diagram. The result of this method of the propagation of the impulse is that the bottom of the ventricles contract first. The wave then passes upward rapidly, increasing the pressure within the chambers and forcing the blood to close the atrioventricular valves and open the semilunars. The blood then leaves the ventricles through the arteries.

Control of the rate of the heart beat. Nervous impulses, constantly flowing between the heart and the central nervous system, control the *rate* of the heart beat. These impulses are of two types: one that *inhibits,* or slows down the rate, and the other that *accelerates* it. The impulses travel over the fibers of the autonomic nervous system. By their mutually antagonistic effect, they keep the heart rate steady.

We have already mentioned the *vagus nerves* in connection with the rate of respiration, because certain branches of these nerves pass to the respiratory apparatus. They may be easily found in an anesthetized animal. One member of the pair lies on either side of the larynx. If one of these nerves is cut, there is little effect on the rate of the heart beat, but if both are severed, the rate is greatly accelerated and quickly reaches a high uniform level. Stimulation of these nerves will have an inhibitory effect on heart action. This may be shown by either a reduction in the rate, the lessening of the force of the beat without a change in rate, or the stoppage of the heart during diastole. It appears, therefore, that of the two types of impulses entering the heart by way of the vagus nerves, the inhibitory ones are the more powerful in maintaining a constant rate (Fig. 25-6).

Nerves carrying accelerating impulses also pass to the heart from one of the **cervical sympathetic ganglia.** The connection between the ganglion and the spinal cord eventually leads to the **cardioaccelerating** center in the medulla. This has connections with the **cardioinhibitory** center from which slowing impulses arise. Thus, if the sympathetic nerve is stimulated, the rate of the heart beat increases and the flow of the inhibitory impulses is lessened.

Within the heart itself and also in the

walls of some of the large vessels, there are nerve endings which help to control the rate of the heart. These nerves may be grouped as follows, depending on their location:

1. Nerve endings in the walls of the venae cavae and the right atrium are stimulated by the presence of blood in the cavities. Whenever a group of body muscles becomes very active, their pressure against the walls of the veins they contain has a milking action on these vessels and forces more blood into the general circulation. This increased flow into the veins results in increased pressure within the right atrium and the venae cavae. In order to prevent the added amount of blood from slowing down as it passes through the heart, the rate of the heart increases. This burst of speed is known as the **Bainbridge reflex.**

2. Another reflex originates in the walls of the aortic arch, where there are nerve endings called the **stretch receptors (pressoreceptors).** If the pressure of blood in the aorta becomes excessively high, these receptors are stimulated by the stretching of the walls of the vessel. Impulses from them pass along the vagus nerve to the cardioinhibitory center and the rate of heart beat is reduced, with an accompanying drop in blood pressure.

If the blood pressure drops to a very low point, as it does following severe hemorrhage, these pressoreceptors are no longer stimulated and their inhibiting action is removed. This results in a rapid rise in heart rate and the small amount of blood left in the system is sent throughout the body as rapidly as possible.

3. The **carotid artery** passing to the right side of the head branches off from the aorta first as the **innominate artery.** As shown in Fig. 25-6, this branches again to form the **right sub-**

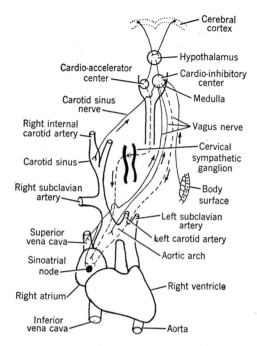

Fig. 25-6. *The principal nerve pathways connecting the heart and the central nervous system. The arrows indicate the directions in which the nerve impulses travel.*

clavian artery that carries blood to the shoulder and arm region, and the **right common carotid artery.** From this latter arise two arteries, the **right internal carotid artery** and the **right external carotid.** The external branch supplies blood to the outer surfaces of the head, while the internal division carries blood to the brain. At the point of their separation, there is a small swelling in the internal carotid artery, known as the **carotid sinus.** Within its walls are stretch receptors from which nerve fibers pass along the ninth cranial nerves, the glossopharyngeal nerves, to the cardioinhibitory center. If the carotid sinus becomes distended with blood, as might occur with high blood pressure, impulses stimulate the center in the medulla and the heart rate is decreased with an accompanying fall in pressure. On the

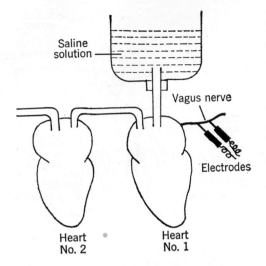

Saline solution

Vagus nerve

Electrodes

Heart No. 2   Heart No. 1

Fig. 25-7. *A diagram to show how a stimulating substance is passed from one heart to another.*

other hand, if there is a decrease in blood pressure the receptors are not stimulated and the rate of the heart beat accelerates.

The name carotid comes from the Greek word, *karos,* meaning "sleep." The ancients found that certain people could be made to sleep by pressure on the carotid arteries below the region of the sinus. This effect is caused by reduction in the amount of blood in the sinus, with the accompanying drop in blood pressure in the vessels of the brain. To-day we would call this loss of consciousness a *fainting spell.* Fainting is the result of a drop in blood pressure in the vessels supplying the brain, due to any of a number of causes, including psychic disturbances. One of the common methods of preventing a fainting spell is to lower the head below the general level of the body. This permits more blood to flow to the sinus so that the rate of the heart is lowered, but the strength of the beat is increased. This results in a rise in the pressure within the vessels in the brain.

Exercise affects heart action. It has been observed that even the slight exercise involved in clenching the fist brings about an immediate response in the heart rate. As soon as the motion of closing the hand begins, the next diastolic phase of the heart is shortened. This indicates a reflex effect, possibly started by the nerves associated with the muscles. Strenuous exercise which involves large numbers of muscles soon has a pronounced effect on the heart rate because the increased flow of blood toward the heart also activates the Bainbridge reflex. The reflexes that are established in muscles result in the stimulation of the cardioaccelerator center, an increase in the activity of the sympathetic accelerator nerves, and a repression of the cardioinhibitory center with a reduction in the strength of the impulses leaving it. Under the influence of these various factors, the heart rate may rise to extremes of around 190 beats per minute.

In addition to neural control of the heart rate, there is chemical control through a number of substances. If the hearts of two animals are connected in the manner shown in Fig. 25-7 and the vagus nerve stimulated electrically, heart No. 1 will be inhibited. If this state of inhibition is continued, heart No. 2 will also become inhibited shortly. This indicates that some material formed in No. 1 passes to No. 2 through the saline solution. It is believed that the substance formed in the first heart is a minute quantity of acetylcholine. The sensitivity of the heart to this compound is so great that 0.000001 milligram of it will produce a noticeable inhibiting action.

Many chemical compounds affect the nerve endings in the heart. For example, *atropine,* the active substance obtained from deadly nightshade, has an action comparable to that obtained by cutting both vagus nerves: the heart beat is greatly accelerated. *Muscarine,* the poisonous substance found in some mushrooms, acts like acetylcholine, and will inhibit heart action to the point where the beat stops entirely. The action of both of these inhibitors can be neutralized by atropine. *Nicotine* has a double action in that it first stimulates the nerve endings and then paralyzes them. It also causes constriction of the coronary arteries that supply blood to the heart muscle. Since the effect of this drug on the heart is a pronounced one, people suffering from certain types of heart disease may be advised to stop smoking.

In a later chapter we will discuss the effects of *adrenalin (epinephrin)* on the rate of the heart beat. This substance is a powerful heart stimulant even when present in very minute quantities. Some years ago, Dr. Cannon and his associates found that if all of the nerves to the heart except those arising in the sympathetic ganglia were cut, the rate of the heart was slowly accelerated. This increase took place as much as a minute after cutting the nerves, and lasted two or three minutes. This occurred even after the adrenal glands had been removed from the body of the anesthetized animal. The cause of this acceleration was attributed to the formation of a substance called *sympathin.* Some conflicting results in later experiments indicated that the sympathin could, under certain conditions, excite the heart (sympathin E), but under other circumstances would inhibit its action (sympathin I). This led to the theory that there were actually two different substances involved. More recent work has shown that the adrenal gland does produce two different substances which have the same effects as sympathin E and sympathin I. These are *noradrenalin* and *adrenalin.* The only known difference between these

hormones and sympathin is that they are produced in different organs.

The rate of the heart beat. The rate at which the heart normally beats is determined by many factors. Age, sex, position of the body, amount of physical activity, temperature of the surroundings, psychic (thought) processes are all reflected in the rate of the heart. Fig. 25-8 shows how the rate of the beat varies with age. Before birth the rate is high, but there is a steady decline after birth until a fairly constant average is reached. The vertical bars show the limits that can be expected among healthy individuals, while the short horizontal bars indicate the average for the group. Thus a person 15 years old may have a normal resting rate between 59 and 98 beats per minute, and the average rate is 72 beats for the entire group. Since these data have not been separated on the basis of the sex of the individuals included, they do not show that women have a slightly higher average rate than men. A sleeping man may average about 59 beats per minute while a woman has a heart rate of approximately 78 while sleeping. On waking, both sexes show an increase, the man's rate going up to an average of 75 beats, while the woman's increases to approximately 84 beats per minute.

Bioelectric currents of the heart. In common with all muscles, the heart develops an electric current when it contracts. This arises within the muscle itself as a result of the movements of ions across cell membranes. Known as the **action current,** it flows between any active tissue such as a muscle, nerve, or gland and an inactive region. In the case of the heart, the production of this current is especially important from a medical standpoint because it means that the various stages in the heart beat can be studied with a great deal of precision.

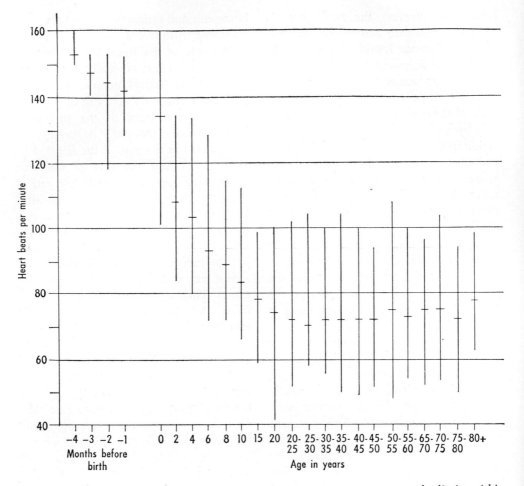

Fig. 25-8. *The relation of age to heart rate. The vertical lines represent the limits within which the normal heart rates may be expected to fall when a person is resting. Mean (average) rates are shown by the small horizontal lines.*

The presence of an action current in the heart can be demonstrated in anesthetized animals. If an electrode is placed on the atrium of a beating heart, and another on the ventricle, and the two connected with a galvanometer, a definite flow of electrical current can be shown. Three stages in the passage of the current are evident. When the atrium contracts, the current flows from the atrium to the ventricle. This is followed by a short period of neutrality in which no current flows, and then the ventricle contracts and the current flows from the ventricle to the atrium.

The study of the electric changes in the human heart was made possible by the invention of the *string galvanometer* by Einthoven in 1903. This consists of a large electromagnet between the poles of which is suspended a very delicate string made of quartz. The surface of this thread, which is about three microns in diameter, is coated with silver so that any change in the electric field of the magnet will affect it. When the current through the coils of the magnet changes its direction of flow (from the south pole toward the north), the thread will be deflected rapidly. Since this thread is extremely delicate, its inertia is small and it responds quickly to any change in the direction of the current. In addition to the string and the magnet, the instrument contains an optical system that throws a bright beam of light on the string. The shadow formed by the thread as it moves in the magnetic field is then projected on a piece of sensitive photographic paper that is moved behind the thread at a constant rate of speed. This photographic record of the electric changes can be analyzed and correlated with the activities of the heart. A record of this type is called an **electrocardiogram** (EKG), and the instrument that is used to obtain it is known as an **electrocardiograph.**

The currents that are generated by the heart pass through the tissues of the body and can be recorded at various points on the surface. To make an electrocardiogram, metal electrodes applied to the skin lead the currents present in that area into the electrocardiograph. Since the various tissues have differing abilities to conduct currents, the location of the electrodes is of extreme importance. Experience has shown that certain regions produce more uniform and easily interpreted results than others. The electrodes are usually applied in the places shown below; these combinations are known as the **standard leads.**

| Lead I .... right arm and left arm |
| Lead II .... right arm and left leg |
| Lead III .... left arm and left leg |

Since each of these pairs of electrodes is in a different position, each shows certain characteristics of the heart beat that differ from each of the others. In Fig. 25-9 is seen a diagram of a typical wave of electricity as it is recorded by Lead I electrodes. Each of the parts of the wave has been assigned a letter, which is purely arbitrary, to identify specific events occurring during the passage of the electric current. The parts of the tracing that rise above the base line are formed by the passage of a positive wave, while those that drop below it indicate a negative wave. Thus, the *P* wave shows the passage of a positive current over the atria. The *Q* wave, which may be absent in a normal electrocardiogram, shows a period of electric neutrality or slight negativity. The *R* wave is tall, upright (positive) and sharply pointed. This represents the period of the contraction of the ventricles. Following this is another brief moment of neutrality which is followed by the *T* wave showing a positive electric condition. In Fig. 25-10 are shown the characteristic forms taken from the three standard leads.

In addition to these standard leads, other regions of the body may be used to produce their own characteristic electric waves. A record from a commonly used chest lead is shown in Fig. 25-10. To obtain a tracing of this type, one

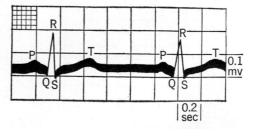

Fig. 25-9. *The parts of a normal electrocardiogram. Each vertical division represents 0.0001 volt (0.1 millivolt). The larger squares are divided into smaller units as shown in the upper left corner.*

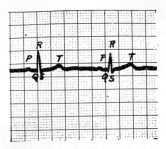

Lead I

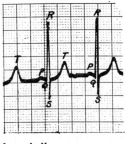

Lead II

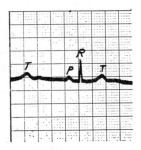

Lead III

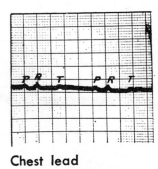

Chest lead

Fig. 25-10. *Photographic reproductions of normal electrocardiograms. (Edward F. Bland, M.D.)*

electrode is placed on the left leg and the other on the chest in the region of the apex of the heart. The tracing is quite different from the standard leads. Here we have a striking example of the result of the difference in the conductivity of body tissues.

Electrocardiograms are of great value to the physician in diagnosing defects of the heart. Some heart diseases can be identified by the abnormal sounds the heart makes, while others can only be detected by the slight changes that occur in the electrical conductivity of the heart muscle. For the diagnosis of such conditions, the electrocardiogram is of great importance.

In Fig. 25-11 is seen an electrocardiogram of a person afflicted with *auricular fibrillation*. This is the most common of all serious heart irregularities. In this condition, the atria are never completely emptied of blood and their walls quiver instead of giving the pronounced contraction typical of a normal heart beat. The impulses which the atria may develop in this condition range from 400

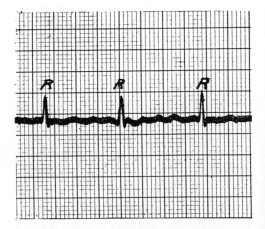

Fig. 25-11. *An electrocardiogram of a person suffering from auricular fibrillation. Note the series of P waves before the appearance of the R wave. (Edward F. Bland, M.D.)*

to 600 flutters per minute. Only a few of these impulses pass through the atrioventricular bundle to activate the ventricle. This accounts for the fact that the R wave appears only after a succession of many minor waves that take the place of the normal P wave.

A second heart ailment that can be identified by the electrocardiogram is *delayed conduction* of the impulse from the atria to the ventricles. In this, the time interval between the contraction of the atria and the ventricles is greatly lengthened. Instead of the normal 0.2 second, the delay may be as much as 0.5 second. In this condition, the atrioventricular bundle fails to conduct the impulse in a normal manner (Fig. 25-12).

Heart sounds. A physician listens to the heart beat for two reasons. First, by noting the beginning and end of the ventricular systole, he can time other events in the cardiac cycle. Second, the sounds produced by the heart indicate the condition of the atrioventricular and semilunar valves.

There are two heart sounds, each of which is related to a phase in the cardiac cycle. The first sound is the result of the closing of the atrioventricular valves and the contraction of the muscles in the walls of the ventricles. This is a low-pitched sound of some duration that coincides with the ventricular systole. Actually, it starts a fraction of a second before there is visible evidence of contraction in the ventricles and represents the instant at which the atrioventricular valves close. In relation to the electrocardiogram, the beginning of this sound corresponds to the upstroke of the R wave and continues to a point between the S and T waves. It sounds like the word *dub*, and can be heard best over the region of the apex of the heart, between the fifth and sixth ribs to the left of the sternum.

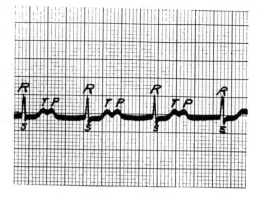

Fig. 25-12. *Electrocardiogram of a case of delayed conduction. Note the interval between the P and R waves and compare this interval with that shown in the normal Lead I tracing in Fig. 25-10. (Edward F. Bland, M.D.)*

The second sound is much shorter in duration and of a higher pitch. This sounds like the word *dip*, and represents the sudden closing of the semilunar valves. It is heard most distinctly in the second intercostal space (between the second and third ribs) near the sternum. When it is correlated with an electrocardiogram, it is heard just before the appearance of the T wave.

Certain abnormal sounds called *murmurs* may be heard occasionally. They are generally low in intensity and quite difficult to identify without considerable practice. These unusual sounds may indicate some imperfection in the valves of the heart and may take the form of indistinct gurgling sounds, or hissings, as the valves fail to close properly. If the murmurs occur during systole, they usually have little significance. They may be the result of a fever or undue physical exertion. If, however, they are heard during the diastolic phases of the heart beat, they may be due to the failure of certain valves to close properly (incompetence) or a tightened condition of other valves (stenosis).

SPEAKING OF Physiology

Briefly identify each of the following:

apex	fainting	oxygenated hemoglobin
atropine	inhibit	reduced hemoglobin
auricular fibrillation	mediastinum	septum (of the heart)
cardiac cycle	muscarine	stretch receptors
diastole	nicotine	systole

Test YOUR KNOWLEDGE

1. How does cardiac muscle tissue differ from striated and smooth muscle tissue? What are the advantages of the cytoplasmic structure of cardiac tissue?
2. Describe the location of the human heart with respect to the other body organs.
3. Why does most of the blood by-pass the lungs during the prenatal period? What would happen if the foramen ovalis did not close at or shortly after birth?
4. Describe the location and function of the pericardium.
5. Trace the path of a drop of blood containing reduced hemoglobin, as it enters the heart from venous circulation. Describe its passage through the various chambers and valves until it leaves the heart again as oxygenated blood.
6. Briefly describe the sequence of events in the cardiac cycle.
7. What is the outstanding structural difference between the heart of a frog and heart of man? Is there any functional advantage of one heart over the other?
8. What is the function of the sinoatrial node? How does this node compare with the bundle of His?
9. What effect does smoking have on heart action?
10. What is the function of the vagus nerve (tenth cranial nerve) in the regulation of the heart? From what point in the central nervous system do its impulses originate?
11. Briefly explain the Bainbridge reflex. How does this reflex compare to the action of the vagus nerve?
12. How does the carotid sinus influence the heart rate? What relationship exists between the action of the carotid sinus and blood pressure to the head?
13. With reference to Fig. 25-8, answer the following: (*a*) At what time of life of the individual does the heart have the highest average number of beats? (*b*) What age group or groups show the greatest distribution in normal heart rate? (*c*) Between what ages does the most consistent mean rate occur?
14. How does the movement of the action current compare with the muscular activity of the heart? How can these activities be shown with a galvanometer? What name is given to the electrical recording of the action current?
15. What information can a physician gain from studying the electrical graphing of a patient's heart?
16. How are heart sounds produced? What does a heart murmur indicate?

See FOR YOURSELF

1. Select 10 students from your class and teach them how to take their own wrist pulse. Keep a record of the changes that occur in heart rate under the following conditions of physical activity: (*a*) after 10-minute rest, lying down; (*b*) standing; (c) hopping on one foot for 30 seconds; (*d*) climbing a flight of stairs; (*e*) run-

ning 100 yards. Plot the results on graph paper. If possible use two or three athletes who have been in training for a period of time. See if their heart rates differ from those of the other students. What conclusions can you draw from this experiment?

2. Get a beef or lamb heart from a butcher. Observe its external features. Is there any evidence of the pericardium? Note the attached blood vessels. Can you identify the major veins and arteries entering and leaving the heart? Make a frontal section and observe the interior chambers and valves. Make a written report of your observations. Illustrate your paper.

3. Find out what you can about modern advances in heart surgery.

4. Make a chart similar to Fig. 25-8, showing the relation of age to heart rate. Use as subjects people of different age groups, such as younger brothers and sisters, parents, grandparents, classmates, etc. Note that your data should be taken while the subjects are resting.

5. Ask your doctor to show you different electrocardiograms and to explain their significance. Compare them with those shown in this book.

6. Listen to the heart sounds of several people, using a stethoscope. If you can find a sufficiently sensitive microphone, try to amplify the heart sounds so that your class can hear them. Perhaps you can make a tape recording of heart sounds.

CHAPTER 26

The General Plan of Circulation, the Spleen, and Lymph

General circulation of blood. After the blood leaves the heart, it passes through two main channels. One goes to the lungs and forms the **pulmonary circulation.** The other carries blood to all other parts of the body and is called the **systemic circulation.** Although the blood flowing through the pulmonary artery contains much less oxygen than the blood passing through the aorta, both vessels are classified as arteries. As we have stated previously, arteries always carry blood away from the heart while veins bring blood to the heart. These two principal types of vessels are connected by the capillaries.

Of the three types of blood vessels, the arteries are the strongest because of the thickness of their walls. Furthermore, since most of the larger arteries are closely surrounded by muscles and other tissues, they are able to withstand sudden large increases in internal pressure better than the other vessels. The walls of arteries are composed of three layers of tissues. On the outside is a layer of connective tissue cells throughout which are scattered bundles of smooth muscle cells. This outermost covering of the artery (Fig. 26-1) constitutes the **tunica externa.** In the larger arteries there is a thin layer of connective tissue which attaches the tunica externa to the middle layer of smooth muscle fibers. The cells making up the muscular layer (**tunica media**) are arranged in a circular pattern so that the diameter of the artery is decreased or enlarged as they contract or relax. The innermost **tunica intima** is an extremely thin layer of endothelial cells. These give the lining of the arteries a smooth surface which does not appreciably obstruct the flow of blood.

The tunica media has the most important function. Because of the smooth muscle fibers in their walls, the arteries are highly elastic. As a wave of blood flows through them, they dilate, and after the wave has passed, they constrict. This action is important because it allows the blood to pass freely through the vessels and keeps the flow even and steady.

The walls of some of the larger arteries are so thick that their cells are unable to obtain sufficient food and oxygen from the blood passing through them. It is necessary, therefore, for them to have their own system of capillaries. The arteries also have an extensive nerve network to control their dilation and

288

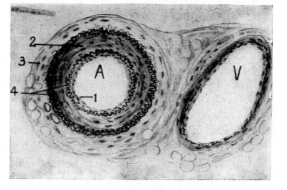

Fig. 26-1. *Sections through an artery,* A, *and a vein,* V. *The other structures shown are: 1, tunica intima; 2, tunica media; 3, tunica externa; 4, elastic tissue.* (*From Marsland,* Principles of Modern Biology, *Holt, 1958*)

thereby limit the amount of blood passing through them.

The pulmonary artery and the aorta branch to form the arterioles, some of which have internal diameters scarcely larger than the width of red blood corpuscles. These smallest arterial branches have the same wall structure as the great arteries, although their size makes it difficult to distinguish them from capillaries. The arterioles give rise to the smallest vessels, the capillaries (Fig. 26-2).

We may consider that in forming capillaries, the arterioles lose their two outer layers and branch into single-layered tubes that are a continuation of the tunica intima. Capillaries are composed of a single layer of endothelial cells between which is a layer of cement substance. The internal diameter of these vessels averages about 8 microns, although some are considerably smaller. These minute dimensions require that the red blood corpuscles pass through them in single file, so that each erythrocyte presents the maximum surface to the surrounding tissues. The extremely delicate walls allow materials in the blood to diffuse outward to the cells of the body and also permit the passage of the cellular products into the blood.

The cement substance which holds the endothelial cells to each other has

two functions. First, it is through this material that the leukocytes migrate when they pass from the blood to combat invading organisms in the tissues. Also, through this binding material substances pass to and fro between the blood and the tissues. Although the cement appears to be highly permeable to some materials, it is selective in its action toward the blood proteins. In health, these proteins cannot escape into

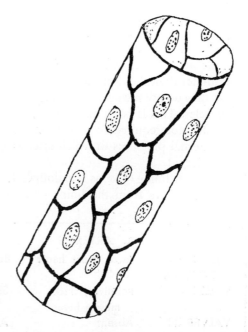

Fig. 26-2. *The cellular structure of a capillary.*

the tissues. This shows the complex nature of the cement.

Although the walls of the capillaries lack muscle cells, the flow of blood through them can be controlled to meet the requirements of the tissues they serve. This control is exercised by small bands of muscle, the **precapillary sphincters** surrounding the capillaries where they branch from the smallest arterioles. In some of the lower vertebrates, such as frogs and salamanders, the capillaries are covered by star-shaped cells, the points of which contract to decrease the diameter of the vessels. These are not found in the circulatory systems of man and other mammals.

The veins are formed by the joining together of capillaries. The distinction between a capillary and the smallest part of the venous system, the **venule,** is in the nature of the vessel walls. The smallest venules are scarcely larger than a capillary, but they have muscle fiber which is entirely lacking in capillaries. The venules rapidly converge to form larger vessels which eventually unite with others to form the great veins entering the heart. The walls of the veins are thinner than those of the arteries because they do not have such a thick layer of muscles. This is not a handicap, since veins are not required to withstand the high internal pressures to which arteries are subjected.

The inner lining of veins is endothelial tissue. It differs from the lining of arteries in that it forms **valves** which help to direct the flow of blood. These are composed of semilunar folds of tissue with their free ends pointing toward the heart. When blood flows toward the heart, they are pressed back against the walls of the vessels so that the blood can flow freely. If a back-pressure develops, the valves close. This prevents the blood from flowing back toward the capillaries.

Valves in the veins are especially abundant in those regions where the blood is raised against the force of gravity, as in the limbs. Valves in the legs may occasionally rupture because of the wearing of tight garters, undue stress resulting from lifting heavy objects, or local injury. In these cases the veins swell and become discolored, a condition known as *varicose veins.*

The table below compares the structure and functions of the three types of blood vessels.

Blood pressure. The human circulatory system, like that of the other vertebrates, is a closed system in which blood travels through the arteries and veins under pressure. The pressure level is fairly constant, although it varies in different parts of the system. The blood pressure is the result of several factors. Variations from the normal in any of the factors cause changes in the blood pressure.

1. The *elasticity* of the vessel walls tends to regulate the pressure. Blood

	ARTERIES	CAPILLARIES	VEINS
DIRECTION OF FLOW	Away from heart	Between arteries and veins	Toward the heart
WALLS	Relatively thick muscle layer	Single layer of endothelium	Less muscle than arteries
VALVES IN WALLS	Absent	Absent	Present

pumped from the heart keeps flowing in a steady stream throughout the system. If the walls of the arteries were rigid, the blood would flow in sudden spurts through them as the ventricles contracted. During the time when the ventricles were filling, there would be almost no flow of blood in the vessels. Because the walls of the arteries are elastic, they tend to expand as the blood pressure increases and contract as it decreases. This alternate expansion and contraction of the artery walls slows or hastens the flow of blood, keeping it steady. In a child the walls of the vessels are highly elastic. With advanced age, the vessels slowly become more rigid and greater internal pressure develops.

2. The *pumping* action of the heart is a major factor in blood pressure. It is difficult to determine just how much blood is forced from the heart with each beat, but it is estimated at approximately four ounces. If we assume that this figure is correct, a heart beating at the rate of 70 beats per minute would discharge about 18 pounds of blood per minute, or about 25,200 pounds in the course of 24 hours. This volume increases in direct relation to the activity of the heart. It has been estimated that the heart of an athlete rowing a strenuous race pumps about 15 gallons (approximately 120 pounds) of blood per minute.

The cardiac output, or amount of blood expelled with each beat, depends on the rate and force of the beat. Measurements taken in the aorta show that the pressure of the wave of blood as it leaves the heart may vary between 90 and 130 millimeters of mercury. This is the **systolic pressure,** since it is produced by the systole of the ventricles. During the relaxation of the heart, the **diastolic pressure** in the aorta drops to

between 60 and 90 millimeters of mercury. Because of the action of the semilunar valves, there is always some blood in the aorta. In ventricular diastole, however, the pressure within the ventricles may drop to between 2 and 8 millimeters of mercury.

3. Blood pressure is partially determined by the *amount of blood* actually present in the system. Normally, this quantity varies only slightly, but conditions may arise in which the volume of the blood may be either increased or decreased. An extra amount of blood may be added to the general circulation when the spleen contracts slightly and gives up some of its stored blood. In this case the blood pressure rises. A fall in blood pressure may result from the loss of blood in hemorrhage. If the blood volume is lowered, the heart is unable to pump blood efficiently. In the preceding chapter, we studied methods to replace the volume of blood fluids.

4. Blood pressure is determined by *peripheral resistance,* the resistance of the narrower arterioles to the flow of blood from the arteries. When a fluid travels from a large tube to several smaller ones, pressure is greater in the smaller tubes because of friction. The slowing up of the flow builds up back pressure in the larger tubes. The constriction of the arterioles and the precapillary sphincters under various stimuli increases the pressure. An example is the response to the secretion of the adrenal glands. In moments of excitement, these glands produce adrenalin, which enters the blood stream and causes the arterioles to contract. The result is a reduced flow of blood to the capillaries and an increased pressure within the arteries. The peripheral resistance is lowered when the arterioles and the sphincters expand, as under psychic stimuli. Thus the pain from an

injury or an unpleasant experience may cause the capillaries to be suddenly filled with blood. Pressure in the brain may then fall to a point where the cells are not receiving a normal supply of blood and the person faints.

5. *Viscosity of the blood* is another factor in determining blood pressure. The viscosity of a liquid is the degree to which it resists flow. Viscosity results from internal friction produced by the rubbing together of the tiny particles in the liquid. Blood is about six times more viscid than water. In health, the viscosity of blood does not change.

If there is a pronounced increase in the number of red cells, as in the condition known as *polycythemia vera,* the viscosity of the blood increases because of friction among the red corpuscles as well as between them and the walls of vessels. This causes the blood pressure to rise.

The measurement of blood pressure. The first attempt to measure the pressure of blood as it flowed through an artery was made in 1733 by an English clergyman, Stephen Hales, who experimented on horses. He inserted a small brass tube into the aorta of a horse at a point near

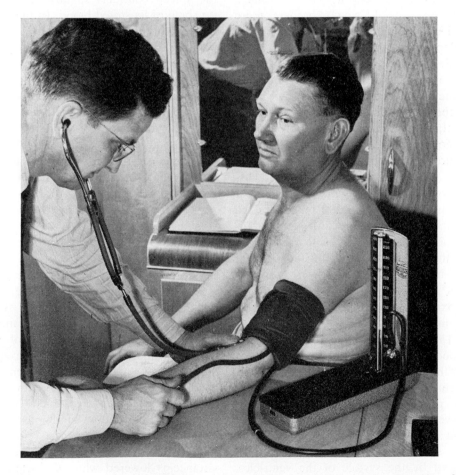

Fig. 26-3. *The measurement of blood pressure using a sphygmomanometer. (Standard Oil Co. of N.J.)*

its junction with the ventricle. To this he attached a long glass tube and found that the blood in the tube rose to a height of slightly over eight feet. He also noted that the level of the blood in the tube rose and fell several inches with each heart beat. This indicated that there was considerable pressure in the aorta and that it fluctuated with the heart beat. In 1896, the modern method of measuring blood pressure was developed by Dr. Ricca Rocci.

This method of measuring blood pressure in the arteries is based on the principle of applying just enough pressure to the artery to stop the flow of blood through it. The apparatus used is called a **sphygmomanometer.** It consists of a cuff, containing an inflatable rubber bladder, which is wrapped around the upper arm. Connected to the rubber bladder are a bulb by which it can be inflated and a pressure gauge (Fig.

26-3). A valve in the bulb allows air to escape slowly from the bladder. A column of mercury is used in some sphygmomanometers, while in others there is a modified aneroid barometer scaled to measure pressure in millimeters of mercury. The use of these devices makes possible a small compact instrument. If water were used in the instrument, it would have to be almost 14 times as big.

When blood pressure is measured, the cuff is adjusted around the upper arm and a stethoscope is placed under the edge of the cuff, above the brachial artery. Air is then pumped into the bladder until the sound of the pulse in the artery can no longer be heard through the stethoscope. Air is then released slowly. The point at which the sound reappears is noted on the pressure gauge. This gives the *systolic pressure,* because it is the pressure exerted by the wave of blood that has been ejected during the

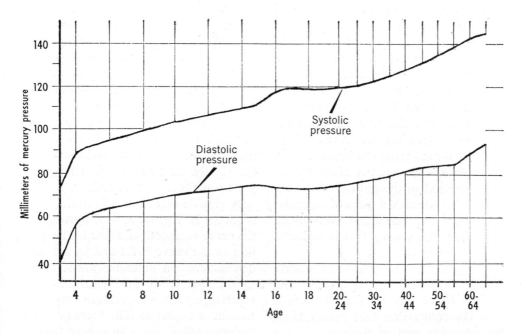

Fig. 26-4. *The relation of blood pressure to age. The lines showing systolic and diastolic pressures are averages for each age group. Some variation from these averages is considered to be within the normal range.*

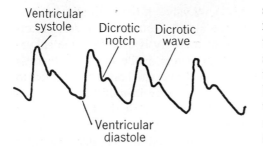

Fig. 26-5. *Tracing of an arterial pulse. Note the irregular nature of the wave after the peak is passed.*

ventricular systole. As air is allowed to escape a change in the quality of the sound is heard just before it disappears. At this point the pressure recorded on the gauge is again noted. This gives the *diastolic pressure,* which is the pressure during the period when the ventricles are filling. Figure 26-4 shows the usual limits of the average blood pressure at varying ages. About a five-percent variation from the extremes is still considered normal.

The pulse. We are all familiar with the fact that blood flows through the arteries in a series of waves and we have all felt the pulse beat at the wrist and elsewhere in the body. However, the motion of the artery that can be felt is not the actual passage of a wave of blood that has started from the heart a short time before. There are two distinct processes involved in the pulsing of the arteries. First, there is a wave of muscular contraction and relaxation that constitutes the **pulse wave.** This is followed by the wave of blood.

The pulse wave originates in the aorta with each systole of the heart and spreads to all the arteries. This is a wavelike contraction that passes along the muscular coat of the arteries at a rate of between 6 and 9 meters per second (approximately 20 to 30 feet per

second). The wave of blood, expelled from the heart at the same instant, travels at a rate of only 4 to 16 feet per second. The pulse we feel does not, therefore, correspond to the wave of blood that has just left the heart. A pulse wave will travel from the heart to the arterioles in the sole of a foot in about 0.25 second, while about 7 seconds are required for the wave of blood that left the heart at the same instant to reach this region.

The pulse wave forces the blood through the arteries. In a young person with highly elastic artery walls, the rate of the pulse wave is relatively slow. With age, the elasticity of the arterial walls decreases so that the wave travels more rapidly. This is comparable to the condition found in certain nonliving objects. For example, if a violin string is drawn slightly taut and then plucked, the wave motion is much slower than when the string is drawn more tightly. Regardless of how rapidly the violin string is plucked the note will be of the same pitch at any given tension of the string, due to its rate of vibration. The same general principle applies to the pulse wave. If the walls of the arteries retain a great amount of elasticity, the pulse wave will travel at a definite rate of speed, regardless of the heart rate. If they become less elastic, comparable to the tightly stretched violin string, the pulse wave travels more rapidly.

A graphic record of an arterial pulse is shown in Fig. 26-5. The upstroke of the curve is smooth and steep. This portion of the curve is formed by the sudden increase in muscular pressure due to the systole of the ventricle. After reaching a peak, the pressure drops and the curve begins to fall. Partway down the descending line is an uneven portion known as the *dicrotic notch,* followed by the *dicrotic* wave. The notch is produced by the closing of the semilunar valves at the opening of the aorta; the dicrotic wave is the result of their bulging back into the ventricle because of the increased pressure of the blood above them.

A venous pulse similar to the arterial pulse cannot be detected in most veins. The reason for this is that the pulse wave is lost when the arteries lose their muscular coat as they merge into the capillaries. The veins arise from the convergence of the capillaries. Although they contain muscle tissue, the pulse wave is not transmitted to them through the capillary bed due to the lack of muscle tissue in capillaries. There is one region where a pulse exists in veins. This is in the large veins leading to the heart, but the origin of this pulse is quite different from that of the arterial pulse. Its cause is purely mechanical and depends on the alternate flow of blood into the atria and its sudden stoppage during systolic periods of these chambers.

Regulation of the blood flow to body regions. The flow of blood to different parts of the body is controlled by nervous impulses to the vessels. If there is an increase in activity in a certain region, more blood passes to that region and another is deprived of a maximum supply. Since there is only a certain amount of blood to supply the entire body, its distribution must be carefully controlled. A good example of this mechanism is seen when a person goes swimming in cold water too soon after a heavy meal. The digestive processes demand a large supply of blood, with the result that other regions of the body are deprived of an adequate supply to meet emergency conditions. In such a case, the muscles may not be supplied with enough blood to maintain the temperatures they require for oxidation. Then they will contract violently under

the stimulus of the cold, and a cramp will result.

The normal distribution of blood to various regions of the body is controlled by the action of two nerve centers in the medulla of the brain. One of these, the **vasoconstrictor center,** is constantly sending out a series of impulses which keep the arterioles in a state of slight contraction, or tonus. These impulses reach the arterioles along paths that originate in the sympathetic ganglia. Impulses which result in the further constriction of the arterioles are generally stimulated by emotional states such as anger or fear, or by changes in normal requirements of some part of the body for an added supply of blood.

Vasodilation, or the relaxation of muscle fibers in the blood vessels, may be controlled by the **vasodilator center** which lies two or three millimeters distant from the vasoconstrictor center. We cannot say definitely that impulses arising in this center are the sole cause for the dilation of the arterioles. There appears to be a reciprocal action between the constrictor and dilator centers, so that when one is stimulated the other is inhibited. At present there is no easy method of distinguishing between the active role of the constrictor center and the more passive part played by the dilator center. Nerves from the vasodilator center pass out to the parasympathetic ganglia and thence to the vessels. Stimulation of these nerves results in the relaxation of the muscle fibers in the arterioles and the precapillary sphincters so that blood flows more readily into the capillaries. This results in a drop in pressure in the arteries which may reach an alarmingly low level.

Several factors control the flow of blood to various regions of the body.

1. The influence of the cerebral cortex. In the cortex of the cerebrum are centers that control a wide variety of reactions. For example, if we meet with an embarrassing situation, our face is apt to become flushed. The steps leading to this reaction are extremely complicated because they involve memory patterns, previous training, and our peculiarly individual reactions to certain situations. The flush is caused by inhibition of the vasoconstrictor center, with the result that the surface of the skin becomes filled with blood as the skin arterioles dilate. Other emotional stresses may have the opposite effect. If one becomes angry, the temperature of the fingers and hands drops because of stimulation of the vasoconstrictor center. (It is interesting to note that there is a decrease in the electrical resistance of the skin accompanying the constriction of the capillaries.) This change in fingertip temperatures has been used in studying the effect of drugs on the nervous system. Nicotine, for example, stimulates the vasoconstrictor center and its effect on the circulatory system can be observed in a lowering of the circulatory rate through the fingers.

2. *The effect of carbon dioxide.* We have already studied the effect of an increased amount of carbon dioxide on the rate of respiration. While there is some debate about the effect of this gas on the vasomotor system, there are certain well-recognized facts connected with its appearance in the blood in greater than normal quantities. It has been found, for example, that in early stages of asphyxiation, blood pressure rises. On the other hand, if the carbon dioxide content of blood is lowered as a result of forced breathing, a feeling of dizziness results which may be attributed to a decrease in blood pressure in the cerebrum. The mechanism involved in these cases appears to be the presence of *chemoreceptors* in the carotid sinus and the

aortic bodies. Impulses arising in these regions result in the stimulation of the vasoconstrictor center. If the activities of these centers decrease as the result of too little carbon dioxide in the blood, the blood pressure is lowered and fainting follows. Conversely, an increase in the amount of carbon dioxide in the blood results in rising blood pressure which has a reflex action on the heart and increases its rate of beating.

3. *Effect of drugs on vasomotor action. Adrenalin,* a product of the adrenal glands, has a profound effect on the action of the precapillary sphincters. Under the influence of this hormone, the vasoconstrictor center is stimulated and the blood pressure rises sharply but remains elevated for only a short time. This effect is used by physicians, who may apply a dilute solution of adrenalin (about 1:10,000 parts of water) locally when performing minor operations on the eye, nasal membranes, or some other local area. This causes constriction of the arterioles in the region and helps to staunch the flow of blood.

Acetylcholine is produced at the junction of nerves and muscles. In most muscles, it has a stimulating action that results in contraction. In the heart and blood vessels it acts as a relaxing agent and causes dilation of vessels.

Histamine is a compound that is found in all tissues. If formed in larger than normal quantities, it dilates the arterioles and capillaries. The congestion of mucous membranes, a common symptom of asthma, the common cold, and certain allergies, is the result of this action. *Antihistamine* drugs have been developed to combat this congestion. These drugs do not affect the underlying causes of the symptoms, and therefore should not be considered a cure.

Alcohol is essentially a vasodilator which may produce a feeling of warmth if taken on a cold day. This effect is caused by dilation of the skin capillaries and may result in loss of heat over the surface of the body. The sensation of warmth may be misleading if the body is later subjected to extremely low external temperatures. Some extremely low internal body temperatures (55° to 65° F.) have been reported following excessive use of alchohol and later exposure to cold.

Nicotine has an effect opposite to that of alcohol: it is a vasoconstrictor. Smoking lowers the skin temperature of the fingers by one or two degrees due to the effect of the nicotine on the vasoconstrictor center. In the treatment of certain types of heart disease, smoking is prohibited because of the effect of nicotine on the coronary vessels that supply an already overtaxed heart.

Ephedrine, a drug obtained from plants, is frequently used in nose drops. It reduces the swelling of nasal membranes by the constriction of blood vessels locally. It is doubtful whether this affects the vasoconstrictor center. The effect seems to be mainly local, confined to stimulation of the constrictor nerves in the region.

The spleen. This is an important organ of the circulatory system. It is not essential, since a person can continue in good health after it has been surgically removed.

The location of this organ is shown in the Trans-Vision insert following page 312. Although its size is variable in different individuals, its average dimensions are about 4.7 inches long, 2.75 inches wide, and 1.8 inches thick. It is slightly concave on its front surface and correspondingly rounded in back. Its blood supply is very extensive, giving it a somewhat purple color. Before birth and for a short time afterwards, the spleen produces both red and white

corpuscles, but in the adult this function is lost. The walls of the spleen are composed of several layers of connective tissue which make up its *capsule.* In the walls are scattered bundles of smooth muscle tissue which enable the spleen to contract slightly. The interior of the organ is composed of loosely connected cells that support many blood vessels, with numerous spaces (sinuses) in which excess blood is stored. This inner region is subdivided irregularly by strands of fibrous tissue, the *trabeculae.*

There are three major functions of the spleen. First, the spleen serves as a reservoir for blood. When it is stimulated by nervous impulses from the sympathetic nervous system, or when there is an increase in the amount of adrenalin in the blood, the muscle fibers contract and blood is forced into the general circulation. Thus in an emergency blood is supplied with an increased number of red corpuscles to carry more oxygen to the tissues.

A second function of the spleen is the destruction of aged or damaged red corpuscles. This is accomplished by the action of large specialized white corpuscles, the **macrophages,** which surround and engulf the erythrocytes in much the same manner that the neutrophils engulf bacteria. Just how the macrophages determine which of the red cells are to be destroyed and which will remain unharmed is unknown. It may be that as hemoglobin is used, it changes in its chemical composition so that it becomes attractive to the macrophages.

The third function of the spleen is the production of lymphocytes. This function it shares with lymphatic tissue.

Extravascular fluids. All of the fluids of the body that are not definitely parts of blood are known as **extravascular fluids.** This refers to the fact that they are outside the blood vessels. Those fluids which are contained within the cells are called *intracellular fluids,* while those lying between the cells are known as the *intercellular* or *interstitial fluids.* In a man of average weight (70 kilograms or 154 pounds) the distribution of these fluids would be approximately as follows:

Fluid	Percent of body weight
Plasma of the blood	5
Intracellular fluid	50
Intercellular fluid	15

The intracellular fluid contains approximately 25 percent protein materials by volume; the remaining 75 percent is aqueous solution of both organic and inorganic salts. Plasma, on the other hand, contains about 2.6 percent protein materials, while there is less than 1 percent protein in the intercellular fluid. The reason for these differences is that protein molecules are generally too large to pass easily through cell membrane. This concentration of protein materials within cells is a highly important factor in maintaining osmotic pressure in the cells.

The intercellular fluid that bathes the cells serves as a middleman between blood and cells. Since capillaries do not come in direct contact with all cells, it is necessary for some fluid to act as a carrier between the blood and cells. This is the primary function of intercellular fluid. It originates from the portion of the blood plasma that diffuses through the walls of the capillaries. This may pass through the walls of the endothelial cells, but most of the fluid is thought to escape through the intercellular cement. Since the cement behaves as a semipermeable membrane, few of

the blood proteins are present in the intercellular fluid. Thus fibrinogen is retained by the blood, with the result that intercellular fluid does not coagulate. We are all familiar with the appearance of this fluid in the form of the clear liquid that collects in a blister or that oozes from a slight abrasion.

The fluid that leaves the blood gradually filters through the spaces among the cells. It carries to the cells those materials that are essential to their maintenance and removes wastes formed during their metabolic activities. Oxygen, for example, is released into the plasma by hemoglobin as it reaches an area of

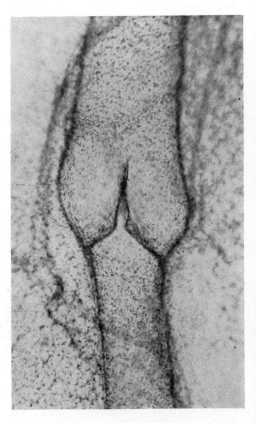

Fig. 26-6. *Valve in a lymphatic. The flaps of the valve are closed to prevent the backflow of lymph. (General Biological Supply House, Inc.)*

low oxygen tension. The gas diffuses through the plasma in solution. The resulting solution then passes through the capillary wall and is carried to cells that lack oxygen. Other materials pass to cells in the same way.

After the required materials have passed into cells, various metabolic wastes diffuse out of the cells into the intercellular fluid. Some of these enter the blood stream directly because of the difference in osmotic pressure of the fluid and plasma. As we have mentioned, osmotic pressure of plasma is lower at the beginning of the capillary where it leaves the arteriole than it is at the end where it unites with others to form a venule. This gradient in the osmotic pressure along the course of the capillary hastens the exit of materials from the blood and then later permits the re-

absorption of other substances. Some materials, however, do not re-enter the blood stream. These continue to flow between the cells until they enter another type of thin-walled vessel that is a part of the **lymphatic system.**

The material in these vessels is known as **lymph,** although the same term is applied loosely to include the intercellular fluid as well. The lymph vessels, or **lymphatics,** form an extensive network throughout the body. They begin as extremely small tubes composed of endothelial tissue. These branch freely and intricately through all the tissues, gradually running together to form larger tubes. In the walls of the larger lymphatics are valves (Fig. 26-6) to control the flow of lymph. Fluids push through these tubes by the massaging or milking action of the tissues in which they lie. In

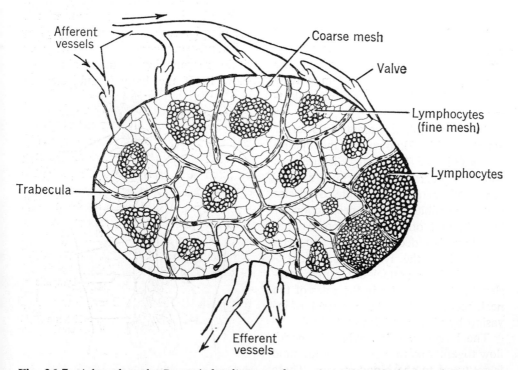

Fig. 26-7. *A lymph node. Part of the diagram shows the node with the lymphocytes removed to make the internal structure clearer. Lymph flows through the coarse mesh, in which there are normally large numbers of lymphocytes.*

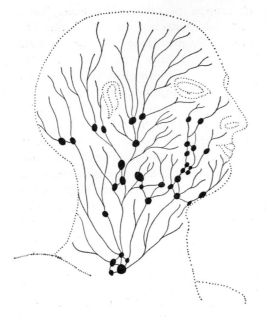

Fig. 26-8. *Distribution of some of the lymphatics in the head region.*

inactive tissues, lymph flows very slowly or is completely stagnant. When activity increases, the fluid flows faster. The valves direct the flow of the lymph away from the tissue toward a central collecting point.

Smaller lymphatics empty into larger lymph cavities known as the **lymph nodes** (Fig. 26-7). Their cells are large and loosely arranged, containing numerous lymphocytes. These white corpuscles are responsible for the destruction of bacteria and other foreign bodies that may have invaded the tissues and been drained into the lymphatics. For example, during an attack of German measles, the lymph nodes in the sides of the neck become enlarged as the result of invasion by virus particles (Fig. 26-8).

The larger vessels leaving the nodes flow together so that eventually the fluid is returned to the blood stream. These large vessels follow two paths. The lymphatics draining the right side of the

head, right half of the thorax, and right arm drain into the *right lymphatic duct.* This duct enters the right subclavian vein through an opening guarded by a semilunar valve to prevent the entrance of venous blood into the duct.

Lymph from the other body regions flows into a large series of vessels that collect to form the *cisterna chyli,* which is located in front of the second lumbar vertebra. Much of the lymph reaching this chamber contains globules of fat that give it a milky appearance. From the cisterna, the *thoracic duct* (Fig. 26-9) passes upward near the vertebral column until it empties into the left subclavian vein.

Effects of changing forces on circulation. Since the heart is a muscular pump that forces blood through the body under normal pressure, any pronounced variation from the normal may have a profound effect on the flow of blood. The blood vessels, also, are designed to withstand pressures at sea level, or within reasonable distances above or below it. If the body is subjected to

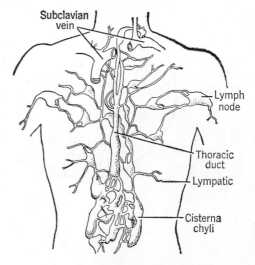

Fig. 26-9. *Lymph flows toward the heart through the main lymph ducts, which collect it from the lymph nodes.*

forces that exceed those normally encountered, the circulatory system has no means of adjusting to these changes. The result may be disastrous unless proper precautions are taken.

For instance, an aviator may be subjected to abnormal forces when he pulls his plane out of a dive or banks it sharply around a curve. In these maneuvers, the blood is forced into the lower parts of the body with a corresponding deficiency in circulation through the brain. This may cause loss of consciousness, commonly known as a *blackout.* If the maneuver forces blood away from the lower organs (as in an outside loop),

the aviator may experience a condition called *redout,* in which he sees everything through a red haze. This effect is probably caused by excess blood in the vessels of the eye, and may be rapidly followed by unconsciousness.

Both of these conditions result from the inability of the circulatory system to cope with the abnormal forces to which the body is subjected. The reactions may be prevented to some degree by the use of pressure suits that can be inflated with air to produce counter-pressures that tend to neutralize the effects of these unusual forces. Placing the pilot in a prone position is also helpful.

SPEAKING OF Physiology

Briefly identify each of the following:

cisterna chyli	**peripheral resistance**	**systemic circulation**
dicrotic notch	**pulmonary circulation**	**varicose veins**
dicrotic wave	**pulse wave**	**vasoconstriction**
endothelial	**sphygmomanometer**	**vasodilation**
macrophages	**stethoscope**	**viscosity**

Test YOUR KNOWLEDGE

1. Describe the structure and function of each of the layers in the wall of a large artery. Which layer has the greatest physiological importance? Why?
2. When the diastolic action of the ventricles occurs, no blood moves out of the heart. Yet, if an artery is cut we see an uninterrupted flow of blood. Explain in detail what makes this possible.
3. What structural similarities and differences exist between arteries, arterioles, and capillaries?
4. How is the control of the flow of blood through the capillaries maintained?
5. How does the elasticity of the arterial walls aid in maintaining blood pressure? What happens in elderly people when the elastic quality of arterial walls decreases?
6. What is cardiac output? How is this related to blood pressure?
7. How can a doctor diagnose internal hemorrhage or bleeding? In what way does your body attempt to offset this condition?
8. How do you know that the pulse you feel is not caused by the flow of blood through the vessel?
9. Why is there no pulse in the veins of the body?
10. How is the flow of blood to the various regions of the body controlled? What bodily activities influence this control?

11.   Briefly summarize the various effects of chemical activity on vasomotor action.
12.   What are the functions of the spleen?
13.   What are the functions of the lymphatic system? What part do lymph nodes play in this system? How does the structure of lymphatics compare with that of blood vessels?
14.   What are the effects on the circulatory system of changes in the gravitational forces?

See FOR YOURSELF

1. With a stethoscope, listen to your own heart sounds or to those of another student. Put the bell of the stethoscope between the second and third ribs just to the left of the sternum. Listen to the sounds at this point. Move the bell down to the space between the fifth and sixth rib and about 2½ inches to the left of the sternum. Explain any differences in the sounds at these two points. Listen to the heart sounds after physical exertion. What changes in beat do you note?

2. Have your teacher or doctor demonstrate the use of the sphygmomanometer. If permissible, take the blood pressure of a fellow student yourself, following the directions of your instructor.

3. Demonstrate various methods used to stop the flow of blood from a surface wound.

4. Examine prepared slides of tissues taken from humans or other mammals. Try to differentiate between arteries, veins, and capillaries in the tissues. Make drawings to illustrate these differences.

5. Prepare a report on how aviators can be protected from changes in forces that affect the efficient operation of the circulatory system.

The Skin, Metabolism, and Excretion

CHAPTER 27

The Skin

CHAPTER 28

The Regulation of Body Temperature

CHAPTER 29

Metabolism

CHAPTER 30

The Kidneys and Their Function

The Skin

Functions of the skin. The covering of an animal's body is called its **integumentary system.** This may consist of a single layer of cells or may be a quite complex system that includes various protective devices. We find, for example, that the scales of fishes and reptiles assume quite strange and unusual forms that may be protective, either by disguising the animal or by helping to prevent it from being attacked by a predator. The scales of fish and reptiles appear to be similar, but their origin is quite different, even though both are products of the skin. Birds have feathers, a highly specialized skin derivative, while mammals have a body covering of hair. Although it is beyond the scope of this text to explain the origin of all these body coverings, it should be pointed out that the scales of reptiles, the feathers of birds, and the hair of mammals are somewhat alike in that they develop from the same general types of tissues.

In man, the **skin** is the primary covering of the body surface. Hair is present over parts of the body, but its distribution is so variable among different people that it cannot be considered as distinctive a feature of the human race as it is of other groups of mammals. The human skin has a variety of different functions which may be briefly outlined.

The skin has several *protective* functions. Its unbroken surface presents a barrier against invasion by bacteria and other foreign bodies. This barrier is chiefly mechanical, but there also appears to be a chemical susbtance produced by the outer layers of the skin which destroys most of the bacteria that come in contact with it. The skin protects the body against the absorption of excessive amounts of water or the loss of fluid through the body surface. There is a small osmotic flow between the cells of the skin and the surrounding air or water, but this is of minor consequence in maintaining the water content of the body. Apparently, this osmotic action is of primary importance only in people who hereditarily lack sweat glands. The underlying tissues are protected by pigments formed in the skin against the injurious effects of ultraviolet radiations in sunlight.

The skin plays a very important role in the *regulation* of body temperature. Heat is lost by the evaporation of sweat, and by the radiation of heat through the skin. Both of these activities will be discussed in detail in the next chapter.

Because it is well supplied with nerves, the skin is *sensitive* to changes in its surroundings. These may be temperature changes or mechanical changes, received in the form of pressure, touch, or pain sensations.

The skin *eliminates* excess water and salts. Although it disposes of these substances, it can hardly be considered a part of the excretory system because the quantity of waste materials liberated is negligible.

The skin has tissues for the temporary *storage* of water, fats, glucose, and some inorganic salts. Most of these are later reabsorbed by the blood and carried to other regions of the body where they may be used.

The structure of the skin. The skin consists of two principal layers; the **epidermis**, or the **cuticle**, and the **dermis, corium**, or **true skin**. The word "dermis" is derived from the ancient Greek word *derma* which meant "skin." The prefix, *epi,* meaning "on top of," is added to designate the outer layer. Below the dermis is a layer of varying thickness, the subdermal layer, which is not properly a part of the skin.

The epidermis is composed of two layers of cells, as shown in Fig. 27-1. The outer of these layers is made up of cells in which the living material has been replaced by a hard, nonliving protein substance, **keratin.** The outermost cells are flattened and scalelike and are constantly worn off by rubbing on clothing or on other objects in contact with the skin. This horny layer, the **stratum corneum,** is replaced by the division of cells that constitute the lower layer of the epidermis, the **stratum germinativum.**

The stratum corneum is one of the principal defenses of the body against invasion by bacteria and against mechanical injury to the delicate underlying tissues. So long as this outer layer

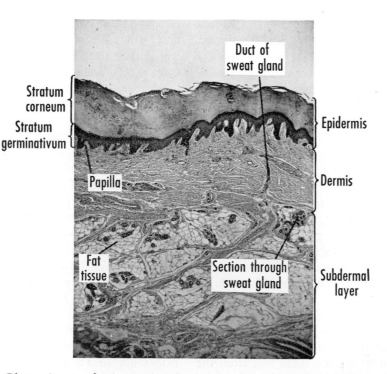

Fig. 27-1. *Photomicrograph of a section through hairless human skin. Note the thickness of the epidermal layer, especially that of the stratum corneum.* (*General Biological Supply House, Inc.*)

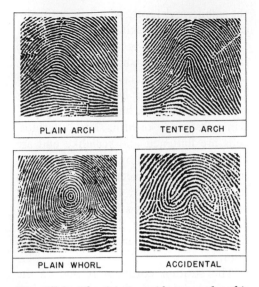

PLAIN ARCH   TENTED ARCH

PLAIN WHORL   ACCIDENTAL

Fig. 27-2. *The friction ridges on the skin of the fingers and the feet form a characteristic pattern in each individual. (U.S. Dept. of Justice)*

remains unbroken, bacteria cannot easily invade the body. In fact, the protective action afforded by this keratinized layer is reportedly equal to the immunizing action of the blood in preventing infections. The thickness of the horny layer varies in different regions of the body. In some areas it is quite thin, while in others it becomes thick as the result of friction against some particular area. When the thickening develops outwardly in a local region, such as the palms of the hands, the enlargement is known as a *callus*. If the thickening results from inward growth of the stratum corneum, as it does occasionally on the toes, the growth is called a *corn*.

The stratum germinativum is made up of cells of various forms. Those at the lowest level are columnar in shape, but this typical form is lost by repeated divisions, as these cells gradually become flattened to replace those lost from the horny layer. Within the columnar cells are the granules of pigment which give the skin its characteristic color. Among the substances that are responsible for the color are *melanin, carotene,* and *hemoglobin.* The various proportions of these substances are responsible for the different shades of color. White races are those in which the amount of melanin is normally reduced, while the colored races have a larger percentage of this material in the skin. An absence of pigments, except for hemoglobin, results in the condition known as *albinism.* This is caused by an inherited defect in the ability of the cells to produce pigment.

The production of excess pigment is stimulated by ultraviolet rays. It is these solar radiations that are responsible for sunburning and the subsequent tanning of the skin. Ultraviolet rays in the neighborhood of 3200 Ångstrom units (the lowest visible violet rays are about 4000 Ångstrom units in length) cause the familiar reddening of the exposed skin. Following the sunburn, a moderate tanning will appear. Continued exposure will darken the skin color as more pigment is formed in the cells. It should be remembered that this effect is a defense mechanism to protect the lower-lying tissues from injury by ultraviolet rays. The wisdom of prolonged exposure to sunlight is being questioned at present because of its possible connection with the development of skin cancers.

As is seen in the photomicrograph (Fig. 27-1), the lower edge of the stratum germinativum is very irregular in outline. The indentations are known as the **papillae** of the skin. In certain areas of the body the papillae are so pronounced that they raise the surface into permanent ridges. This occurs in the skin of the fingers, the palms of the hands, and the soles of the feet. The ridges are so arranged that they offer maximum resistance to slipping, either in walking or in grasping an object. They are therefore known as *friction ridges.*

Those on the inner surfaces of the fingers are used for purposes of identification by means of fingerprints (Fig. 27-2).

The corium, or dermis, like the epidermis, varies in thickness in different regions of the body. It is especially thick over the palms of the hands and the soles of the feet. Also, it is thicker in the skin covering the back of the body than it is over the front of the thorax and abdomen. This layer is composed of matted masses of connective tissue and elastic fibers through which pass numerous blood vessels, lymphatics, and nerves.

Appendages of the skin. Certain well-defined structures form what are called the **appendages of the skin.** These are *hairs,* the *nails* of fingers and toes, the *sweat glands* and the *sebaceous* (oil) *glands.* In Fig. 27-3 the relation of these to other parts of the skin is shown diagrammatically.

Although a part of each hair lies within the dermis, it is actually surrounded by an inward projection of the epidermis which forms a sloping tube, the **hair follicle.** At the lower end of this tube is an upward projection of the surrounding tissue, the *papilla* of the hair. The papilla contains capillaries to nourish the cells of the follicle, from which the hair is formed by the rapid division of cells at its lower end.

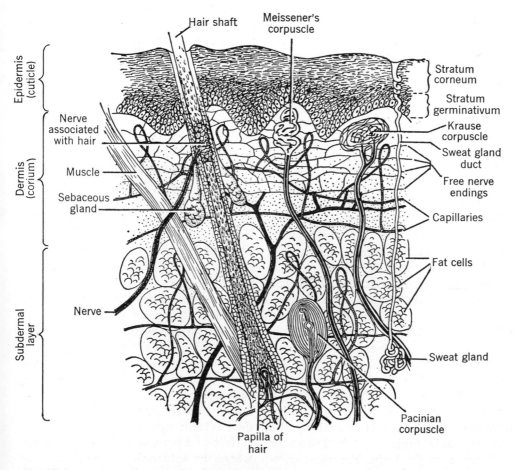

Fig. 27-3. *A section through the skin showing the structures in the epidermis and dermis.*

Microscopic examination of a hair shows that it is composed of three distinct parts. On the outside is the *cuticle,* a single layer composed of flat scalelike structures in which the protoplasm has been replaced by keratin. These overlap each other slightly and give the surface a scaly appearance. Within the cuticle is a keratinized layer of elongated, nonliving cells that make up the *cortex* of the hair. The pigment of the hair is in the cortex. A central cavity, or *medulla,* appears in some types of hair.

The distribution of hair over the body, its type, and its color are the result of hereditary factors that are primarily racial, and beyond the scope of this text. However, two common conditions should be discussed briefly: these are the graying of hair and the loss of hair. In white hair, the pigment is lost and air takes its place in the cells of the cortex. The air serves as a reflecting medium. The period of life at which graying of the hair occurs appears to be genetically determined. There is no evidence that it is connected with any vitamin deficiency, as is the case in some animals. The loss of hair may be due to several causes. First, if the scalp is too tightly drawn over the bony framework of the skull, a temporary loss of hair may occur. This condition is the result of interference with the blood circulation to the hair follicles and can be relieved by massage. Illness, when accompanied by a very high fever, may result in the loss of hair. If the body temperature does not reach a point where there is destruction of the cells in the hair follicles, the hair will return. Local diseases of the scalp may also cause the loss of hair over small areas. A common infection of this type is caused by the growth of a fungus and is known as *ringworm* of the scalp. The most common type of baldness seems to be hereditary. Inheritance of certain factors determines not only the loss of hair but also the approximate time of life when this occurs and the pattern that it follows. Aging and the activities of the male sex hormones are also factors connected with baldness.

Attached to each hair follicle on the side toward which it slopes is a small bundle of smooth muscle fibers, the **arrector pili muscle.** This has its origin on the upper surface of the dermis and its insertion on the wall of the follicle. In some animals, the contraction of this muscle causes the hair to be erected, but in man the hair is too weak to allow this action to occur. When this muscle of the skin is stimulated, as by sudden chilling, it contracts and causes the skin to pucker around the hair. This produces the condition commonly called *goose flesh.* Contraction of the muscle also results in pressure on the sebaceous glands and the secretion of a small amount of oil.

The **sebaceous glands** lie along the walls of the hair follicle. They may also be present in hairless regions of the skin. They are especially numerous on the face and scalp, but absent from the palms of the hands and the soles of the feet. The product of these glands is composed of fats, proteins, salts, and water. Due to its oily nature, this secretion keeps the hair and the surface of the skin flexible. It also helps to prevent excessive absorption or loss of water over the surface of the body.

A third group of skin appendages is the **sweat glands.** These are small glands, the *body* of which consists of a coiled tube which lies in either the corium or the subdermal layer. From this a duct extends upward and opens on the surface as a *pore.* In regions of the body where the epidermis is thick, the outer end of the duct may be twisted or coiled.

Elsewhere, in thinner skin, this tube is usually straight. The number of sweat glands varies in different regions of the body. They are very plentiful on the palms and the soles, where the openings of the ducts are evenly distributed along the friction ridges. Their approximate numbers are as follows:

Palms of the hand ..	370 per sq. cm.
Back of the hand ..	200 per sq. cm.
Forehead	175 per sq. cm.
Breast, abdomen, and forearm	155 per sq. cm.
Leg and back	70 per sq. cm.

It has been estimated that the total number of sweat glands is approximately 2 million.

Sweat is composed principally of water (99 percent) and salts, of which sodium chloride is the most common. There are traces of other substances, including urea. The chemical composition can vary considerably in different regions of the body and under differing circumstances. Sweat may at times be very acid, with pH of about 3, or it may shift toward the alkaline side. The quantity of sweat also varies, depending on the temperature of the air and the amount of physical activity. The glands are continually secreting sweat, but it is usually in such small quantities or is removed so quickly by evaporation or absorption by clothing that we are not conscious of it. This is called insensible perspiration. The total amount of sweat formed during twenty-four hours may be quite small (about a half liter) or it may reach two liters. Under extreme conditions of high temperature, a person may secrete about 10 liters per day. As a general rule, when the loss of water by sweating is great, the quantity of urine produced by the kidneys is reduced.

The activities of the sweat glands appear to be under the control of a sweat center located in the hypothalamus of the brain. Impulses from this center pass along sympathetic nerve fibers to the glands. The center is stimulated when the temperature of the blood passing over it rises by 0.3 to 0.9° F., as the result of increased muscular activity or a rise in external temperature. It may also be reflexly stimulated when the skin temperature rises above 94° F. Emotional conditions may also increase the production of sweat, as we know when we experience the cold sweat of fear. The role of sweat in helping to control the body temperature will be discussed in the next chapter.

The **nails** are also classified as appendages of the skin. These are hard structures, slightly convex on their upper surfaces and concave on the lower surfaces. They are formed by the epidermis, where they first appear as elongated cells which then fuse together into plates. During this process their protoplasm is replaced by keratin. The area producing the nail is called the **nail bed,** or matrix. As long as any part of this region remains intact, it will produce the nail substance. It is possible, therefore, for a finger nail to be lost and later on replaced by a new one. At the back of the nail bed, the skin forms a fold in which the base of the nail is embedded.

Sense receptors in the skin. Among the functions of the skin mentioned at the beginning of this chapter was its sensitivity to stimuli. Both afferent and efferent nerves pass through the skin, and some of these end in receptors which lie either in the dermis or the subdermal layer. Motor nerve fibers are distributed to the walls of the blood vessels and the arrector pili muscles. The sensory nerves end in receptors sensitive to heat (*end organs of Ruffini*) and cold (*end organs of Krause*). The sense of touch is the result of stimulation of other specialized nerve cells, *Meissner's corpuscles,* while pressure can be detected by the deeper lying *Pacinian corpuscles.* In addition to these specialized receptors, there are nerve endings for the sensation of pain just under the epidermis and around the hair follicles.

Skin sensitivity varies from one part of the body to another. Pain receptors are quite plentiful on the forehead, breast, and lower arm. On the forehead, for example, there are about 200 of these per square centimeter of skin surface. On the nose and thumb there are only about 50 per square centimeter, while a small area on the inside of each cheek just opposite the second molar tooth lacks them completely. Touch spots also differ in their distribution. On the lips these spots are less than one millimeter apart but in the middle of the back this distance is increased to over 10 millimeters. Sensitivity to heat or cold is not due to a temperature sense but to the presence of definite receptors that are sensitive to either heat or cold. The cold receptors are more numerous than those sensitive to warmth.

Subdermal tissues. The subdermal tissues contain fat cells, connective tissue, blood vessels, lymphatics, and nerves. This region serves primarily as a connection between the skin and the deeper tissues. In some areas of the body, such as the neck, the connecting fibers are loose, so that the skin can be moved quite freely. In other regions, like the palms and the soles, the skin is attached much more firmly, so that very little motion is possible. The adipose tissue in the subdermal area stores fats. The subdermal layer of fat is generally thicker in women than in men, due to the action of sex hormones.

Care of the skin. Bathing removes the secretions of the sebaceous and sweat glands that adhere to the body surface. The oily nature of the sebaceous secretion is responsible for the clinging of dirt to the skin, and its removal is a physiological as well as esthetic necessity. A common cause of skin eruption (acne) is the clogging of the openings of the sebaceous glands. The accumulated secretion encourages the growth of bacteria which cause pimples. Thorough cleansing of the skin helps to prevent clogging of the pores. However, if too much soap and hot water are used, the beneficial lubricating action of the oils may be lost. Water with a temperature between 80 and 90° F. is the most satisfactory for bathing. The widely held idea that cold baths (below 65° F.) will toughen the body and thus make it more resistant to colds has been disproved.

The skin is subject to a variety of injuries, cuts and burns being the most common. First aid treatment for a simple cut is to clean the wound, apply a mild antiseptic, and cover with a sterile dressing. The use of harsh antiseptics is not recommended because they may damage the surrounding tissues and delay the healing process.

If a burn is of the first degree, with an unbroken reddened area of skin, the application of a mild ointment and covering with several layers of sterile gauze is usually all that is required. Second degree burns, in which the skin becomes blistered, should be treated by covering with moist sterile gauze. The blisters should not be opened because the enclosed tissue fluid helps the healing process. Third degree burns, involving serious destruction of tissues, should receive immediate medical care. The burned area should be covered lightly with a moistened sterile cloth until such time as a physician can treat the victim. Greases should not be applied to second or third degree burns unless prescribed by a physician. Dressings may be moistened with some mild anti-septic, such as that made by dissolving three tablespoonfuls of either sodium bi-carbonate (baking soda) or Epsom salts in a quart of warm water.

SPEAKING OF Physiology

Briefly identify each of the following:

corn	**hair follicle**	**ringworm**
cuticle	**melanin**	**stratum corneum**
epidermis	**papillae**	**stratum germinativum**
goose flesh	**pore**	**ultraviolet radiation**

Test YOUR KNOWLEDGE

1. How does the skin prevent bacteria and other foreign substances from entering the body? How does it prevent injury from the sun's radiations?
2. In what ways does the skin aid in the regulation of body temperature?
3. Why do we often consider the skin to be a sense organ?
4. What types of tissues are found in the epidermis? What part does keratin play in this layer?
5. We are constantly rubbing off the outer cells from the skin. How are these cells replaced?
6. Why do we tan? How is tanning produced? What is an albino?
7. What are fingerprints? Why is their pattern constant in any individual?
8. What types of tissues are present in the dermis? How does this layer provide for the nutritional requirements of the skin?
9. Describe the function of the following accessory skin structures: (*a*) hair and arrector pili muscles; (*b*) sweat glands and their ducts; (*c*) sebaceous glands; (*d*) fingernails and toenails; (*e*) sensory nerve endings.
10. What is the function of the subdermal layer? How is this layer different in men and women?
11. Why is it necessary to keep the skin clean?

See FOR YOURSELF

1. Write a report on the tanning of leather. Relate each of the steps in this process to the structure of the skin and point out how the parts of the skin and ac-cessory structures require special treatment.

2. Prepare a report on the fur industry discussing the types of hair and the rel-ative value of fur and guard hairs. Make a microscopic examination of hair from several different kinds of animals and sketch the appearance of each, paying par-ticular attention to any pattern that may be present on the surface of the hair.

3. Study how the hair grows on a dog or cat. Note the pattern of growth in various regions of the body. If possible, watch and report on the growth of hair over the body of some small animal, like a mouse, that is born hairless.

4. Write a report on fingerprinting as a means of positive identification. Ask one of your local police officers to demonstrate how fingerprints are taken.

CHAPTER 28

The Regulation of Body Temperature

Variations in body temperature. The members of the Animal Kingdom can be roughly classified in two groups, depending on their ability to regulate their internal body temperatures. The temperature of cold-blooded (poikilothermic) animals changes with that of their environment, while warm-blooded (homoiothermic) animals maintain a relatively constant temperature. This grouping does not take into consideration those animals that hibernate. The temperature of the big brown bat (*Eptescius fuscus*) varies from 101.4° F. when active to approximately 50° F. during hibernation.

At birth, the human infant has an imperfectly developed heat-regulatory mechanism. Infants are, therefore, quite susceptible to cold air, which is apt to lower their body temperature to a dangerous limit. Even children of school age may show large variations in body temperature as a result of exercise or emotional disturbance. In old age, there is a similar inability to regulate the body temperature, with the result that the aged are easily affected by changes in temperature.

We are apt to think of the body temperature as remaining at a constant level of 98.6° F. This is the average normal temperature shown by a clinical thermometer placed under the tongue. Normal average rectal temperature is considered to be 99.6° F. Probably the oral temperature is closer to the real average of the whole body. Studies show there is considerable variation in temperature among the members of any group. For example, 276 medical students, all members of one class, took their oral temperatures while seated in the classroom. The temperatures ranged from 96.5° to 99.3° F. with an average of 98.1° F. Of these, 95 percent fell between 97.3° and 98.9° F.

During the course of 24 hours, the oral temperature of an individual fluctuates to a greater degree than is generally realized. As Fig. 28-1 shows, the body temperature drops below the generally accepted average during the night and then rises above this point during the day. The data for this graph were obtained from one person, and undoubtedly show some slight variations from similar data that might be obtained from another individual. Some interesting observations have been made on people who have changed their employment so that their working hours come during

THE HUMAN BODY
IN ANATOMICAL TRANSPARENCIES

By GLADYS McHUGH, Medical Artist
Associated with the University of Chicago Clinics

The "Trans-Vision" process presents the human body in a unique manner in which you can perform a "dissection" and proceed through the depths of its structures by turning transparent pages. You can see organs overlying other organs in a three-dimensional effect. As you turn the pages, a layer of anatomy is removed and a deeper layer comes into full view. The right pages give you a front view of the structures. To see the same structures from the back side, you turn the page. Thus, you can see the relation of organs to the body as a whole and to each other. You can single out an individual part for more detailed observation.

The pages preceding and following the anatomical transparencies give you a description of each view—how it was made and what it shows. The numbers you find on many of the structures refer to an identification key on the back of Plate 6. This will identify any structure you wish quickly and easily. Numbers have been omitted where they would detract from structural detail. Many such structures are referred to in the description of the various plates.

The structures shown are detailed and accurate. This presentation of the human body will serve as an adequate basis for anatomical study in any degree of thoroughness and complexity you may desire.

Key identifying numbered structures on back of Plate 6.

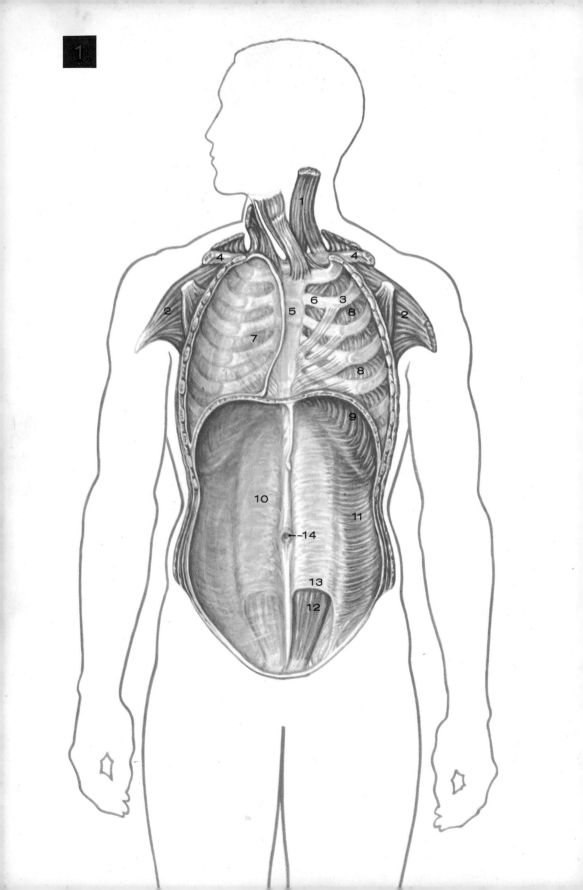

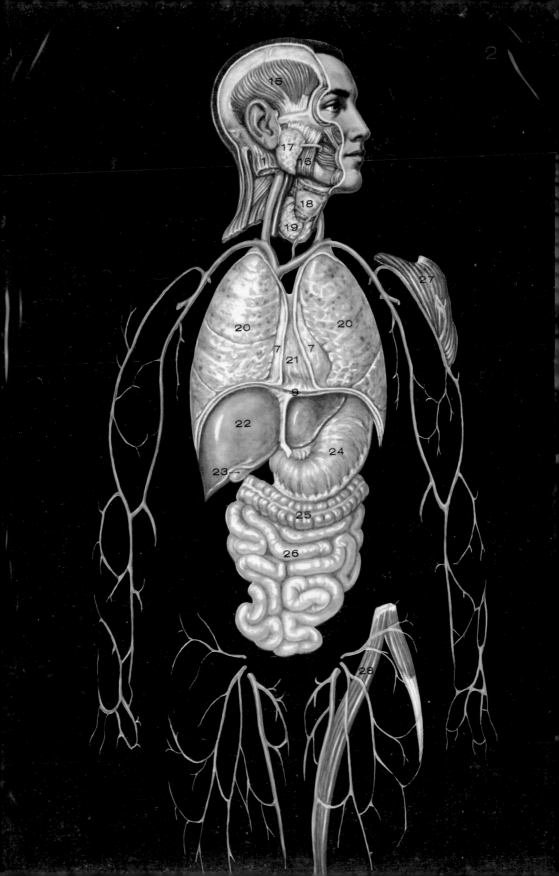

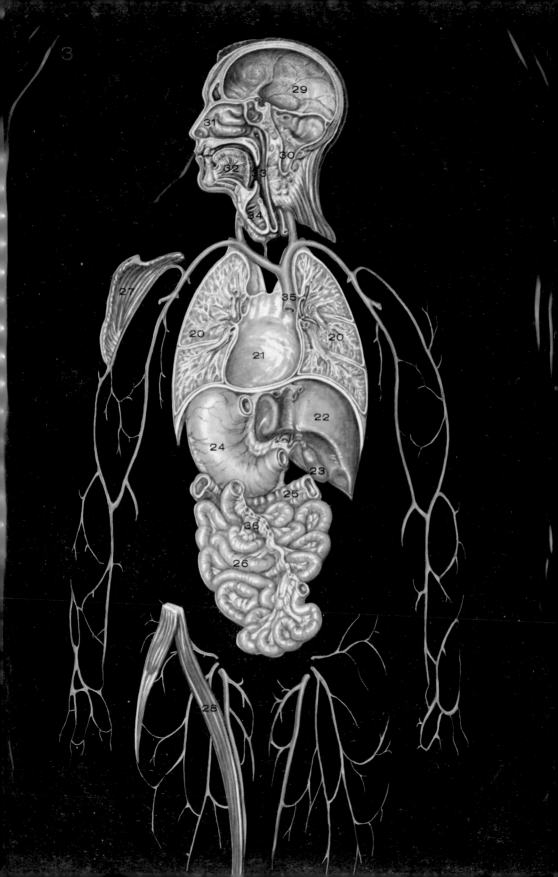

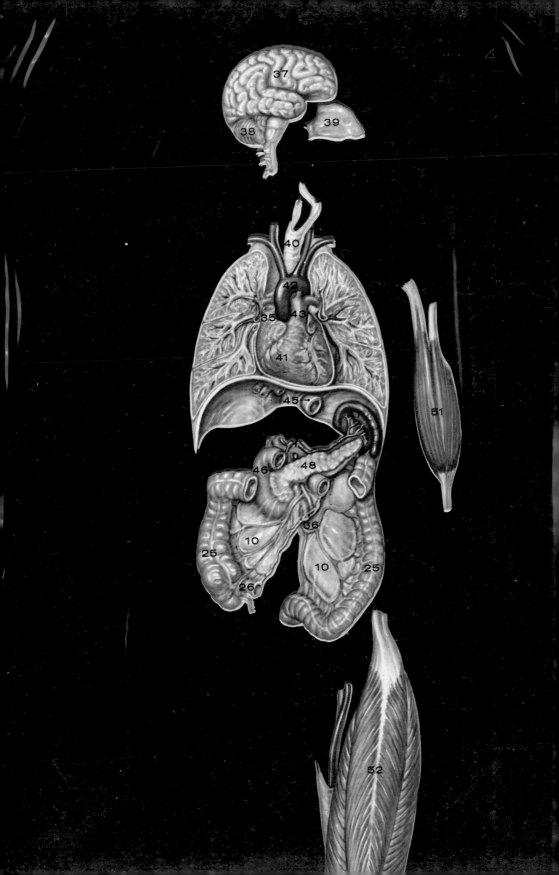

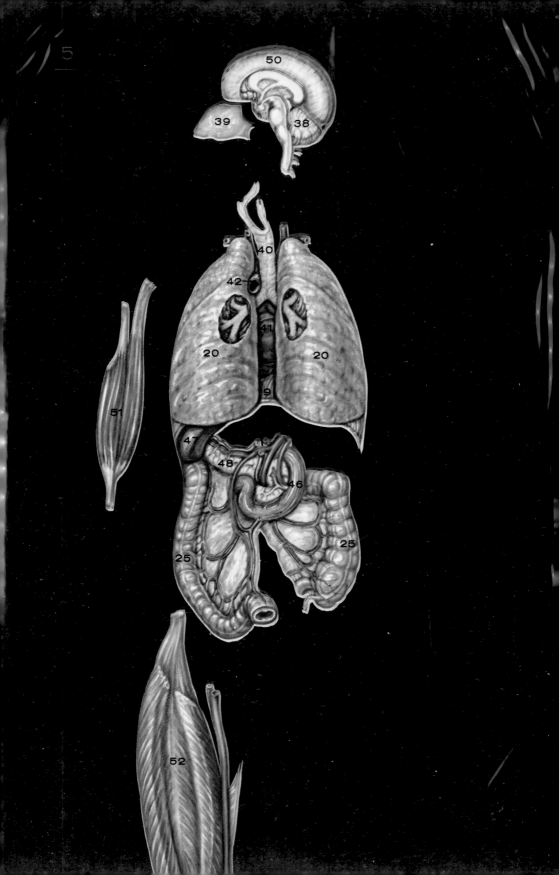

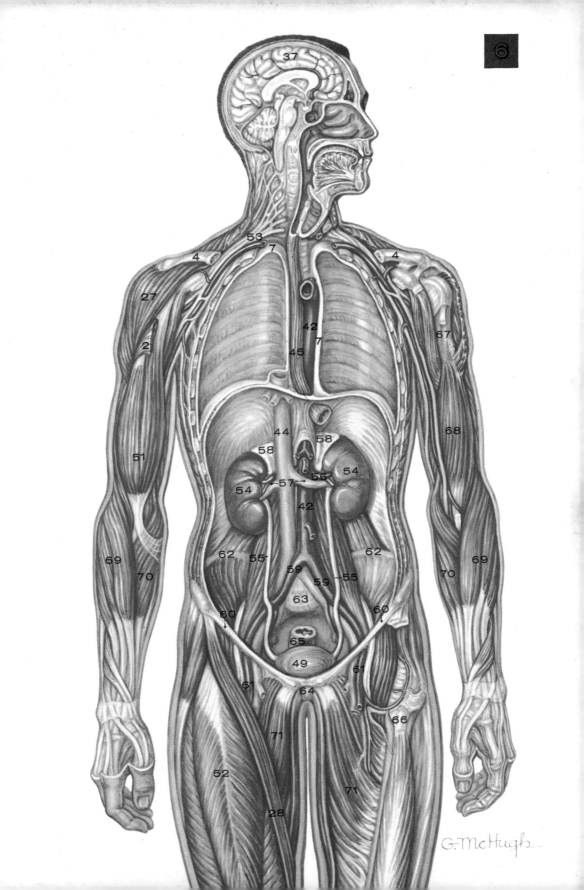

Key to the Structures of the Human Body

1. Sterno-mastoid muscle, used in turning the head
2. Pectoral muscle, used in moving the arm across the chest
3. Rib
4. Clavicle
5. Sternum
6. Rib cartilage
7. Pleural membrane
8. Intercostal muscles, used in breathing
9. Diaphragm
10. Peritoneum
11. Transverse abdominal muscle, supporting the abdominal wall
12. Rectus abdominal muscle, used in flexing the trunk
13. Rectus sheath
14. Umbilicus
15. Temporal muscle, used in chewing
16. Masseter muscle, used in chewing
17. Parotid salivary gland
18. Thyroid cartilage
19. Thyroid gland
20. Lung
21. Pericardium
22. Liver
23. Gall bladder
24. Stomach
25. Colon
26. Small intestine
27. Deltoid muscle, used in raising the arm
28. Sartorius muscle, used in crossing the leg
29. Cranial cavity
30. Spinal canal
31. Nasal cavity
32. Tongue
33. Pharynx
34. Larynx
35. Superior vena cava
36. Root of the mesentery
37. Cerebrum
38. Cerebellum
39. Nasal septum
40. Trachea
41. Heart
42. Aorta
43. Pulmonary artery
44. Inferior vena cava
45. Esophagus
46. Duodenum
47. Spleen
48. Pancreas
49. Urinary bladder
50. Cerebral septum
51. Biceps muscle, used in flexing the arm
52. Flexor muscles of front of thigh
53. Brachial plexus
54. Kidney
55. Ureter
56. Renal artery
57. Renal vein
58. Adrenal gland
59. Iliac artery
60. Inguinal ligament
61. Femoral artery
62. Crest of hip bones
63. Lumbo-sacral joint
64. Pubis
65. Rectum
66. Femur
67. Humerus
68. Brachial muscle, which works with biceps as a flexor of the arm
69. Extensor muscles of hand
70. Flexor muscles of hand
71. Adductor muscles which bring legs together

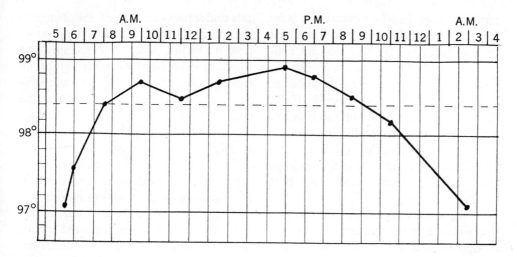

Fig. 28-1. *A graph of a person's body temperatures during a twenty-four hour period. Note how the temperatures deviate from the usually accepted average oral temperature.*

the night instead of the day. Such persons show a reversal of the normal temperature patterns after a few weeks so that their maxima are reached during the early hours of the morning.

The idea that the blood is of a uniform temperature throughout the body has been shown to be incorrect. Some relatively recent work by Dr. H. C. Bazett indicates that the temperature of

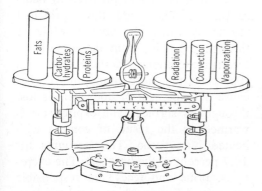

Fig. 28-2. *The balance between heat loss and heat gain. The "weights" on the left side of the balance represent the relative importance of the three organic nutrients in the production of heat. The three principal methods of heat loss are shown on the right side of the balance.*

the blood within arteries varies to a considerable degree. He placed thermocouples (electrical devices for measuring small differences in temperature) in the brachial and radial arteries (those of the upper and lower parts of the arm). Dr. Bazett found that the temperature of the blood in the brachial artery varied between 96.8° and 98.6° F. In the radial artery the temperature of the blood was between 95.9° and 98.9° F. These measurements were made in a room where the temperature was comfortable. If, however, he exposed himself to cold, but "without the subject's being unduly cold or the rectal temperature particularly low," the temperature in the brachial artery fell to 87.9° F. and that in the radial artery to 70.7° F.

The maintenance of normal body temperature may be compared to the balancing of a scales. We can imagine that on one side of the scales we have the factors that are basic to the *production* of heat on the body and on the other those that are basic to its *elimination*. Under ideal conditions, the two sides would balance (as illustrated in Fig. 28-2). On the one side of the scales we have proteins, carbohydrates, and fats because it is by the *oxidation* of these materials that heat is produced. On the other side are convection, radiation, and vaporization, since these are the three most important ways in which heat is lost from the body. Physical processes maintain the balance. Any change in activity will alter the rate at which the nutrient materials are oxidized. Likewise, a change in the environment will affect the rate at which heat is lost.

In the next chapter the function of each of the organic nutrients in the production of heat will be discussed. Oxidation of nutrients in the body cells accounts for virtually all of the heat that is produced. Some tissues, however, are more active than others, and it is in these that the major production of heat occurs. Muscles make up over one half of the soft structures of the body, and oxidation in muscle tissue supplies the largest quantity of heat. If, for example, a warm-blooded animal receives an injection of curare, which renders its muscles incapable of movement, its body temperature varies in the same way as that of a cold-blooded (poikilothermic) animal. Active glands add a little heat, the liver being the greatest heat-producing gland. The amount of heat supplied by warm food or drinks plays a negligible role in this process.

Temperature control. Body temperature is controlled by several different processes operating within the body or over its surface. Some of these are internal adjustments while others are responses to the temperature of the surrounding air. We can summarize these processes as follows:

1. Heat regulation by nervous control. In previous chapters we have mentioned several factors which influence body temperature. These include the dilation and constriction of the blood vessels under nervous control, the change in the tonus of the muscles and the production of sweat. The centers controlling these activities lie in the lower part of the medulla, but their function in temperature regulation appears to be under the control of a *heat-regulating center* located in the hypothalamus. It has been found, for example, that if the hypothalamus is separated from these lower centers in an experimental animal, all control over heat regulation is lost.

There are two distinct areas in this center. One of these controls the loss of heat and the other its production. If the anterior part of the center is destroyed or injured, a person adjusts his temperature normally in cool surroundings. However, in a warm place his body temperature rises because he cannot dispose of excess heat. When this anterior region is warmed in an experimental animal, all of the outward signs of heat loss are shown: the animal pants, sweats, and its body temperature drops. If the posterior part of the center is injured, heat production lags behind heat loss and the body temperature falls.

2. Physical factors involved in heat-regulation. There are three principal means by which the body loses heat: through the skin, from the lungs, and through excretions. Of these three, the skin plays the most important role because 87.5 percent of body heat is lost through its surface. The expired air is warmed as the result of contact with heated lung tissue. This accounts for 10.7 percent of the heat lost. The excretions, urine and feces, are responsible for only 1.8 percent of the heat loss. This quantity is so small that it is taken into consideration only when making the most exact measurements of loss of body heat.

Loss of heat over the surface of the body may occur in any of several ways, depending on environmental conditions. *Conduction* of heat may occur when the skin comes in contact with a surface of lower temperature, as when a lightly dressed person lies on cold ground. In general, however, we are protected from heat loss by conduction. We wear clothing that is made from materials that are poor conductors of heat because of numerous small pockets of air trapped within the fibers. The body does not normally lose much heat by conduction.

Body heat is lost by *radiation,* in the form of invisible waves in the infrared region of the spectrum (Fig. 28-3). These wave lengths are longer than those of the longest visible red rays. Radiation occurs whenever an object is warmer than its surroundings. A radiator in a cold room gives off infrared (heat) waves which are absorbed by the walls and furniture. The air itself is not appreciably warmed by radiation, however. The body is constantly radiating heat.

Convection is partly responsible for loss of body heat. If a person is at rest in a cool room, he loses heat as a result of the convection currents that are set up over his skin. The layers of warmed air next to his skin are constantly replaced by cooler air that flows in as the lighter warm air rises. The same process occurs when a person swims in cold water. The thin layer of warmed water that has been in contact with the skin is replaced by cold water. In this condition

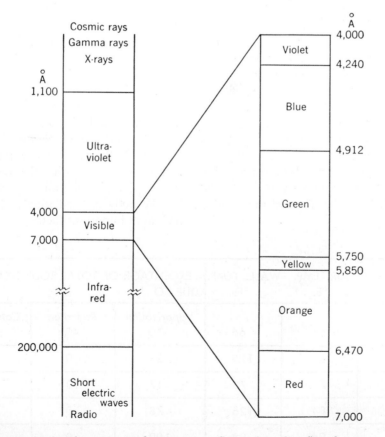

Fig. 28-3. *The parts of the spectrum that ordinarily affect humans.*

the loss of body heat by convection is very great.

Vaporization, or evaporation, of sweat from the surface of the skin is the method we are most apt to think of as the principal means of heat loss. This is because we are more conscious of the cooling effects of the evaporation of sweat than we are of the other methods.

The capacity of a fluid to lower the temperature of the surface from which it is evaporating depends on its ability to absorb heat from the surface. This heat is the energy which converts the fluid into a vapor, and is known as the *heat of vaporization.* It can be defined as the amount of heat needed to vaporize one gram of a liquid without changing the temperature of the liquid. The amount of heat absorbed is measured in terms of small calories. It varies with each fluid and also with its temperature. Water has a very high heat of vaporization in comparison to other liquids, which means that its rate of evaporation is sufficiently slow to prevent too rapid chilling. At a skin temperature of 86° F. each gram of water that evaporates requires 579.5 calories of heat. However, the rate of evaporation of sweat depends on factors such as the rate of the movement of air, the temperature of the air, and the relative humidity.

It must be kept in mind that relative humidity refers to the amount of moisture present in the air at a given temperature in relation to the absolute amount of moisture it could hold at that same temperature. As air becomes warmer it can hold more moisture. Therefore on a hot and humid day the body is still able to lose heat by evaporation of sweat, although there is a general feeling of discomfort. A relative humidity between 40 and 60 percent is generally considered to be the most desirable for health and comfort.

In a series of ingenious experiments conducted by Drs. Winslow and Herrington, the relative roles of radiation, convection, and vaporization under differing conditions of temperature were demonstrated. The experimenters constructed a booth in which air could be circulated freely, and in which the temperature of the air could be changed independently of that of the walls. Unclothed subjects were then placed in the booth and the conditions altered as shown in the table below.

In *Series A* the temperature of the air and the walls was considerably below that of the skin, with the result that evaporation played a minor part in cooling the body but radiation and convection were important factors. In *Series B*

SERIES	AIR TEMP. °F.	WALL. TEMP. °F.	PERCENTAGE OF TOTAL BODY HEAT LOST DUE TO		
			Vaporization	*Radiation*	*Convection*
A	63	66	10	40	50
B	61	120	21	0	79
C	73	73	17	13	70
D	84	126	78	0	22
E	96	92	100	0	0

the high temperature of the walls prevented the radiation of heat, as it also did in the last two series. In *Series B,* convection again was important because the air temperature was too low to permit much evaporation of sweat. In *Series C* we see that when the air temperature and the wall temperature were equal, but still somewhat below normal skin temperature, vaporization and radiation were about equally responsible for heat loss. *Series D* shows that as the temperature of the air was increased, the effect of sweating became more marked while convection was decreased. With a high wall temperature, such as the one found here, the body may even have absorbed some heat from the walls. In *Series E* the evaporation of sweat was the only method of losing heat because the air and wall were at about the same temperature as the body.

3. *The chemical control of temperature.* The range of external temperature in which man can regulate his body temperature effectively lies between 77 and 95° F., depending on the clothing worn and the presence of fat deposits. In this range of temperatures he loses the least heat and his rate of oxidation is lowest. In a resting state, the most economical temperature for the human body in terms of the balance between heat loss and oxidations is about 65° F.

If the body temperature falls because physical processes cannot keep heat loss at a normal level, chemical processes are initiated to increase production of heat. We have already mentioned some of these in connection with the neural control of heat regulation. When an excessive heat loss occurs, we have such activities as shivering, the chattering of the teeth, and the involuntary tensing of muscles which increase the rate of oxidation. These may be under the control of the nervous system, but it is the chemical reactions in the muscles that are chiefly responsible for the rise in temperature.

Some disturbances of heat balance. One of the most common types of disturbance of the heat-regulating mechanism is **fever.** In the past some people held the idea that fever was the result of an increased rate of oxidation in the cells. There is little evidence to support this idea, since a fever produces an increase of only 20 percent in the rate of oxidation while muscular activity may raise the rate as much as 200 percent with no symptoms of a fever. Currently, it is thought that a fever is a result of the temporary failure of the "thermostat" in the hypothalamus to function properly, due to the action of bacterial or viral toxins, or to serious emotional upsets. The hypothalamus controls activities of the lower centers that are directly responsible for the operation of the heat-regulating processes. This theory is supported by the fact that a young child develops fevers very easily under conditions which cause a much slower response in adults. Nervous control of the heat-regulating mechanisms is not well established in babies and young children. A fever is accompanied by lack of sweat and constriction of the skin capillaries. This latter condition may cause the victim to feel cold, even though his temperature is higher than normal. Fever is the usual indication that infection of some kind is present in the body.

A second type of disturbance of heat regulation is **heatstroke,** or **sunstroke.** Both of these terms refer to the same condition, which is brought about by high external temperature and high humidity. The body is unable to lose heat normally and the temperature rises. Heatstroke is characterized by a dry, hot skin, a rapid pulse, and high blood pressure. The internal body temperature may rise as high as 110° F. At this temperature, destruction of brain cells results and death follows. Care for a victim of heatstroke may include external application of ice packs or the wrapping the person in sheets soaked in cold water in order to reduce the body temperature rapidly. Overweight, the drinking of alcohol, and the wearing of unsuitably heavy clothing are all factors which may contribute to heatstroke.

Heat exhaustion, or **heat prostration,** occurs when the circulatory system fails to function properly under adverse temperature conditions. In this condition the pulse is weak, the blood pressure low, and the skin moist and clammy. A person suffering from heat exhaustion should be kept warm. Complete rest is the best method of caring for this condition.

Heat cramps develop when a person has been subjected to a high temperature and has been sweating profusely, with the loss of an excessive amount of sodium chloride from the body. The cramps are not accompanied by any rise in body temperature. The main characteristic of this condition is the painful cramps in the muscles that have been used most. People can tolerate surprisingly high temperatures if they take in enough salt. At zero humidity, experimenters have withstood temperatures between 200 and 250° F. for a few hours without any harmful effects. A 0.2 percent solution of salt in the drinking water will safeguard a person against heat cramps. Many industries encourage their employees to avoid heat cramps by providing salt tablets in dispensers near the drinking fountains.

SPEAKING OF Physiology

Briefly identify each of the following:

conduction	**homoiothermic**	**relative humidity**
convection	**poikilothermic**	**thermometer**
heat-regulating center	**radiation**	**vaporization**

Test YOUR KNOWLEDGE

1. How do you account for the fact that your body temperature varies during a 24-hour period?
2. How does your body maintain the balance between the production of heat and its elimination? What effect does physical activity have on this balance?
3. If the muscles of your body were rendered inactive by some drug, what would happen to your body temperature? How is this condition similar to the normal state of cold-blooded animals?
4. What is the function of the nervous system in the control of body temperature? Where is the center for this control?
5. What tissue of the human body accounts for the greatest amount of heat loss? Why?
6. Explain how the mechanisms of conduction, radiation, and convection affect the control of body temperature.
7. How much heat is lost by evaporation of sweat? What effect does the humidity of the air have on this loss of heat?
8. What theory may explain fevers in the human body? What changes occur in the body during a fever?

9. What is the difference between heat exhaustion and sunstroke? How does the treatment vary?

10. How does the drinking of a dilute salt solution help a person to endure high atmospheric temperatures?

See FOR YOURSELF

1. How much does your own temperature vary throughout a day? Learn how to take your own temperature with a clinical thermometer. Keep a record of your body temperature for a week, taking readings when you wake up in the morning, when you get home from school, and in the evening when you go to bed. Plot the results on a graph. What conclusions can you draw from this information?

2. Try to find out why a person's temperature is elevated during illness. What effect does aspirin have on body temperature? Why?

3. Prepare a report on the best first aid treatments for heat exhaustion, heat-stroke, and heat cramps. Give a physiological explanation for the effectiveness of these treatments.

4. Write a report on the research being done by the armed forces and other agencies on preventing heat loss by persons who must be active under the extremely low temperatures found in the Arctic and Antarctic.

5. Demonstrate to the class the physical processes of conduction, convection, radiation, and vaporization. Make a chart showing the relative importance of these four methods of losing body heat under various environmental conditions.

6. Prepare a chart of the body temperature variations of some cold-blooded animals, such as a frog, a turtle, or a snake.

7. Write a report on the ability of some warm-blooded animals to lower their body temperature during periods of true hibernation.

CHAPTER 29

Metabolism

The term *metabolism* includes all those chemical processes within cells from which any living thing derives its energy. The processes are of two kinds. If a process is primarily constructive and results in the building of protoplasm, it is classed as *anabolism*. If it is a destructive process, it is called *catabolism*. As a result of anabolic processes, the protoplasmic materials of the cells either increase in quantity or are replaced. The catabolic processes, on the other hand, result in the destruction of substances and the conversion of the potential energy they contained into kinetic energy. Youth is the period in life when anabolism is the characteristic process; middle age is represented by a balance between the two, and old age is a period in which the catabolic processes are dominant.

We have already studied the nature of the various food materials and their preparation for distribution by the blood. We have also become acquainted with some of the processes involved in muscular contraction, the secretion of materials by glands, and the development of various parts of the body. All of these processes require transformations of energy which are basic to the study of metabolism.

Calorimetry. In Chapter 13 we mentioned the uses of organic nutrients and the role each plays in producing energy or building protoplasm. The unit used in measuring the energy production of foods is the Calorie. The energy value of any food is measured by an apparatus such as the one diagrammed in Fig. 29-1. This is known as a *bomb calorimeter*. It consists of several vessels placed one inside another for complete insulation from changes in the outside temperature. The innermost chamber is sur-

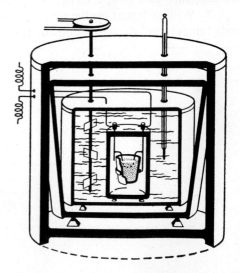

Fig. 29-1. *A bomb calorimeter. The food is placed in the crucible and ignited by an electric arc. The heat generated by burning the food can be calculated from the rise in temperature of the water in the surrounding water bath.* (*Bawden,* Matter and Energy, *Holt, 1957*)

rounded by a water bath fitted with a stirring rod to keep the water in circulation. An accurate thermometer is inserted into the water bath. The material to be tested is put into a crucible in the innermost compartment, the *bomb*. By means of electrical connections, an arc is produced which ignites the food. As the food burns, the water outside the bomb is heated and any rise in temperature is read on the thermometer. After subtraction of the heat produced by the arc, the rise in temperature of the water can then be translated into Calories produced by the complete combustion of the food.

The heat produced by an animal can also be measured directly in a similar device. This method of *direct calorimetry* employs a chamber large enough to accommodate the animal under investigation. Direct measurements of the heat produced by animals as large as an elephant have been made. Essentially, a calorimeter of this type consists of a fully insulated, airtight chamber through the walls of which pass tubes containing water in constant circulation. The temperature of the water is read as it enters the tubes and again as it leaves. The outgoing air is passed through sulfuric acid to remove moisture, and through soda lime to absorb the carbon dioxide. The air from which the water and the carbon dioxide has been removed is then mixed with a known amount of oxygen and recirculated through the chamber. At the conclusion of the test, the sulfuric acid and the soda lime are weighed to determine the amount of water and carbon dioxide that the animal has produced. Since the amount of oxygen entering the chamber during any given period of time is known, its conversion into water and carbon dioxide can be measured. These substances are the products of oxidations occurring within the cells, as shown in the following chemical equation for the oxidation of glucose:

$$C_6H_{12}O_6 \ + \ 6\ O_2 \ \rightarrow$$
glucose   oxygen

$$6\ CO_2 \ + \ 6\ H_2O.$$ (+4.1 Calories per
carbon   water   gram of glucose)
dioxide

Direct calorimetry requires the use of cumbersome and complicated apparatus. To simplify the procedure, a method of *indirect calorimetry* has been developed to measure human metabolic rates. In Fig. 29-2 is shown a person undergoing a metabolism test in a hospital. The apparatus pictured here is a modification of the spirometer described in Chapter 20. The patient breathes into a closed system. The floating bell of the spirometer is filled with oxygen which the patient inhales. Provision is made for the absorption of carbon dioxide by soda lime. Attached to the respiratory calorimeter is a revolving drum on which is recorded the rate at which oxygen is used. Figure 29-3 is a reproduction of a graph obtained from this apparatus.

A person who is scheduled to undergo a metabolism test is required to rest quietly in a comfortable room for at least an hour before starting the test. Also, he should not have eaten for a period of at least 12 to 14 hours so that the presence of food in the digestive system will not affect the metabolic rate.

Since the test determines the amount of oxygen consumed in a given period of time (usually six minutes), certain facts regarding the oxidation of the organic nutrients must be taken into consideration. These are:

1. To oxidize 1 gram of carbohydrates and liberate 4.1 Calories, 0.812 liter of oxygen is required. Hence when 1 liter of oxygen is used, 5 Calories will be generated.

2. To oxidize one gram of fat and

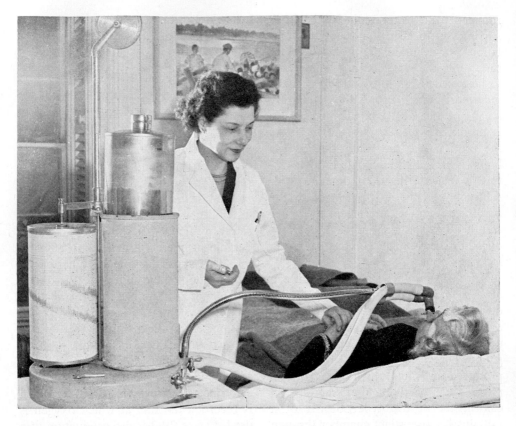

Fig. 29-2. *A person undergoing a BMR test. The kymograph at the left records the amount of oxygen consumed during a measured period of time.* (*Massachusetts General Hospital*)

liberate 9.3 Calories, 0.71 liter of oxygen is needed. One liter of oxygen will therefore produce 13.098 Calories.

3. The oxidation value for the proteins must be reached by indirect methods because of the extreme complexity of their chemical structure. It has been determined, however, that 1 gram of protein requires 0.95 liter of oxygen for its combustion and will supply 4.1 Calories. One liter of oxygen therefore produces 4.5 Calories of heat when proteins are oxidized.

If we assume that all three nutrients are present in the patient's diet in the usual proportions (carbohydrates, three parts; fats, two parts; proteins, one part), and are completely oxidized, the consumption of 1 liter of oxygen will produce a total of 7.616 Calories. If, therefore, in the six minutes required by this test, he uses 1.25 liters of oxygen, the patient will generate 9.59 Calories ($7.616 \times 1.25 = 9.59$). If we then assume that the patient remains quiet for a total of twenty-four hours, his total heat production during this period will be 2301.6 Calories.

Basal metabolic rate. The results obtained by the method just described constitute the *basal metabolic rate* (*BMR*). Since the activity of the person undergoing such a test is controlled, the rate of oxidation is considered to be the fundamental rate for that individual.

Two factors which influence the BMR

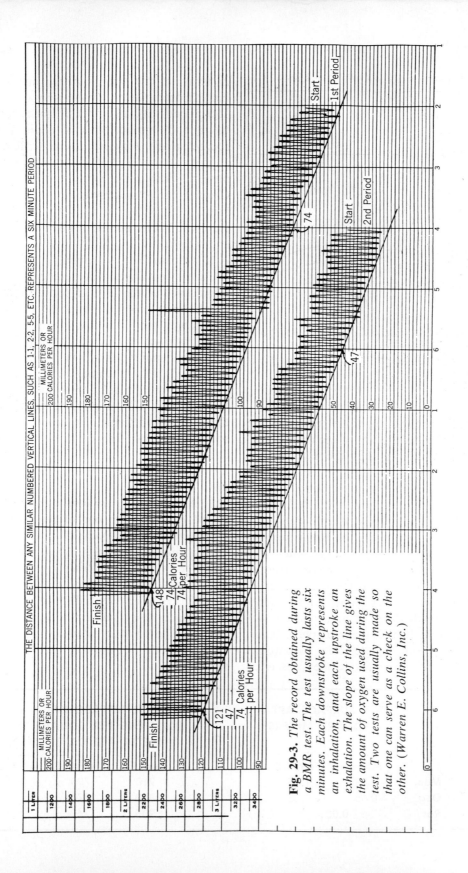

Fig. 29-3. The record obtained during a BMR test. The test usually lasts six minutes. Each downstroke represents an inhalation, and each upstroke an exhalation. The slope of the line gives the amount of oxygen used during the test. Two tests are usually made so that one can serve as a check on the other. (Warren E. Collins, Inc.)

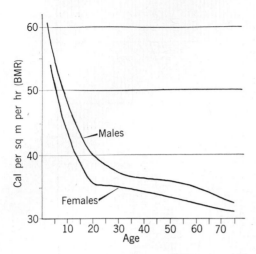

Fig. 29-4. *The relation between BMR and age. These are smoothed curves, based on averages obtained by three separate research groups who studied results from 1762 men and 2254 women.*

are the age and sex of the person. Figure 29-4 shows the effect of age on the basal rate. It is seen that the rate is high among young children and decreases as they grow older, until the period of rapid growth has been completed. From that point on, there is relatively little decline. The reason for this pattern is not clearly understood at present.

The rate of metabolism is given in terms of Calories per square meter of body surface per hour. Most energy is lost in the form of heat, and the surface of the body is the principal radiator. Because body surface varies with weight and height, the metabolic rate is described

in terms of the heat lost per unit of body surface. An adult male who weighs 150 pounds and is 5 feet 7 inches tall has a body surface area of about 1.7 square meters. He will have a BMR of approximately 38 Calories per square meter of body surface per hour, or 912 Calories per square meter per day. The chart in Fig. 29-5 is used to find the surface area of a person of known height and weight.

If we consider two animals of different sizes, we will get a clearer idea of the significance of the area of body surface in relation to heat loss. A mouse, for example, will lose more heat in proportion to the amount of heat it produces than a larger animal, such as a dog. The reason for this is that the mouse has a greater surface area in relation to its weight than the dog. If, however, we calculate the heat loss in terms of a unit of body surface, we find that all mammals are approximately alike in this respect. The table of averages below illustrates this.

Factors affecting metabolic rates. As we have mentioned, one of the results of muscular activity is the production of heat within the muscles. Since muscle tissue forms a large percentage of the body's mass, it is reasonable to expect that muscular activity will have a proportionately large relation to heat production. The list of activities on page 326 shows the effect of muscular activity on the BMR.

	BODY SURFACE AREA (IN SQUARE METERS)		BASAL METABOLISM (CALORIES PER SQUARE METER PER DAY)	
	MALE	FEMALE	MALE	FEMALE
Man	1.83	1.65	910	790
Dog	0.65	0.58	800	770
Rat	0.031		905	760

BODY SURFACE CHART

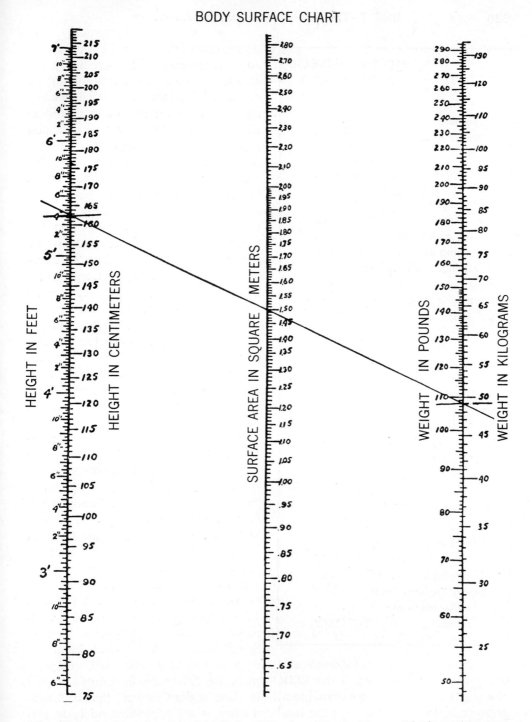

Fig. 29-5. *A chart showing the relationship of weight, height, and body surface area. To use the chart, lay a ruler across it so that one end intersects the weight line at your own weight and the other end intersects the height line at your own height. You then read your body surface area (in square meters) where the ruler intersects the middle line. The line drawn on this chart gives the body surface area of a person who was 5 feet 4 inches tall and who weighed 108 pounds. (Warren E. Collins, Inc.)*

ACTIVITY	PERCENT INCREASE IN BASAL RATE
MEN	
Sleeping	— 0.1
Working as draftsman	+ 54
Sitting, reading	69
Working as radio mechanic	131
Driving car	139
Dressing	242
Using pick to dig earth	498
Walking at 4.2 mph	678
Farming: hoeing, deep ridging	712
Lumbering; horizontal chopping	1028
Walking in loose snow carrying 40-lb weight at 2.4 mph	1627
WOMEN	
Sleeping	— 0.1
Darning	+ 29
Typing (40 words per minute)	51
Washing dishes	54
Washing floor on knees	66
Sweeping	89
Carrying tray in hands	130
Washing clothes by hand	175
Changing bed linen	451
Skiing on level hard snow, moderate speed	1002

Changes in *external temperature* also affect metabolic processes. If the BMR of a dog is measured at an external temperature of 45.7° F. and then the temperature is raised to 86° F., it will be found that the BMR has dropped by 65 percent. The higher rate of metabolism at the low temperature can be explained by the fact that muscle tonus (and,

hence, rate of oxidations) has increased. At low temperatures, there is an increased rate of heat loss over the surface of the body and this must be balanced by an increase in the rate of heat production. This applies to humans also, and accounts for our feeling of general well-being on a cool, clear day. Although our reaction may be pleasurable, from a physiological standpoint we are paying for our pleasure by increasing our rate of cellular oxidations to offset the loss of heat from the surface of the body. It was found that American soldiers in tropical countries with daily air temperatures that approached 90° F. needed only 3100 Calories per day, while soldiers serving under Arctic conditions required a much higher average of 4900 Calories per day.

A consistently high external temperature influences basal metabolism. If we examine the basal metabolism of people who are acclimatized to tropical conditions, we find that there is considerable variation from the expected response. Studies made on a group of male Brazilians showed that their BMR was less than that of a comparable group of men in northern parts of the United States. On the other hand, the BMR of natives of Yucatan averaged about 8 percent above that of a comparable group of Americans. In India, a group of women showed an average BMR of 17.4 percent lower than that of a comparable group of American women. Since Yucatan, Brazil, and India are tropical countries with high temperatures, the differences in results obtained in these regions indicate that heat production is not dependent on body surface area alone.

Altitude evidently plays no part in determining the basal metabolic rate of an individual. Many BMR tests have been made on people who live at high altitudes and are acclimatized to them. When their test results are compared with those of people living at lower elevations, no significant differences appear. Likewise, no change in the rate has been observed in aviators flying at different altitudes nor in people who have been placed in low-pressure chambers where the effects of increased altitudes could be imitated.

Food itself has an effect on the BMR. Experimental evidence of this was obtained by putting a person on a starvation diet. At the end of the first day it was found that he liberated only 718 Calories. On the second day of the experiment he received 400 grams of proteins in addition to his starvation diet and his heat liberation jumped to 1046 Calories. The third day he again went on starvation rations and his Calorie output dropped to 746, but rose to 1105 on the fourth day when he again received an additional 400 grams of protein. Other experiments have shown conclusively that this is not due to the presence of food in the digestive system because such inert materials as agar (a complex carbohydrate that cannot be digested) do not increase the BMR. This action of foods, especially proteins, is known as the *specific dynamic action* (SDA) of foods.

The reason for the SDA of foods is not clearly understood at present. Currently, experimental evidence points to the liver as the controlling factor in this action. Studies indicate that if this organ is removed from an experimental animal, the addition of large amounts of protein to its diet does not result in an increase in the BMR. These experiments lead us to the conclusion that the specific dynamic action of foods is connected with deamination (removal of NH_2 from the protein molecule). It is possible that the presence in the body of proteins that cannot be immediately utilized will help to keep the body warm.

Thyroxin also influences the BMR. This hormone is a secretion of the thyroid gland, which will be discussed later. The malfunctioning of this gland is one of the abnormal conditions revealed by a basal metabolism test. If the gland produces too little thyroxin, the BMR will be low, but if it is overactive, the BMR will be above normal. Other conditions which may lower the metabolic rate of the body are lack of proper amount of one of the pituitary secretions, starvation, and kidney disorders. An elevation of the rate may be the result of an overproduction of the pituitary secretion, severe anemia, certain types of leukemia, or too rapid growth.

Relative energy value of nutrients. Carbohydrates, fats, and proteins, as we have seen, vary in their ability to produce heat on oxidation. Other factors in the metabolism of these nutrients must be considered, however, in judging their value as energy-giving foods.

The idea that a good day's work requires a diet that is primarily composed of proteins has little basis in observed fact. Physiologists working on this problem report that the protein content of the diet has little effect on the physical vigor or efficiency of the individual. This is due to the fact that proteins are rarely oxidized to produce energy.

A person with a diet low in protein (50 grams per kilogram of body weight per day) did not show any difference in physical vigor or efficiency when he was changed to one rich in protein (160 grams per kilogram of body weight per day).

As we have previously said, the function of proteins is to build tissue. They can be replaced by carbohydrates, the protein-savers, as sources of energy. Fats are the best sources of energy, but

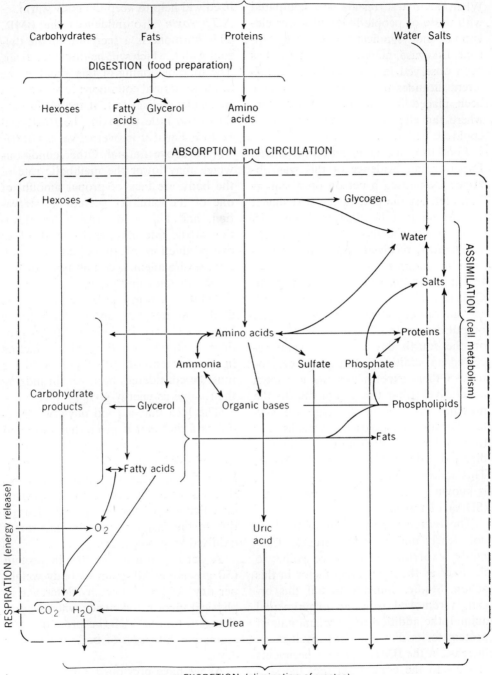

Fig. 29-6. *Diagram summarizing the interrelations of the most important activities in metabolism. The area within the broken line includes processes that occur within the cells.*

when they serve as the exclusive energy-producing materials, there is an increase in the amount of ketones formed. Since ketones are acid in their reaction, they threaten the acid-base equilibrium of the blood, and the condition of ketosis develops. We will have more to say about this later in connection with diabetes and the action of insulin.

It is a well recognized fact that eating sugar before an athletic contest increases one's ability to combat exhaustion. This is because carbohydrates are quickly digested and made available for oxidation. We can conclude, therefore, that while all three types of organic nutrients are capable of supplying energy, carbohydrates are preferred. In this connection, it is interesting to note that the majority of the most muscular animals are herbivorous in their diets. It appears therefore, that plant nutrients can supply the major part of the carbohydrates needed for energy.

The chart in Fig. 29-6 summarizes human metabolism and shows the interrelationships and interactions of many of the body processes.

SPEAKING OF Physiology

Briefly identify each of the following:

anabolism	**catabolism**	**ketosis**
basal metabolic rate	**direct calorimetry**	**metabolism**
bomb calorimeter	**indirect calorimetry**	**specific dynamic action**

Test YOUR KNOWLEDGE

1. List separately various bodily activities which fall under the headings of anabolism and catabolism.
2. Define the term Calorie. How can the caloric value of different foods be determined?
3. What is the chief value of the indirect calorimetry method in determining the metabolic rate of an individual? Describe the procedure used in this method.
4. Why do we normally get most of our Calories from carbohydrates in spite of the fact that fats have a much higher energy value than carbohydrates?
5. Why is the metabolic rate shown in terms of Calories per square meter of body surface per hour?
6. How does muscular activity affect the metabolic rate?
7. Is there any relationship between diet and the rate of metabolism? How does temperature change affect food consumption?
8. Why does the administration of thyroxin increase the BMR?
9. Does altitude have any effect on the rate of metabolism?

See FOR YOURSELF

1. Determine your own Calorie needs per day based on your sex, weight, and height. Using food charts, determine the number of Calories in your daily diet. Is it adequate for your energy needs? Explain.

2. During a seven-day period, weigh yourself each morning. Keep an account of the total Calories taken into your body each day. At the end of the week, note any changes in your body weight. Explain any differences that occur.

3. Devise a set of sensible rules to follow in order to gain weight. How would you change these rules to lose weight? Explain why your rules should be effective.

4. Collect a series of advertisements for various drugs or pills for reducing weight. What dangers are there in taking these drugs?

5. Find out all you can about past and present fads in foods and diet. What are some of the dangers in following food fads?

6. If your doctor has a BMR apparatus, ask him to demonstrate its operation. Report on this to your class.

CHAPTER 30

The Kidneys and Their Function

The elimination of waste materials from the cells is the primary concern of the excretory system. The catabolic activities of cells produce waste materials of various types. If these were allowed to accumulate in the body, serious injury would result. The **kidneys,** with their associated structures, are the most important organs of excretion, but as we have seen, other organs take a lesser part in the process. The principal types of waste materials and the way in which they are eliminated are shown in the table below.

The kidneys are especially concerned with eliminating salts, particularly if the salts contain nitrogen. The primary excretory function of the kidneys is the elimination from the body of the products of protein catabolism. Only small amounts of these nitrogenous wastes leave by any other pathway. So long as the kidneys continue to excrete these nitrogenous compounds, the processes of anabolism and catabolism are kept in balance. A *dynamic equilibrium* is thus established in the body.

Kidney functions. The functions of the kidneys are not limited to the elimination of waste materials. These organs are the primary regulators of our internal environment since they are largely responsible for maintaining balance in the composition of the blood. The kidneys perform three functions. First, they help to maintain the water balance of the body

SUBSTANCE	SOURCES	ELIMINATED BY
WATER	Cellular oxidations	Skin
	Ingestion of liquid and solid food substances	Lungs Kidneys
GASES	Cellular oxidations	Lungs
SALTS	Products of catabolic processes	Principally by the kidneys, although some are lost in sweat
	Ingested in excess in food	

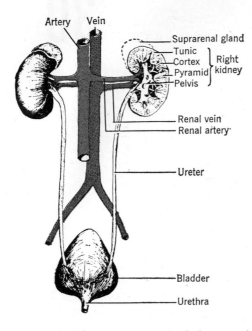

Artery   Vein

Suprarenal gland

Tunic
Cortex   } Right
Pyramid } kidney
Pelvis

Renal vein
Renal artery

Ureter

Bladder

Urethra

Fig. 30-1. *The structure of the kidneys and their associated parts. (After B. F. Edwards, from MacDougall and Hegner,* Biology, *McGraw-Hill Book Co., 1943)*

by excreting or conserving water as required. Second, they are essential in regulating the acid-base equilibrium of the body. As well as excreting fixed acids, the kidneys manufacture materials which help to neutralize excess acids or bases. Third, the kidneys help regulate the osmotic action of the blood and maintain a balance between its salt content and that of the cells. This is accomplished by the excretion of excess amounts of sodium, potassium, calcium, and magnesium.

Structure of the kidneys. The kidneys (as shown in the Trans-Vision which follows page 312 lie against the dorsal wall of the abdominal cavity between the peritoneum and the muscles of the back. They are enclosed in capsules of fatty tissue. Each kidney is about 4.4 inches long, 2 to 3 inches broad, and about 1 inch thick. Their combined weight is approximately 10 ounces. The **renal artery** and the **renal vein** enter

the concave side of the kidney at the **hilum.** The **ureters** also leave at the hilum and carry the urine to the **urinary bladder** which lies on the floor of the abdominal cavity. From the bladder, a tube called the **urethra** carries the urine to the outside (Fig. 30-1).

If a kidney is cut lengthwise, a definite arrangement of tissues can be seen. On the outer surface is a layer with a fine granular texture called the **cortex** of the kidney. Within it is a layer composed of tissues arranged in lines that radiate outward from the central part toward the cortex. This layer is the **medulla** of the kidney. On its inner margin are numerous rounded projections, the **pyramids.** The cavity into which the pyramids protrude forms the **pelvis** of the kidney, which is the uppermost end of the ureter.

A microscopic examination of the various layers shows that they have a very extensive blood supply. The renal artery branches extensively immediately after it enters the kidney. The branches give rise to numerous capillaries. The blood supply to the kidneys is so great that when the body is at rest, about one fourth of the total output of the heart passes through them. This means that a volume equal to the total blood supply of the entire body enters and leaves the kidneys every four or five minutes.

The kidney tubule or nephron. There are approximately 1 million highly specialized tubules within each kidney. Each tubule is about 14 millimeters long and 0.055 millimeter in diameter. The upper end of the tubule is expanded into a saclike structure known as **Bowman's capsule.** It is composed of two layers of cells and its shape is like that obtained by pushing a blunt object against one side of a thin-walled rubber ball to form an indentation. The **affer-**

ent blood vessel, a minute branch of the renal artery, enters at this indentation. The afferent vessel then forms a knot of about fifty separate capillaries, the **glomerulus,** which fills the cavity of the capsule. Although the diagram of the nephron in Fig. 30-2 does not show it, the inner wall of Bowman's capsule dips between the capillaries to surround them. This brings each blood vessel into direct and intimate contact with the capsule wall.

Beyond the capsule, the nephron becomes tubular and quite convoluted (twisted) for a short distance. Both the capsule and the convoluted tubule lie in the cortex, but the tube suddenly dips into the medulla to form the **loop of Henle** and then returns to the cortex. It once more becomes convoluted before opening into a **collecting tubule.** This larger vessel is joined by other tubules which open into the pelvis from the surface of a pyramid.

As Fig. 30-2 shows, the walls of the tubule are surrounded by capillaries. After the afferent vessel has formed the glomerulus, it continues out of the capsule as the **efferent vessel** and this again branches to form the capillaries which surround the tubules. These eventually flow together to form a small branch of the renal vein which takes the blood from the kidney.

The filtering action of the nephron. We have already mentioned that the renal artery branches into smaller vessels immediately upon entering the kidney. The result of the sudden lessening in size of the vessels is a sudden increase in pressure, like that which would occur if we attached many small rubber tubes to the end of a garden hose. Thus, when the blood flows into the glomerulus, the pressure rises as the artery branches into capillaries. In most of the capillaries throughout the body, pressure is about

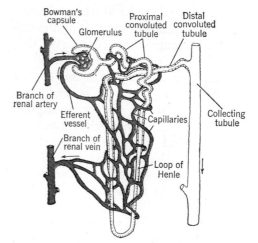

Fig. 30-2. *A diagram showing the close relationship of the nephron and the blood vessels by which materials are reabsorbed into the blood.*

25 millimeters of mercury, but within the glomerulus it rises to between 60 and 70 millimeters. As a result of this high pressure, blood fluids are filtered through the capillary wall and pass into the capsule.

The total amount of fluid passing from the capillaries is astounding. It is estimated that approximately 125 milliliters of fluid leave the blood each minute. In the course of 24 hours this amounts to about 180 liters, or 190 quarts. In spite of this tremendous withdrawal of fluid from the blood, the body loses only 1½ to 2 quarts of fluid per day in the form of urine. The reason may be found in the relationship of the blood capillaries to the tubular parts of the nephron.

Due to the loss of large amounts of fluid in the capsule, the blood in the efferent vessel is highly concentrated and viscous. The various blood proteins do not filter through the walls of the capillaries. Since these proteins have a high colloidal osmotic action, much of the fluid is reabsorbed by the blood as it passes through the capillaries surrounding the convoluted tubule. With the water that reenters the blood go other materials of relatively low molecular weight. Thus all the glucose that left the blood in the capsule is normally returned to it so that there is none present in the urine. The same is true for a small portion of the salts and other wastes that have passed out of the blood, but most of these substances are retained in the tubule and excreted in the urine.

Under normal conditions, very few proteins leave the blood in the kidneys. As numerous experiments have shown, this is due to the large size of the protein molecules. Their retention by the blood is of primary importance in maintaining the protein balance of the body. It has been found that if gelatin (molecular weight: 35,000) or egg albumin (molecular weight: 34,500) are injected into the blood, they pass out of the blood into the urine quite easily. The same is true of other proteins with molecular weights lower than that of hemoglobin (molecular weight: 68,000). Hemoglobin, however, may appear in the urine when it is present in plasma in excessively large quantities. Such a condition arises when there is an abnormally great destruction of red blood corpuscles, as in a disease such as *malignant malaria.*

Excess albumin in the urine produces a condition known as **albuminuria,** found in four to five percent of healthy individuals. The amount present is very small (about 0.2 percent). If a person with no previous history of albuminuria takes a cold bath or performs severe muscular exercise, the excretion of albumin in the urine increases. In **nephritis,** a condition of inflammation and degeneration of the kidneys, the glomeruli fail to prevent the loss of albumin from the blood. Therefore albumin appears in the urine in large amounts. Other conditions such as scarlet fever, pneumonia, decaying teeth, streptococcic sore throat, and sinus infections may result in temporary albuminuria. The loss of blood protein lowers the osmotic action of the blood with the result that fluids tend to collect in the tissues and cause edema. The presence of glucose in the urine, called **glycosuria,** indicates either a loss of ability of the tubules to reabsorb sugar or an excess of sugar in the blood.

When glycosuria is *not* accompanied by an increase of sugar in the blood, it is called **renal glycosuria.** If there is an increase in both blood sugar and sugar in the urine, the condition is called **diabetes.** This disease will be discussed in a later chapter.

The concentration of various materials in the urine as compared with their presence in the plasma of the blood is shown in the following table adapted from the work of Dr. A. R. Cushny:

PERCENTAGE COMPOSITION OF PLASMA AND URINE		
	PLASMA %	URINE %
Water	90–93	95
Proteins, other colloids and fats	8.0	
Glucose	0.1	
Urea	0.03	2.0
Sodium	0.32	0.35
Chlorine	0.37	0.6
Uric acid	0.004	0.05
Creatinin	0.001	0.075
Phosphates	0.009	0.15
Ammonia	0.001	0.04

Formation of the organic excretory products. The principal organic excretions are *urea, uric acid,* and *creatinin.*

In addition to these, other organic substances may be present in the urine at various times and in differing amounts depending on the composition of the food ingested. *Ammonia,* in the form of ammonium salts, is also present. Though not one of the organic compounds, it is an intermediate product in their formation.

Urea is a product of the decomposition of amino acids formed by the digestion of proteins. The disposition of the products of amino acid decomposition is shown in Fig. 30-3. The liver is the only place in the body where urea is formed. This can be demonstrated by removing the liver from an anesthetized experimental animal. When this is done, the volume of urea excreted by the kidneys drops to zero. The processes involved in the formation of urea from amino acids are quite complicated and are generally beyond the scope of this book. In brief, the formation of urea includes the breaking down of the amino acid molecule into simpler substances

including ammonia (NH_3). The ammonia is then combined with an amino acid (citrullin) that is present in the liver, resulting in the formation of urea ($CO(NH_2)_2$). This enters the systemic circulation through the hepatic vein.

Creatinin ($C_4H_7N_3O$) is evidently formed in the muscles from creatine (N_3H_8COOH), a normal constituent of muscle tissue. It may also be ingested. By the use of radioactive isotopes of nitrogen (N^{15}) and hydrogen (H^2), the formation of creatinin from creatine has been traced. The amount excreted by any one individual remains quite constant but is dependent on his size. Its production is therefore reported in terms of body surface area in the same manner as the BMR, and for the same reason.

Uric acid ($C_5H_4O_3N_4$) is normally present in the blood in small quantities. The source of this acid is the destruction of nucleoproteins. It varies in quantity in the urine depending on the amount of protein material ingested. Following a heavy protein meal, the kidneys will

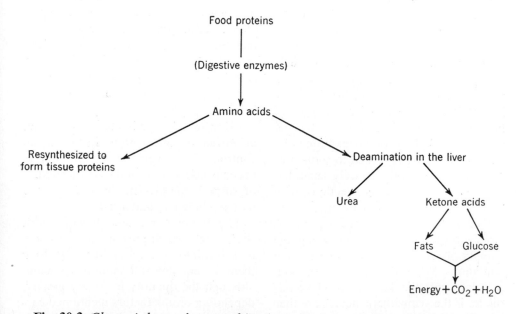

Fig. 30-3. *Chart of the products resulting from the decomposition of amino acids.*

excrete an additional amount of uric acid. Leukemia, a disease characterized by the production of leukocytes, results in an increase of uric acid excretion. Gout also is believed to be the result of an upset in the uric acid balance in the body, but some question regarding this has been raised recently.

Ammonia (NH_3) is a highly toxic material that the cells cannot tolerate, but its compounds help in the maintenance of the acid-base equilibrium of the blood. As we have learned, acids which might cause a shift in the pH of the blood are neutralized by basic ions. In the kidney, certain of these acids are combined with ammonia and excreted as ammonium salts. The basic ions thus freed help to maintain the body's alkaline reserve. When the diet is rich in acid-forming food, such as proteins, the excretion of ammonium salts increases. Excretion decreases when alkali-producing foods are eaten in quantity. Formation of ammonia in the kidneys is a result of the deamination of amino acids.

Factors influencing kidney function. In common with most organs in the body, the kidneys receive branches from the sympathetic nervous system which help to regulate their activities. Stimulation of these nerves may control the amount of urine excreted, but has very little effect on the cellular activities of the organs. This is illustrated by the fact that a kidney of an experimental animal can be transplanted to some other region of the body, entirely separated from its normal nerve connections, with little effect on its cellular functions.

The blood supply to the kidneys is largely responsible for determining the amount of urine produced under normal conditions. When the nerves to the kidneys are cut, the kidney blood vessels dilate. If the sympathetic nerves are then stimulated, raising the blood pressure, more blood passes through the kidneys, resulting in greater production of urine by the kidney.

The amount and concentration of the urine is affected by ingestion of water or salt. As we all know, if we drink large quantities of fluid, the amount of urine increases. This urine is quite dilute due to the presence of an increased amount of water. On the other hand, if very salty substances are eaten, the quantity of urine is reduced, but the concentration of dissolved materials increases. The events which bring about these reactions are rather complicated because they involve both the nervous and endocrine systems. Intake of fluid or salt changes the osmotic pressure of the blood. This in turn apparently affects certain receptors (osmoreceptors) which lead to the hypothalamus of the brain. The hypothalamus then sends impulses to the posterior lobe of the pituitary gland, which produces an **antidiuretic hormone.** (Diuretic refers to urine production.) If too much fluid has been taken into the body, the production of this hormone is reduced and the liquid is excreted in order to maintain the correct osmotic state of the blood. On the other hand, if an excess of salt has been eaten, the osmoreceptors are stimulated and the amount of antidiuretic hormone is increased.

Urination. The elimination of urine, **urination** or **micturition,** is under the control of the nervous system and is brought about by stimulation of bundles of smooth muscles in the walls of the ureters, bladder, and urethra.

The ureters enter the bladder at a sharp angle which prevents the backflow of urine into them. Liquid flows along them in an almost continuous stream, although the quantity may vary greatly, depending on the factors mentioned earlier. The normal capacity of the bladder is about one pint. Its opening into the urethra is controlled by two groups of sphincter muscles which are under voluntary control.

The process of voiding the urine is the result of a combination of involuntary and voluntary processes. In the first place, the presence of urine in the pelvis of the kidney stimulates peristaltic waves in the walls of the ureters, which pass urine to the bladder. The bladder becomes distended as the quantity of fluid in it increases, and receptors in its walls are stimulated. A feeling of fullness results when the bladder contains between 250 and 300 milliliters of liquid. In the infant, the flow of urine is purely reflex in nature and will continue to be until proper training (conditioned reflex) has been established. In an adult, the nerve impulses from the bladder pass to a center in the spinal cord just as they do in an infant. However, in the adult they continue upward to the cerebral cortex and result in the control of the expulsion of urine through the urethra.

SPEAKING OF Physiology

Briefly identify each of the following:

albuminuria	excretion	micturition
Bowman's capsule	glomerulus	nephritis
convoluted	glycosuria	nephron
cortex (of the kidney)	loop of Henle	pelvis (of the kidney)
diuretic	medulla (of the kidney)	ureter

Test YOUR KNOWLEDGE

1. Why are the kidneys considered the primary regulators of our internal environment?
2. Briefly describe the general location and structures that make up the urinary system.
3. Why must there be an extensive blood supply to the kidneys?
4. Why is the nephron considered the unit of structure and function of the urinary system?
5. Is the fluid which enters the Bowman's capsule classified as urine? Why?
6. How are the blood proteins prevented from entering the Bowman's capsule from the glomerulus?
7. If urinalysis shows a positive reaction for the presence of sugar, what might this indicate, especially if blood sugar is also high?
8. What differences exist between the contents of the fluid filtered through the Bowman's capsules and the urine?
9. Where is urea produced? How is it eliminated?
10. What is the function of ammonium salts in maintaining the acid-base equilibrium?
11. Under what conditions might the urinary output be increased? Under what conditions might it decrease?
12. Describe the nerve control of micturition.
13. Explain the work of the kidney in filtration as well as excretion.
14. Trace the path of a molecule of urea from the liver to the urinary bladder.

See FOR YOURSELF

1. Get a beef or lamb kidney from a meat market. Dissect the kidney into front and back halves. Note the internal structure of this organ. Identify the following: (1) capsule, (2) cortex, (3) medulla, (4) pyramids, (5) pelvis, (6) hilum, (7) ureter, (8) renal vein, (9) renal artery. Make a detailed drawing of the structures seen and label the parts.

2. Using available reference materials, find the major differences between *chronic* and *acute nephritis*. What are the symptoms of acute nephritis and how is this disease treated? Is there any predominance of this disease with respect to age or sex?

3. From a physician or hospital laboratory technician, learn what you can about urinalysis and the use of such analysis for diagnostic purposes. Ask your physician or druggist about simple methods you might use to identify some of the common substances in urine.

4. Consult zoology texts to find information about the development of kidneys in such animals as earthworms, fish, frogs, and mammals. Prepare a series of charts comparing kidney structure in lower and higher forms of animal life.

UNIT **8**

The Endocrine System

CHAPTER 31

The Endocrine Glands: the Pituitary and the Thyroid

CHAPTER 32

The Parathyroids, the Adrenals, the Pancreas, the Pineal Body, and the Thymus

The Endocrine Glands:
The Pituitary and the Thyroid

ENDOCRINE GLANDS

There are certain types of epithelial cells in the body which are grouped together to form glands that do not have any apparent outlet for their secretions through ducts. These are **endocrine glands,** whose secretions are emptied directly into the blood stream. Occasionally, but not always correctly, these are called **ductless glands;** the error lies in the fact that some, like the pancreas or the reproductive organs, do have ducts, but also produce substances that pass directly into the blood.

Because the products of the endocrine glands enter the blood stream, the effect of these secretions is widespread. They bring about changes in the reactions of body parts which are frequently at a great distance from the point of secretion. This is an important distinction between the secretions of the endocrine glands and those of the *exocrine,* or ducted, glands; the latter usually have a very local action. The products of the endocrine glands are known as **hormones,** from the Greek verb, *hormodzein,* meaning "to arouse." This original meaning of the word describes the function of many of these secretions.

The hormones play a tremendous role in our general activities, growth, mental development, metabolism, and relationships with other people. The entire field of endocrinology (the study of the secretions of endocrine glands) is very complex. These glands form an "interlocking directorate" over the activities of the body. Although each hormone has a specific function, this can be modified by the effects of hormones from some of the other glands. This interdependence of one gland on another results in the *endocrine balance* of the individual. When all glands are functioning properly, a person is considered to be normal. An excellent example of this interlocking directorate of the glands is shown by the action of the pituitary gland. As you will see, the pituitary influences other endocrine glands so that their activities are either accelerated or depressed. The form -tropic (Greek *tropos,* a turning) is used to make up words which refer to this action, as in thyrotropic hormone, one affecting the thyroid. It is only by careful and exhaustive tests that the actual effects of the secretions of these endocrine glands can be determined. Endocrinology is currently a most rewarding field for research.

Figure 31-1 shows the location of some of the more important endocrine glands. Some of these are known to have definite hormonal secretions, while the secretions of others are not well understood.

The products of these glands exercise a *chemical control* of bodily function as opposed to *neural* (nervous) *control,* described in Chapters 8 and 9. Neural control of a function is usually quite local in its effects and immediate in its

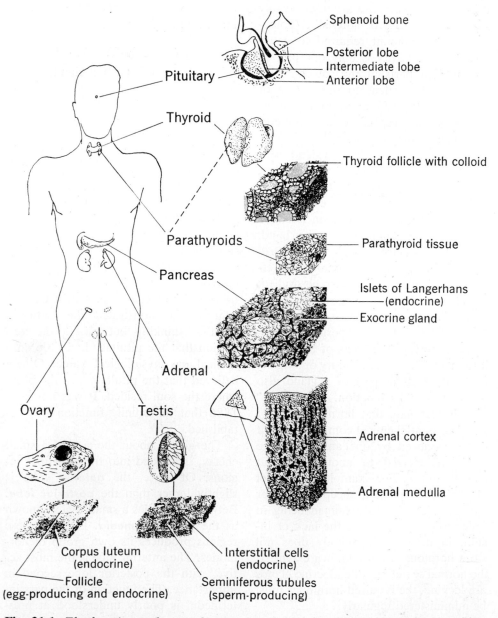

Sphenoid bone

Pituitary

Posterior lobe
Intermediate lobe
Anterior lobe

Thyroid

Thyroid follicle with colloid

Parathyroids

Parathyroid tissue

Pancreas

Islets of Langerhans (endocrine)

Exocrine gland

Adrenal

Ovary   Testis

Adrenal cortex

Adrenal medulla

Corpus luteum (endocrine)

Interstitial cells (endocrine)

Follicle (egg-producing and endocrine)

Seminiferous tubules (sperm-producing)

Fig. 31-1. *The location and general structure of the principal glands of the endocrine system.* (*From Johnson, Laubengayer, De Lanney,* General Biology, *Holt, 1956*)

action. Hormonal control, on the other hand, is slower in showing its effects, more widespread in its action, and slower in disappearing, because hormones remain in the blood for a relatively long period.

The amounts of hormones needed to bring about a response are unbelievably small. In the case of adrenalin (epinephrin), the amount required to cause appreciable activity is only one part in 400 million parts of the solvent. This would be equivalent to one ounce of adrenalin dissolved in 12,500 tons of solvent. In this respect, hormones resemble some of the enzymes.

The functions of endocrine glands may be determined in several ways. When a gland shrinks in size its secretions are reduced, with observable effects on body functions. The condition is called **atrophy** of the gland. On the other hand, if a gland enlarges (called **hypertrophy**), it increases its secretions. The effects of this increase can also be studied. Another way to learn about the functions of endocrine glands is to feed portions of the glands to experimental animals, or to inject extracts of the glands into them. The effect of injury or surgical removal of all or part of a gland also gives clues to its function.

It is fortunate that hormones are of such constant chemical composition that those produced by one animal can be safely transferred to another without causing injury. For example, an extract of the pancreas of a sheep or a steer can be injected into a human being in order to compensate for the lack of insulin in diabetes. The body does not store hormones to any known extent. If the normal secretions of endocrine glands are lacking, the required hormones must be administered regularly.

Two prefixes are commonly used to refer to the relative amount of hormones produced by an endocrine gland. **Hypo-** refers to a subnormal secretion, the term being derived from the similar Greek word meaning "under." The prefix **hyper-** means "over," and is used to describe overproduction of a secretion. For example, undersecretion of the thyroid gland is *hypothyroidism;* oversecretion is *hyperthyroidism.*

THE PITUITARY GLAND

The **pituitary** is a small gland, weighing about 0.5 grams, attached to the lower surface of the brain just behind the optic chiasma (see Fig. 11-1) and connected with the brain by a short stalk, the **infundibulum.** The pituitary body is partly enclosed by bone, which makes any surgical operation on this structure a most difficult procedure. The pituitary was so named by the great anatomist, Vesalius (1514–1564) because he thought that it produced a lubricating substance (Italian, *pituita,* mucus) that found its way into the nose. In 1660, the German anatomist Conrad Schneider demonstrated the error in Vesalius' thinking, but came to the conclusion that the pituitary had little anatomical or physiological value. Others believed that the pituitary was the place where the soul resided. It was not until 1886 that its definite function was established.

The gland, about the size of a small cherry, is divided into three distinct regions. Of these, the **anterior lobe** is slightly larger than the **posterior lobe.** Between them lies a small region known as the **pars intermedia.** Each of these regions produces its own group of hormones. The anterior lobe is the most active, with the posterior lobe second in importance. The function of the pars intermedia is poorly understood at present.

In Fig. 31-2 are shown some of the

far-reaching effects of this gland. Some of these will be discussed in this chapter, but others will be left for later chapters where pituitary influence on other glands can be more fully appreciated. In view of its many activities, the pituitary has sometimes been called the "master" gland of the body.

Functions of the anterior lobe. The anterior lobe secretes several different hormones which have two general functions. One group of hormones affects various parts of the body by controlling their metabolic activities. The other group exerts control over other endocrine glands, thus regulating various body processes by remote control.

Abnormal variations in production of some hormones by the anterior lobe have startling effects. One of the most striking evidences of a disturbance in this portion of the gland is the effect of the **somatotropic hormone** (growth hormone) on physical development. If this hormone is produced in greater than normal quantities, the bones grow to unusual length. The hormone acts to prevent the epiphyseal junction from forming in a normal manner, thus making continued growth possible.

A child who is the victim of this condition may have a normal birth weight but quickly shows signs of excessive growth. This accelerated growth results in the condition known as **gigantism** (Fig. 31-3). Giants have been reported

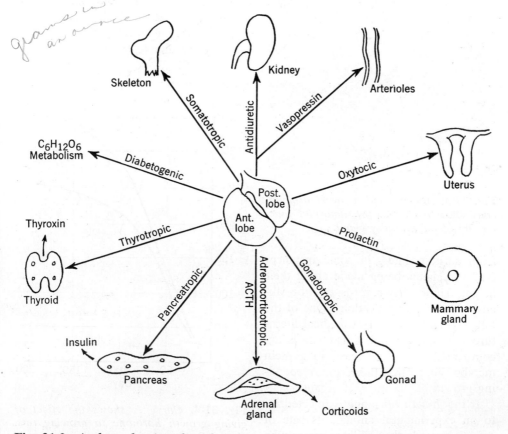

Fig. 31-2. *A chart showing the relationship of the pituitary hormones to other body organs and functions.*

Fig. 31-3. *A giant and a dwarf dramatically show the effects of abnormal functioning of the pituitary gland.*

from earliest times, in some instances fantastic claims being made about their height. These early records must be taken with certain reservations. One of the tallest giants reported in medical literature was 9.2 feet tall. Gigantism is accompanied by an increase in protein metabolism, so that there is corresponding growth of the internal organs.

If the growth hormone is injected into an experimental animal, its rate of growth exceeds that of litter mates who were not given the treatment (see Fig.

31-4). Thus far, however, little success has been obtained when this hormone is administered to humans in an attempt to stimulate growth.

If increased secretion of the somatotropic hormone occurs after adult size has been reached, the long bones are no longer affected, but those of the face, hands, and feet may show marked changes. The lower jaw enlarges and spaces appear between the teeth. Other bones of the face enlarge and the person's expression is greatly changed. The bones of the hands also become larger, especially in the region of the knuckles. This condition is called **acromegaly** (Gk, *akron,* extremity + *megas,* large).

Deficiency of the somatotropic hormone gives rise to **dwarfism.** In this condition the skeletal structures reach their maximum development early in life and are unable to grow any larger.

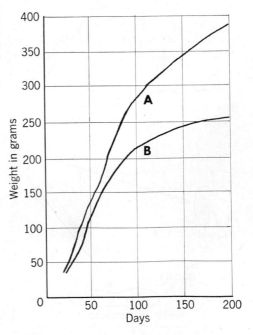

Fig. 31-4. *Curve A shows the effect of giving growth hormone to growing rats. Curve B shows the normal increase in weight of untreated rats.*

The result of this stoppage of growth is a miniature person (sometimes called a *midget*) whose bodily proportions and mental ability are generally normal.

In human beings there does not appear to be any inheritance factor that controls either gigantism or dwarfism. Among some breeds of animals, on the other hand, there is evidently a hereditary agent involved. We are all familiar with small breeds of horses called ponies, and various miniature types of dogs and chickens. In these animals there appears to be an inherited deficiency of the anterior lobe of the gland which is perpetuated by selective breeding.

A second hormone formed by the anterior lobe of the pituitary is **prolactin,** or the **lactogenic** hormone. Some of the earliest experimental work on this hormone was done in studying the secretions of the esophageal glands of pigeons, the only vertebrates known to have these specialized glands. Normally, the gland is active only during the breeding season, since its secretion is used to feed the young squabs. It was found that if prolactin was injected into female pigeons during the nonbreeding season, they showed all of the characteristics typical of the nesting period. Also, the secretion of the esophageal glands appeared and continued as long as injections were continued. In mammals, the injection of the lactogenic hormone stimulates the production of milk and arouses other reactions associated with the care of the young. If a female rat is given injections of prolactin, she will attempt to mother not only young rats belonging to another parent, but also mice, and even young birds. She will build an elaborate nest for them and hover around showing all the signs of a true mother.

A third hormone produced by the anterior lobe affects the thyroid gland. The absence of this **thyrotropic** substance, following the removal of the pituitary gland from an anesthetized experimental animal, results in the degeneration of the thyroid gland. Also, if a purified form of this secretion is injected into a normal animal, the thyroid gland enlarges and the animal shows all the effects of an increased amount of thyroid secretion.

The anterior lobe also produces a secretion known as the **adrenocorticotropic hormone (ACTH)**. This influences the amount of various *corticoids* produced by the cortex of the adrenal glands. These substances in turn affect the production of insulin (**diabetogenic** and **pancreatropic hormones**).

Functions of the posterior lobe. The posterior lobe of the pituitary secretes several hormones. One of these, the **antidiuretic hormone (ADH)** appears to control the reabsorption of water from the kidney tubules. When the blood stream fails to reabsorb water from the nephron, urine is formed in copious quantities but in a very dilute condition. This disease is known as **diabetes insipidus** and may result in the excretion of as much as 10 gallons of urine per day. ADH failure is apparently not the only cause of this condition. Neural control of the process of reabsorption may also be involved, as well as the action of some secretions of the adrenal cortex.

Closely related to ADH is the hormone **vasopressin**. The exact relation of this hormone to normal blood pressure has not been established, but it does stimulate the contraction of smooth-muscle sphincters in the arterioles. Some investigators also report that it stimulates the contraction of muscle fibers in the walls of the intestine.

A third hormone produced by the posterior lobe affects the uterus (womb).

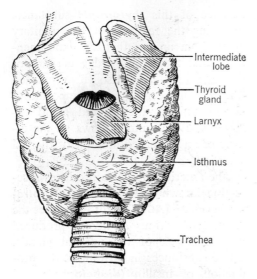

Intermediate
lobe

Thyroid
gland

Larnyx

Isthmus

Trachea

Fig. 31-5. *The thyroid gland is located in the neck region, partly surrounding the larynx.*

This is called the **oxytocic hormone,** and is normally produced in increased quantities at the time of childbirth. Its presence in the blood stream causes a series of contractions of the smooth-muscle bundles of the uterus which bring about the birth of the child. It also depresses the formation of urine and increases blood pressure and respiratory rates. Highly purified salts of this hormone have been found to produce an effect on uterine muscle when they were in a concentration of 1:15 billion parts.

The pars intermedia. The remaining part of the pituitary gland, the pars intermedia or intermediate lobe, is reported to produce a hormone called **intermedin.** Little is known about the effects of this material on human beings. In fish and amphibia, injection of this material increases the production of *melanophores,* the parts of the scales or skin responsible for dark colors. In some work on higher animals, intermedin has been reported to reduce the loss of water from the blood through the kidneys

without changing the salt content of the urine.

THE THYROID GLAND

The thyroid gland is a dark red structure in the neck, lying along the sides of the larynx (Fig 31-5). Its general shape is that of the letter H with the upright members about two inches long and approximately 1.2 inches broad. These are joined by a bridge of tissue, the **isthmus,** which lies in front of the second and third cartilage rings of the trachea and is about one-half inch wide. From the isthmus, or from the region on either side near it, an **intermediate lobe** of varying length projects upward toward the floor of the mouth. This third part may extend to the hyoid bone, or it may be attached to the bone by means of a continuing cord of connective tissue. The thyroid gland produces only one secretion **thyroxin.**

Microscopically, the gland is composed of groups of cells that surround open spaces, the **follicles.** These cells secrete a viscous material of uniform structure known as *colloid,* which is deposited in the follicles. Each follicle is richly supplied with blood vessels through which cells of the gland extract materials they need. The colloid is composed of a protein-iodine combination known as **thyroglobulin.** This is changed into a more fluid form by an enzyme formed in the surrounding cells. In this less viscous condition it is absorbed by the blood. The formation of the enzyme appears to be controlled by the thyrotropic hormone produced by the anterior lobe of the pituitary gland.

The microscopic structure of the thyroid shows such wide variations in detail that it is impossible to describe or picture a normal section through the gland. The supply of iodine in the diet or drinking water determines the microscopic appearance of the gland as well as its activities. Since a large percentage of the world's population lives in regions where there is a deficiency of iodine, the structure of a gland that might be considered normal in one region would be abnormal in another. These variations in structure may not be sufficiently great to cause external symptoms of thyroid disorder. A section through the thyroid gland of a rabbit is shown in Fig. 31-6.

The thyroglobulin is formed by a combination of the amino acid, *tyrosine,* with iodine. Although iodine in its pure form is a violent cellular poison, it is present in all body fluids in minute amounts in the form of iodides. Approximately one half of the body's total supply of iodine (about 50 milligrams) is concentrated in the thyroid in the form of thyroglobulin. Before it enters the blood, thyroglobulin undergoes several chemical changes to convert it into the hormone thyroxin (empirical formula, $C_{15}H_{11}I_4NO_4$). Thyroxin is not stored in the thyroid gland.

The formation of thyroxin and the functions of the thyroid gland have been clarified in recent years by the use of a radioactive isotope of iodine, I^{131}. The functions of the gland are of two types: those concerned with control of cellular metabolism, and those influencing growth and development. In a sense, the second type is the result of the first. In the majority of cases in which the metabolic activities are adversely influenced by the thyroid, alterations in growth, development, or changes in tissue structure occur.

Hypothyroidism, the deficency of thyroid secretion, is characterized by a reduction in the metabolic rate: the fires of life burn low. If the thyroid gland is removed from an eight-day-old lamb, its gain in weight over a seven-month period will be only about one-third that of

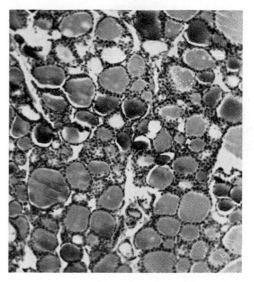

Fig. 31-6. *Photomicrograph of a section of a rabbit's thyroid gland.*

a normal lamb. In humans a somewhat similar condition develops in the absence of a normal amount of thyroxin. If a child is born with a defective thyroid gland or develops one early in life, a type of dwarfism appears. Whereas a pituitary dwarf is usually of normal intelligence and bodily proportions, a thyroid dwarf is of low mental ability and subnormal physical development. Such an individual is called a **cretin,** or is said to show signs of **infantile myxedema.**

Hypothyroidism in childhood prevents the normal growth of the bones. Cretins are frequently bow-legged, and have dry scaly skin. The abdomen usually protrudes, due to weakness of the muscles in its walls, and the tongue projects slightly between the characteristically open lips. The face is puffy due to the formation of an excess amount of connective tissue. Mental ability is retarded, so that the victim is hardly able to take care of himself. All of these signs point to a marked retardation of the metabolic rate. If a child in this condition is treated regularly with thyroid extract,

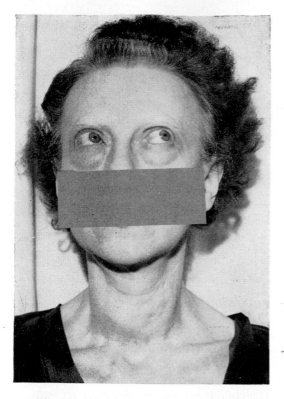

Fig. 31-7. *An example of exophthalmos with a slight enlargement of the thyroid gland. (George J. Hamwi photo, Ohio State University Health Center)*

his improvement is usually spectacular. He will become normal in appearance and reactions, and will remain normal as long as treatment is continued.

Hypothyroidism in an adult results in the reduction of the BMR by between 30 and 45 percent. This causes a drop in body temperature so that the person feels cold, especially in his hands and feet, even when in comfortably warm surroundings. There is also a decrease in heart rate and blood pressure, and the muscle tone is lowered so that slight exertion quickly brings on fatigue. This combination of symptoms indicates the condition known as **adult myxedema.** There may also be changes in skin texture, puffiness of the face, and a decrease in mental capacity. As in the case

of the cretin, administering thyroxin will relieve the symptoms.

The condition of **hyperthyroidism** results from overproduction of thyroxin. This condition may be caused by gland enlargement or by oversecretion. Just as the undersecretion of thyroxin results in a lowering of the rate of metabolism, so an excess will lead to an increase in metabolism. We may therefore expect that a person suffering from hyperthyroidism will show symptoms that are almost the opposite from those displayed by a victim of hypothyroidism.

In hyperthyroidism the BMR may exceed the normal by 50 to 75 percent. Although there is a tendency to consume large amounts of food, there is usually a loss in body fat and weight. There is also an increase in heart rate and blood pressure. Since the BMR has risen, the person feels uncomfortably warm and sweats profusely. More glucose is freed by the liver, so that blood sugar content is slightly higher than normal. This produces a mild condition of glycosuria.

People who suffer from hyperthyroidism show nervous excitability and have a tendency to react to an emergency or unpleasant situation in an exaggerated manner. In some cases, the eyeballs become prominent and protrude from their sockets. This is accompanied by dilated pupils and widely opened eyelids (Fig. 31-7). The cause of this condition (*exophthalmos*) is not clearly understood, as it is apparently not the direct result of the hyperthyroid state. Thus, removal of the thyroid does not always cause the eyeballs to return to their normal condition. Treatment of hyperthyroidism may involve removal of all or part of the gland, or the use of certain drugs which reduce the secretion of thyroxin.

Enlargement of the thyroid results in **goiter,** a swelling in the neck region. It may be associated with either hypothyroidism or hyperthyroidism (*toxic goiter*). If it is not accompanied by symptoms of either of these, it is known as a *simple goiter*. Experiments on animals show that if they are deprived of iodine, goiter develops soon after. However, if iodine is added to their drinking water, the goiter does not form. The amounts required to maintain the thyroid in proper condition are almost unbelievably small. Slightly more than 1 milligram of iodine in 1 million parts of water is all that is needed. In areas where iodine is lacking, thyroid defects are common.

Cretinism, myxedema, and goiter are especially prevalent in the Himalayas, the Alps, and the Andes. In the United States, such conditions are most common in the Pacific northwest, the Great Lakes basin, and the St. Lawrence region. Most of the iodine has been leached out of the soil and rocks in these regions, probably by the action of the great continental glaciers that covered them in recent geologic times. Areas along the oceans are seldom affected in the same way because of the availability of saltwater fish and the presence of iodine in the soil. Goiter has become less common, due to modern methods of preventing this disease. The easiest method is the use of table salt to which about 0.02 percent of potassium iodide has been added. A good example of the effect of this iodized salt is seen in an experiment started in Denver in 1924. Here the number of goiter cases among the total school population fell from 36 to 2.1 percent following the introduction of iodized salt for cooking and table use. However, the use of excessive amounts of iodized salt in regions where it is not necessary may have a serious effect on the activities of the thyroid.

In the absence of sufficient iodine, the thyroid cannot supply the body's needs. Formation of a simple goiter is the result of an attempt by the thyroid gland to increase its production. The lowered concentration of thyroxin in the blood evidently stimulates the anterior lobe of the pituitary gland and an excess of thyrotropic hormone is formed. This in turn brings about the enlargement of the follicles of the gland, and even the development of new follicles. Administration of proper amounts of iodine results in the shrinking of the gland to normal size.

The thyroid gland plays another role among the Amphibia. If bits of thyroid gland are fed to some of the tailless amphibians (frogs and toads) when they are in the tadpole stage, they rapidly pass through their metamorphosis and become adults (Fig. 31-8). Not all frogs and toads respond in this manner, but if the bullfrog (*Rana catesbiana*) tadpole is fed thyroid, it metamorphoses within about two weeks. Normally, this frog requires two to three years to accomplish these changes. It has also been found that if the thyroid is removed from this species in the tadpole stage, feeding the tadpole iodine or even adding a small amount of iodine to the water in which it swims is all that is required to bring about metamorphosis. The use of frog tadpoles is one of the most delicate tests for thyroid secretions.

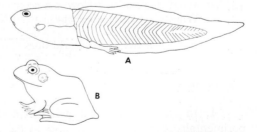

Fig. 31-8. *The effect of feeding thyroid to a bullfrog tadpole (A). The change to the adult form (B) occurs rapidly without appreciable growth in size. Both figures are drawn to the same scale.*

SPEAKING OF Physiology

Briefly identify each of the following:

ACTH	exophthalmos	melanophores
ADH	hormone	metamorphosis
atrophy	hyperthyroidism	myxedema
colloid (of the thyroid gland)	hypertrophy	pars intermedia
diabetes insipidus	hypothyroidism	prolactin
endocrinology	goiter	somatotropic horomne
exocrine	infundibulum	thyroglobulin

Test YOUR KNOWLEDGE

1. What are the differences between endocrine and exocrine glands?
2. Why is it essential that only physicians prescribe hormones for patients?
3. What does the expression "interlocking directorate" mean, with reference to the activities of the endocrine glands?
4. How does chemical control differ from neural control of bodily functions?
5. In general, what treatment may be used to offset the hypofunction of an endocrine gland? How do doctors treat some types of endocrine hyperfunction?
6. Where is the pituitary gland? Why is it almost impossible to operate on this gland?
7. Why is the pituitary gland sometimes called the master gland of the body?
8. What is the cause of gigantism? What effect does this condition have on the metabolic rate of the body? Can anything be done for victims of gigantism?
9. What are the symptoms of acromegaly? Why does this condition not occur in young children?
10. What does the form -*tropic* mean? How is it used in the terms thyrotropic and adrenocorticotropic (ACTH) hormones?
11. Which pituitary hormone depresses normal urinary output? In what portion of the pituitary gland is this hormone produced? What other hormones are produced by this lobe?
12. Describe the location and the external and internal structure of the thyroid gland.
13. What influence does thyroxin have on the activities of the body? What part does iodine play in the production of thyroxin?
14. What is cretinism? How is a cretin different from a pituitary dwarf?
15. What disease is caused by a thyroxin deficiency in an adult? How can this be corrected?
16. In what areas of the world does simple goiter occur most commonly? Why?

See FOR YOURSELF

1. In order to determine whether a gland has an endocrine function, what experimental procedures would have to be followed? Write a hypothetical procedure for obtaining this information. What would be the importance of a control animal in your experiment? Would you use humans for this type of experimentation? Why?

2. How are hormones procured commercially? Choose one of the hormones listed in your text and write a report on its extraction and use.

3. Write a report on famous examples of gigantism and dwarfism.

4. Get an outline map of the world. By using library references, show on the map the incidence of simple goiter. If you can, show these areas as of 1900 and again in 1950 (or the present). Has the prevalence of simple goiter increased or decreased? What conclusions can you draw as to the cause of this distribution?

5. Write a report on the use of radioactive iodine in diagnosis and treatment of thyroid disorders. Are there any other radioactive elements used for clinical diagnosis of disease? Discuss.

6. Ask your doctor or a hospital laboratory technician to explain how a basal metabolism test is used to diagnose abnormalities of the thyroid function.

nephron)
renal = kidney

The Parathyroids, the Adrenals, the Pancreas, the Pineal Body, and the Thymus

THE PARATHYROID GLANDS

The parathyroid glands are usually embedded in the posterior part of the thyroid gland, but occasionally they may be located a short distance from it on either side. They are four small bodies, each about 8 millimeters in length.

The parathyroids were not well understood until recent times. Following the introduction of aseptic methods of surgery by Lister, removal of the thyroid gland became easier and safer. It was found, however, that when the entire gland was removed, the patient frequently developed tetanic contractions of the muscles (convulsions), often followed by death. There was considerable confusion regarding these unfortunate incidents until 1881, when it was demonstrated that the parathyroids were usually removed with the thyroid gland. When there were no adverse symptoms, the parathyroids were evidently not embedded in the thyroid and hence escaped removal.

The parathyroids control the amount of calcium and phosphorus in the blood.

If they are completely removed from the body of an animal, the calcium content drops by about 3 percent, while the phosphorus rises as much as 10 percent. The critical effect of the loss of the parathyroids seems to be the failure of the kidneys to reabsorb calcium into the blood after it is removed by the Bowman's capsules. When the concentration of blood calcium falls, the nervous system becomes highly irritable and muscular twitching appears. A profound drop in blood calcium leads to death. The maintenance of the normal content of the blood is the primary function of the parathyroid hormone, **parathormone**. Injections of extracts of the parathyroids and increasing the calcium content of the diet will offset the lack of the hormone.

Increase in the amount of parathormone may occur in a normal individual at certain periods in life. Lactation (milk production) or pregnancy may cause a heavy drain on the mother's calcium. Milk is rich in calcium, and the developing fetus requires calcium for the formation of its bones. Lowered blood calcium evidently stimulates production of para-thormone. Therefore, the mother's diet should be adequate in both calcium and the Vitamin D needed for absorption of calcium. Otherwise, excessive *resorption of bone* may occur. This involves the removal of calcium from the mother's bones to maintain her blood calcium level. The mother's bones may then become soft and weak. The critical time is during the last two months of pregnancy.

THE ADRENAL GLANDS

The **adrenal glands** resemble small caps, resting above each kidney, as shown in the Trans-Vision insert following page 312, and in Fig. 30-1. They are occasionally termed suprarenal glands (Lat., *supra,* above), because of their position over the kidneys in man, but this term is applicable only in those cases where the organism has assumed an upright position. In other animals, the adrenal glands bear various relations to the kidneys. In some of the lower fish, the tissue corresponding to the adrenals is embedded in the kidneys. In man, the right adrenal has the general outline of a cocked hat, while the left is somewhat more curved.

The human adrenal glands appear early in embryonic life and at one stage of development are the most conspicuous organs in the abdominal cavity. At birth they are approximately one-third the size of the kidneys, but in early infancy they become smaller. Each gland is composed of two distinct regions: an outer area that makes up the **cortex** of the gland; and an inner part, the **medulla** (Fig. 32-1). These two parts have very different and distinct secretions, and their origins in the embryo are equally different. The cortex is derived from the same group of tissues which produce the reproductive organs, while the medulla develops from the embry-

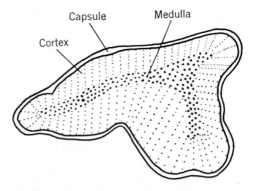

Fig. 32-1. *A section through the adrenal gland showing the relationship of its parts.*

onic tissues which also produce the sympathetic nervous system. The entire gland is surrounded by a firm layer of connective tissue, the **capsule.**

The adrenal cortex. This part of the adrenal gland is absolutely essential to life. Its removal, or extensive injury, in experimental animals invariably leads to death unless its secretions are replaced artificially. In man, the diseased cortex produces symptoms known as **Addison's disease,** which will be discussed later.

The hormones formed by the cortex belong to a group of chemical compounds known as **steroids,** of which cholesterol is an example. As a result of research carried on during the past twenty-five years, 28 different steroids have been isolated from the cortex and as many more from urine. It is assumed that those in urine also originate in the adrenal glands. These steroids are frequently called **corticosteroids,** or **corticoids.** Of these, the best known is **cortisone.** The structural formula for cortisone is given in Fig. 32-2.

The removal of the adrenal glands from an experimental animal, or their hypofunction in man, results in a drop in the BMR. This is a symptom of Addison's disease. It is brought about by a

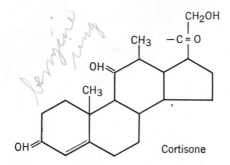

CH₂OH

CH₃   −C=O

OH

CH₃

OH   Cortisone

benzine ring

Fig. 32-2. *Structural formula of the corti-sone molecule. This is typical of the structure of the other steroids.*

decrease in the amount of glycogen stored in the liver and an accompanying loss of available glucose in the blood. Body temperature falls, and the weakened heart is unable to maintain normal blood pressure. Appetite declines and satisfactory absorption of food is impaired, with the result that the body weight drops alarmingly.

One of the most important functions of the adrenal cortex is to maintain a proper balance between the water content of the blood and its salt content. In man, lack of this balance is characteristic of Addison's disease. If the cortical hormones are lacking, the kidneys excrete an increased amount of sodium salts. Since these affect the osmotic pressure of the blood, there is gradual dehydration of the tissues because fluid passes from them into the blood. If an animal from which the adrenal glands have been removed is given the choice of drinking fresh water or a 3 percent solution of water and table salt, it will choose the latter. This compensates for the loss of sodium through the excretory system.

Another characteristic of Addison's disease is the failure of the kidneys to excrete a proper amount of potassium salts.. Potassium ions cause the heart muscle to relax. If they are in too great concentration, they bring about the stop-

page of the heart during diastole. Thus, insufficiency of cortical hormones directly affects the heart as well as influencing the composition of blood. Injections of cortisone will alleviate the acute effects of this disease.

One of the most obvious symptoms of Addison's disease is the bronze coloration of the skin of the face. As the disease progresses, the skin becomes darker in color due to formation of a greenish-yellow pigment in it. This condition has not been satisfactorily explained.

The cortical hormones have definite effect on the leukocytes. If cortisone or ACTH is injected into an experimental animal, there is a rapid destruction of eosinophils and lymphocytes. Lymphoid tissue is also affected. At one time, cortisone and/or ACTH were widely used as a treatment for various conditions, such as arthritis. Spectacular cures were reported following their administration, but their continued use had some undesirable side effects. One was that the feeling of well-being following their use sometimes hid the underlying disease symptoms. Another was their effect on the blood and lymphoid tissue. Since this tissue is the principal source of gamma globulin, the carrier of antibodies, any lessening of its activities will decrease the person's general resistance to disease. Stomach ulcers, high blood pressure, edema, and even atrophy of the adrenal glands have followed excessive use of cortisone. However, with moderate dosage and under careful medical supervision, cortisone is a valuable weapon against a variety of human diseases.

The adrenal medulla. This part of the adrenal glands is not as vitally important as the cortex. The loss of the hormones of the medulla does not result in death, nor does replacement of these

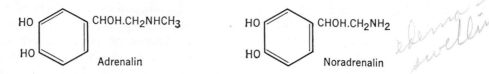

Fig. 32-3. *The structural formulas of adrenalin and noradrenalin molecules. Their functions are quite different even though their chemical structures are very similar.*

hormones save the life of an animal from which the adrenal glands have been removed.

In earlier research, it was believed that the secretion of the medulla consisted of only one hormone, **adrenalin** (sometimes *adrenin* or *epinephrin*). Thus the pronounced vasoconstrictor effect of extracts made from the medulla was understood to be due to adrenalin. More recently a second hormone, **noradrenalin** (*norepinephrin*) has been found to be responsible for the over-all constriction of the blood vessels. In some other respects, noradrenalin has an action similar to that of adrenalin, though weaker. Adrenalin is still listed in many texts as the most powerful vasoconstrictor in the body. Actually it is a vasodilator with only local constricting effects. The human medulla forms noradrenalin and adrenalin in the ratio of approximately 1 : 5. Commercial preparations of adrenalin contain from 10 to 20 percent noradrenalin.

As we have said, the over-all effect of adrenalin itself is vasodilation. However, it does cause constriction of the small vessels passing to the skin, with resulting paleness. It also causes constriction of the vessels in the kidneys and a corresponding reduction in the amount of urine. Its major effect is the dilation of the vessels in the liver, heart, brain, and skeletal muscles. Adrenalin also causes a rise in the systolic blood pressure, and an increase in the respiratory rate. Another important effect of adrenalin is that it converts glycogen, stored in the liver, into glucose, which then enters the blood stream. Thus there is an extra supply of energy available to the tissues in cases of emergency. Some of this excess glucose is excreted by the kidneys, resulting in temporary glycosuria.

Smoking influences the normal secretion of adrenalin and the release of sugar from the liver. Experiments have shown that the nicotine in tobacco stimulates the sympathetic nervous system. This stimulation then brings about a slight increase in the secretion of adrenalin, with a corresponding increase of blood sugar. The added blood sugar dulls the sensation of hunger slightly, since hunger is partly induced by a decreased supply of sugar in the blood. Thus we can explain, at least in part, why smoking sometimes causes a loss of weight. Conversely, we have a possible explanation of the observation that those who stop smoking often gain weight unless they consciously control their food intake.

Increased production of adrenalin results in increased muscle tone in skeletal muscles but decrease in tone of the smooth muscles of the stomach and intestines. Thus the injection of adrenalin into an experimental animal, such as a rabbit, causes the inhibition of intestinal movements and twitching of the skeletal muscles. In human physiology this effect plays an important role. If we are eating a meal when an unpleasant situation arises, the adrenalin content of the blood increases. We tense our muscles, become pale, and perhaps later feel some abdominal distress. Similar effects occur when we are frightened. We suddenly feel weak in the pit of the stomach (stoppage of normal peristalsis) and break out in a cold sweat due to the constriction of the skin capillaries. Noradrenalin has the same effect when injected into an animal, but to a lesser degree.

The amount of adrenalin present in the blood stream under normal resting conditions is minute. It has been determined that adrenalin is normally present in the blood in the ratio of 1 part of adrenalin to from 2 billion to 1 billion parts of blood. This concentration has no effect on the body. On stimulation of the adrenals, the concentration may rise to 1 : 4 million.

The presence of an appreciable amount of adrenalin in the blood increases the BMR by as much as 20 percent. Oxygen use may rise 20 to 40 percent above the resting rate, while CO_2 production may mount by 40 percent. If 0.5 cubic centimeters of a 1 : 1000 solution of adrenalin is injected into a human subject, these increases occur within a few minutes and last for about two hours. If adrenalin is injected into an experimental animal from which the liver has been removed, comparable results are not obtained. It is therefore thought that the increase in the BMR, use of oxygen, and carbon dioxide production are the result of the release of glycogen from the liver (glycogenesis). Other factors that contribute to these effects are the constriction of skin capillaries, which prevents the loss of heat, and an increase in muscle tone.

As we have already pointed out, the relation of the adrenal glands to the sympathetic nervous system is a close one. It has been found that in moments of stress, such as those occasioned by fear, anger, pain, and exposure to cold, the medulla is stimulated to produce more adrenalin. The effects of this increased supply of adrenalin seem to be independent of normal nerve control. For example, the rate of a cat's heart action increases by 15 to 20 beats per minute on hearing a dog's bark, even after the nerves to the heart have been cut. When the same cat struggles against a restraining device, its rate of heart beat may increase by 40 to 50 contractions per minute when the dog barks. This increase is usually accompanied by dilation of the pupils and erection of hair. On the other hand, if the nerves to the adrenal glands are cut or veins leading from the glands are tied off, these reactions do not occur at all.

PANCREAS

We pointed out in Chapter 31 that some glands that produce hormones also form exocrine secretions. The pancreas is one of these. It forms two types of materials: one that digests food materials (Chapter 17); and another that helps to control the metabolism of carbohydrates. Digestive enzymes pass from the pancreas to the duodenum through the pancreatic duct, but **insulin**, formed in the pancreas by the Islands of Langerhans (Figs. 17-6 and 31-1), is a hormone and enters the blood stream directly. Thus the pancreas may be considered a *mixed gland* because of its ability to produce both exocrine and endocrine secretions.

Diabetes. The failure of the Islands of Langerhans to produce sufficient insulin results in the disease known as **diabetes mellitus.** Until 1922, a victim of this disease was doomed to a restricted life centered about a diet in which all ingested food was carefully measured and weighed. Up to that year, the prognosis (forecast) was not heartening; life expectancy in diabetes was short. Since 1922, the outlook for diabetics is immeasurably brighter. By the use of insulin and a sensibly controlled diet, the diabetic can look forward to a long and relatively unrestricted life.

Diabetes affects people of all ages and economic conditions. Children may be born with defective Islands, and the type of diet, unless excessively heavy in carbohydrates, appears to have little effect on the disease. Inheritance may be a factor in its appearance. Early symptoms include paleness, loss of weight, excessive thirst, increase in the amount of urine, and a feeling of fatigue following moderate exercise. There is also an extensive itching of the skin. It is estimated that there are about a million known diabetics in this country, and a like number of people who have diabetes but are not aware of it. The prevalence of the disease and the lack of recognition in its early stages have prompted some local boards of health to establish mobile units to identify the condition and help the victims to receive early treatment. There are also simple test kits for sugar in the urine available at any drug store.

Lack of insulin results in several reactions. In the first place, there is a sharp rise in the amount of sugar in the blood (*hyperglycemia*) and a corresponding rise in the excretion of glucose by the kidneys (glycosuria). This is due to the body's inability to convert glucose into glycogen and to store it in the liver. A second effect is the use of proteins for energy, since the tissues are unable to use carbohydrates properly. When proteins are used for energy, they can no longer serve their primary function of repair and replacement of protoplasm. The result is loss in weight.

A third effect of the lack of insulin is related to the use of lipids by the body. In the absence of insulin, abnormal quantities of fat are oxidized. This results in formation of large amounts of ketones, which have a toxic effect. Acetoacetic acid is the ketone body most commonly formed. It is thought that this acid is responsible for the *diabetic coma* (unconsciousness) which results from lack of insulin. Many of the ketones have a sweet odor which can be detected in the breath of a diabetic.

The anterior pituitary gland may also be concerned in the development of diabetes. Its *diabetogenic hormone* may influence the production of insulin. A secretion of the adrenal cortex may have a similar effect. Details of the action of these hormones can be found in more advanced texts. This illustrates again how the effect of a gland on the body functions can be influenced by hormones from another gland.

Insulin is administered by hypodermic injection. Many attempts have been made to produce it in a form that could be taken by mouth, but such preparations are ineffective. Since insulin is a protein, it is easily digested in the stomach and small intestine. Its molecular structure is thus completely changed before it can be absorbed into the blood. There are indications, however, that biochemists may be able to change the structure of the insulin molecule so that it can be absorbed unchanged through the walls of the intestine. This advance would be of tremendous benefit to those who suffer from diabetes.

When there is an upset in the hormonal balance of the body, the injection of the missing hormone does not cure the condition; it simply alleviates the symptons. This is true of insulin in diabetes or thyroxin in cretinism, or cortisone in Addison's disease. In the case of diabetes, the injection of insulin results in an immediate drop in the blood sugar level. What happens to the sugar is a matter of conjecture, but it is thought that some of it is stored as glycogen, some forms fats, and some is used for energy. With the injection of insulin, the characteristic thirst of the diabetic decreases because less fluid is excreted by the kidneys.

One of the dangers of using insulin is the possibility that too much will be injected at one time. The dose usually prescribed is based on the supposition that the diabetic will take a normal amount of exercise for his age group and thus oxidize carbohydrates moderately. When too much insulin is taken, *insulin shock* develops. This condition is marked by such a sudden lowering of blood sugar (*hypoglycemia*) that the central nervous system lacks sufficient glucose to function normally. Convulsions and death may result unless the sugar level is raised immediately either by injections of glucose or by eating carbohydrates that can be absorbed rapidly. Many diabetics therefore carry tablets of sugar or pieces of candy with them to offset such an eventuality. Insulin shock has been found effective in the treatment of certain types of mental disorder. Under the severe shock to the nervous system, there is frequently a favorable response, and the distressing symptoms of depression and some cases of schizophrenia can be eased.

THE PINEAL BODY

The **pineal body** is a small organ attached to the lower surface of the brain between the anterior corpora quadrigemina. It is about 8 millimeters long and is reddish gray in color. In humans after the age of seven, it begins to degenerate and is represented in the adult only by a mass of fibrous tissue. During its development, the cells are glandular in nature, but no specific secretion has been isolated from them. In most lizard embryos, the pineal body develops briefly into a structure resembling a third eye, but this disappears before the animal hatches from the egg. In higher vertebrates, including man, it does not show this curious development and its function is unknown.

THE THYMUS GLAND

The **thymus gland** has occasionally been called the *gland of childhood*. It is located between the upper part of the sternum and the pericardium in the thoracic cavity. In the newborn child it weighs about 13 grams and continues to grow until puberty is reached, when its weight approaches 35 grams. The gland then gradually degenerates until in the adult of middle age it is scarcely recognizable from the surrounding tissues. Sexual maturity hastens its disappearance.

Structurally, the thymus has all of the features of a gland, but no definite function has been assigned to it. It has been blamed for the untimely death of infants on the basis that its overgrowth may interfere with respiration and circulation, but this theory has been questioned.

In Chapters 31 and 32 we have tried to point out how some of the activities of the body are interrelated. Throughout the text this same theme has been emphasized, but there are few better examples of this correlation than those shown by the nervous and endocrine systems.

We must constantly remember that each living thing succeeds because of the coordination of its chemical and physical activities. If any of these fail, the organism suffers.

The greater the complexity of its body structure, the more dependent the organism becomes on the proper functioning of its body parts. Basically, the activities of the human body depend on the action of its individual cells. Although some of the structures mentioned in Chapter 3 may be lacking in some types of cells, their absence is balanced by the activities of other cells that are specialized for definite functions. Thus the body may be said to represent a community of interests in which each cell, tissue, organ, and system plays an important part.

SPEAKING OF Physiology

Briefly identify each of the following:

adrenal capsule	dehydration	lactation
adrenal cortex	glycogenesis	noradrenalin
adrenal medulla	hyperglycemia	resorption of bone
adrenalin	insulin shock	steroid
cortisone	ketones	suprarenal

Test YOUR KNOWLEDGE

1. What is the relationship of the parathyroid glands to the thyroid?
2. Summarize the functions of the secretion of the parathyroid glands. Of what special importance is this hormone during pregnancy?
3. Why is the thymus gland often called the gland of childhood?
4. Why are the adrenal glands also called suprarenal glands?
5. What are the cortical hormones? Of these, which one seems to have the greatest therapeutic use?
6. What symptoms accompany the removal of the adrenal glands from experimental animals?
7. What are the symptoms of Addison's disease? What medical treatment is used for victims of this disease?
8. What side effects may develop after too frequent injections of cortisone?
9. What part does adrenalin play in the body's emergency responses?
10. Discuss the relationship of the sympathetic nervous system to the secretion of adrenalin.
11. What endocrine function does the pancreas perform? Describe the disease associated with failure of the hormone-producing portion of this gland.
12. Discuss the uses of insulin.

See FOR YOURSELF

1. What is the incidence of diabetes in the United States? Describe the urinalysis test to determine the absence or presence of sugar in urine. If laboratory materials are available, test your own urine for sugar.

2. Find out about the method of treating diabetes by interviewing a diabetic. Write a report of your findings.

3. Construct a chart summarizing the information you have learned in this unit on each of the endocrine glands. Use the following headings: name and location of gland; secretions; functions; effects of abnormal secretion (hyper- or hypofunction).

4. When diabetes appears in adults, various chemical compounds in tablet form may be prescribed by a physician. These are advised only when some of the islands of Langerhans are intact and can produce some insulin. Obtain information from Eli Lilly, Pfizer, Merck, or some other pharmaceutical firm that produces these materials. The Josyln Clinic in Boston, Mass., may be able to furnish data on the effectiveness of these substitutes for insulin.

UNIT **9**

Genetics

CHAPTER 33

The Inheritance of Characteristics

The Inheritance of Characteristics

In Chapter 3 we learned that cells are the basic units of the body and that their structure is specialized according to their activities. We have also learned that within the nucleus of each cell are the materials that control the heredity of the individual. It must be remembered that only the chromatin in the gametes is involved in heredity and then for just a brief period of time during the process of **fertilization.** It is in this union of the nuclei of the egg and sperm that the hereditary characteristics of the individual are determined. The science that deals with the inheritance of characteristics is called **genetics.**

Genes. We may say that a person has inherited the color of his eyes from one parent and the color of his hair from the other. This of course, does not mean that there are small bits of eye color or hair in the gametes. However, each of us has in his cells the determinants of physical and mental traits. These are called the **genes.** Although we cannot be certain that the genes are composed of definite chemical substances that control the appearance of the heritable characteristics, there is increasing evidence to support this idea.

Some early studies by Drs. Morgan, Bridges, and Sturtevant indicated that some of the hereditary characteristics of the fruit fly, *Drosophila,* could be related to definite regions in the chromosomes of this animal. Later, by a careful analysis of the results from breeding flies with different features, these men were able to locate within the chromosomes the regions that determine specific hereditary characteristics.

Investigation of the structure of the chromosomes in the salivary glands of Drosophila has produced very interesting and significant results. The chromosomes in these glands are many times larger than those in the gametes or the other body cells of the animal. If these giant chromosomes are properly stained, alternating bands of dark and light materials can be seen (Fig. 33-1). Through comparison of these with ordinary chromosomes, it has been determined that bands are present at exactly the same points (*loci*) on the chromosomes at which previous methods forecast the presence of genes. Although it is still too early to make a definite statement that these bands are genes, it is becoming more apparent that what we call genes are actually these alternating bands of material.

362

Chemical nature of genes. Let us now consider the chemical nature of chromosomes. We have already described their physical changes in the process of mitosis (Chapter 3). Many of the details of this process have been known for a long time. It is only within the past few years that the science of biochemistry has advanced to the point where it is possible to analyze the chemical substance that appears to be responsible for heredity. This substance is called **desoxyribonucleic acid (DNA)**.

We have already pointed out that carbohydrates with fewer than six carbon atoms in their molecules (hexoses) cannot be used in cellular oxidations. The molecule of DNA contains a five-carbon sugar, **desoxyribose** ($C_5H_{10}O_4$), and therefore is not involved in normal metabolism. In the DNA molecule this sugar alternates with a phosphate (PO_4) group to form a central rodlike structure. Around this are grouped molecules of protein, purine ($C_5H_4N_4$), and pyrimidine ($C_4H_4N_2$). Several theories have been advanced to explain the relationship of these parts. According to one theory, the DNA molecule is built like a spiral staircase in which the desoxyribose and phosphate groups form the central supporting pillar, and the protein, purine, and pyrimidine groups are the steps and the railing. Another theory is that the desoxyribose and phosphate parts form a central band from which the others project as double tightly coiled spiral structures twisted around each other. Regardless of the exact form of the molecule, its spiral nature is well established. It is also believed that this particular form of the molecule permits it to branch and change in structure so as to produce macromolecules that give the characteristic banded appearance of the giant salivary chromosomes. The molecule of DNA has a calculated mo-

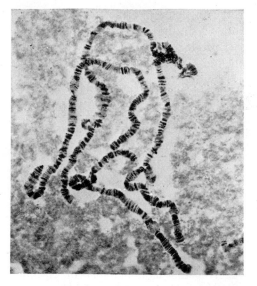

Fig. 33-1. *Photomicrograph of the giant chromosomes from the salivary glands of Drosophila. Note the pronounced banding in the chromosomes.*

lecular weight exceeding one million.

DNA is not normally found outside the nucleus of a cell except in one case. The egg cell has a relatively large amount of this material stored in its cytoplasm. This reserve supply is distributed to the rapidly forming nuclei of the cells that arise from the division of the fertilized egg. Within these new cells, the DNA is formed into chromosomes.

Differentiation and development of gametes. Following its fertilization, the egg cell is known as a **zygote** (Greek, *zygosis,* joining). It then divides by mitosis to form two cells, and later, four, eight, sixteen, and so on. At first these divisions are very regular, but soon the mathematical exactness is lost since some cells start dividing more rapidly than others. As a result of this change in division rate, certain tissues develop earlier in life than others. This **differentiation** into various types of cells appears to be the result of the action of materials in the cytoplasm of the egg. These serve to determine the fate of the cells into which they are eventually segregated, producing muscle or nerve or epithelium or whatever other type of tissue is required. As Fig. 33-2 shows, this has been demonstrated in the case of the frog's egg. If the shaded area in the egg is destroyed, no reproductive system can develop. Other regions are responsible for the development of still other organ systems. It is the eventual separation of these regions into groups of cells that determines the development of the animal.

During the development of the reproductive organs, the cells divide by mitosis just like the other body cells. Each receives the *same number* of chromosomes as the others as well as the *same*

types of chromatic materials. Some of these cells of the gonads will eventually produce the mature eggs or sperm. However, the mature gametes have only half the number of chromosomes that body cells have. In man, for example, the number of chromosomes present in **somatic** (body) cells is 46, but this is reduced to 23 in the mature **germ** (reproductive) cells.

Until quite recently, the number 48 was generally accepted as the chromosome count for man. However, researchers using much improved methods of staining have found that the basic number is apparently 46. Variations of 47 and 48 may appear occasionally.

The full number of chromosomes

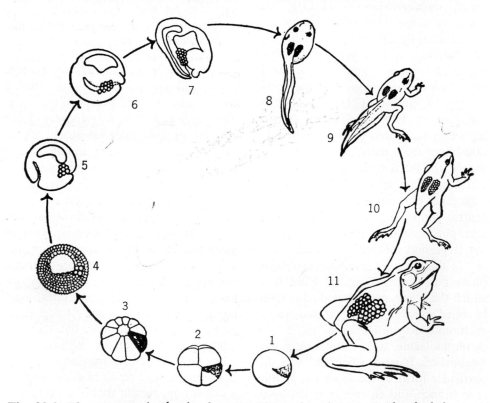

Fig. 33-2. *The sequence in the development of eggs in a frog. In 1, the shaded area of the fertilized egg contains materials that determine the development of the reproductive system. In 2 through 10 are shown various stages in tadpole development. In 11 we see the adult frog with mature eggs in the ovaries. (After Conklin from Guyer,* Animal Biology, *permission of Harper and Bros.)*

found in each somatic cell is called the **diploid (2n) number,** while that of the germ cells is known as the **haploid (n) number.** Each species of animal or plant has a constant diploid number of chromosomes. The number of chromosomes is not the important consideration: the quality of the genes is the principal factor in determining the characteristics of an organism. The following table shows how the number of chromosomes varies among a few selected animals and plants:

ORGANISM	DIPLOID NUMBER (2n)	HAPLOID NUMBER (n)
Honey bee	16	8
Fruit fly (Drosophila)	8	4
Crayfish	196	98
Rabbit	44	22
Pig	40	20
Cattle	60	30
Horse	66	33
Monkey (Rhesus)	48	24
Man	46	23
Corn	20	10
Wheat	82	41
Black pepper	128	64
Edible pea	14	7

As these data indicate, the structural or physiological complexity of an animal or plant is not solely dependent on the number of chromosomes present in its cells.

Meiosis. The process by which the number of chromosomes is reduced from the diploid to haploid number is known as **meiosis** (Greek, meaning "lessening"). This usually occurs just before the gametes become mature within the gonads, although in a few forms the process may not take place until after fertilization. In Fig. 33-3 are shown the important steps in the process, the details of which are beyond the scope of this text. Plants undergo a similar series of nuclear changes, but these are somewhat more complex than those found in animals.

There are two features of the process of meiosis that should receive special attention. During the formation of the sperm (**spermatogenesis**), most of the cytoplasm disappears from the cell, since the sperm contributes only chromatin material to the egg cell at the time of fertilization. There is no reduction in the number of sperms formed. The cytoplasm of the egg, on the other hand, supplies the early stages of the developing embryo with nourishment. It is therefore of extreme importance that the mature ovum retain as much cytoplasm as possible. During meiosis, the reduction division of chromosomes in the egg is accompanied by unequal division of the cytoplasm. As a result, a miniature cell (**polar body**) is formed, which contains the same number of chromosomes as the egg but has a minimum amount of cytoplasm (Fig. 33-4). These small polar bodies may be considered as waste products of the process of reproduction, since they cannot normally be fertilized.

During meiosis, the distribution of specific chromosomes to the mature cells is purely a matter of chance. Since they are present as pairs of **homologous** (Greek, homo, equal + logos, origin) **chromosomes,** the members of the pairs separate at the time of reduction and each passes into a different cell. For example, if we consider a cell with a diploid number of 6 chromosomes (3 pairs of homologous chromosomes) which we label Ee, Ef, and Gg, we find that the separation of the members of these pairs may take any of the eight patterns shown in the table on page 366.

1	2	3	4	5	6	7	8
E	e	E	e	E	e	E	e
F	f	F	f	f	F	f	F
G	g	g	G	G	g	g	G

If only three pairs of chromosomes result in eight (2^3) different combinations of mature gametes, it is not difficult to see how 46 (23 pairs) of human chromosomes may result in many more possible combinations. Mathematically, the number of possible combinations of chromosomes appearing in either the mature egg or sperm cell would be 2^{23} or 8,388,608. Since fertilization consists of the union of any sperm with any ovum, the number of possible combinations of chromosomes in the zygote reaches the amazing total of 70,368-744,177,664 ($8,388,608^2$). If each chromosome contained only one gene, this alone would explain why the possibility of any two people being exactly alike is infinitesimally small. It has been estimated that the chances are about 300 trillion to 1 against the occurrence of the same gene content in two people. Of course, the possibility of similarity between closely related people would be considerably greater.

By the process of fertilization, the new individual receives specific hereditary

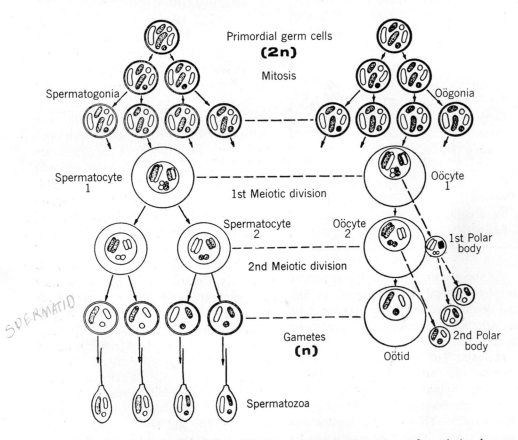

Fig. 33-3. *The process of meiosis in an animal having a diploid number of six chromosomes. Note the reduction in the number of chromosomes in the gametes.* (*From Miller and Haub,* General Zoology, *Holt, 1956*)

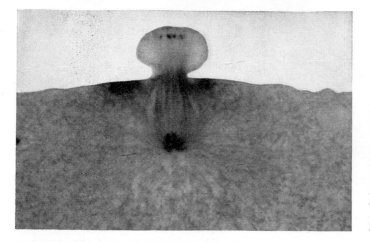

Fig. 33-4. *Photomicrograph of the formation of a polar body on a whitefish egg. The number of chromosomes is the same in both cells, but the volume of cytoplasm is very much smaller in the polar body. (General Biological Supply House, Inc.)*

characteristics from his parents. Fertilization also stimulates the egg cell to start dividing. As Dr. Jacques Loeb demonstrated in the early 1900's, a mature unfertilized frog egg need only be pricked by a sharp needle in order to start its division. Normally, the stimulus that starts cell division is provided by the penetration of the sperm through the cell membrane of the egg. If, however, an artificial stimulus is used to start division, the animal that develops has only the haploid number of chromosomes. This process, known as **parthenogenesis,** occurs normally among some animals, notably certain insects. In these forms, the stimulus that starts the division is presumably chemical.

Principles of heredity. Studies of heredity before 1866 were not conclusive. The results obtained by earlier investigators offered little explanation of the way inheritable features are transmitted from one generation to the next. This was due either to faulty techniques or failure to interpret the results correctly. In 1866 an Augustinian monk who lived in the monastery in Brünn (Brno), Moravia, published two small treatises on the laws of heredity in the journal of the local natural-science society. This monk, Johann Gregor Mendel, later became

the head of the monastery. His many added duties prevented him from continuing his study of inheritance. He died in 1886 without realizing that his two small contributions would form the foundation for all the work that has since been done in this field.

It was not until 1900 that three investigators (de Vries, Correns, and Tschermak) discovered what they thought to be new facts about heredity. In searching through literature in this field, they found Mendel's earlier reports on the same subject. They realized immediately that Mendel was the pioneer in this investigation and gave him full credit for these basic discoveries. The principal reason for the delay in recognizing the value of Mendel's experiments was that they ran counter to the thought of the period on the inheritance of characteristics. In the middle of the nineteenth century, many biologists were seeking material to support Darwin's idea that variations in animals and plants were responsible for their evolutionary progress. Mendel's work very definitely denied variability in those characters he had observed, and it was therefore not acceptable to other workers. A second reason for the lack of recognition was that Mendel's papers were published in a

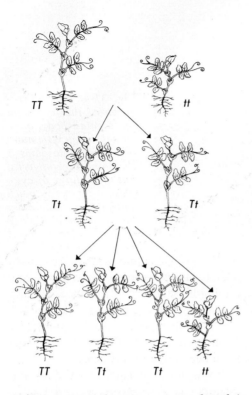

Fig. 33-5. *The inheritance of stem length in the edible pea. In the F₂ generation it is impossible to distinguish between the homozygous and heterozygous plants because the gene for tallness is dominant.*

small journal that usually contained only natural-science articles of a very generalized type. Although the publication was received by large libraries, Mendel's reports were apparently disregarded by outstanding biologists of that area.

Mendel's work was concerned with the inheritance of various characteristics shown by the edible pea (*Pisa sativum*). He grew plants of this species in the monastery garden and kept very careful notes on the results he obtained. Because peas are normally self-pollinating, Mendel could control his experiments. He concentrated on one characteristic at a time, and made his crosses between plants which had shown the trait through several generations.

In this way, Mendel discovered that when he pollinated plants having long stems with pollen from those having short stems, all of the offspring were as tall as the tall parent. He also found that whenever he cross-pollinated two plants showing any pair of contrasting characteristics, one of these appeared in the offspring while the other did not. To the characteristic that appeared in the offspring he gave the name of **dominant characteristic**, while the characteristic of the pair that did not appear he called the **recessive characteristic**. The following table shows some of the dominant and recessive pairs discovered by Mendel in his work with garden peas.

DOMINANT	RECESSIVE
Tall plants	Short plants
Round seeds	Wrinkled seeds
Green pods	Yellow pods
Gray seed coat	White seed coat

Mendel found that if he crossed two plants which were the offspring of parents showing contrasting characters, the following generation contained some plants showing the recessive feature. If we use the same pairing given in the preceding table, Mendel's actual results are shown in the table on page 369.

The diagram in Fig. 33-5 illustrates the results obtained in crossing tall and short plants. It will be noted that the letters *T* and *t* are used to designate the traits of tallness and shortness. The capital letter, *T,* designates the dominant feature, and the small letter, *t,* the recessive one. Thus the sperm and egg cells of the tall plant each contain one gene for tallness. The genes for shortness are separated in the same manner.

Since the parents in this case show pure characteristics for tallness and

FEATURE	CHARACTERISTIC		RATIO
	DOMINANT	RECESSIVE	
Stem length	787 tall	277 short	2.84 : 1
Seed shape	5474 round	1850 wrinkled	2.96 : 1
Pod color	428 green	152 yellow	2.82 : 1
Seed coat color	705 gray	224 white	3.15 : 1
Average ratio	———	———	2.94 : 1

shortness, they are said to be **homozygous** (Greek, *homo,* equal + *zygosis,* joining). After fertilization, the offspring of these parents contain one gene for tallness and one for shortness, and are said to be **heterozygous** (Greek, *heteros,* different). The term **hybrid** is often used for the heterozygous condition.

The generation that results from breeding together the pure (homozygous) parents is called the **first filial generation** (F_1). All these offspring are heterozygous. However, if these heterozygous plants are bred with each other, the **second filial generation** (F_2) will show an approximate ratio of three plants with the dominant characteristic (tallness) to every plant with the recessive characteristic (shortness). This 3 : 1 ratio is seen in the above table of Mendel's results. It is based on the probable sorting out of the genes into different gametes and their random recombination in the zygote. It should be pointed out that the 3 : 1 ratio holds only when the offspring are numerous; the data given above are based on the observation of 9,897 individual plants.

Unless you are familiar with the ancestry of an organism, it is impossible to tell by inspection whether it is heterozygous or homozygous for any *dominant* characteristic, since its appearance gives no clue to the genetic content of its cells. Because of this, we need terms to differentiate appearance from genetic makeup. The appearance of the organism is known as the **phenotype** (Greek, *phaino,* to show + *typos,* model). The assortment of genes in the cells is the **genotype** (Greek, *genos,* race). Thus, in the pea plants mentioned above, there is no way of knowing which tall offspring in the F_2 generation are heterozygous and which are homozygous. The phenotype (tallness) is the same in all of them, but they may be of two different genotypes (*TT* or *Tt*). In order to determine whether a specific individual is homozygous or heterozygous for the dominant characteristic, it is necessary to perform a **back cross**. This is done by crossing the unknown individual with one showing the *recessive* feature.

The use of the back cross can be illustrated in the case of mice. If a mouse having black hair is crossed with a white mouse, the black color is dominant and the offspring in the F_1 generation are all black. If two of these mice that are heterozygous for color are crossed, the members of the F_2 generation are in the ratio of three black mice to one white mouse, the same ratio that Mendel found in his pea plants. Since all of these black mice are as black as the parents and the black grandparent, it is impossible to determine visually their genetic makeup. A back cross, using one of the black mice and a white mouse (which is necessarily homozygous) will reveal the genotype of the black mouse. Figure 33-6 shows the results obtained when a homozygous black mouse is crossed with

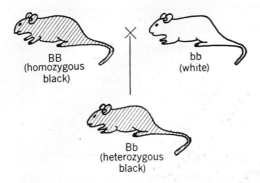

Fig. 33-6. *A back cross between a homozygous black and a recessive white mouse.*

a white mouse. The details of this cross may also be shown as follows:

Genes from one parent	Genes from the other parent	
	b	b
B	Bb	Bb
B	Bb	Bb

The offspring of a cross between a homozygous black and a white, represented by the symbols in the boxes, would all be black (phenotype) and heterozygous (genotype *Bb*).

If the heterozygous mouse is crossed with a white mouse (Fig. 33-7) the results shown graphically are as follows:

Genes from one parent	Genes from the other parent	
	b	b
B	Bb	Bb
b	bb	bb

Half of the offspring of a cross of this type will be heterozygous black and half will be white.

Sex determination. In one instance, the *entire* chromosome, rather than the gene, controls a definite characteristic of an organism. The sex of an individual

is determined by the presence of certain definite chromosomes, known as the **X** and **Y** *chromosomes*. In the human male there are 22 pairs of homologous chromosomes plus one pair in which the members are quite unlike each other. The larger of this pair is known as the *X* chromosome and the smaller the *Y* chromosome. Together they constitute the sex chromosomes. In females we find the pair consists of two *X* chromosomes.

During meiosis, the number of chromosomes is halved so that each mature gamete receives 23 chromosomes, distributed as follows:

SPERM	OVA
22 + X	22 + X
22 + Y	22 + X

Fertilization of an ovum by a sperm containing an *X* chromosome results in the development of a female child, while a male develops if the sperm contains a *Y* chromosome. Theoretically, this should result in an equal distribution between male and female births in the population as a whole. Actually, however, there is a slight tendency in favor of male births. It has been suggested that an explanation of this is the greater

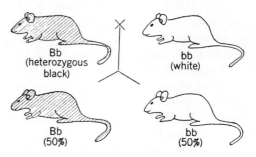

Fig. 33-7. *A back cross between a heterozygous black mouse and a recessive white. Compare this with Fig. 33-6.*

speed of movement of the sperm carrying the Y chromosome. Some students of population trends consider the idea that the male is the stronger sex to be a myth. Data from various life insurance companies lend weight to the idea that two X chromosomes are more effective in promoting longevity (long life) than the X–Y combination. At present the average married woman has a life expectancy of six or seven years more than the average married man.

Sex-linked characteristics. Color blindness has already been discussed briefly in Chapter 11. It is a hereditary defect that is transmitted from one generation to the next by a defective gene on the X chromosome. Hemophilia (Chapter 24) is inherited in the same way. Both of these are recessive characteristics.

As Fig. 33-8 shows, a major part of the X chromosome does not have a homologue (similar part) on the smaller Y chromosome. If, therefore, this nonhomologous region of the X chromosome contains the gene for color blindness or hemophilia and the X is com-

bined with a Y chromosome, there is no gene for the normal condition to overcome the defect. The male will therefore inherit color blindness or hemophilia. If, however, two X chromosomes join in the zygote, and one contains a defective gene and the other a gene for the normal characteristic, the female will not inherit the defect although one of her chromosomes still carries the defective gene. Characteristics that are transmitted in this fashion are known as **sex-linked** traits. In Fig. 33-9 are shown several crosses between individuals carrying the gene for color blindness. It will be noted that a woman can be color blind only if she has two genes for the condition, which means that she must inherit the characteristic from both her father and her mother.

If a gene on the Y chromosome determines a characteristic, it is termed **sex-limited.** Again referring to Fig. 33-8, it will be noted that there is a region of the Y chromosome that has no homologue on the X. It is in this region that the sex-limited genes are found. Only a few of these have been identified with certainty.

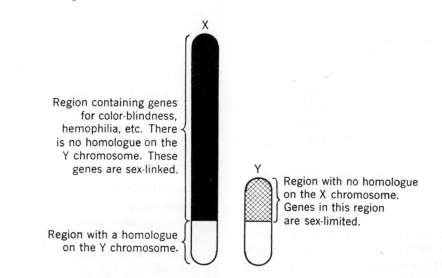

Fig. 33-8. *A diagram of the X and Y chromosomes showing the homologous and non-homologous regions.*

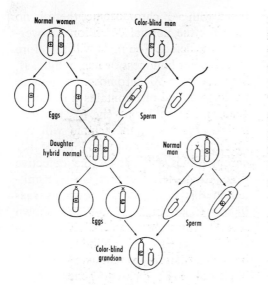

Fig. 33-9. *Diagrams showing how the gene for color blindness* (C) *can be transmitted from a man through his daughter to his grandson. Note that there is the probability that half of his grandsons will inherit color blindness. (From Altenburg,* Genetics, *Holt, 1957)*

One results in the webbing of the second and third toes, another the appearance of excess hair in and around the ears, and a third (sometimes fatal) condition characterized by a barklike skin.

A few of the human characteristics for which the inheritance pattern has been determined are shown in the tables at the right and in Fig. 33-10.

We have thus far discussed only the results obtained when one pair of contrasting characteristics is crossed (**monohybrid cross**). In such a mating, one member of the pair is dominant over the other in the ratio of 3 : 1 in the F_2 generation. If we want to determine the ratios that result from crossing two pairs of characteristics, we make a **dihybrid cross.** Mendel also performed experiments of this type. He crossed plants which consistently yielded round green seeds with those yielding wrinkled yellow seeds. The resulting seeds were all round and yellow. The plants which grew from these seeds by normal self-pollination produced seeds in the following ratios: 9 yellow-round : 3 green-round : 3 yellow-wrinkled : 1 green-wrinkled. The reason for this distribution is shown diagrammatically in Fig. 33-11. If these results are analyzed in terms of dominant and recessive characteristics, it will be seen that the basic ratio of 3 dominants to one recessive still exists. There

DOMINANT	RECESSIVE
Black hair	All other colors
Dark brown hair	Light browns and reds
Curly hair	Straight hair
Brown eyes	Blue eyes
Astigmatism	Normal vision
Double-jointedness	Normal condition of joints
Normal pigmentation	Albinism
Cleft palate	Normal palate
Lack of musical ability	Musical ability
Normal hearing	Deaf mutism
Tongue-curling	Lack of ability to curl tongue
Free ear lobes	Attached ear lobes
Ability to taste PTC (phenyl-thiocarba-mide)	Inability to taste PTC

SEX—LINKED CHARACTERISTICS

Broad terminal joints of the digits
Red-green color blindness
Hemophilia
White forelock of hair
Baldness
Icthyosis simplex (scaly skin)

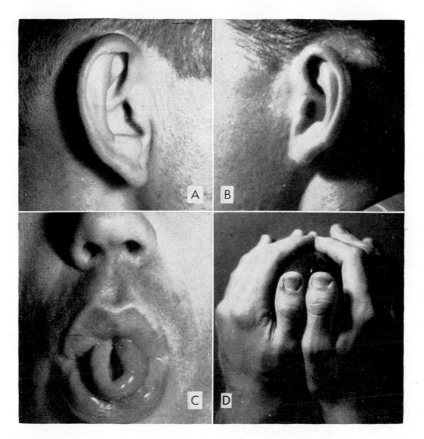

Fig. 33-10. *Photographs of several inheritable human traits. A, free ear lobe; B, attached ear lobe; C, tongue curling; D, broad terminal ends of the fingers. (From Miller and Haub,* General Zoology, *Holt, 1956)*

are still 3 round-seed plants for each wrinkled-seed, and 3 yellow-seed plants for each green-seed.

Mendel's Laws. Mendel's work laid the basis for the formulation of three laws, which control the inheritance of most known characteristics. These are called **Mendel's Laws** and may be stated as follows:

1. *The Law of Dominance.* The offspring of parents which are pure for contrasting characteristics will resemble one parent only. The hereditary unit (gene) for one characteristic, the dominant, prevents the other, the recessive, from expressing itself when the two are combined in the same organism.

2. *The Law of Segregation.* When hybrids are crossed with other hybrids or with individuals showing either the dominant or recessive characteristic, the dominant and recessive both appear in the offspring, in a definite ratio. The results obtained by various types of matings are shown in the table on page 374.

3. *The Law of Unit Characters.* Each pair of characteristics operates independently of others, following the laws of dominance and segregation.

Incomplete dominance. Since Mendel's time, some apparent contradictions of his basic findings have been discovered. However, if these are examined critically, they will be found to follow

MATING	OFFSPRING
Heterozygous × Heterozygous	75% show the dominant feature : 25% the recessive This may also be shown as 25% homozygous dominants : 50% heterozygous dominants : 25% recessives.
Heterozygous × Recessive	50% heterozygous : 50% recessives
Heterozygous × Homozygous dominant	50% homozygous dominants : 50% heterozygous

the fundamental laws. One of these contradictions is a condition known as *incomplete dominance,* or *blending,* in which neither of the contrasting genes appears to be strictly dominant or recessive in the heterozygous condition. The result is an apparent blending of the characteristics so as to produce an intermediate condition. This is well illustrated in the case of certain flowers such

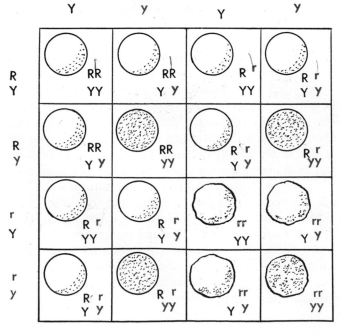

Fig. 33-11. *Chart showing the results of a dihybrid cross. The genes from one parent are across the top while those from the other parent are along the left side. Dominant characteristics are in black letters and recessives are shown in red.*

as zinnias or four o'clocks. A pink hybrid results from the crossing of a red flower with a white flower in these species. The same is true of some of the colors shown by cattle (Fig. 33-12). In these animals, the roan is a hybrid showing incomplete dominance.

The inheritance of skin color in man is another example of blending, but the condition is not as simple as that shown by either flowers or cattle. There are evidently two pairs of genes involved in human skin color. Therefore, the inheritance of skin color resembles the dihybrid cross shown in Fig. 33-11. If we consider *AB* as representing the genes for dark skin color, and *ab* those for white skin color, then *ABAB* would represent the homozygous condition existing in the dark-skinned races, and *abab* that of the white-skinned races. A mating between two individuals who are homozygous for these characteristics would produce a heterozygous person with a genotype of *AaBb*. A cross between two people having this hybrid condition could produce any of sixteen possible combinations illustrated in Fig. 33-11. The occurrence of intermediate shades of color is due to differences in the total number of genes for dark or white skin color which the individual has received.

Mutations. A new hereditary characteristic that appears in any species of animal or plant is known as a *mutation.* Any such change must, of course, be the result of alterations in the pattern of the genes, otherwise it could not be inherited. The explanation for mutations is most frequently found in changes that occur during mitosis or meiosis. When a cell divides, the cytoplasm moves in a vigorous manner. During this cytoplasmic

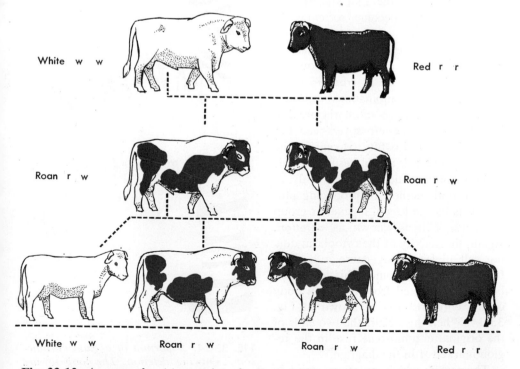

Fig. 33-12. *An example of incomplete dominance (blending). Note that neither the red nor the white color is dominant in the hybrid.*

Crossing over

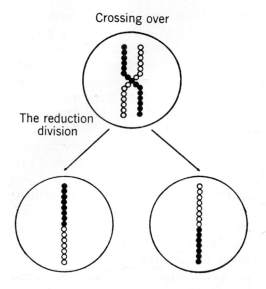

The reduction division

Fig. 33-13. *In a crossover, the homologous chromosomes become entwined. When they separate, a new arrangement of genes results* (*From Altenburg,* Genetics, *Holt 1957*)

activity it is possible that the strands of chromosomes become so entwined that when they separate to form the haploid number, new combinations of genes occur. This process, as shown in Fig. 33-13, is known as **crossing over,** and these new combinations can give rise to new groupings of characteristics. Theoretically, such crossovers can occur in from one to fifty percent of the offspring, but the actual results of this process appear much less frequently.

A second method of producing mutations is by the loss of a gene, or group of genes. This is known as **deletion.** Again, the activity of the cytoplasm during cell division may cause a loop to form in a chromosome. This loop then becomes separated from the main body of the chromosomes as shown in Fig. 33-14. When this occurs the two ends of the original chromosome fuse in the region marked *A* in the diagram.

The rate at which mutations occur in man is very difficult to determine. This

is primarily due to the small number of offspring resulting from one mating. Thus far sixteen changes have been found that may be considered mutations because of their recognizable effects on the phenotype. Since all of these result in abnormalities which require medical treatment, they have been brought to the attention of students of human heredity. Figure 33-15 shows the inheritance of a condition known as *multiple cartilaginous exostoses,* in which numerous bony projections form on the skeleton. Since both of the victim's parents were normal, as were his nine brothers

A

Fig. 33-14. *A portion of a giant chromosome showing deletion. The loop toward the right is lost as the original thread reunites in the region at the base of the loop.*

and sisters, we can consider the appearance of this disease in him as a mutation. It should be noted that four of his children also showed this condition. We can therefore assume that this mutation is dominant.

A mathematical study of the sixteen mutations previously mentioned shows that only about 48 germ cells per 100,000 should contain a gene for one of these. Considering the tremendous number of possible combinations of germ cells, it is evident that the chances of the appearance of one of these mutations are extremely slight.

The question of the effects of atomic radiations and other penetrating radiations (X rays) on the occurrence of mutations has been the subject of much speculation during recent years. Since 1946, geneticists have been studying the effects of the atom bombs dropped on Hiroshima and Nagasaki. They have attempted to determine whether there has been any change in the sex ratio of children born to survivors of the bombings, the birth weight of children, their size at the age of nine months, and the rate of death during the first nine months. Thus far, little information of a really conclusive nature has been obtained. This might be expected because of the shortness of the time that has elapsed since the bombings. Whether future generations will show an increase in mutations is, of course, a question that cannot be answered now.

Experiments on fruit flies, mice, and various types of plants have been undertaken to determine the effects of radiations on germ cells. Many of these have indicated that radioactive materials and powerful X rays can produce mutations. It must be remembered, however, that these experiments have been carried out under very carefully controlled laboratory conditions. In the case of atomic

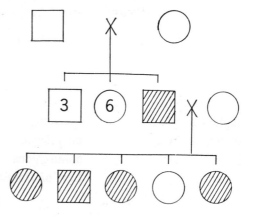

Fig. 33-15. *Pedigree of a family in which a mutation appeared. The squares represent males and the circles females. The figures containing diagonal lines represent individuals that show multiple cartilaginous exostoses. The numbers 3 and 6 indicate normal brothers and sisters of the male in which the mutation appeared.*

radiations, the animals and plants have not been subjected to the blast of an atom bomb. Since the effects of the radiations decrease with distance from the center of the blast area, the chances of a survivor of an atomic attack receiving a harmful dosage are also reduced by distance. The preliminary studies from Hiroshima and Nagasaki indicate that the human genes are not unusually sensitive to atomic radiations, nor do they have any special ability to resist them. Studies of the effects of X-ray radiations on human heredity are not conclusive. Because of the possibility that such radiations may cause mutations, health authorities are now cautioning us against the indiscriminate use of X rays, particularly in the region of the sex organs. Physicians and dentists are advised to be more careful than they formerly were in shielding both themselves and their patients from excessive exposure to X rays and to avoid "routine" use of X rays where they are not necessary.

SPEAKING OF Physiology

Briefly identify each of the following:

back cross	gene	Law of Segregation
blend	genotype	Law of Unit Characters
differentiation	haploid number	mutation
diploid number	heterozygous	phenotype
dominant trait	homologue	recessive trait
fertilization	homozygous	spermatogenesis
gamete	Law of Dominance	zygote

Test YOUR KNOWLEDGE

1. During what process are the hereditary traits established in a new organism?
2. Why is the fruit fly *Drosophila* frequently used for laboratory experiments in heredity?
3. Why is there special interest in the giant chromosomes found in the salivary glands of *Drosophila?*
4. What is believed to be the chemical composition of chromosomes? What is unique about the structure of this substance?
5. How are gametes different from somatic cells in cytoplasmic and nuclear structure?
6. Does the number of chromosomes in the sex cells of an animal have any relation to the complexity of the animal? Explain.
7. How does meiosis differ from mitosis in nuclear division? In cytoplasmic division?
8. What are the polar bodies and what functions do they perform?
9. How can you determine mathematically the number of different combinations of chromosomes that can occur in the mature gametes of organisms that have 6 homologous pairs of chromosomes in immature sex cells?
10. What is parthenogenesis? Under what conditions can it occur?
11. Why did Mendel's experiments have no immediate effect on theories about heredity?
12. Why has Mendel often been called the *father of genetics?*
13. How could you determine the difference between animals which are heterozygous for a given trait and dominant homozygous litter mates?
14. In humans, what determines the sex of the offspring? What other characteristics are linked with the inheritance of sex?
15. What is the difference between a monohybrid and dihybrid cross?
16. What are mutations? Do they often occur in humans? How may they be caused?

See FOR YOURSELF

1. Using library reference material, write a report comparing the work of Gregor Mendel in his Laws of Heredity and Charles Darwin in his Theory of Natural Selection. Include a brief biographical sketch of each scientist and show the various similarities and differences between their two theories. Show how these theories have contributed to our present knowledge and research in these fields.

2. As a student, you can raise a culture of fruit flies (Drosophila), crossing them to study heredity. Complete instructions and pure strain cultures may be obtained from various biological supply houses or from the science department of some college or university. You could start with wild fruit flies gathered near a fruit stand or market.

You will need a number of half-pint milk bottles, sterile cotton to plug the end of each bottle, a hand magnifier for easy identification of structures, ether to anesthetize the flies for close observation, and ripe bananas as their food. A new generation is hatched in from 12 to 15 days, so you can study many generations in a fairly short time. Ask your instructor for further information that will be valuable for this experiment.

3. Report on the most recent findings regarding the effects of atomic and other penetrating radiations on the development of mutations.

Appendix

UNITS OF MEASUREMENT

1 Ångstrom Unit (Å) = 3.937×10^{-9} inch (in.)

$= 1 \times 10^{-10}$ meter (m.)

$= 1 \times 10^{-4}$ micron (μ)

1 Atmosphere = 33.899 feet of water at 39.1° Fahrenheit (F.)

= 760 millimeters (mm.) of mercury (Hg) at 0° Centigrade (C.)

= 29.921 inches of mercury at 32° F.

1 centimeter (cm.) = 0.3937 inch.

1 gram (g.) = 0.03527 avoirdupois (av.) ounce.

1 liter (l.) = 0.028378 U.S. bushels.

= 1.816192 U.S. dry pints.

= 1.056681 U.S. fluid quarts.

1 meter = 1×10^{10} Ångstrom Units.

= 3.280833 U.S. feet.

= 39.3700 U.S. inches.

1 micron = 10^{-3} millimeters.

= 3.937×10^{-5} U.S. inches.

1 millimeter (mm.) = 0.1 centimeter.

= 10^{-3} meter.

= 0.03937 U.S. inch.

1 milligram (mg.) = 3.352739×10^{-5} ounce.

1 milliliter (ml.) = 1.000027 cubic centimeters (cc.)

= 0.061025 cubic inch.

= 0.0338147 U.S. fluid ounce.

1 U.S. inch = 2.5400×10^{8} Ångstrom Units.

= 2.540 centimeters.

= 25.40005 millimeters.

TEMPERATURE CONVERSION FACTORS

1° Fahrenheit (F°.) = 0.5556° Centigrade (C°.)

1° Centigrade = 1.8° Fahrenheit.

0° Kelvin = -273° C. = -459.4° F. (Absolute Zero)

To convert Fahrenheit or Centigrade readings: $\dfrac{C°}{F° - 32} = \dfrac{5}{9}$

381

Bibliography

ADVANCED TEXTS FOR TEACHER REFERENCE.

Human Physiology.
Bard, P., ed., MEDICAL PHYSIOLOGY. 10th ed., 1956. C. V. Mosby Co.
Best, C. H., & Taylor, N. B., PHYSIOLOGICAL BASIS OF MEDICAL PRAC-
TICE. 6th ed., 1955. Williams & Wilkins Co.
Starling, E. H., PRINCIPLES OF HUMAN PHYSIOLOGY. 12th ed., 1956.
Lea & Febiger.

Human Anatomy.
Goss, C. M., ed., GRAY'S ANATOMY. 26th ed., 1954. Lea & Febiger.
Schaeffer, J. P., ed., MORRIS' HUMAN ANATOMY. 11th ed., 1953. Williams
& Wilkins Co.
Spalteholtz, W., HAND ATLAS OF HUMAN ANATOMY. 7th ed., 1937. J. B.
Lippincott Co.

Organic and Biological Chemistry.
Amundsen, L. H., ORGANIC CHEMISTRY. 1954. Henry Holt & Co., Inc.
Bodansky, M., & Bodansky, O., BIOCHEMISTRY OF DISEASE. 2nd ed., 1952.
The Macmillan Co.
Fieser, L. F., ORGANIC CHEMISTRY. 3rd ed., 1956. Reinhold Publishing Co.
Harrow, B., & Mazur, A., TEXTBOOK OF BIOCHEMISTRY. 6th ed., 1954.
W. B. Saunders Co.
Hawk, P. B., PRACTICAL BIOLOGICAL CHEMISTRY. 13th ed., 1954.
McGraw-Hill Book Co.
Sherman, H. C., THE CHEMISTRY OF FOOD AND NUTRITION. 8th ed.,
1952. The Macmillan Co.

Biophysics.
Stacy, R. W., Williams, D. T., Worden, R. E., & McMorris, R. O., ESSENTIALS
OF BIOLOGICAL AND MEDICAL PHYSICS. 1955. McGraw-Hill Book
Co.

Histology.
Ham, A. W., HISTOLOGY. 3rd ed., 1958. J. B. Lippincott Co.
Jordan, H. E., TEXTBOOK OF HISTOLOGY. 8th ed., 1952. Appleton-Century-
Crofts, Inc.
Maximow, A. A., & Bloom, W., TEXTBOOK OF HISTOLOGY. 7th ed., 1957.
W. B. Saunders Co.

TEXTS SUITABLE FOR STUDENT REFERENCE.

Human Anatomy and Physiology.

Anthony, C. P., TEXTBOOK OF ANATOMY AND PHYSIOLOGY. 4th ed., 1956. C. V. Mosby Co.

Best, C. H., & Taylor, N. B., THE HUMAN BODY. 3rd ed., 1956. Henry Holt & Co., Inc.

DeCoursey, R. M., THE HUMAN ORGANISM. 1955. McGraw-Hill Book Co.

Edwards, E. F., CONCISE ANATOMY. 2nd ed., 1956. McGraw-Hill Book Co.

Kimber, D. C., Gray, C. E., & Stackpole, C. E., TEXTBOOK OF ANATOMY AND PHYSIOLOGY. 13th ed., 1955. The Macmillan Co.

Millard, N. D., HUMAN ANATOMY AND PHYSIOLOGY. 4th ed., 1956. W. B. Saunders Co.

Primarily Physiological in Nature.

Amberson, W. R., & Smith, C. D., OUTLINE OF PHYSIOLOGY. 2nd ed., 1948. Williams & Wilkins.

Best, C. H., & Taylor, N. B., THE LIVING BODY. 4th ed., 1958. Henry Holt & Co., Inc.

Carlson, A. J., & Johnson, V. E., THE MACHINERY OF THE BODY. 4th ed., 1953. University of Chicago Press.

Hickman, C. P., PHYSIOLOGICAL HYGIENE. 3rd ed., 1950. Prentice-Hall, Inc.

Zoethout, W. D., & Tuttle, W. W., TEXTBOOK OF PHYSIOLOGY. 13th ed., 1957. C. V. Mosby Co.

Miscellaneous.

Altenburg, E., GENETICS. Rev. ed., 1957. Henry Holt & Co., Inc.

Bogert, L. J., NUTRITION AND PHYSICAL FITNESS. 6th ed., 1954. W. B. Saunders Co.

Dobzhansky, T., EVOLUTION, GENETICS, AND MAN. 1955. John Wiley & Sons, Inc.

Dull, C. E., Metcalf, H. C., & Williams, J. E., MODERN CHEMISTRY. Rev. ed., 1958. Henry Holt & Co., Inc.

Edsall, J. T., ENZYMES AND ENZYME SYSTEMS: THEIR STATE IN NATURE. 1951. Harvard University Press.

Gamble, J. L., CHEMICAL ANATOMY, PHYSIOLOGY, AND PATHOLOGY OF EXTRACELLULAR FLUID. 6th ed., 1954. Harvard University Press.

Harrow, B., ONE FAMILY: VITAMINS, ENZYMES, HORMONES. 1950. Burgess Pub. Co.

Hoskins, R. G., ENDOCRINOLOGY. Rev. ed., 1950. W. W. Norton & Co., Inc.

Jordan, H. E., & Kindred, J. E., TEXTBOOK OF EMBRYOLOGY. 5th ed., 1948. Appleton-Century-Crofts, Inc.

Laidler, K. J., INTRODUCTION TO THE CHEMISTRY OF ENZYMES. 1954. McGraw-Hill Book Co.

McEwen, R. S., VERTEBRATE EMBRYOLOGY. 3rd ed., 1949. Henry Holt & Co., Inc.

McLean, F. C., & Urist, M. R., BONE: AN INTRODUCTION TO THE PHYSI-
    OLOGY OF SKELETAL TISSUE. 1955. University of Chicago Press.
Rose, M. S., FOUNDATIONS OF NUTRITION. 5th ed., 1956. The Macmil-
    lan Co.
Saunders, F. A., & Kirkpatrick, P., COLLEGE PHYSICS. 4th ed., 1953. Henry
    Holt & Co., Inc.
Scheinfeld, A., YOU AND HEREDITY. Rev. ed., 1950. J. B. Lippincott Co.
Wenger, M. A., Jones, F. N., & Jones, M. H., PHYSIOLOGICAL PSYCHOL-
    OGY. 1956. Henry Holt & Co., Inc.

Glossary

Abdomen. The lower part of the trunk below the level of the ninth pair of ribs. It contains the major parts of the digestive and excretory systems as well as many endocrine glands.

Absorption. The passage of materials through a cell membrane by either diffusion or osmosis.

Acetylcholine. A substance produced at the junction of nerve and muscle fibers which results in the contraction of the muscle.

Actin. One of the two proteins concerned in muscle contraction.

Adipose tissue. A type of tissue in which each cell contains a single large vacuole filled with oil.

Afferent. Any blood vessel or nerve which carries blood or impulses toward a region of the body.

Afterimage. The retention of a visual image on the retina of the eye after the light stimulus has been cut off.

Agglutination. The clumping together of cells, caused by the chemical action of agglutinins on their surfaces.

Agglutinin. A chemical substance which affects the outer layer of a cell's membrane and makes it sticky.

Agglutinogen. A chemical substance in the cell's membrane toward which the agglutinin is antagonistic.

Albumin. A relatively simple type of protein.

Albuminuria. The excretion of albumin in the urine.

Amino acid. A chemical compound that contains both the amine (NH_2) and the organic acid (COOH) radicals.

Anabolism. Those chemical processes occurring during the life of a cell that result in the formation of new protoplasm or the replacement of old.

Anaphase. A stage in mitosis that is characterized by the migration of chromosome halves to opposite poles of the cell.

Anatomy. The branch of the biological sciences dealing with visible body structures.

Anemia. A condition resulting from a lowering of the amount of hemoglobin in the body.

Anoxia. The condition arising from a lack of oxygen.

Antagonistic action of muscles. The opposing action of the members of a pair of skeletal muscles.

Anterior. Referring to the front of the human body. Also at or toward the head end of an animal.

Anvil. See *incus.*

Appendage. Any structure having one end attached to the main part of the body and the other end more or less free.

Appendicular skeleton. The skeletal structures composing and supporting the appendages. These include the shoulder and hip girdles as well as the arms and legs.

Arachnoid. The middle layer of the tissues covering the brain and spinal cord.

Arteriole. A fine branch of an artery.

Artery. A muscular blood vessel carrying blood away from the heart.

Arthritis. An inflammation of the joints, sometimes resulting in fusion of the bones.

Assimilation. The formation of new protoplasm from nonliving materials within cells.

Aster. A series of cytoplasmic fibers which radiate from the centriole during mitosis.

Astigmatism. A defect of vision caused by abnormal curvature of the surface of either the cornea or the lens.

Atom. The smallest unit of matter.

Atrio–. A prefix referring to the atrium of the heart.

Atrioventricular bundle. A bundle of nerve fibers that transmits impulses from the atria to the ventricles.

Atrium. A chamber of the heart that receives blood.

Atrophy. A decrease in size of some organ or structure of the body.

Auricle. See *atrium.*

Autonomic nervous system. A portion of the nervous system formed of two chains of ganglia lying outside of the central nervous system but connected to it by branches (rami).

Axial skeleton. The central, supporting portion of the skeleton composed of the skull, vertebral column, ribs, and breast bone.

Axon. That portion of the neuron that carries impulses away from the cell body.

Back cross. A cross between either a homozygous dominant or a heterozygous dominant of the F_2 generation and a homozygous recessive.

Barometer. A device for measuring air pressure.

Basal metabolic rate. The basic rate of the body's metabolism.

Basophil. A type of white blood corpuscle in which the cytoplasmic granules stain blue with methylene blue.

Bel. A unit used to measure the intensity of sound.

Bilateral symmetry. A type of body structure in which bisection through the vertebral column and the breast bone results in two halves which are mirror images of each other.

Binocular vision. The ability to see an object with both eyes simultaneously.

Biological sciences. The sciences that deal with living organisms.

Blending. See *incomplete dominance.*

Blind spot. The region of the retina that is insensitive to light because it has no rods and cones.

Blood. The circulating tissue of the body.

Blood platelets. The smallest of the blood solids, which aid in the formation of a blood clot.

Blood pressure. The pressure exerted by flowing blood on the walls of an artery.

Bolus. A ball of food which passes along the digestive canal.

Bone. A relatively hard porous substance containing a high percentage of calcium and phosphorous salts. It forms the major part of the skeleton.

Bone marrow. The fatty tissue lying within the central cavity of many bones. See *red bone marrow* and *yellow bone marrow.*

Boyle's law. The gas law which deals with the relation of pressure to the volume of a gas.

Brain. The part of the central nervous system contained within the cranium of the skull.

Brain stem. Structurally, the lowest part of the brain. It is composed of the pons, midbrain (thalamus and hypothalamus) and the medulla oblongata.

Brownian movement. Movement of small particles which results from their bombardment by smaller invisible particles.

Bursa. A sac of fluid between the bones of a joint.

Bursitis. An inflammation of a bursa, frequently accompanied by the formation of calcium salts in the cavity.

Callus. Any thickening of a tissue resulting from the normal growth of cells.

Calorie. The amount of heat required to raise the temperature of 1,000 grams of water one degree Centigrade.

Calorimeter. A device to measure heat production.

Capillary. A minute blood vessel that arises from an artery and joins with other small vessels to form a vein.

Carbohydrate. A chemical compound composed of carbon, hydrogen, and oxygen, with hydrogen and oxygen in the ratio of $2:1$.

Cardiac muscle. A branching, lightly striated type of muscle found only in the heart. It contracts rhythmically.

Cartilage. A flexible supporting tissue composed of a nonliving matrix within which are the living cartilage cells.

Catabolism. Those processes occurring with living cells that result in the breaking down of protoplasm and the release of energy.

Cell. The unit of structure and function in a living body.

Cell membrane. A membrane surrounding a cell. It is highly selective in controlling the passage of materials into and out of the cell.

Central nervous system. The brain and spinal cord.

Centriole. A small body lying within the centrosphere, which can be stained by hemotoxylin.

Centromere. A small centrally located body which attaches the two chromosome halves to each other.

Centrosphere. A granular area lying near the nucleus of an animal cell, containing the centriole.

Cephalin. A chemical produced by blood platelets.

Cerebellum. The region of the brain that coordinates muscular activities.

Cerebral hemisphere. One of the two principal divisions of the cerebrum.

Cerebrum. The largest of the three principal parts of the brain.

Cerumen. The waxy secretion formed by glands in the external acoustic meatus.

Cervical. Referring to the neck region.

Charles' law. The gas law dealing with the relation between the volume of a gas and its temperature.

Chemical compound. A substance composed of two or more unlike atoms which are chemically united in definite percentage.

Chemical formula. A method of stating the composition of a substance by the use of chemical symbols and numbers.

Cholinesterase. A substance produced at the junction of a nerve and muscle fiber which neutralizes the action of acetylcholine.

Choroid layer. A pigmented, highly vascular layer of the eye that lies between the retina and the sclera.

Chromatic abberation. The scattering of light rays at the edges of a lens so that rings of color appear to surround the object that is being viewed.

Chromatin. The material within the nucleus of a cell that is easily stained by basic dyes.

Chromosome. One of the rodlike bodies appearing during the mitotic division of a cell.

Chyle. The fluid form of food in the small intestine.

Chyme. The fluid form of food within the stomach.

Cilium. A small, whiplike projection from a cell.

Coccyx. The end of the vertebral column beyond the sacrum.

Cochlea. The spiral bony canal of the inner ear in which are located the auditory receptors.

Cold-blooded. A term used to describe animals which cannot maintain a constant body temperature.

Colloid. Matter in a very finely divided state. Colloidal particles vary in size from large molecules to the threshold of visibility with a high power optical microscope.

Colon. The large intestine.

Cone. A receptor in the retina of the eye that is sensitive to light of high intensity and color.

Conjunctiva. A delicate layer of epithelium that covers the outer surface of the cornea and is continued as the lining of the eyelids.

Convolution of the brain. The raised area between two sulci.

Cornea. The transparent layer in the front of the eye, the outer surface of which is covered by the conjunctiva.

Coronary circulation. The arteries, capillaries, and veins of the heart.

Corpus callosum. A band of white matter that connects the two cerebral hemispheres. It is present only in mammals.

Cortex. A general term applied to the outer region of an organ.

Cranial nerve. A nerve that arises from the brain and passes to some region of the body. There are twelve pairs of cranial nerves.

Crossing over. The recombination of genes resulting from the twining of chromosomes during meiosis and their later separation.

Cytoplasm. The material lying within the cell membrane and outside of the nucleus. It contains both living and nonliving substances.

Dalton's law of partial pressures. The gas law which describes the effect of the pressure exerted individually by each of the gases in the atmosphere.

Decibel. A unit used to measure sound intensity. One-tenth of a bel.

Deciduous. Describing any structure which is lost during the normal growth period of an animal or plant. It is applied to the milk teeth or the leaves shed by a tree.

Deglutition. The act of swallowing.

Deletion. In genetics: the loss of a part of a chromosome during meiosis.

Dendrite. The nerve cell process that carries impulses toward the cell body. There may be many dendrites on one nerve cell.

Dentin. The hard bonelike material that forms the major part of a tooth.

Dialysis. The separation of a colloidal material from other substances through a semipermeable membrane.

Diaphragm. A wall of muscle separating the thoracic and abdominal cavities. It is present only in mammals.

Diaphysis. The main part, or shaft, of a bone.

Diastole. The period during the beat of

the heart when the atria and the ventricles fill with blood.

Diffusion. The movement of molecules of a substance from a region where it is in relatively high concentration to an area of lower concentration.

Diploid number. The number of chromosomes present in the somatic (body) cells of an individual. It is usually twice that of the haploid number.

Disaccharide. A type of carbohydrate formed by the chemical union of two hexoses.

Dislocation. The forcing of a bone out of its normal position in a joint.

Distal. Toward the free end of an appendage. The hand, for example, is distal to the arm.

Division of labor. The division of the activities of the body among specialized organs and tissues.

Dominant characteristic. The member of a pair of contrasting characteristics which appears in the phenotype.

Dorsal. Referring to the back of an animal; the side along which the backbone passes; sometimes called the posterior side.

Dura mater. The outermost of the meninges.

Ear drum. See *tympanum*.

Edema. Swelling caused by the collection of fluids in a tissue.

Effector. A muscle, gland, or other type of tissue that responds to a definite stimulus.

Efferent. Referring to any nerve or blood vessel that carries an impulse or blood away from a central point.

Electrocardiogram. A record of the electric currents produced by a beating heart.

Electroencephalogram. A record of the electric currents produced by the brain.

Electron. A negatively charged particle of an atom.

Elements. The basic forms of mttaer.

Embryology. A study of the early stages in the development of the individual. The embryonic period extends up to the time when the individual assumes the general characteristics of the race.

Emulsion. The suspension of an insoluble liquid in another liquid in the form of small droplets.

Enamel. The hard outer layer of a tooth.

Endocrine gland. A gland lacking ducts and secreting directly into the blood stream,

Endothelium. A type of tissue resembling squamous epithelium.

Enzyme. A chemical compound which affects the rate of a chemical reaction.

Eosin. A commonly used biological stain that is bright red in color.

Eosinophil. A type of white corpuscle in which the cytoplasmic granules stain deeply with eosin.

Epiphyseal line. The line between the epiphysis and the diaphysis (shaft) of a bone.

Epiphysis. A bony process attached to another bone by a layer of cartilage.

Epithelium. The type of tissue which covers all body surfaces.

Erythrocyte. See *red blood corpuscle*.

Excretion. The elimination of liquid wastes.

Exocrine gland. A gland with a duct or ducts.

Extension. The movement of one part of the body away from another.

External acoustic meatus. A slightly curved canal in the temporal bone which conducts sound waves from the exterior to the tympanum.

Extrinsic muscles of the eye. The muscles attached to the outer surface of the eyeball.

Farsightedness. See *hyperopia*.

Fat. A simple type of lipid composed of one molecule of glycerine and three molecules of fatty acid.

Fatty acid. A weak organic acid present in lipids.

Fertilization. The union of egg and sperm nuclei.

Fibrinogen. A plasma protein responsible for the formation of a blood clot.

Fissure. A deep indentation on the surface of the cerebrum.

Flexion. The bending of one part of the body on another.

Focal point. The point at which the rays of light passing through a lens are focused.

Food. Any substance which may supply energy to the body, increase or repair protoplasm, or be stored for future use.

Foramen. A normal opening in a tissue through which fluids, nerves, or blood vessels pass.

Fovea centralis. The most sensitive region of the retina.

Galvanometer. A device used to measure the flow of an electric current.

Gamete. A general term applied to either egg or sperm cells.

Gametogenesis. The processes involved in the maturation of the gametes.

Gas. A state of matter characterized by an indefinite volume and shape.

Gene. The determiner of a heritable characteristic.

Genetics. The study of the inheritance of characteristics.

Genotype. The genetic makeup of an individual.

Gland. A specialized group of cells that manufactures materials which are released in the form of secretions.

Globulin. A type of protein.

Glycosuria. The excretion of sugar in the urine.

Golgi network. Small bodies in the cytoplasm of most animal cells, evidently concerned with protein formation.

Gonad. A general term applied to a reproductive organ.

Gray matter. Those parts of the central nervous system having nerve tissue lacking a medullary sheath.

Gyrus. See *convolution of the brain.*

Hammer. See *malleus.*

Haploid number. The number of chromosomes present in the mature gametes.

Haversian canal. A small canal in bone tissue, occupied by a blood vessel.

Heart muscle. See *cardiac muscle.*

Hematin. The iron compound that is combined with globin to form hemoglobin.

Hemoglobin. A chemical compound of iron and protein that is responsible for the transport of oxygen around the body.

Hemophilia. An inherited defect in which the blood does not clot normally.

Hemorrhage. The loss of blood from the circulatory system.

Henry's law. The statement of the solubility of gases in a liquid.

Heterozygous. The condition in which an individual possesses both genes for a pair of contrasting characteristics. The hybrid condition.

Hexose. A form of carbohydrate in which there are six carbon atoms.

Histology. The branch of the biological sciences dealing with the microscopic structure of tissues.

Homologous. A term used in describing parts of the body that are similar in structure and origin.

Homozygous. Referring to the condition in which an individual possesses only one type of gene for a given characteristic. The pure condition.

Hormone. A product of an endocrine gland.

Hydrogen ion concentration. The degree of acidity or alkalinity of a substance measured in terms of the concentration of hydrogen ions.

Hydrolysis. A chemical process in which a molecule of water combines with another compound, reducing it to a simpler form.

Hyper–. A prefix denoting an excess of a substance.

Hyperopia (farsightedness). A defect of vision in which the focal point of the lens falls behind the retina due to a shortening of the eyeball.

Hypertrophy. An increase in size of some organ or region of the body.

Hypo–. A prefix denoting a subnormal amount of a substance or the lower position of one object in relation to another.

Incomplete dominance. A type of inheritance in which neither of a pair of genes for contrasting characteristics is completely dominant or recessive.

Incus (anvil). The middle of the three small bones of the middle ear.

Infrared radiations. The wave lengths of light lying just beyond the red end of the visible spectrum.

Ingestion. The intake of solid or liquid food materials through the mouth.

Inhibit. An action which slows down an activity or prevents it from occurring.

Integument. The skin and its appendages.

Interphase. The period in the life of a cell when it is not dividing.

Invertebrate. An animal lacking a backbone.

Inverted retina. The type of retina in which the rods and cones point toward the choroid layer.

Iodopsin. A pigment in cones which is sensitive to color differences.

Ion. An electrically charged atom, or group of atoms.

Iris. The colored portion of the eye.

Irritability. The ability of protoplasm to respond to a stimulus.

Islands of Langerhans. Small groups of

isolated cells embedded in the pancreas. They form insulin.

Isotopes. Forms of the same element whose atoms differ in the number of neutrons they contain.

Jaundice. Yellow color of skin due to blockage of bile ducts causing excess bile pigments to accumulate in blood.

Joint. The point of union between two bones.

Karyolymph. The fluid within the nucleus of a cell.

Kyphosis. The abnormal curvature of the vertebral column or the sternum in an anterior-posterior plane.

Lacteal. A lymph duct in a villus in which fat accumulates.

Larynx. The voice box, or Adam's apple.

Lens. An optical device that refracts light so that its rays either diverge (biconcave lens) or converge (biconvex lens).

Leukemia. A disease of the blood characterized by an abnormally large number of white blood corpuscles.

Leukocyte. See *white blood corpuscle.*

Leukocytosis. An increase in the number of white blood corpuscles during certain types of infection.

Leukopenia. A decrease in the normal number of white blood corpuscles due to bone marrow damage or certain infections.

Ligament. A tough band of connective tissue which connects bones to each other.

Lipids. Chemical compounds usually composed of the elements carbon, hydrogen, and oxygen, in no special relation to each other. The simplest forms are the fats and oils.

Liquid. The state of matter that is characterized by a definite volume but indefinite shape.

Lordosis. An abnormal curvature of the lumbar vertebrae in an anterior direction resulting in a swayback condition.

Lumbar. Referring to the region of the back extending from the thorax to the sacrum.

Lymph. A colorless fluid within the lymphatics, derived from the extracellular fluid.

Lymphocyte. A type of white blood corpuscle formed in lymph tissue.

Malleus. One of the small bones in the middle ear, one end of which is attached to the tympanum and the other to the incus.

Mammals. A group of verebrates possessing hair, giving birth to living young, and capable of producing milk.

Mastication. The act of chewing food.

Matter. Any substance that has weight and occupies space.

Medulla. A general term applied to the internal region of a solid organ.

Medulla oblongata. A part of the brain stem.

Megakaryocyte. A primitive type of blood cell formed in the red marrow. It breaks up to form blood platelets.

Meiosis. The type of cell division which occurs during maturation of gametes. It results in the formation of the haploid number of chromosomes.

Mendelian laws. The laws formulated by Gregor Mendel to explain the inheritance of characteristics.

Meninges. The coverings of the brain and spinal cord.

Mesentery. A fold of the peritoneum that supports parts of the digestive system.

Metabolism. The chemical processes occurring within cells.

Metaphase. A stage in mitosis in which the halves of the chromosomes separate.

Metaplasm. Nonliving materials formed by the cytoplasm of a cell.

Micella. A subdivision of a myofibril.

Mitochondria. Small living structures lying within the cytoplasm of a cell, associated with energy transformations.

Mitosis. The process of cell division which results in the chromatin material of a cell being divided into equal halves.

Mixed gland. A gland possessing both exocrine and endocrine parts; for example, the pancreas.

Mixed nerve. A nerve containing both efferent and afferent fibers.

Monosaccharide. A form of carbohydrate containing a single saccharide group. These may be either pentoses or hexoses.

Mucosa. The mucous membrane lining an organ.

Muscle tissue. A type of tissue that has the ability to contract.

Muscle tone. The constant state of partial contraction of a muscle resulting from a subthreshold flow of nervous impulses to it.

Mutation. A suddenly appearing new characteristic that can be inherited.

Myasthenia gravis. A condition of easy fatigability of voluntary muscles thought to be caused by an excess of a chemical which blocks acetylcholine at the myoneural junction.

Myelin (medullary) sheath. A covering of fatty material over a nerve fiber or process.

Myofibril. A subdivision of a striated muscle fiber.

Myopia (nearsightedness). A defect of vision resulting from an elongation of the eyeball and the failure of the lens to focus the image on the retina.

Myosin. One of the two proteins concerned in muscle contraction.

Nearsightedness. See *myopia*.

Nephron. A tubule in the kidneys.

Nerve. A cablelike structure composed of axons, dendrites, or both.

Nerve impulse. A wavelike impulse passing over a nerve cell process that is characterized by both electrical and chemical effects.

Nerve tissue. A specialized tissue that is adapted to respond to a stimulus.

Neural. Referring to the nervous system.

Neurofibrils. Strands of cytoplasm in the nerve cell body that connect the dendrites and the axons.

Neuron. The unit of structure in the nervous system. A nerve cell.

Neutron. An electrically neutral particle in the nucleus of an atom.

Neutrophil. A type of white blood corpuscle in which the cytoplasm does not stain with either hemotoxylin or eosin.

Nissl body. One of many small cytoplasmic inclusions in the nerve cell body.

Nuclear membrane. A semipermeable membrane surrounding the nucleus of a cell and separating it from the cytoplasm.

Nucleic acid. A complex type of organic acid found in chromatin.

Nucleolus. One or more bodies within the nucleus that appear to be associated with the formation of nucleoproteins.

Neucleoplasm. A general term used to identify the living material of the nucleus.

Nucleoprotein. A type of protein found in the nucleus of a cell.

Nucleus. (1) The controlling center of a cell's activities; (2) the center of an atom, composed of protons and neutrons; (3) a group of specialized nerve cells lying within the white matter of the central nervous system.

Nutrient. See *food*.

Oil. A type of relatively simple lipid that is fluid at ordinary temperatures.

Olfaction. The process of smelling.

Optic nerve. The nerve passing from the eye to the occipital lobe of the cerebrum.

Orbit (orbital cavity). A cavity in the upper half of the anterior surface of the skull; the eye cavity.

Organ. A group of tissues which function together in the performance of a definite body function.

Organ of Corti. The structure in the inner ear which contains the sense organs of hearing.

Organ system. A group of organs with related functions.

Organic nutrient. Any carbohydrate, lipid, or protein.

Osmosis. Diffusion through a semipermeable membrane.

Osmotic pressure. The pressure that is established on one side of a semipermeable membrane as a result of the passage of a material through it.

Ossification. The process of bone formation.

Osteoclast. A cell which destroys bone to form channels through it for the passage of blood vessels and nerves.

Osteocyte. A bone-forming cell after it has left a Haversian canal.

Osteomyelitis. An infection of bone tissue.

Ovary. The egg-producing organ.

Ovum. A female reproductive cell; an egg cell.

Oxyhemoglobin. Hemoglobin containing oxygen. It is bright red in color.

Papilla. Any projection of tissue above a normal surface.

Pathology. The study of disease.

Pericardium. A double-walled sac of endothelial tissue surrounding the heart.

Periosteum. The tissue which covers the outside of a bone.

Peripheral nervous system. The part of the nervous system lying outside of the central nervous system and containing the receptors and effectors.

Peristalsis. A rhythmic, wavelike series of contractions moving over the walls of a tube and resulting in the passage of materials along the tube.

Peritoneum. A layer of tissue that lines the abdominal cavity and surrounds many of the abdominal organs.

pH. The symbol for hydrogen ion concentration.

Phagocyte. A type of white blood corpuscle that devours bacteria and other foreign bodies.

Pharynx. The cavity in back of the mouth which is a common passageway to both the respiratory and digestive systems.

Phenotype. The visible characteristics of an individual as determined by the genes.

Phonation. The ability to produce sounds by means of vocal cords.

Photopic vision. Vision in a bright light resulting from the activities of the cones.

Physiology. The study of the functions or activities of the various parts of the body.

Pia mater. The innermost of the meninges.

Plasma. The fluid part of the blood.

Pleura. A two-layered sac of endothelial tissue surrounding each lung.

Polar body. A small cell that is formed during the maturation of the ovum. It cannot be fertilized by a sperm.

Polysaccharide. A complex form of carbohydrate composed of many hexose groups.

Portal vein. A large vein, formed from capillaries in the walls of the digestive system, that passes to the liver.

Posterior. Referring to the back of the human body. Also at or toward the tail end of an animal.

Presbyopia. A condition of old age in which the lens of the eye becomes fixed at a universal focal distance.

Prophase. A stage in the mitotic division of a cell in which the chromatin network becomes thicker and individual chromosomes appear.

Protein. An extremely complex chemical compound composed of carbon, hydrogen, oxygen, nitrogen, and other elements. It forms the basis of protoplasm.

Proton. A positively charged particle within the nucleus of an atom.

Protoplasm. The living material in cells.

Proximal. The part of an appendage that is toward the main part of the body.

Psychology. The study of an organism's responses to its environment (behavior).

Pulmonary circulation. The path of the blood through the lungs.

Pulse. A wave of blood flowing along the arteries.

Pulse wave. A wave of muscular contraction that passes along the walls of the arteries.

Pupil. The opening in the iris of the eye.

Receptor. The ending of a nerve fiber that is specialized to receive one particular type of stimulus.

Recessive characteristic. The member of a pair of opposing characteristics which does not appear in the phenotype when the dominant is present.

Reciprocal innervation. A condition in which the members of a pair of antagonistic muscles are stimulated and inhibited simultaneously by nerve impulses.

Red blood corpuscle. A nonnucleated, biconcave disk containing hemoglobin.

Red bone marrow. The principal site of the formation of blood corpuscles.

Referred pain. A feeling of pain in one part of the body resulting from the stimulation of nerves in another region.

Refraction. The bending of a beam of light as it passes from one medium into another.

Reproduction. The ability of a living organism to produce similar living things.

Respiration. The exchange of gases between cells and their surroundings.

Retina. The innermost layer of the eye composed of nerve endings that are sensitive to light.

Rhodopsin (visual purple). A reddish-blue pigment present in the choroid layer and in the rods in the retina.

Rod. A light receptor in the retina that is sensitive to low intensities of light but not color.

Sacrum. The region of the vertebral column composed of fused vertebrae that forms part of the hip girdle.

Sclera. The tough outer layer of the eye; the white of the eye.

Scoliosis. A sideward curvature of the vertebral column.

Scotopic vision. Vision in a dim light due to the activities of the rods.

Secretion. The act of releasing a product of a gland from the cells that formed it. Also, the product of the gland.

Secretagogue. An endocrine secretion that stimulates another gland to activity.

Semicircular canals. Three bony canals in the inner ear, concerned with maintenance of balance.

Semipermeable membrane. A type of membrane that will permit the passage of certain materials but prevent the movement of others through it.

Septicemia. A generalized type of infection

caused by bacteria or other pathogenic organisms in the blood.

Septum. A wall of tissue dividing a cavity.

Serum. Plasma lacking fibrinogen.

Serum albumin. A type of protein present in plasma and concerned with the maintenance of osmotic pressure.

Serum globulin. A type of plasma protein that contains antibodies.

Sex-limited characteristic. A characteristic which is determined by a gene that is present on the nonhomologous portion of the Y chromosome.

Sex linkage. The type of inheritance in which the gene is carried on the nonhomologous portion of the X chromosome.

Sinoatrial node. A bundle of nerve fibers in the wall of the right atrium that serves as the pacemaker for the heart beat.

Sinus. A normal cavity within a bone or other organ.

Skeletal muscle. See *striated muscle*.

Skeleton. The bony and cartilaginous framework of the body.

Smooth muscle. Elongated, thin, spindle-shaped muscle fibers that are involuntary in their action.

Sociology. A study of the relation of human beings to each other and their environment.

Solid. The state of matter that is characterized by definite shape and volume.

Sperm. A male reproductive cell.

Spherical aberration. The scattering of beams of light at the edges of a lens so that they are not focused sharply.

Sphincter muscle. A layer of smooth muscle arranged in a circular manner around a tube or opening. It behaves like a drawstring in controlling the size of the opening.

Sphygmomanometer. A device for measuring blood pressure.

Spinal nerve. One of thirty-one pairs of nerves arising in the spinal cord.

Spindle. A series of elongated cytoplasmic fibers connecting the two centrosomes during mitosis.

Spirometer. A mechanical device used to measure the capacity of the lungs.

Sprain. The result of tearing or straining of tendons and ligaments at a joint.

Stapes. The innermost of the three small bones of the middle ear. It articulates with the incus at one end and the membrane of the oval window at the other.

State of matter. The form taken by matter; solid, liquid, or gas.

Stereoscopic vision. The ability to see in three dimensions.

Stimulus. Any change in the environment that brings about a response.

Stirrup. See *stapes*.

Striated muscle. Tissue composed of spindle-shaped fibers with striations; its action is voluntary.

Subarachnoid space. The space between the arachnoid and pia mater containing the cerebrospinal fluid.

Substrate. The material affected by an enzyme.

Sulcus. A relatively shallow indentation on the surface of the brain.

Suspension, colloidal. The suspension of finely divided particles of one substance in another.

Synapse. The meeting place of two nerve cell processes.

Systemic circulation. The path followed by the blood in flowing through all organs of the body except the lungs and the tissues of the heart.

Systole. The period of active contraction of the atria and ventricles.

Telophase. The final stage in mitosis in which a new cell membrane appears and the cytoplasm of the parent cell divides into two halves.

Tendon. A tough band of connective tissue that attaches a muscle to a bone.

Testis. The male sperm-producing organ.

Tetanus. A state of sustained contraction of a muscle caused by the repeated flow of nerve impulses to the muscle. Also, a bacterial disease in which the muscles contract and fail to relax.

Thoracic. Referring to the region of the thorax.

Thorax. The upper part of the trunk.

Threshold. The minimum stimulus required to bring about a response.

Thrombocyte. See *blood platelet*.

Thrombus. A clot of blood that forms within a blood vessel.

Tissue. A group of similar cells performing a specific function.

Tourniquet. A mechanical device to prevent excessive loss of blood.

Trabecula. A wall of firmer and more compact tissue lying within an organ.

Transformation of energy, Law of. The

conversion of energy from a quiet (potential) form to an active (kinetic) state.

Trunk. The main part of the body.

Tympanum. A thin membrane covering the internal end of the external acoustic meatus. It vibrates when struck by sound waves.

Tyndall effect. The scattering of a beam of light by the particles of a colloidal suspension.

Ultraviolet radiations. That region of the spectrum lying just beyond the shortest visible violet rays.

Vacuole. A space within a cell that is filled with a fluid.

Vaso–. A prefix referring to a blood vessel.

Vein. A blood vessel carrying blood back toward the heart.

Ventral. Referring to the side of an animal opposite to that along which the backbone passes; sometimes called the anterior side.

Ventricle. (1) A chamber of the heart from which blood flows to various parts of the body. (2) One of several cavities in the brain.

Venule. A small vein.

Vertebral column. The backbone.

Vertebrate. An animal possessing a backbone.

Villus. A small, fingerlike projection from the mucosa of the small intestine, through the walls of which digested foods are absorbed by the blood.

Visual acuity. The ability to see objects clearly with the naked eye.

Visual purple. See *rhodopsin.*

Vitamin. An essential accessory food substance.

Voluntary muscle. See *striated muscle.*

White blood corpuscle. A relatively large, nucleated blood cell having the power of independent movement.

White matter. That part of the central nervous system characterized by neurons having medullary sheaths.

Yellow bone marrow. Marrow in the medullary cavities of long bones, containing many fat cells.

Yolk. Nonliving material in the cytoplasm of an ovum. It serves as food for the developing embryo.

Zygote. A fertilized egg cell.

Index

Abdomen, **5**–6
Abdominal wall, **200**
Abduction, 44–46
Aberration, chromatic, **135;** spherical, **134**–135
Absolute refractory period, **89**–90
Accommodation, of eye, 124, 136–137
Acetabulum, **55**
Acetylcholine, 63–64; effect on heart rate, 280; effect on nerve fibers, 92–93; functions in autonomic nervous system, 112; as vasodilator, 296
Achilles' tendon, **75, 77,** 79
Achrodextrin, 156
Acid(s), amino, *see* Amino acids; ascorbic, 178–179; butyric, 157; capric, 157; caproic, 157; caprylic, 157; cerotic, 157; fatty, 157–158, 207, 209; hydrochloric, 167, 191–192, 196; lauric, 157; myristic, 157; oleic, 157; palmitic, 157; para-aminobenzoic, 177–178; phosphoric, 164; stearic, 157; uric, 164
Acid-base equilibrium of blood, 247; maintenance of, 266–267; regulation of, by kidneys, 332, 336
Acidity, and pH, 16; of blood, effect of exercise on, 70
Acromegaly, 344
Acromion process, 53, **55**
ACTH, **343,** 345, 354
Actin, 62, 66–67; molecular weight of, 159
Action current, 281–282
Action potential, 89
Actomysin, 67–68
Adam's apple, 218, 241
Adaptation, dark, 129–130; light, 130–134
Addison's disease, 353–354
Adduction, 46
Adenoids, 181, **182, 217,** 218
Adenosine diphosphate (ADP), 67–68
Adenosine triphosphate (ATP), 67–68
ADH. *See* Antidiuretic hormone
Adipose tissue, 34–**35**
ADP. *See* Adenosine diphosphate
Adrenal glands, 204; cortex of, **341,** 345, **353;** effects of malfunction of, 353–354; hormone of cortex, 353; hormone of medulla, 355–356; location and structure of, **341, 353;** medulla

of, **341, 353,** 354–356; and sympathetic nervous system, 355, 356
Adrenalin (epinephrin), 111, 112, 281, 342, 355–356; and conversion of glucose, 204; effect on basal metabolic rate, 356; effect on blood pressure, 291–292; functions of, 355; structural formula for, 355; as vasoconstrictor, 296; as vasodilator, 355
Adrenin. *See* Adrenalin
Adrenocorticotropic hormone (ACTH), **343,** 345, 354
Adult myxedema, 348
Afterimages, positive and negative, 133
Agglutination, 269–271
Agglutinins, 269–271
Agglutinogens, 269–271
Air, atmospheric, composition of, 225; in respiration, 227–228
Air passages, 216–219, **217**
Air sac, **219**
Alanine, 159
Albinism, 306
Albumins, of plasma, 264–265
Albuminuria, 334
Alcohol, as end-product of enzyme reaction, 169; as vasodilator, 296–297
Alkalinity, and pH, 16
All-or-none law, 90–91
Alpha-tocopherol, 173
Alveolus (i), **219**
Ameloblasts, 184
Amino acids, 207; amount of in certain proteins, 159; composition of, 159; conversion of by liver, 204; decomposition of (chart), 335; essential, 159, 160; nonessential, 159, 160
Aminopeptidase, 206
Ammonia, 335
Amphiprotic compound, 159
Amphoteric compound, 159
Ampulla, **142,** 149
Amylase, pancreatic. *See* Amylopsin
Amylopsin, 205, 206, 207
Anabolism, 320
Anaphase, 25, 26
Anatomy, science of, **2**–3
Anemia, 258–260; Cooley's, 259; iron-deficiency, 259–260; pernicious, 259; sickle cell, 259
Anesthetics, spinal, 96
Ångstrom units, 122, 130, 131, 133

Angular joint, 44, **45**
Ankle, bones of, **49,** 56–57
Anomaly, 148
Anoxia, 231
Antagonistic muscles, 73–74
Anterior side, 5
Antidiuretic hormone (ADH), 336, **343, 345**
Antihistamine, 296
Antitoxins, 265
Antrum (a), **217**
Anus, 211
Aorta, **275, 276, 279,** 288, 289
Apex, of heart, 273, **274**
Apparatus, for decomposition of water, **9;** to demonstrate breathing, **222;** for demonstration of sound waves, **144;** to record sound waves, **145**
Appendage, 5–6, 52
Appendicitis, 212
Appendicular skeleton, 47, 52–57
Appendix, **201;** inflamed, **212**
Appetite, 164
Aqueous humor, 122
Arachnoid mater, 96, 99, **100**
Arch(es), of aorta, **274, 279;** of human foot, **57;** pelvic, **55;** pharyngeal, 218; pubic, **55;** zygomatic, 50
Arginine, 159, 204
Arm, bones of, **49,** 53–55; regions of, 53–55
Arrector pili muscles, 308, 309
Arterioles, 248, 289; effect on blood pressure, 291–292; and regulation of blood flow, 295
Artery (ies), 248; afferent and efferent of renal glomerulus, 332–**333;** carotid, **279;** central retinal, 119, **120;** common carotid **274, 279;** coronary, **274**—; hardening of, 158; elasticity of, 290–291—and rate of pulse wave, 294; external carotid, 279; of eye, 116, 119; hepatic, **201, 249;** innominate, 279; internal carotid, **279;** of intestine, 206; pulmonary, **274, 275, 276,** 288, 289; renal, **332, 333;** structure and functions of, 288–**289,** 290; subclavian, **274, 279;** variations of temperature in, 313
Arthritis, hypertrophic, 57; rheumatoid, 57–**58**
Articular cartilage, **46**
Articular processes, of vertebra, 51, **52**

Articulation, 43–47, 52–57; types of, 44, **45**. *See also* Joints
Artificial respiration, 231, 234–240; methods of applying, 236–240
Ascorbic acid. *See* Vitamin C
Assimilation, 23–24
Asters, **25**
Asthma, white cell count in, 257
Astigmatic dial, **135**, 136
Astigmatism, 135–136, 372
Atmosphere, composition of, 225
Atmospheric pressure, 226; effects of changing, 230–232—on ear, 141; measurement of, 222–223
Atom(s), 8–16; carbon, 8; hydrogen, 8; motion of, 13–15; oxygen, **8**; radioactive, 9–10; structure of, 8–9; sulfur, 8; uranium, 8
Atomic weight, 8
ATP. *See* Adenosine triphosphate
Atrial appendage, 277
Atrioventricular bundle, **278**
Atrium (a), 250, **274, 275, 279**
Atrophy, 69; of gland, 342; of muscles, 69, 106, 107
Atropine, 280–281
Audition, 85
Auditory canal, **50**
Auricle, of ear, 139; of heart, *see* Atrium
Auricular fibrillation, 284
Autonomic nervous system, 83, 108–112; chemicals in, 112; in control of blood vessels, 112; functions of, 109–112; organs supplied by, **111**; parasympathetic (craniosacral) division of, 110, **111**; structure of, 110–111; sympathetic (thoracolumbar) division of, 110–112, **111**
Avidin, 177
Avogadro's Law, 226
Axial skeleton, 47–52
Axis cylinder, **86**, 87, **88**
Axon, 85, **86**–87; of cortical cells, 103–104

Back cross, illustration of, 369–**370**
Bacteria, and bone infection, 57; digestion of by leukocytes, **255**–256; in feces, 213; in large intestine, 213; protection against by epithelium, 28
Bainbridge reflex, 279, 280
Balance, physiology of, 148–149
Ball and socket joint, 44, **45, 55**
Barometer, **223**
Basal metabolic rate (BMR), 322–327; effect of adrenal glands on, 353–354, 356; effect of thyroid gland on, 347–348; factors affecting, 324, 326–327; record of, **323**; relation of to age and sex, 323–**324**
Base (alkali), and pH, 16
Basophil, **253**, 257
Bayliss, Sir William, 166
Beaumont, Dr. William, 196
Bel, 145
Bell, Alexander Graham, 145
Belly, of muscle, 73

Bends, the, 232
Benedict's solution, 156
Berger, Hans, 112
Beriberi, 169, 174–175
Bicuspids. *See* Premolar teeth
Bilateral symmetry, 4–5
Bile, 201–203, **202**, 207; composition of, 202–203; digestive action of, 203; source of, 201–202
Bile salts, 202, 203
Bilirubin, 202–203
Biliverdin, 202
Binaural perception of sound, 147
Biological sciences, 2–3; relationships of, **2**
Biotin, 177
Bipolar neuron, 86, **87**
Bird, brain of, **101**
Blackout, 301
Bladder, urinary, **200, 332**, 336–337
Blending (incomplete dominance), 373–**375**
Blind spot, 121, **122**
Blood, 246–250; abnormal conditions affecting, 258–260; circulation of, 248–250, **249**; coagulation of, *see* Coagulation of blood; compatible, 270; composition of, 247–248—and osmotic pressure, 15; control of distribution of, 295–297; deoxygenated, 250; general functions of, 246–247; maintenance of pH of, 266–267; oxygenated, 250; pH of, 16; plasma of, *see* Blood plasma; Rh factor in, 270–271; solid parts of, 248, 252–260; solubility of gases in, 226–227; and tissues, principal materials exchanged between, 250; transfusions of, 269–271; typing of, 269–271; viscosity of and effect on blood pressure, 292; volume of, 247; white cell content of, 257
Blood plasma, 33, 246; composition of, 247–248—table, 262; inorganic substances in, 262, 266; proteins of, 264–265
Blood pressure, and blood volume, 291; diastolic, 291, 293, 294; during hemorrhage, 267–268; during shock, 265–266; effect of adrenalin on, 296, 355; effect of carbon dioxide on, 296; effect of exercise on, 71; and elasticity of vessels, 290–291; during sleep, 113; and fainting, 280; factors affecting, 290–292; and heart action, 291; measurement of, **292**–294; and peripheral resistance, 291–292; relation of to age, 293; systolic, 291, 293–294; and viscosity of blood, 292
Blood proteins, in plasma, 262
Blood sugar, and adrenalin, 355; in diabetes, 357, 358; effect of insulin on, 357, 358
Blood vessels, in Haversian canals, 43; type of cells in, 29
BMR. *See* Basal metabolic rate
Body, human, anterior view of, **5;**

ciliary, 116, 119; general regions of, **5**–6; of olfactory cell, **218;** polar, 365, **366, 367;** of stomach, **190**, 194; of sweat gland, 308; of vertebra, 51, **52;** of sternum, 51–52, **53;** vitreous, 122
Body temperature, and blood, 247; control of, 314–317; during sleep, 113; effect of exercise on, 71; factors disturbing, 317–318; and fat, 35; graph of, 313; regulation of, by skin, 304, 314–317; variations in, 312–314
Body surface (chart), 325
Bolus, **187**–188
Bomb calorimeter, **320**–321
Bone(s), *see also,* individual, specifically named: anvil, *see* incus; breast, *see* sternum; calcaneus, **49**, 56; carpal, **42, 43, 49**, 54, **58**; clavicle, **48, 49**, 52, **53, 55**; coccyx, **49**, 51, **55**; collar, *see* clavicle; cranium, 47, **48, 50**; ethmoid, **50**, 115, **116**; femur, **48**, 55–56; fibula, **48**, 56; humerus, **41, 49**, 53, **55, 59, 74**; hyoid, **240**; ilium, **48, 55**; incus (anvil), **140**–141; ischium, **48, 55**; lacrimal, 115, **116**; malleus (hammer), **140**; mandible, **50**; maxilla, **50**, 115, **116**; metacarpals, **43, 49, 54**; metatarsals, **48**, 57; nasal conchae, 216–**217**; occipital, **50**; palatine, **50**, 115, **116**; parietal, **50**; patella, **48**, 56; phalanges, of fingers, **43, 49**, 54–55—of toes, **48**, 57; pubis, **48, 55**; radius, **42, 43, 49**, 53–54, **58, 59, 74**; ribs, **48**, 51–52, **53, 54, 200, 229**; sacrum, **49, 55**; scapula, **49**, 52–53, **55, 74**; sesamoid, **43**, 55–56; sphenoid, **50**, 115, **116, 341**; spiral lamina, 142, **143**; stapes (stirrup), **140**–141, 146, 147; sternum, **48**, 51–52, **53, 54, 220**, 221; talus, **49**, 56; tarsal, **48**, 56–57; tarsus, 56–57; temporal, **50**; thoracic, **49, 54**; tibia, **48**, 56; trochlea, 117; turbinate, 216–**217**; ulna, **42, 43, 49**, 53–54, 58–60, **74;** vertebrae, **49**, 50–**51, 52**; zygomatic, **50**, 115, **116**
Bone(s), 40–60; of ankle, **49**, 56–57; of arm, **49**, 53–54; articulation of, 43–47, 52–57; canaliculi of, 42, 43, **44**; cells of, 35–36, **41**, 42–43, 44; compact, 40–**41**, 43; constituents of, 40; covering of, 41, 42, 46; dislocation of, 59–60; of ear, **140**–142, **143**, 146; facial, 47, **48, 50**; of fingers, **43, 48**, 54–55; of foot, **48**, 57; formation of, 35–36, 41–43; fractures of, **58–59**; of hand, **49**, 54–55; of head, 47, **50**; healing of broken, 59; of heel, **49**, 56–57; of hip, **48, 55**; infections of, 57; internal structure of, **41;** of jaw, **50, 184**, 185; lamellae of, 43, **44;** of the leg, **48**, 55–57; as levers, 46–47; marrow of, **41,**

43—red, 252, yellow, 252; nasal, 47, **50**; of orbital cavity, 115–**116**; ossification of, 41, 42–43; of pelvic girdle, **48, 49, 55**; and radioactive calcium, 9; resorption of, 353; of shoulder girdle, **48**, 52–**53**; spongy, 40–**41**, 42–43; structure of, 40–**41**; thumb, 54–55; of toes, **48**, 57; trabeculae of, **41**, 42, 43; of vertebral column, **49**, 50–**51**, **52**; of wrist, **49**, 54–55; xiphoid process, 51–52, **53**
Bony labyrinth, 141–142
Bowman's capsule, 332, **333**
Boyle, Robert, 226
Brain(s), 99–108; base of, **108**; electrical activity of, 112–113; of invertebrates, 100; membranes of, 99; origin of, 83; prenatal development of, 100–101; subdivisions of, **100**–104; of vertebrates, 100, **101**
Brain stem, 100, 101–102
Breathing, mechanics of, 221–223. *See also* Respiration
Bronchiole, **219**
Bronchus (i), **219**
Brown, Robert, 14
Brownian movement, **14**
Buffers, action of in blood, 266–267
Bundle of His, **278**
Bursa (ae), **46**; of knee joint, 56

Caecum, 211, **212**
Caisson disease, 231–232
Calcification, of cartilage matrix, 42
Calcium, 154; and arthritis, 57–58; of bone, 40; in clotting of blood, 263; and digestion of milk, 167; and parathyroid glands, 352–353; radioactive, 9; requirement in pregnancy, 352–353; sources, 154; and vitamin D, 171
Callus, 59, 306
Calorie(s), 320–321, 322 324; daily requirements of, 161; definition of, 160; distribution of in some common foods, 162–163; values of different nutrients, 160
Calorimetry, 320–322
Canal, anal, 211, 213; auditory, **50**, 139–140; Haversian, 43, **44**; medullary, **41**, 43; root, **184**, 185; semicircular, 141, **142**, 148, 149
Canaliculi, 42, 43, **44**
Cancer, and cell division, 24: gastric, 196, **197**
Canine teeth, **183**, 184
Capillary (ies), 201, **205**, 248–250, **249**; absorption of nutrients by, 209; bile, **201**; of intestine, **206**, 209; of lungs, **219**; in muscular contraction, **70**; renal, 332–**333**; in skin, **307**; structure and functions of, **289**–290
Capsule, of adrenal gland, **353**; fibrous, **46**; internal, 105, 106; of spleen, 297

Carbohydrates, 153; definition of, 153; digestion of, 207; formulas for, 155; general divisions of, 153, 155; metabolism of, and diabetes, 356, 357; molecular structure of, 155–156; oxidation of, 156–157; oxidation value of, 321; as protein savers, 157; as source of energy, 156; storage of in body, 156–157
Carbon, 8, 153; radioactive, 9–10
Carbon dioxide, in air, 225; effect of on circulation, 296—on respiration rate, 230; percentage of in inhaled and exhaled air, 228; solubility of in blood, 226–227
Carbon monoxide poisoning, 235–238, **237**
Carboxypeptidase, 205, 207
Cardiac cycle, 274–278; sequence of, **276**
Cardiac muscle tissue, **32**, 33
Cardiac orifice, **190**
Cardiac output, 291–292
Cardioaccelerating center, 278, **279**
Cardioinhibitory center, 278, **279**
Cardiovascular disease, 158
Carotene, 170, 171, 306
Carotid channel, **143**
Carpus, 54, **58**
Cartilage, articular, **46**; arytenoid, **240**, 241, 242; of bronchi, 219; cells, **36**, 37—in bone formation, 42; costal, 52, **53**, **54**; cricoid, **240**, 241; elastic, **36**; epiphyseal, **41**, 42; functions of, 35, 36; hyaline, 36, **41**; of skull bones, 47; thyroid, **240**–241; of trachea, 218, **240**; types of, 36
Casein, 192–193; amino acids in, 159
Catabolism, 320
Catalyst, 166–167
Cavity, abdominal, section through, **200**; chest, 227, **220**; glenoid, 53; mouth, **181, 182**; nasal, **182**, 216–**217**; olecranon, 53, 54; orbital, 115–**116**; pleural, **219**, 220; in pulp of tooth, **184**, 185; thoracic, and breathing, 220–221; tympanic, **140**
Cell(s), of adipose tissue, **35**; animal, **21**; blood, types of, 33—see also Erythrocyte, Leukocyte, Platelet; of bone, 35–36, 37, **41**–**46**, **44**; of capillary, **289**; cartilage, **36**, 37, 42; connective tissue, 35–36, 37; of epidermis, **305**, 306; epithelial, 28–**30**, **29**, 37; fat, in skin, **307**; functions of, 20–27; of gastric glands, 191, **192**; germ, 364, 365; goblet, **29**—in trachea, 218; growth of, 23–27; hair, of inner ear, 147, 148, 149—of organ of Corti, 142–144, **143**; and heredity, 20–21, 24; interstitial (endocrine), **341**; of Island of Langerhans, **205**; Kupffer, 202, 204; liver, 201, **202**; of lymph

nodes, 300; muscle, 20, 30–**32**, 37; nerve, 20, 32–33, 37—*see also* Neuron, Nerve(s); and nonliving material, 18; olfactory, 217, **218**; pancreatic, **205**; of Paneth, **206**; and protoplasm, 17–18; reproductive (gametes), 33–**34**, 37, 362–367; reticular, 252; saliva-forming, **186**; somatic, 364, 365; specialization of, 18, 20–21, 28; of stomach, 191, **192**; structure of, 20–23; taste, **183**
Cell body, of nerve, 85, **86**
Cell division, 23–27
Cell membrane, **21**–22; diffusion through, 14–15
Cellulose, 156, 164, 213
Cementum, **184**, 185
Center of ossification, 42
Central nervous system, development of, 82–**83**; and rate of heart beat, 278–281; structure and functions of, 83, 95–113
Centriole, **21**, 22, **25**
Centromere, 26
Centrosome, **21**, 22
Cephalin, 263
Cerebellum, **100**, 148, 149; structure and functions of, **102**–103
Cerebral aqueduct, **102**
Cerebral cortex, **104, 105, 106, 107, 279**; associative activities of, 104–105; and conditioned reflexes, 113; effect of on blood flow, 295–296; functions of, 104–**105**; injury to fibers of, 106; motor activities of, **105**; motor pathways from, 105–107, **106**; removal of, 104–105; sensory activities of, **105**; sensory pathways to, **107**; structure of, 103–104
Cerebral peduncles, 101, **102**
Cerebrospinal fluid, 96, 99–100
Cerebrum, **100**–101, **229**; cortex of, *see* Cerebral cortex; structure of, 103–105
Cerumen, 140, 147
Characteristic(s), dominant, 368, 369, 372; recessive, 368, 369, 372; sex-limited, 371; sex-linked, 371–373
Charles, Jacques, 226
Cheeks, 181
Chemical activity, in nerve impulse, 91, 92–93
Chemical compound(s), **10**–11
Chemical control, by hormones, 341–342; of respiration, 228–229, 230
Chemical formula, 11
Chemicals, autonomic, 112; in retina, 120–121, 129–130
Chemistry, of muscular contraction, 63, 64–68; relation of to biological sciences, **2**, 4
Chemoreceptors, 296
Chlorine, 154
Chokes, the, 232
Cholecystokinin, 205
Cholesterol, 158, 202, 203, 353
Choline, 177, 178

Choline acetylase, 92
Cholinesterase, 63; effect of on nerve fibers, 92–93
Chordae tendineae, **275, 276**
Choroid layer, 118–119
Chromatic aberration, **135**
Chromatic vision, 121
Chromatin, 21, 23, **25,** 26, 362; and heredity, 24
Chromosomes, 23, **25, 26,** 364; of Drosophila, 362, **363;** homologous, 365–366, **371;** nonhomologous regions of, **371;** number of in various organisms, 365; deletion in, **376;** *X* and *Y,* 370–371
Chylomicrons, 209
Chyme, 194, 199, 205, 206, 208
Chymotrypsin, 205–206, 207
Chymotrypsinogen, 205
Cilia, **29**
Ciliary body, 116, 119
Ciliated columnar epithelium, in paranasal sinuses, 50
Ciliated epithelium, **29**–30
Circular folds, of small intestine, 209
Circulating tissue, 28, 33
Circulation, control of, 295–297; during shock, 265–266; effect of acetylcholine on, 296—of carbon dioxide on, 296, of changing forces on, 300–301, of drugs on, 296–297; general, 288–290; Harvey's studies of, 4; influence of cerebral cortex on, 295–296; Paracelsus' concept of, 4; portal, **201,** 202, 203; pulmonary, 288; systemic, 288; through heart, 274–276
Circulatory system, 246–301; closed, 248–250; diagram of, **249;** effect of exercise on, 69–71; open, 248; types of tissues in, 37
Cisterna chyli, **300**
Clotting. *See* Coagulation of blood
Coagulation of blood, factors affecting, 263–264; processes of, 262–**263**
Cobalt, sources and biological effects of, 154
Cochlea, 141, **142–143,** 147, 148, 149
Cohnheim's fields of myofibrils, 63
Collar bone. *See* Clavicle
Colloid, of thyroid gland, 346
Colloidal suspensions, 11–13
Colon, ascending, **211, 212;** descending, **211;** movement of, 213–214; sigmoid, **211,** 213; structure of, 211–212; transverse, **211**
Color(s), absorption of, **132;** compound, 131; primary, 131; receptors of. *See* Cones, of retina; of spectrum, 130, **131**
Color blindness, 134, 371, **372**
Color vision, characteristics of, 133–134; defects in, 134; theories of, 132–133
Columnar epithelium, **29**

Columns, of spinal cord, 96–**97,** 107
Compact bone, 40–**41,** 43
Complemental air, 227
Compound(s), chemical, 10–11
Compound fracture, 59
Compressions, of molecules, 144, 145
Conchae, nasal, 216–**217**
Conduction, 82, 315
Cones, of retina, 119–**121, 120,** 130, 132, 133; and color blindness, 134; and visual acuity, 134
Conjunctiva, 117, 118
Conjunctivitis, 117
Connective tissue, 28, 34–36
Constipation, 212, 213–214
Contractions, muscular. *See* Muscular contractions
Convection, 315–316
Convergence, of eyes, 123, **128;** of light rays, **124**
Convolutions, of cerebral cortex, 103, **104**
Cooley's anemia, 259
Copper, and formation of hemoglobin, 259–260; sources and biological effects of, 154
Coracoid process, 53
Cord(s), gangliated, of sympathetic, 110–111; of liver cells, **201;** prevertebral, 110–111; spinal, *see* Spinal cord; vertebral, 110–111; vocal, **217,** 218, **240, 241**–242
Corium. *See* Dermis
Corn, 306
Cornea, 118; and astigmatism, 135–136
Corpora quadrigemina, 101–**102**
Corpus luteum (endocrine), **341**
Corpuscles, red. *See* Erythrocytes; white. *See* Leukocytes
Cortex, adrenal, **341,** 345, **353,** 354; of cerebellum, **102;** of cerebrum, *see* Cerebral cortex; of hair, 308; of kidney, **332,** 333
Corti, organ of, 142–144, **143,** 148
Corticoids, 345, 353
Corticosteroids, 353
Cortisone, 353, 354; structural formula for, 354
Covering tissue. *See* Epithelium
CP. *See* Creatine phosphate
cps, 145, 146
Creatine phosphate, in muscle, 67–68
Creatinin, 334, 335
Cretin, 347
Crista acoustica, 149
Crossing over, during meiosis, 375–**376**
Crown, of tooth, **184**
Crypts of Lieberkuhn, 206
Crystalline lens, of eye, 121–122
Cuboidal epithelium, **30**
Cupula, 149
Cusps, of teeth, 184
Cutaneous senses, 84
Cuticle, of hair, 308. *See also* Epidermis
Cycle, of sound, 145

Cyclotron, 9
Cystine, 159
Cytoplasm, **21,** 22–26

Dalton's Law, 226, 231
Deafness, 147–148
Deamination, in liver, 204
Decibel, 145
Deep muscles, 74
Defecation, 213
Degeneration, of nerve fiber, **88**
Deglutition, 187–188
7-dehydrocholesterol, 172
Deletion, producing mutation, **376**
Dendrite(s), 85, **86**–87
Dentate nucleus, **102**
Dentin, **184**–185
Dentinal tubules, 185
Depth perception, 128
Dermis, **305, 307**
Desoxyribonucleic acid (DNA), 23, 363
Desoxyribose, 363
Detoxification, in liver, 213
Deuterium, 9
Dextrin, 156, **207**
Dextrose. *See* Glucose
Diabetes, 334; insipidus, 345; insulin and, 356–358; mellitus, 356–358
Diabetic coma, 357
Diabetogenic hormone, 357
Dialysis, 12–**13,** 15
Diaphragm, **219,** 220, 221, 222, **229**
Diaphysis, **41**
Diastole, 276
Diastolic pressure, 291, 293, 294
Dichromats, 134
Dicrotic curve, **294**–295
Dicrotic notch, **294**–295
Dicumarol, 264
Diencephalon. *See* Interbrain
Diet, 161–164; balanced, 161, 164; effects of vitamin deficiency in, **172, 174, 175, 176, 178, 179;** general grouping of foods in, 161
Differentiation, of gametes, 363–**364**
Diffusion, 14
Digestion, 161, 164; of casein, 167; in mouth, 181–188; and pH, 16; of proteins, 192–193; in small intestine, 199, 206–209; and smooth muscle cells, 31–32; in stomach, 190–197
Digestive juices, action of (table), 207
Digestive system, 152–214; types of tissues in, 37
Dihybrid cross, 372, **374**
Dipeptidase, 206
Diploid (2n) number, 365
Disaccharides, 155, 156
Dislocation, of bones, 59–60
Disorders, of skeletal structure, 57–60
Distal end, 5–6
Divergence, of light rays, 123, **124**
Diver's palsy, 232
DNA, 23, 363
Dog, brain of, **101**

Dominance, incomplete (blending), 373–**375**
Donor, blood, 270
Dorsal side, 5
Drosophila, 362, **363,** 365
Drugs, bacteriocidal, 178; bacteriostatic, 177–178; effect of on vasomotor action, 296–297
Duct, bile, **201–202;** common bile, **202,** 205; cystic, 201, **202;** hepatic, 201, **202;** lacrimal, 118; nasolacrimal, 118; pancreatic, **202,** 205; right lymphatic, 300; semicircular, of ear, 149; of sweat gland, **305, 307,** 308–309; thoracic, 209, **300**
Duodenal ulcer, **196**
Duodenum, **190, 191,** 194, 197, **202,** 204; hormones of, 205; structure of, 199
Dura mater, 96, 99, **100**
Dwarfism, **344**–345, 347–348
Dynamic equilibrium, 331

Ear, defects in, 147–148; effects of changes in pressure on, 141; external, 139–140; inner, 141–144, **142,** 146–147, 148; middle, **140**–141, 146; structure of, 139–144
Ear drum, 139–**140**
Ear lobe, 139
Echo, 144
Ectoderm, as origin of nervous system, 82–83
Edema, 265
Egg cells, DNA in, 363
Egg white, amino acids in, 159
EKG, **283,** 284, 285
Elastic cartilage, **36**
Elbow, dislocation of, **59**
Electrical activity, in nerve fiber, **89**–90
Electrical current, demonstrations of in heart, 282–283
Electrical potential, **89**–90
Electrocardiogram (EKG), **283, 284, 285**
Electrocardiograph, 283, 284
Electroencephalogram, **112**–113
Electroencephalography, 112
Electrolysis, 10
Electrons, **8**
Element(s), 10; in formation of mineral salts, 154; of protoplasm, 17
Embryology, **2, 3**
Emotions, and stomach disorders, 196–197
Empirical formula, 155
Emulsifying agent, 13
Emulsions, 13
Enamel, tooth, **184**
Encephalon. *See* Brain
End organs, of Krause, 309; of Ruffini, 309; sensory. *See* Receptors
End-loaded compound levers, examples of, 47
Endocrine balance, 340
Endocrine glands, 340–358; interdependence of, 340; location and structure of, **341.** *See also* individual glands

Endocrine system, 340–358; types of tissues in, 37
Endolymph, 142, 149
Endosteum, **41;** and healing of bones, 59
Endothelium, 30
End-products, of enzymes, 168–169
Energy, and chemical compounds, 10–11; conversion of by muscle fibers, 62; and fat, 35; food as supply of, 152; kinetic, 62; and metabolism, 18; from oxidation of carbohydrates, 156–157 —of fats, 157, 158, of proteins, 157, 160; and physiology, 2; potential, 62; release of by mitochondria, 22
Energy level, 8
Enterokinase, 205, 207
Enzymes, 166–169; definition of, 166; effect of pH on, 168; end-products of, 168–169; of gastric juice, 192–193; of intestine, 205, 206–207; and nature of substrate, 168; optimum temperature of, 167; pancreatic, 205–206
Eosin, 256
Eosinophil, **253,** 257
Ephedrine, 297
Epidermis, **305–307**
Epiglottis, **182,** 188, **217, 240**
Epimysium, 62
Epinephrin. *See* Adrenalin
Epiphyseal cartilage, **41,** 42
Epiphyseal line, X-ray of, **47**
Epiphyses, **41,** 42
Epithelium, 28–30; ciliated, **29**–30—of bronchi, 219, in trachea, 218–219; columnar, **29;** cuboidal, **30;** as protection against bacteria, 28; shape of cells, 29–30; squamous, 28–**29;** stratified, 30
Equator, of cell, 26
Equilibrium, 148–149
Erepsin, 206–207
Ergosterol, 172
Eruption, of teeth, 183–184
Erythroblastosis fetalis, 271
Erythrocytes, **33,** 248; deficiency of, 258–260; destruction of, 256; formation of, 252, **253;** increase of at high altitudes, 231; outline and dimensions of, 20, **254;** structure of, 252–254
Erythrodextrin, 156
Esophagus, **182, 187,** 188, **191, 202, 217,** 218, **220**
Ethnoid sinus, **50**
Eustachian tube, 141, **182**
Eve's technique, of artificial respiration, 238
Excretion(s), definition of, 203; by kidneys, 331–337; by lungs, 331; principal organic, 334–336; by skin, 331
Excretory system, types of tissues in, 37
Exophthalmos, **348**
Expiration, **220**–223, **221**
Expiratory reserve volume, 227
Extension, 44; of muscles, 73, **77**

External acoustic meatus, 139–140, 146
External respiration, 216
Extrafoveal (peripheral) region, of retina, 121, **122**
Extremities, **5**–6
Eye, accessory organs of, 117–118; accommodation of, 124, 136–137; anterior chamber of, 122; arteries of, 116, 119; convergence of, 123, **128;** coordinated movements of, 117; cornea of, 118; crystalline lens of, 121–122; defects of, 134–137; fatigue of, 124; layers of, 118–120; muscles of, 116–117; nerves controlling movement of, 117; pigment of, 118–119; protection of, 115–118; refraction in, 123; structure of, 115–122
Eyebrows, 117
Eyelashes, 117
Eyelids, 117

Fainting, 280
False ribs, **48,** 52, **53**
Familial hemolytic jaundice, 259
Fascia, in orbital cavity, 116
Fasciculi, 96–97
Fat(s), 153; digestion of, 207—in liver, 202, 203, by steapsin, 206; emulsions of, 207, 209; excess, and cardiovascular disease, 158; importance of to body, 35; oxidation value of, 321–322
Fats, true, 157–158. *See also* Lipids
Fatigue, of muscles, 65–66, **67**
Feces, 203; formation of, 213
Fehling's solution, 156
Fehling's test, 166–167
Fertilization, 362, 366–367
Fever, 317
Fibrin, 263
Fibrinogen, 247, 262–265
Fibroblasts, 256
Fibrous capsule, **46**
Fibrous pericardium, 273
Field of vision, 126
Filaments, in muscle cell, 31
Fish, brain of, **101**
Fissure(s), of Rolando (central fissure), 103, **104, 105;** superior orbital, 116; of Sylvius, 103, **104, 105**
Fistula, 196
"Flat-footedness", 57
Flexion, 44; of muscles, 73, **77**
Floating ribs, **48,** 52, **53**
Fluids, body, 246, 248—effect of exercise on, 69–71; and osmotic pressure, 15, and relative pH, **16;** cerebrospinal, 96, 99–100; extracellular, 246; extravascular, 246, 297–300; of eye, 122; of inner ear, 141–142, 146, 147; intercellular, 298–299; interstitial, 298; intracellular, 246, 297–298; intravascular, 246; pericardial, 29, 274; pleural, 29, 220; serous, 28, 29; synovial, 46
Fluorine, of bone, 40

Focal length, of lens, 123
Focus, principal, 123, **124**
Folds, circular, of small intestine, 209
Folic acid, 178
Follicle, egg-producing and endocrine, **341**; hair, **307**, 308; of thyroid gland, **341**, 346
Food, acid, 164; alkaline, 164; compositions of, 153–161; digestion of, 161, 164, 194; groups of, 152–161; ingestion of, 161; irradiated, 173; principal groups of, essential for life, 152; requirements of, 152; value of some common, 162–163; varying needs of body for, 161, 164
Foot, arches of, 57
Foramen (foramina), magnum, 95; neural, 95; optic, 115–116; ovalis, of fetal heart, 273
Forebrain (prosencephalon), 100–101
Formula, chemical, 11; empirical, 155; structural, 155
Fovea centralis, 121, **122**, 134
Fracture(s), compound, 59; of femur, 56; green-stick, 58–59; of hip, **59**; simple, **58**–59; of skull, 50; types of, **58–59**
Frequency, of sound, 145
Friction ridges, 306
Frog, brain of, **101**
Frontal bone, **50**, 115, **116**
Frontal sinus, **50**
Fructose, 155, 207; composition of, 11; structural formula for, 11
Fruit fly (Drosophila), 362, **363**, 365
Fulcrum, 46–47
Fundus, of stomach, **190**, 194, **196**

Galactase, 207
Galactose, 155
Galen, 3, 229
Gall bladder, 200, 201–**202**; disease of, 203; stimulation of, 205
Gall stones, 158, 203
Galvanometer, 89; string, 282–283
Gamete, 33–**34**, 37, 362, **366**; differentiation and development of, 363–367
Gamma globulin, 265
Ganglion (a), 84; autonomic, 110; cervical sympathetic, 278, **279**; of parasympathetic, 110; posterior root, **97**, 98, **107**; of retina, 119, **120**; of sensory nerve, **97**; of sympathetic, **97**; 110–111
Gangrene, 268
Gas(es), 8; absorption of into blood, 226–227; inert, 225; molecular movement in, 14; respiratory, 225, 227, 228
Gas laws, 226–227
Gastric juices, 191–193; and pH, 16; secretion of, 193–194
Gastric mucosa, **191**
Gastric phase, of stomach secretion, 194
Gastric secretion, 193–194
Gastrin, 193–194

Gel, 12–**13**
Gelatin, amino acids in, 159, 160
Genes, 362, 363
Genetics, **2**, 3, 362–377
Genotype, 369
Germs, 259
Gigantism, 343–**344**
Girdle, pelvic, 52; bones of, **55**; shoulder (pectoral), 52–53
Glands, adrenal. *See* Adrenal glands; ceruminous, 140; ductless, *see* Endocrine glands; endocrine, *see* Endocrine glands; exocrine, 340, **341**, 356; gastric, 191, 192; intestinal, **206**; lacrimal, 118; mixed, 356; parotid, **186**, *see* Pituitary gland; salivary, 185–187, **186**; sebaceous, 117, **307**, 308; sublingual, **186**; submaxillary, **186**; suprarenal, **332**—*see also* Adrenal glands; sweat, **305**, **307**, 308–309
Glaucoma, 122
Glenoid cavity, 53
Gliding joint, 44, **45**
Globin, 254
Globulins, of plasma, 264–265
Glomerulus, **333**
Glottis, 218, **219**, 242
Glucose, 155, 156, 168, 194, 207; composition of, 11; structural formula for, 11; in urine, 156; use of by liver, 22
Glutamic acid, 159
Glycerol, 157
Glycerin, 207, 209
Glycine, 159
Glycogen, 155, 156; in liver, 22, **202**, 203–204; in muscular contraction, 67–68
Glycosuria, 204, 334, 348, 355, 357; renal, 334
Goblet cells, 29, **30**; in trachea, 218
Goiter, simple, 349; toxic, 348–349
Golgi bodies, **21**, 22–23
Golgi network, 22–23
Gonadotropic hormone, **343**
Goose flesh, 308
Gray matter, 87; of cerebellum, 102; of cerebrum, 103; of interbrain, 103; of medulla, 101; of midbrain, 101–102; of spinal cord, **96**
Gray rami communicantes, 111
Green-stick fracture, 58–59
Growth, of cells, 23–27; effect of thyroid on, 347–349
Growth hormone (somatotropic), **343**–345
Gum, **184**

Hair(s), **307**; graying of, 308; loss of, 308; olfactory, 217, **218**; structure of, 308
Hair follicle, **307**, 308
Hales, Stephen, 292–293
Hand, main sections of, 54–55
Haploid (n) number, 365
Harvey, William, **4**
Haustra (ae), **211**, 213
Haversian canals, 43, **44**

Haversian system, 35, 43
Head, **5**–6; of femur, 55–56; of pancreas, 204; of rib, 52; of sperm, 33–**34**
Hearing, defects in, 147–148; physiology of, 146–147
Heart, **201**, **249**, 250; action of, 274–276; bioelectric currents of, 281–285; chambers of, **274**, **275**; conducting pathways in, **278**; cycle of, *see* Cardiac cycle; diastole of, 276, 277; effect of acetylcholine on, 280—of adrenalin on, 281, of atropine on, 280–281, of exercise on, 280, of muscarine on, 281, of nicotine on, 281, of pumping action on blood pressure, 291, of sympathin on, 281; of frog, **277**; impulses of, 278; inhibition of, 278, 280–281; irregularities of, 284–285; murmurs in, 285; nerve pathways connecting with central nervous system, 278–**279**; layers of, 273–274; pacemaker of, 277; rate, chemical control of, 280–281—neural control of, 278–280; section through, **275**; size and weight of, 273; sounds of, 285; stimulation of, 277–278; structure of, 273–276, **274**, **275**; systole of, 276, 277; valves of, **274**, **275, 276**
Heart beat, control of rate of, 278–281; origin of, 277–278; rate of, 281—during sleep, 113, in exercise, 71, in relation to age, **282**
Heat, loss of, *see* Heat loss; production of by body, measurement of, 320–322; by oxidation, 313–314; regulation of by nervous control, 314; of vaporization, 316
Heat cramps, 318
Heat exhaustion, 318
Heat loss, by conduction, 315; by convection, 315–316; through excretions, 314; from lungs, 314; by radiation, 315; through skin, 314–317; by vaporization, 316; under varying conditions (table), 316
Heat prostration, 318
Heat-regulating center, 314
Heatstroke, 317–318
Heel bone. *See* Calcaneus
Heister, spiral valves of, 202
Hematin, 254
Hemin, 254
Hemiplegia, 106
Hemispheres, of cerebellum, **102**; of cerebrum, 103
Hemoglobin, 248, 306; and anemia, 258–260; breakdown of in liver, 202; decomposition of, 256; deoxygenated (reduced), 273; function of, 254; oxygenated, 273
Hemophilia, 264, 371
Hemorrhage, 267–269; methods of checking, 268–269; physiological effects of, 267–268

Hemosiderin, 256
Hemotoidin, 256
Henle's loop, **333**
Henry's Law, 226
Heparin, 264
Hepatitis, 203
Heredity, 362–377; and cell division, 24; control of by cells, 20–21; of dominant characteristics, 368, 369, 372; incomplete dominance in, 373–**375**; mutations in, 375–377; principles of, 367–370; and radiation, 377; of recessive characteristics, 368, 369, 372; and sex determination, 370–371; of sex-linked characteristics, 371–373
Heterozygous, 369
Hexoses, 155, 156
Hilum, of kidney, 332
Hindbrain (rhombencephalon), 100
Hinge joint, 44, **45**
Hip, fracture of, **59**
Histamine, 296
Histidine, 159
Histology, **2**, 3
Hohenheim, Theophrastus. *See* Paracelsus
Hooke, Robert, 20
Homoiothermic animals, 312
Hormone(s), 193, 340; of adrenal cortex, 353; of adrenal glands, 204; of adrenal medulla, 355–356; adrenalin, 355–356; of anterior lobe of pituitary, **343**–**345**; antidiuretic (ADH), 336, **343**, 345; control by, 341–342; diabetogenic, **343**, 345, 357; of duodenum, 205; gonadotropic, **343**; growth, **343**–345; intermedin, 346; lactogenic, **343**, 345; noradrenalin, 355; oxytocic, 343, 345–346; of pancreas, 204, 356–358; pancreatropic, **343**, 345; parathormone, 352–353; of pars intermedia of pituitary, 346; in plasma, 248; of posterior lobe of pituitary, **343**, 345–346; prolactin, **343**, 345; somatotropic, **343**–345; steroids, 353; of stomach, 193–194; thyrotropic, **343**, 345, 346; thyroxin, 346, 347, 348, 349; vasopressin, **343**, 345
Horns, of spinal cord, **96, 97**, 106, 107
Hunger, 164
Hyaline cartilage, 36, **41**
Hybrid, 369
Hydrogen, atomic structure of, 8–9, **10**; atomic weight of, 8; heavy, 9
Hydrogen ion concentration (pH), 16
Hydrogenation, 158
Hydrolysis, of sugars, 155
Hyper-, definition of, 342
Hyperglycemia, 357
Hyperopia, 137
Hyperthyroidism, 348–349
Hypertrophy, 69; of gland, 342; in muscles, 69
Hypo-, definition of, 342

Hypoglycemia, 358
Hypothalamus, **279;** as center of emotions, 103; as heat-regulating center, 314; injury to, 103
Hypothyroidism, 347–348

Ileum, 199, **212**
Impulse, nerve. *See* Nerve impulse
Incisor teeth, **183**, 184
Incus (anvil), **140**–141
Infantile myxedema, 347
Infections, of bone, 57; of ear, 141; signs of, 256; of throat, 141
Infectious hepatitis, 203
Infrared rays, 131
Infundibulum, 342
Ingestion, 161
Inhalation. *See* Inspiration
Inhalator, 237
Inheritance, of characteristics, 362–377. *See also* Heredity
Inhibition, of muscles, 99
Inorganic substances, in plasma, 262, 266
Inositol, 177
Insertions, of muscle, 73–79, **74**
Inspiration, **220**–223, **221**
Inspirator, 237
Inspiratory reserve volume, 227
Insulin, 204, **343**, 345, 356–358; action on glycogen of, 204; amino acids in, 159
Insulin shock, 358
Integumentary system, 304–311; types of tissues in, 37
Intelligence, and the brain, 100; and cerebral cortex, 105
Interbrain (diencephalon), 100–101; functions of, 103; injury to, 103
Intercostal muscles, 52
Intermedin, 346
Internal capsule, 105–106
Internal respiration, 216
Interphase, 25
Intestinal juice, 206–207; and pH, 16
Intestine(s), large, **200, 201**, 211–214—bacterial action of, 213, structure of, 211–212, water absorption by, 212–213, X ray of, **211**, *see also* Colon; small, **200, 201**, 203—absorption from, 209, autonomic control of, 209, cells of, **206**, digestion in, 199, 206–209, enzymes of, 206–207, glands of, **206**, lining of, **209**, movements of, **208–209**, smooth muscle in, 208–209, wall structure of, 208
Inulin, 156
Invertebral disks, **48**, 51, **52**
Inverted retina, 119–120
Involuntary muscles, 31–**32**, 33. *See* Muscle, smooth
Involuntary nervous system. *See* Autonomic nervous system
Iodine, and formation of goiter, 349; radioactive, 9; sources and biological effects of, 154; and tests for disaccharides, 156; and thyroid gland, 346–347
Iodopsin, 120–121

Ions, 10; calcium, and formation of cell membrane, 21–22
Iris, 116, 135; layers of, 118–119
Iron, of bone, 40; sources and biological effects of, 154
Iron-deficiency anemia, 259–260
Iron lung, 234, **235**, 237
Irreversible shock, 266
Irritability, 82; as characteristic of protoplasm, 18
Islands of Langerhans, 204, **205**, **341**, 356
Isoleucine, 159
Isotopes, 9–10
Isthmus, of thyroid gland, **346**

Jaundice, 173, 203; familial hemolytic, 259
Jejunum, 199
Joints, 43–47; angular, 44, **45**; and arthritis, 57–**58**; ball and socket, 44, **45**, **55**; dislocation of, **59**–60; as fulcra in leverage, 46–47; gliding, 44, **45**; hinge, 44, **45**; immovable, 43, **45**; movable, coverings of, **46**— lubrication of, 46; partially movable, 43, **45**; pivot, 44, **45**; sacroiliac, 55; saddle, 44, **45**; sprained, 60; symphysis pubis, **55;** types of movable, 44, **45**
Juices, digestive, action of (table), 207

Keratin, 30, 305
Ketones, and insulin, 357
Ketosis, 329
Kidney(s), 204, 331–337; disease of, 334; effect of antidiuretic hormone on, 336; factors influencing function of, 336; functions of, 331–332; structure of, **332–333**
Kinetic energy,
Knee, **46**
Kneecap. *See* Patella
Krause corpuscle, **307**
Kupffer cells, 202, 204
Kymograph, 64, **65**, 194, **322**
Kyphosis, 58

Labyrinth, bony, 141–142; membranous, of ear, 141, 146, 147, 149; nonauditory, 148–149
Lacrimal apparatus, 116, 117–118
Lactase, 206–207
Lacteal, of intestine, **206**, 209
Lactic acid, formation of by muscle contraction, 67–68, 70
Lactose, 155
Lacunae, 43
Lamella (ae), 43, **44**
Lamina, of vertebra, **52**
Langerhans, Islands of, 204, **205**, **341**, 356
Laryngeal pharynx, 181
Larynx, 188, **217**, 218, **229**, **240**–242, **346**; structure of, 239–240
Lateral column, 96–97
Lateral surface, 5–6
Law(s), all-or-none, 90–91; Avogadro's, 226; Boyle's, 226, 230; Charles', 226; Dalton's, of par-

tial pressures, 226, 231; of dominance, 373; Henry's, 226; Mendel's, 373; of segregation, 373; of unit characters, 373
Laxatives, 214
Lead line, 258–259
Leads, standard, of electrocardiograph, 283, 284
Lecithin, 158
Lens, biconcave, 123; biconvex, 123; concave, 123, **124, 136**–137; convex, 123, **124**, 134–**136**, 137; crystalline, of eye, 121–122, 124, 135–137; focal length of, 123; refraction by, 123, **124**
Leucine, 159
Leukemia, 260, 336
Leukocytes, **33,** 247, 248; basophil, **253,** 257; classification of, 257; digestion of bacteria by, **255**–256; effect of cortical hormones on, 354; eosinophil, **253,** 257; formation of, 252; functions of, **255**–256; lymphocyte, 257; monocyte, 257; movements of, 254–256; neutrophil, **253, 255,** 257
Leukocytosis, 257; physiologic (activity), 257
Leukopenia, 257
Levers, end-loaded compound, 47; simple, 46–**47**—classifications of, **47**
Levulose. *See* Fructose
Lieberkuhn, crypts of, 206
Life, physical basis of, 8–18
Ligaments, 40; and articulation, 43–44; function of, 46; in movable joints, **46;** and sprains, 60; suspensory, 121–122, 124
Light, invisible rays of, 130–131; measurement of, 122; refraction of, 122–**123, 124,** 130, 131; separation of by prism, 130, 131; wave lengths of, and hue, 133; waves of, 122, 130–131, 132; white, 130–134
Light rays, convergence of, **124;** divergence of, 123, **124**
Light-producing organisms, 167–**168**
Limbs, **5**–6
Lipase, gastric, 193, 207; of intestinal juice, 206–207; pancreatic, *see* Steapsin
Lipids, 153, 157–158; storage of, 158; tests for, 158
Lips, 181
Liquid, 8; molecular movement in, 14
Litmus, 16
Liver, **200**–204, **201;** deamination in, 204; detoxification in, 213; disease of, 203; as excretory organ, 203; and fat digestion, 202–203; formation of glycogen in, 203–204—of urea in, 335; functions of, 201, 203–204; as secretory organ, 201–203; storage by cells of, 22; structure of lobule of, 200–**201**
Lobe(s), anterior, of pituitary, **341,** 342–345; frontal of cerebrum, 103, **104, 105;** intermediate of thyroid, **346;** of lungs, 220; occipital of cerebrum, 103, **104, 105;** parietal of cerebrum, 103, **104, 105;** posterior, of pituitary, **341**–343, 345–346; temporal of cerebrum, 103, **104, 105**
Lobule, of ear, 139; liver, structure of, 200–**201**
Loeb, Dr. Jacques, 367
Longitudinal arch, of foot, **57**
Longitudinal fissure, of cerebrum, 103, **104**
Loop of Henle, **333**
Lordosis, 58
Loudness, of voice, 242
Luciferase, 167–168
Luciferin, 168
Lung(s), **229;** capacity of, 227–228; structure of, **219**–220; type of cells of, 29; X ray of, **221**
Lymph, 299
Lymph node, **299, 300**
Lymph vessel, of intestine, **206,** 209
Lymphatic(s), **249,** 299–**300;** in Haversian canals, 43
Lymphatic system, 299–300
Lymphocyte, 257, **299**
Lymphoid tissue, effect of cortical hormones on, 354
Lysine, 159

Macrophages, 297
Macula, 148
Macula lutea, 121, **122**
Magnesium, of bone, 40; sources and biological effects of, 154
Malaria, malignant, 334; white cell count in, 257
Malleus (hammer), **140**
Malocclusion, 185
Malpighi, Marcello, 4, 20
Maltase, 168, 206–207
Maltose, 155, 168, 207
Manubrium, 51–52, **53**
Marrow. *See* Bone, marrow of
Mastication, 183, 185
Mastoid process, **50,** 140, 141
Mastoiditis, 141
Mathematics, **2, 4**
Matrix, bone, formation of, 42–43; of cartilage, **36;** gelatinous, of cartilage, 42
Matter, composition of, 8; as colloidal, 11–13; definition of, 8
Maxillary sinus, **50**
Meatus, external acoustic, 139–140, 146
Mediastinum, **219,** 221
Medulla, adrenal, **341, 353,** 354–356; of the brain (oblongata), 100, **106,** 148, 149—as control of heart rate, 278, **279,** gray matter of, 101, importance of, 101, and vomiting, 194–195, white matter of, 101; of hair, 308; of kidney, 332, 333.
Medullary canal, **41,** 43
Megakaryocyte, 252, **253**
Meiosis, 365–**366;** crossing over during, 375–**376**
Meissner's corpuscle, **307,** 310
Melanin, 306; of choroid, 118–119
Melanophores, 346
Membrane(s), basilar, 142, **143,** 147, 148; cell, **21**–22; of cystic duct, 202; fibrous, 41; of liver, 200; of lungs, *see* Pleura; mucous, 117, 140, 141—nasal, 216–217; nuclear, **21,** 23, 26; periodontal, **184,** 185; periosteum, 41; plasma (cell), **21**–22; of red corpuscle, 254; of Reissner, 142, **143;** semipermeable, 14–15, 21; of small intestine, 199; of stomach, 190–**191;** tectorial, **143,** 144; tympanic, 139–**140,** 146, 147; vacuolar, 22; vestibular, 142, **143.** *See also* Meninges
Memory, and cerebral cortex, 105
Mendel, Johann Gregor, 367–370, 372–373
Mendel's laws, 373
Meninges, 96, 99
Meningitis, detection of, 96
Mercury baromoter, **223**
Mesencephalon. *See* Midbrain
Mesenteries, 199, **200**
Mesial surface, **5**–6
Metabolism, 18, 320–329; and body surface, 324; of cell, nuclear control of, 23; effect of activity on, 324, 326—external temperature on, 326, of food on, 327, of thyroxin on, 327; measurement of, *see* Basal metabolic rate; summary of (chart), 328
Metaphase, 24, **25**
Metaplasmic inclusions, **21,** 22
Metastasis, 197
Methionine, 159
Methylene blue, 256
Micellae, 62, 66–68
Microscope, compound, 20; importance of, 3, 4
Micturition, 336–337
Midbrain (mesencephalon), 100; areas of, 101–102; section through, **102**
Milk, digestion of, 192–193; production of and prolactin, 345
Mineral content, of bone, 40; of skeletal muscle, 64
Mineral salts, 152; functions of, 153, 154; sources of, 154
Minimal air, 228
Mitochondria, **21,** 22
Mitosis, 24, 363, 364; phases of, 24–27
Modiolus, 142, **143**
Molar teeth, **183,** 184
Molecule(s), 10; compressions of, 144, 145; hydrogen, **10;** motion of, 13–15; of proteins, 159, 334; rarefactions of, 144, 145; of water, **10**
Monkey, brain of, **101**
Monochromats, 134
Monocyte, 257
Monohybrid cross, 372
Monosaccharides, 155, 156
Motion sickness, 149
Motor area, of cerebral cortex, **105**

Motor neurons, upper and lower, 106–107

Motor pathways, from cerebral cortex, 105–107, **106**

Mouth, digestion in, 181–188; structures of, 181–185

Mucin, 186, 191

Mucosa, intestinal, **206, 208,** 209

Mucus, 29

Multiple cartilaginous exostoses, 376–377

Multipolar neuron, **87**

Muscarine, 281

Muscle, cardiac, **32,** 33, 273—papillary, **275, 276;** sphincter. *See* Sphincter; tissue, 28, 30–**32,** 33

Muscle(s), involuntary, *see* smooth; striated, *see* skeletal; voluntary, *see* skeletal

Muscle(s), skeletal (striated, voluntary), *see also* individual, specifically named; abdominal, 78; antagonistic, 73–74; belly of, 73; composition of, 62–64, **63;** deep, 74; efficiency of, 62; extension, 73, **77;** of eye, 116–117; facial, 74; flexion, 73, **77;** of forearm, **77,** 78; insertions of, 73–79, **74;** of leg, **75,** 78–79, **77;** movements of, 73–79; of neck, 74–76, **75, 77;** origins of, 73–79, **74;** physiology of, 62–71; and radioactive calcium, 9; reciprocal innervation of, 74, 99; structure of, **63;** superficial, action of, 74–79; of trunk, **75,** 76–78, **77;** of upper arm, 73, **74, 75**

Muscle(s), skeletal, individual, specifically named: biceps, 73, **74, 75;** biceps femoris, **77,** 79; brachioradialis, **75,** 78; deltoid, **75, 76, 77;** extensor corpi, **75, 77,** 78; external intercostals, 221; external oblique, **75, 77,** 78; external rectus (eye), 116; flexor carpi, **77,** 78; gastrocnemius, **75, 77,** 79; gluteus maximus, **77,** 79; inferior oblique (eye), 116–117; inferior rectus (eye), 116; intercostal, 52, 221, **229;** internal intercostal, 221; internal rectus (eye), 116; lateral rectus (eye), 116; latissimus dorsi, **75, 76, 77,** 78; linea alba, 78; masseter, 74, **75;** orbicularis oculi, 74, **75,** 117; orbicularis oris, 74, **75;** pectoralis major, **75, 76, 77;** platysma, 74, **77;** pterygoideus internus, 74; rectus abdominis, **75, 77,** 78; rectus femoris, **75, 77;** serratus anterior, **75, 76, 77;** soleus, **75, 77,** 79; stapedius, **140,** 141; sternocleidomastoideus (sternomastoid), **75,** 76; superior oblique (eye), 116–117; superior rectus (eye), 116; tensor tympani, **140,** 141; tibialis anterior, **75, 77,** 79; trapezius, 76, **77;** triceps, 73, **74, 75;** vastus lateralis, **75, 77,** 79; vastus medialis, **75, 77,** 79

Muscle(s), smooth (involuntary), 31–**32,** 33; arrector pili, 308, 309; of arteries and arterioles, 288–289; of eye, 119, 124; functions of in small intestine, 208–209; of stomach, **191**

Muscle fiber(s), 62–**63, 64,** 70

Muscle spasm, in arthritis, 57–**58**

Muscle tone, 68; effect of adrenalin on, 355, 356

Muscle twitch, analysis of, 65–68, **67;** apparatus for recording, 65, **66;** contraction period of, 65, **67;** latent period of, 65, **67;** recovery period of, 65, **67;** relaxation period of, 65, **67;** use of frog muscle in study of, 64

Muscular activity, effect of on metabolic rate, 324, 326

Muscular contractions, 62–68; acetylcholine in, 63; analysis of, 65–68, **67;** chemistry of, 64–68; cholinesterase in, 63; effect of temperature on, 65—neostigmine on, 63–64, **65;** energy produced in, 62, 65, 67–68; fatigue in, 65–66, **67;** glycogen in, 67–68; heat production in, 62; impulses governing, 105–106; lactic acid in, 67–68; malfunction of, 63–64; method for studying, 65–66; proteins in, 66–68; of stomach, 194, **195;** table of chemical reactions in, 68; tetanic, 66, 68; theory of mechanism, 66–68; use of oxygen in, 65, 66, 67–68. *See also* Muscle twitch

Muscular exercise, 68–71; and atrophy, 68–69; blood pressure in, 71; changes in circulatory system due to, 69–71; effect of on acidity of blood, 70—on body fluids, 69–71, on heart rate, 71, 280, on urine, 71; heat produced in, 71; and hypertrophy, 68–69; lactic acid in, 70; oxygen debt in, 69; oxygen requirements during, 69; and pH, 70; respiration in, 69; rise of body temperature in, 71

Muscular weakness, 63–64

Mutation, 375–377; by crossing over, 375–**376;** by deletion, **376;** and radiation, 377

Myasthenia gravis, 63–64, **65**

Myelin sheath, **86,** 87, **88**

Myeloblasts, 252, **253**

Myofibrils, 62, **63**

Myoneural junctions, 62–63, **64**

Myopia, 136–137

Myosin, 62, 66–67; molecular weight of, 159

Mysticism, and Galen, 3

Myxedema, adult, 348; infantile, 347–348

Nachmansohn, Dr. D., 92–93

Nail(s), 307, 309

Nail bed, 309

Nasal bones, **50,** 217

Nasal conchae, 216–**217**

Nasopharynx, 181, 188

Neck, **5**–6; of femur, 56; of rib,
52, **54;** of sperm, **34;** of tooth, **184**

Negative after-potential, **89**

Neostigmine, 63–**65**

Nephritis, 265, 334

Nephron, 332–334

Nerve(s), *see also* Nerve fibers, Nerve impulse, Neuron; afferent process, 86; cranial, 84, **107**–109, 117, 119; efferent process, 86; intercostal, 98; microscopic structure of, 87–88; mixed, 96; processes of, 85, **86**–87; receptors, 82; and reciprocal innervation, 99; sensory, ganglion of, **97;** in skin, **307;** spinal, 84, **96**–**98,** 106–107; structure of cell body, 85–87, **86;** theory of growth of, 85

Nerve(s), individual, specifically named: abducens, 109, 117; accessory, 109; auditory, 109, 147, 148; carotid sinus, **279;** cochlear, 142, **143;** facial, 109, 110; glossopharyngeal, 109; 110; hypoglossal, 109; oculomotor, **102,** 109, 110, 117, 119; olfactory, 109, 183, **218;** optic, 109, 116, 119, **120, 127;** pelvic, 110; phrenic, **229;** trigeminal, 109; trochlear, 109, 117; vagus, 108, 109, 110, **111, 229,** 278, **279;** vestibular, 148, 149

Nerve cell. *See* Neuron

Nerve endings, in muscle fibers, 62–64

Nerve fiber(s), 84; adrenogic, 112; association, 103–104; autonomic, 108; of brain, 101; of cerebral cortex, 103–104; cholinergic, 112; commissural, 103–104; controlling rate of heart, 278–280; degeneration, 88; electrical charges in, **89**–90; mixed, 84; motor, 84, **97,** 105–106; neurofibrils, 85, **86;** olfactory, **218;** postganglionic, 110; preganglionic, 110; projection, 103–104; refractory periods of, **89**–90; regeneration, **88;** sensory, 84, **97;** in spinal cord, 96–**97;** structure of, 87–88; subnormal period of, **89**–90; of taste bud, **183;** theory of neural connection, 91–92

Nerve impulses, 82, 88–92; behavior of, 90–91; chemical activity in, 91, 92–93; directions of travel, **92;** electrical pattern of, **89**–90; oxygen consumption in, 91; pathways of in reflex, 98–**99;** propagation of, 88–89, 90–91; refractory periods of, **89**–90; speed of, 88, 90–91; subnormal period of, **89**–90; theory of as electrochemical phenomenon, 92–93

Nerve-muscle preparation, 65–66

Nerve pathways, in control of respiration, **229**

Nervous system, 82–149; characteristics of, 82; development of, 82–83; diseases of and electroencephalography, 112–113;

general functions of, 82–113; origin of, 82–83; peripheral, 83–85; types of tissues in, 37. *See also* Autonomic nervous system, Central nervous system
Neural fold, 82, **83**
Neural foramina, 95
Neural groove, 82, **83**
Neural plate, 82, **83**
Neural tube, 82–**83**
Neurilemma, **86**, 87–**88**
Neurofibrils, 85, **86**, 88
Neuroglia, 83, 85
Neuron, 32–33, 83, 84, **86**; connecting, **99**; effector (motor), 98–**99**; lower motor, **106**, 107; processes of, 85, **86**–87; receptor (sensory), 98–**99**; of spinal cord, **87**; types of, 86–**87**; upper motor, **106**
Neuroplasm, structure of, 85–**86**
Neutrons, **8**
Neutrophil, **253**, **255**, 257
Niacin, 176
Nicotine, and adrenalin, 355; effect of on heart rate, 281; as vasoconstrictor, 297
Nicotinic acid. *See* Niacin
Nielson, Hilger, 238–240
Nielson method of artificial respiration, 238–240, **239**
Night blindness, 130, 170
Nissl, Franz, 85
Nissl bodies, 85–**86**
Nitrogen, in caisson disease, 232; elimination of by kidneys, 331; as essential element of protein, 160; excretion of, 204; percentage of in inhaled and exhaled air, 228; solubility of in blood, 226–227
Node, atrioventricular (A-V), **278**; lymph, **299**, **300**; of Ranvier, **86**, 87–88; sinoatrial, 277, **278**, **279**
Noradrenalin, 281, 355
Norepinephrin. *See* Noradrenalin
Normoblast, **253**
Nose, **229**
Nostrils, **217**
Nuclear reactors, 9
Nucleolus (i), **21**, 23, 26; of nerve cell, **86**
Nucleoplasm, **21**, 23
Nucleoprotein, 23
Nucleus (i), of animal cell, **21**; of atom, 8; of cardiac muscle, **32**; of cell, functions of, 23; important parts of, 23; of muscle fiber, **63**; of nerve cell, **86**, **88**; of ovum, 34; of smooth muscle tissue, 31, **32**; of striated muscle tissue, **31**, **32**; unstable, 9–10
Nutrients, organic, 152, 153–160; absorption of from intestine, 209; fuel value of, 160; oxidation of, 321–322; relative energy value of, 327, 329. *See also* Food
Nutritive materials, in plasma, 247

Obstructive jaundice, 203
Odontoblasts, 184

Odontoclasts, 184
Oils, 153. *See also* Lipids
Olecranon cavity, 53, 54
Olecranon process, **48**, 54, **59**–60
Olfactory organ, **217**
Omentum, greater, 190–191, **200**
Oöcyte, **366**
Oögonia, **366**
Oötid, **366**
Ophthalmoscope, 121, 122
Optic chiasma, **127**, 128
Optic disk, 121, **122**
Optical illusion, 128, **129**
Oral pharynx, 181
Organ(s), 28, 36; of Corti, 142–144, **143**, 148; supplied by autonomic nervous system, 111
Organ system, 36; table of, 37
Orifice, cardiac, **190**; pyloric, *see* Pylorus
Origins, of muscle, 73–79, **74**
Oscilloscope, **145**
Osmosis, **15**
Osmotic pressure, 15, 298, 299; control of by serum albumin, 265; regulation of by kidneys, 332
Ossicles, **140**–141, 147
Ossification, 35, 41–43, 59; center of, 42
Osteoblasts, 35–36, **41**–43
Osteoclasts, 35–36, 43
Osteocytes, 35, 43, **44**
Osteomyelitis, 57
Otoliths, 148
Oval window 141, **142**, 146, 147
Ovary (ies); 30, 33, 341
Ovum (a), 33, **34**, **336**
Oxidation, and maintenance of body temperature, 313–314, 317
Oxygen, in air, 225; atom, **8**; atomic weight of, 8; deficiency of, *see* Anoxia; dissolution of by hemoglobin, 254; in muscular contractions, 65, 66, 67–68; percentage of in air of high altitude, 230–231; percentage of in inhaled and exhaled air, 228; solubility of in blood, 226–227; use of in measuring metabolism 321–322; use of by nerve cells, 91
Oxygen debt, 69; in nervous system, 91
Oxygen requirements, in muscular exercise, 69
Oxyhemoglobin, 228, 267
Oxytocic hormone, 343, 345–346

Pacemaker, of heart, 277
Pacinian corpuscle, **307**, 310
Palate, **217**; hard, 181, **182**, 188; soft, **181**, 188
Palm, of hand, bones of, 54
Palmar surface, 6; of carpals, 54
Pancreas, **200**, **202**, 204–206, 356–358; enzymes of, 205–206; hormones of, 356–358; location and structure of, **341**; secretion of, 204–205
Pancreatic juice, 204–205, 207
Pantothenic acid, 177
Papilla (ae), of hair, **307**; of skin, **305**, 306; on tongue, **181**, 182

Para-aminobenzoic acid, 177–178
Paracelsus, 3–4
Parallax, 128
Paralysis, flaccid, 106–107
Paranasal sinuses, **50**
Parathormone, 352–353
Parathyroid glands, 341, 352
Parotid gland, **186**
Pars intermedia, of pituitary, **341**, 342, 346
Parthenogenesis, 367
Pathology, **2**, 3
Pavlov, Ivan, 113
Pea, edible, Mendel's experiments with, **368**–369
Pectoral girdle. *See* Shoulder girdle
Pedicle, of vertebra, **52**
Peduncles, cerebral, 101
Pellagra, **176**
Pelvic arch, **55**
Pelvic girdle, 52; bones of, **55**
Pelvis, bones of, **55**; of kidney, **332**, 333
Pendular movement, of small intestine, 208
Pepsin, 168, **192**–193, 194, 207; amino acids in, 159
Pepsinogen, 191, 192
Peptones, 192, 207
Pericardial fluid, 29
Pericardium, 29, 273, **274**
Perilymph, 141–142, 149
Perimysium, 62, **63**
Periosteum, **41**, 42, 46, 59
Peripheral nervous system, 83–85
Peripheral vision, 121, 126
Peristalsis, 188, 194, 208, 213
Peritoneum, 190, **200**
Pernicious anemia, 178, 259
pH, 16; of blood, maintenance of, 266–267; of blood plasma, 248; effect of on enzymes, 168; effect of exercise on, 70; of gastric juice, 191–192, 193; of pancreatic juice, 205; of saliva, 186; scale of, 16; of sweat, 309
Phagocyte, 256
Phagocytosis, 256
Pharynx, **181**, **182**, 187, **217**–218
Phenotype, 369
Phenylalanine, 159
Phonation, 240–243
Phospholipids, 22, 157–158
Phosphorus, of bone, 40, 154; control of blood content of by parathyroids, 352–353; and vitamin D, 171
Photosynthesis, 155
Physics, importance of to physiology, **2**, 4
Physiology, 2–6
Pia mater, 96, 99, **100**
Pigments, of bile, 202–203; of choroid (melanin), 118–119; primary colors of, 131; of retina, 129; of skin, 306
Pineal body, 358
"Pink eye," 117
Pinna, 139
Pitch, 145; thresholds of, 146; of voice, 241, 242
Pituitary gland, **100**, 340–346; effects of on body organs and

functions, **343;** hormones of, **343**–345

Pivot joint, 44, **45**

Place Theory, 146–147

Plasma. *See* Blood plasma

Plasma expanders, 269

Plasma membrane, **21**–22

Plasma proteins, 247

Platelets, **33,** 248; in clotting, 263, 264; content of in blood, 258; formation of, 252, **253**

Pleura (ae), 29, **219, 220**

Pleural fluid, 29

Pleurisy, 221

Plexus(es) (nerve), brachial, 98; cervical, 98; lumbar, 98; sacral, 98

Pneumonia, white cell count in, 257

Poikilothermic animals, 312, 314

Polar body, 365, **366, 367**

Polariscope, 156

Poliomyelitis, anterior, 234, **235;** detection of, 96

Polycythemia vera, 292

Polyneuritis, **174**

Polypeptids, 205, 207

Polysaccharides, 155–156

Pons, **100,** 101, **106, 107**

Pore, 308

Portal circulation, **201,** 202, 203

Position, prone, 6; supine, 6

Positive after-potential, **89**–90

Posterior area, 5

Potassium, 154; adrenal cortex and, 354; of bone, 40

Potential energy, 62

Premolar teeth, **183,** 184

Presbyopia, 137

Pressoreceptors, 279

Pressure, effect of on hearing,141; atmospheric, 222–223, 226—effects of changing, 230–232, relation of to altitude, 230–**231**

Pressure point, 268

Prism, 130, **131**

Process(es), afferent, 86; articular, of vertebrae, 51, **52;** coracoid, 53; efferent, 86; mastoid, 140, 141; of nerve cell, 85, **86**–87; olecranon, **48,** 54, **59**–60; transverse, of vertebrae, 51, **52;** xiphoid, 51–52, **53**

Prolactin, **343,** 345

Proline, 159

Prone position, 6

Prophase, 24–25

Prosencephalon, 100–101

Protease, pancreatic. *See* Trypsin

Proteins, 153; action of digestive juices on, 207; of blood plasma, 264–265; as builders of protoplasm, 160; in cell membrane, 21; composition of, 159–160; digestion of by pepsin, 192; in mitochondria, 22; molecules of, 159, 334; in muscular contractions, 66–68; oxidation of for energy, 157, 160; oxidation value of, 322; percentage of in skeletal muscle, 64; plasma, 247; storage of, 160; tests for, 160–161; varying requirements of, 164

Proteoses, 192, 207

Prothrombin, 173, 263

Protons, 8

Protoplasm, 17–18

Provitamin, 170

Proximal (as term), **5**–6

Psychic phase, of gastric secretion, 193

Psychology, **2,** 3

Psychosomatic conditions, 3

Ptyalin, 167, 168, 186–187, 207

Pubic arch, 55

Pubic symphysis, **55**

Pulse, arterial, 294–295

Pulse wave, **294**–295

Pupil, of eye, **119,** 130, 135

Purkinje shift, 133

Pus, 256

Pyloric orifice. *See* Pylorus

Pyloric portion, of stomach, **190,** 193, 194

Pylorus, **190, 191,** 194, 197, **202,** 204

Pyramid(s), of kidney, **332,** 333

Pyridoxine, 176–177

Quadrants, of abdomen, 6

Quality, of voice, 242

Racemose gland, 204

Radiation, 315

Radioactive atoms, 9–10

Ramus (i) anterior primary, of nerves, **97,** 98; communicantes, gray, 111; white, 110; posterior primary, of nerves, **97,** 98

Rarefactions, of molecules, 144, 145

Reaction time, 88

Receptors, 32, 82; auditory 85, 142; cutaneous, 84, 309–310; general description of, 84; for smell, 84; stretch (pressoreceptors), 279; taste, 84; visual, *see* Rods and cones

Reciprocal innervation, 74, 99, 229–230

Recovery period, of muscle, 65, **67**

Rectum, **200, 211,** 213

Red blood cells. *See* Erythrocytes

Redout, 301

Reflex(es), Bainbridge, 279, 280; conditioned, 113; during sleep, 113; for protection of eye, 117; protective value of, 99; and secretion of saliva, 186–187; unconditioned (involuntary), **98**–**99,** 113

Reflex action. *See* Reflex

Reflex arc, 98–**99**

Refraction, 122–**123, 124;** through prism, 130, 131

Regeneration, of nerve fiber, **88**

Regions, of human body, **5**–6

Reissner's membrane, 142, **143**

Relative humidity, 316

Relative refractory period, **89**–90

Relaxation period, of muscle twitch, 65, **67**

Renal glycosuria, 334

Rennin, 167, 192–193

Reproduction, as characteristic of protoplasm, 18

Reproductive system, types of tissues in, 37

Reproductive tissue, 28; functions of, 33–34

Residual volume, 227–228

Respiration, action of gases in, 225–227; artificial, *see* Artificial respiration; control of, 228–230; effect of carbon dioxide on, 230—of changing atmospheric pressure on, 230–232, of exercise on, 69; external and internal, 216; forced, 234, **235,** 236–240; gas laws affecting, 226–227; mechanics of, 220–223; physical and chemical processes in, 225–232

Respiratory center, 228–**229**

Respiratory failure, causes of, 234–236

Respiratory rate, effect of adrenalin on, 355

Respiratory system, 216–242; structures of, 216–220; types of tissues in, 37

Resuscitator, **237,** 238

Reticulocytes, 252–253

Retina, 119–121; areas sensitive to color, 121, **132**–133; blood supply of, 119, **120, 122;** chemicals of, 120–121; divisions of, 127–128; formation of image on, 126, 127–128; inverted, 119–120; layers of, 119, **120;** posterior surface of, **122;** structures of, 119–121

Retinal image, 126–127

Retinene, 129

Reversible shock, 265–266

Rh factor, 270–271

Rheumatoid arthritis, 57–**58**

Rhodopsin, 120, 129–130, 170

Rhombencephalon, 100

Ribs, **48,** 51–**54, 220;** movement of in breathing, **220,** 221

Riboflavin, **175**–176

Rickets, 171–**172**

Ringworm, 308

Rocci, Dr. Ricca, 293

Rods and cones, of retina, 119–**121, 120,** 129, 130, 132–134

Root(s), of spinal nerves, anterior and posterior, **96, 97, 106, 107;** of tooth, **184**

Root canal, **184,** 185

Rotation, 44

Roughage, 164, 213

Round window, 142, 147

Rugae, **191**

Saccule, 148–149

Sacroiliac joint, 55

Saddle joint, 44, **45**

Saliva, 207; in digestion of starch, 167; formation and composition of, 186; functions of, 185; and pH, 16; secretion of, 187

Salts, elimination of by kidneys, 331; inorganic, of plasma, 247; mineral, *see* Mineral salts

Sarcolemma, 31, 62, **63**

Scala(e), of ear, 142, **143,** 146–147

Schneider, Conrad, 342

Sclerotic coat (sclera), 118

Scoliosis, 58
Scurvy, 169, 178–179
SDA. *See* Specific dynamic action
Secretagogues, 194, 204–205
Secretin, 205
Secretion, definition of, 203; of bile, 201–203
Segmental action, of small intestine, **208**
Selective action, by semipermeable membrane, 21
Semicircular canals, 141, **142**, 148, 149
Sense(s), of balance, 148–149; cutaneous, 84, 309–310; of hearing, 139–149; olfactory, **217**; of taste, 182–**183**; special organs of, 84–85; receptors, *see* Receptors
Sensory area, of cerebral cortex, **105**
Sensory pathways, to cerebral cortex, **107**
Septicemia, 259
Septum, 273, **275**; nasal, **217**
Serene, 159
Serous fluid, 28, 29
Serous pericardium, 273
Serum, 247, **263**, 264, 269; albumin, 264; function of, 265; globulin, 264; functions of, 265; hepatitis, 203
Sesamoid bones, **43**, 55–56
Sex determination, 370–371
Sex-limited characteristics, 371
Sex-linked characteristics, 371–373
Shafer-Nielson-Drinker method of artificial respiration, 240
Shafer prone method of artificial respiration, 238
Shaft, of rib, **54**
Shells, 8
Shock, irreversible, 266; physiological, 265–266; reversible, 265–266
Shoulder, X ray of, **55**
Shoulder girdle, 52–53
Sickle cell anemia, 259
Simple fracture, **58**–59
Simple levers, classes of, **47**
Sinus(es), carotid, **279**; ethmoid, **50**; frontal, **50**; maxillary, **50**; paranasal, **50**, **217**; venosus, **277**
Sinusoids, **201**, 202
Skeletal muscle. *See* Muscle(s), skeletal
Skeletal system, types of tissues in, 37
Skeleton, 40–60; appendicular, 47, 52–57; axial, 47–52; disorders of, 57–60; functions of, 40; human, back view of, **49**; front view of, **48**; main divisions of, 47; structure of, 47–57
Skin, **229**; appendages of, 307–309; care of, 310–311; friction ridges on, **306**; functions of, 304–305; importance in temperature control, 314–317; pigments of, 306; section through, **307**; sense receptors

in, 309–310; sensory pathways from, **107**; structure of, 305–307
Skull, fractures of, 50; regions of, 47, 50
Sleep, 113
Smooth muscle tissue, 31–**32**, 33
Snellen eye chart, 134
Sociology, **2**, 3
Sodium, 154; bicarbonate, in plasma, 266, 267; of bone, 40; chloride, 10, 11, 153; glycocholate, 203; taurocholate, 203
Sol, 12–**13**
Solid, 8; molecular movement in, 14
Sound, amplitude of, 145; binaural perception of, 147; cycle of, 145; frequency of, 145–146; human, characteristics of, 242–243; measurement of, 145; physical nature of, 144–146; and physiology of hearing, 146–147; quality (timbre) of, 146; speed of, 144–145
Sound waves, vibration of in ear, 140
Spatial relationships, judgment of, 128
Specific dynamic action (SDA), 327
Spectrum, **130**, **131**; parts of affecting humans, 315
Spermatocyte, **366**
Spermatogenesis, 365
Spermatogonia, **366**
Spermatozoa (sperm), 33–**34**, **366**
Spherical aberration, **134**–135
Sphincter(s), 74; anal, 213; cardiac, 188; of eye, 117, 119, 135; ileocolic, **212**; precapillary, 290 —effect of adrenalin on, 296; pyloric, 194, 199
Sphygmomanometer, **292**, 293
Spike potential, **89**
Spinal anesthetics, 96
Spinal column, **182**
Spinal cord, 95–98, **100**, **229**; anterior horns of, **96**, **97**, 106, 107; as conducting pathway, 96, 97; cross section of, **96**, **97**; functions of, 95; gray matter of, **96**; membranes (meninges) of, 96; nerves of, **97**–98; origin of, 83; posterior horns of, **96**, **97**; protection of, 95–96; as reflex center, 99; regions of, 97–98, **111**; white matter of, **96**–97
Spinal nerve roots, **96**, **97**, 98, **106**, **107**
Spindle, **25**, 26
Spine, of scapula, 53. *See also* Vertebral column
Spinous processes, of vertebra, 51, **52**
Spiral lamina, 142, **143**
Spirometer, **228**
Spleen, **201**; structure and functions of, 297
Spongy bone, 40–**41**, 42–43
Sprain, of joints, 60
Squamous epithelium, 28–**29**
Stapes (stirrup), **140**–141, 146, 147

Starch(es), 153, 155; digestion of, 156—by ptyalin, 187; effect of saliva on, 167; test for, 156
Steapsin, 203, 205, 206, 207
Steroids, 157, 158, 353
Stimulus (i), achromatic, 129; chromatic, 129; effect of on respiration, 229; reaction of neuron to, 88–90; summation, 90; threshold, 90
Stomach, **200**, **202**; cancer of, 196, **197**; digestion in, 190–197; dispensability of, 197; movements of, 194; in vomiting, 194–196; psychosomatic influences on, 196–197; structure of, 190–191; X ray of, **190**, **195**
Stratified epithelium, **30**
Stratum corneum, 305–306, **307**
Stratum germinativum, **305**, 306, **307**
Stretch receptors (pressoreceptors), 279
Striated muscle. *See* Muscle, skeletal
Striation, 31, 32
String galvanometer, 282–283
Sty, 117
Subarachnoid space, 96, 99–100
Subdermal layer, **305**, **307**, 310
Sublingual gland, **186**
Submaxillary gland, **186**
Subnormal period, 89–**90**
Substantia nigra, 101, **102**
Substrate, 168
Sucrase, 167, 206–207
Sucrose, 155, 207
Sugar(s), 153, 155–156
Sulcus (i), of cerebral cortex, 103
Sulfanilamide, 177–178
Sulfur, 8, 154
Summation, of stimuli, 90
Sunstroke, 317–318
Superficial muscles, 74–79
Supine position, 6
Supplemental air, 227
Surfaces, of body, 6
Surface area, of body, relation of to vital capacity, 228; in cell growth, 23–24
Suture, of cranium, 47, 50
Swallowing, process of, 187–188
Swammerdam, Jan, 20
Sweat, evaporation of, 316; production and control of, 309
Sylvester method, of artificial respiration, 236–237
Sympathetic nervous system, 110–112; relation of adrenal glands to, 355, 356
Sympathin, 281
Symphysis pubis, **48**, **55**
Synapse, 91–92
Synovial fluid, 46
Systems. *See* Organ systems
Systole, 276
Systolic pressure, 291, 293–294

Table(s), action of digestive juices, 207; additional calories needed for certain types of work, 161; approximate composition of muscle tissue, 64; average composition of blood, 248; average percentages of leukocytes, 257; common fatty acids, 157; compatible blood types, 270; composition of air, 225; composition of air, inhaled and exhaled, 228; composition of butter fat, 157; composition of plasma, 262; content of amino acids in certain proteins, 159; cranial nerves, names and actions of, 109; distribution of blood groups, 271; distribution of compounds in protoplasm, 17; distribution of fluids by percent of body weight, 298; distribution of sweat glands, 309; duration of phases of cardiac cycle, 277; effect of activities on metabolic rate, 326; effect of altitude on red blood corpuscles, 231; food value of some common foods, 162, 163; fuel values of organic nutrients, 160; human lung capacity, 227; inheritance pattern of certain characteristics, 372; layers of cerebral cortex, 104; number of chromosomes in various organisms, 365; organ systems and principal types of tissues, 37; oxygen requirements during exercise, 69; percentage of body heat loss under varying conditions, 316; percentage composition of plasma and urine, 334; percentage by weight of elements in protoplasm, 17; principal groups of foods, 152; principal materials exchanged between blood and tissues, 250; ranges of human voice, 242; relation of body surface to basal metabolism, 324; solubility of gases in blood, 227; sound levels, 145; sources and biological effects of important elements, 154; speed of sound, 145; structure and functions of blood vessels, 290; summary of chemical reactions in muscle contraction, 68; types of waste materials and ways eliminated, 331

Tadpole, thyroid experiments on, **349**

Tail, of sperm, **34**

Taste buds, 182–**183**

Tears, 118

Teeth, **183**–185; decay of, 184; deciduous, **183**–184; permanent, **183**–184; structure of, **184**

Tegmentum, 101, **102**

Telencephalon. *See* Cerebrum

Telophase, 25, **26**

Temperature, body. *See* Body temperature; external, effect of on metabolic rate, 326

Tendon(s), **46**; Achilles', **75**, **77**, 79; and sprains, 60

Terms, descriptive, 4–6

Testis (es), 33; location and structure of, **341**

Tetanus, 66

Thalamus, **107**; damage to, 103

Thiamin hydrochloride, 174–175

Thorax, **5**–6

Threonine, 159

Threshold, 90; of pitch, 146

Thrombin, 263

Thrombocytes, **33**, 248. *See also* Platelets

Thromboplastin, 263, 264

Thrombosis, 264

Thrombus (i), 264

Thumb, action of human, 54–55

Thymus gland, 358

Thyroglobulin, 346, 347

Thyroid gland, 346–349; effects of malfunction of, 347–349; hormone of, 346; influence of on metabolic rate, 347–348; location and structure of, **341**, **346**; microscopic section of rabbit's, **347**; and radioactive iodine, 9

Thyrotropic hormone, **343**, 345, 346

Thyroxin, 346, 347, 348, 349; influence of on metabolic rate, 327

Tidal volume, 227

Timbre, 146; of voice, 242

Tissue, adipose, 34–**35**; of arteries, 288, **289**; bone, **44**—types of, 40–41; circulating, 28, 33; classification of, 28; connective, 28, 34–36; covering (epithelium), 28–30; fascia, 116; formation of by cell division, 24; functions of, 28–38; glandular, of pancreas, 204–**205**; ligamentous, 40; moving (muscle), 28, 30–**32**, *see also* Muscle(s), skeletal; nervous, 28, 32–33; parathyroid, **341**; reproductive, 28, 33–**34**; structure of, 28–38; subdermal, 310; supporting, 35–36

Tocopherols, 173

Tonal gaps, 148

Tone, pure, **146**; of skeletal muscle, 68

Tongue, **181**–183, **182**, 187, **217**

Tonsil, **181**, **182**, **217**, 218

Tooth. *See* Teeth

Tourniquet, 268

Toxins, 265

Trabecula (ae), **41**, 42, 43; of femur, 56; of spleen, 297

Trachea, **182**, **217**, 218–**219**, 240, 241, **346**

Tracts, anterior corticospinal (direct pyramidal), 97; anterior spinothalamic, 97; ascending, 96–97; descending, 96–97; fasciculus cuneatus, 97; fasciculus gracilis, 97; internal capsule, 105–106; lateral corticospinal (crossed pyramidal), 97; lateral spinothalamic, 97; pyramidal, 105–**106**; of spinal cord (fasciculi), 96–97; spinocerebellar, 97

Transfusions, blood, 269–271

Transportation, of materials by blood, 246–247

Transverse arch, of foot, **57**

Transverse processes, of vertebra, 51, **52**

Trichinosis, white cell count in, 257

Trichromats, 134

Trochlea, 117

True ribs, **48**, 52, **53**

True skin. *See* Dermis

Trunk, of body, **5**–6

Trypsin, 205, 207

Trypsinogen, 205, 207

Tryptophan, 159, 160

Tube, Eustachian, 141, **182**

Tubercle, of rib, 52

Tubule(s), dentinal, 185; of kidney, 332–334, **333**—collecting, **333**, convoluted, **333**; seminiferous, **341**

Tumor, and cell division, 24

Tunic, of kidney, **332**

Tunica(e) of arteries, 288, **289**

Tympanic cavity, **140**

Tympanic membrane, 139–**140**, 146, 147

Tyndall effect, **12**

Typhoid fever, white cell count in, 257

Tyrosine, 159, 347

Ulcer, duodenal, **196**; gastric, 196–197

Ultraviolet rays, 130–131; and formation of vitamin D, 171–172; and production of pigment, 306

Unipolar neuron, 86, **87**

Universal donor, 270

Universal recipient, 270

Uranium, 8

Urea, 204, 334, 335

Ureter(s), **332**, 336–337

Urethra, **332**, 336–337

Uric acid, 334, 335–336

Urinary bladder, **200**, **332**, 336–337

Urination, 336–337

Urine, 333, 334; effect of exercise on, 71; formation of, 334–336; and pH, 16; production of, during sleep, 113; sugar in, 204

Urobilinogen, 203

Utricle, 148, 149

Uvula, **181**, **182**, 188

Vacuole, **21**, 22; bile, 201, **202**

Valine, 159

Valves, atrioventricular, **274**, **275**; colic, 212; in lymphatic, **298**, **299**; mitral (bicuspid), 274, **275**, **276**; semilunar, **275**, 276; spiral of Heister, 202; tricuspid, 274, **275**, **276**; of veins, 290

van Leeuwenhoek, Anton, 20

Vaporization, 316

Varicose veins, 290

Vasoconstrictor center, 295, 296, 297

Vasodilator center, 295, 296

Vasopressin, **343**, 345

Vein(s), 250; *See also* Vein(s), individual, specifically named; of intestine, **206**; structure and functions of, 290; varicose, 290

Vein(s), individual, specifically

named: central, of liver, **201**; coronary, **274**; hepatic, **201**; inferior venae cavae, **274, 275, 276, 279**; portal, **201**, 204, **249**; pulmonary, **275, 276**; renal, **332, 333**; subclavian, **300**; superior venae cavae, **274, 275, 276, 277, 279**

Vena cava, **201, 274, 275, 276,** 277, **279**

Ventral side, 5

Ventricle, of heart, 250, **274, 275, 279**

Venule, 250, **255**, 290

Vermiform appendix, **212**

Vermis, of cerebellum, **102**

Vertebra (ae), 50–51, **52, 200**; cervical, **49**; lumbar, **49, 52**; relation of to spinal cord, 95; sacral, **51**; thoracic, **49, 54**, 220

Vertebral column, 50–**51**, 95; abnormal curvatures of, 58; regions of, **51**

Vertebral foramen, 51, **52**

Vesalius, 342

Vestibular membrane, 142, **143**

Vestibule, of inner ear, 141, **142**

Villus (i), of intestine, **206**, 208, **209**

Viscosity, of blood, 292

Vision, binocular, 127–128; cerebral cortex as center for, 115; color. *See* Color vision; field of, 126; general description of,115; monocular, 127; near and far, 123–124; night, 129–130; peripheral, 121, 126; photopic, 130–134; physics of, 122–124; scotopic, 129–130, 133; stereoscopic, 128

Visual acuity, 134, 135

Visual pathways, central, **127**

Visual purple, 120, 129–130; chemical changes in, **129**

Visual white, 129

Visual yellow, 129

Vital capacity, 228

Vitreous body, 122

Vitamins, 169–180; antineuritic, 174–175; antiscorbutic, *see* Vitamin C; categories of, 170; discovery of, 169; as essential food, 152; oil-soluble, 170–174; water-soluble, 174–180

Vitamin A, 170–171; and dark adaptation, 130

Vitamin B Complex, 174–177; B_1, *see* Thiamin hydrochloride; B_2 or G, *see* Riboflavin; B_6, *see* Pyridoxine; B_{12}, 178, 179; and pernicious anemia, 259

Vitamin B Complex. *See also* Folic acid, Biotin, and Paraaminobenzoic acid

Vitamin C, 178–179

Vitamin D, 171–173; and calcium, 171

Vitamin E, 173

Vitamin H. *See* Biotin

Vitamin K, 173–174; and clotting, 264

Vocal cord(s), **217**, 218, **240, 241–** 242

Voice, ranges of human, 242–243

Voice box. *See* Larynx

Voluntary muscles. *See* Muscle, skeletal

Vomiting, 194–196

Walker, Mary B., 63

Waste products, in plasma, 248

Water, absorption of in large intestine, 212–213; apparatus for decomposing, **9**; chemical formula for, 11; decomposition of, 10; elimination of by skin, 305; as essential food material, 152;

functions of in body, 153; percentage of in plasma, 262—in skeletal muscle tissue, 64; storage of, in salivary glands, 186

Water balance, and adrenal cortex, 354; maintenance of by kidneys, 331–332

Water content, of tissues, maintenance of by blood, 247

Water vapor, in air, 225

Wave(s), pulse, **294**–295; sound, 139, 140, 144–146

Weight, atomic, 8

White blood cells. *See* Leukocytes

White matter, 87; of cerebellum, 102; of medulla, 101; of spinal cord, **96–97**

White rami communicantes, 110

Window, oval, 141, **142**, 146, 147; round, 142, **143**, 147

Wisdom teeth, 184

Wright's stain, 256

X chromosome, 370–371

Xanthoproteic test, 160

Xerophthalmia, 170, **171**

Xiphoid process, 51–52, **53**

X rays, and mutations, 377

Y chromosome, 370–371

Yeast, enzyme of, 169

Yolk, of ovum, 33

Young-Helmholtz theory of color vision, 132

Zinc, sources and biological effects of, 154

Zygomatic arch, 50

Zygomatic bone. *See* Bone(s), individual

Zygote, 363

Zymase, 169